S0-BSB-469

WITHDRAWN

DATE DUE		
9 00AM	Jan 26	
9 00AM Jan 2		
9 00AM Jan 25		
Feb 11 '64	Oct 29 '74	
IN LIBRARY	Mar 24 '75	
	Dec 15 '75	
Mar 4 '64		
Apr 2 '64		
Aug 18 '64		
Feb 17 '65		
Dec 18 68		
Sep 15 '69		
Jan 12 '70		
May 14 70		
Oct 17 '72		
Jan 12 '73		
Jan 19 '73		
Jan 26 '73		
GAYLORD		PRINTED IN U S A

PHYSIOGRAPHY OF WESTERN
UNITED STATES

A Companion Volume

BY

NEVIN M. FENNEMAN

•

PHYSIOGRAPHY OF
EASTERN UNITED STATES

The purpose of this book is to establish
order in the vast amount of geologic
literature on the eastern United States
and to organize the knowledge in an
attempt to interpret the physiographic
history of this area.

714 *pages,* 6 x 9, 197 *illustrations
and* 7 *maps in two colors*

PHYSIOGRAPHY

OF

WESTERN UNITED STATES

NEVIN M. FENNEMAN

Professor of Geology, University of Cincinnati

McGRAW-HILL BOOK COMPANY, Inc.

NEW YORK AND LONDON

1931

CARL A. RUDISILL LIBRARY
LENOIR RHYNE COLLEGE

551.40978
F36p

Copyright, 1931, by the
McGraw-Hill Book Company, Inc.

Printed in the United States of America

*All rights reserved. This book, or
parts thereof, may not be reproduced
in any form without permission of
the publishers.*

XIII

20420

45,100

July, 1963

PREFACE

In calling this book "Physiography" we are merely accepting the American usage of a not very fortunate term. The central theme of the work is the land forms of western United States and how they came about. There is no doubt about this center of interest, but the circumference of an appropriate mass of fact may be hard to fix. A companion volume on the "Physiography of Eastern United States" is now in preparation.

It may be assumed that geologists and geographers have equal interest in land forms, but the quality of their interests is very different. To the geologist land forms are a kind of final product, the end of a story. To the geographer they offer a beginning, a point of departure. To the former, land forms depend on all the physical processes of geology. To the latter, they depend on nothing; almost everything else depends on them in some measure.

According to the above-made statement of our central theme this book is mainly geological. It treats land forms as effects, not as causes. But before doing so, or while doing so, it is necessary to devote a large share of space to the description of forms as they are. Such descriptions have equal interest to the geographer. Moreover, to a writer who shares the geographic interest there is a constant temptation to clothe these land forms with life by pointing out their influence on climate and life and habitation and civilization. No attempt has been made to resist this impulse but, on the other hand, there is no attempt to treat such matters systematically or symmetrically for all parts of the territory. They belong to the illustrations, not to the systematic framework. If industries are named in one section of the country and not in another it is merely because they serve to illuminate a point in one case and not in the other.

Natural resources are given some mention in connection with most of the divisions, but their critical discussion does not belong here. Minerals, like land forms, are products of the geological past. Generally these two things are not closely related though there are cases in which economic physiography plays an impor-

tant rôle, as in the accumulation of soluble salts under certain
climatic and drainage conditions like those of the Great Basin.
Agriculture and grazing are so plainly related to climate and
topography that a brief mention is adequate. Ground water is
so closely related to physiography that frequent mention of it
is inevitable.

Necessarily the material for such a treatise must be found
largely in the geological literature. The writer has been in all
of the provinces and most of the sections and has done geologic
work in several of them. Such personal observations have
made reading more profitable and writing more critical, but the
great mass of the material must necessarily be taken from others.

A relatively small part of the literature on which this work is
based was produced with a direct physiographic purpose.
Most of the facts were ascertained in the course of areal or
economic studies in geology and published in official reports or
as papers read before geologic societies or as magazine articles
of geologic character.

Some parts of the territory have been studied by geologists
for many years and are adequately treated in the literature both
on their own account and as types of physiographic development.
The temptation to elaborate disproportionately on these was
steadily resisted. On the other hand, there was constant effort
to fill in the picture with respect to the great intervening areas.
In a sense, all places are of equal interest when one is trying to
get a mental picture of a great area. With respect to some
areas it has not been possible to give much more than a
geographic description.

Some parts of western United States are sufficiently well
known to make much fuller treatment possible. Others will be
better known in the future. In either case, or in any other case,
the aim in writing these chapters has been to give a consistent
frame in which additional knowledge may find a setting. It is
only by having some such framework of larger facts and theory
that a great mass of areal information may be made to bring
light instead of confusion. It is highly desirable that the
physiography of smaller units, counties, sections, and districts
variously defined, be studied and published for local use. Some
such treatises already exist. Such local treatises will be vastly
more useful if all conform to some previously accepted scheme

of physical units for the entire country. They will thus conform with one another.

The student of a small area may well find the treatment here given inadequate to his district. In describing or discussing large units covering 10,000 to 50,000 square miles, it is of the essence of the problem to ignore details which may be vastly important locally. Especially in the vicinity of physiographic boundary lines is it necessary to take into account the difference between describing a large area and a small one. Most of the physiographic boundaries thus far published have been drawn by students of large areas on small-scale maps. The discrepancies arising from generalization need not be faced here, except to point out that they are to be expected. Generalization would not be properly done if such things did not occur. On the other hand, it is to be expected that the critical student of a small area bounded or traversed by any of the lines here used will delineate such boundaries with a degree of detail suited to the scale on which he works.

A knowledge of the elements of geology and physiography on the reader's part is assumed. The book is addressed to those who have such elementary knowledge. While not written as a textbook, the interests of advanced students were kept uppermost in mind throughout the writing. For a number of years the writer has used manuscript copies in his class composed of men who have had general and historical geology and were studying at the same time structural and economic geology and other advanced phases.

A matter of interest to geographers is the division of the country into natural physical units called provinces and sections. Fortunately the most obvious divisions are much the same whether made by the geologist or the geographer. The map of physical divisions of the United States which accompanies this volume is the product of development through more than 30 years. The early work of Powell and others was exceedingly general and no attempt was made to locate boundaries. The first attempt to define the actual boundaries of natural units seems to have been by the present writer in the "Annals of the Association of American Geographers" for 1914. On the map published in that volume some of the divisions now recognized appear for the first time. In 1916 a committee of the Association of American Geographers (with the writer as chairman) elaborated the map, leaving it in a form not very different from the one that accompanies this volume. The last revision was made under the auspices of the United States Geological Survey, which issues the map as a public document. For many years to come, all maps of this kind must be subject to alteration and refinement as knowledge increases.

NEVIN M. FENNEMAN.

CINCINNATI, OHIO,
December, 1930.

ACKNOWLEDGMENTS

Acknowledgments of assistance are due to more men than can be mentioned here. Each chapter was sent in manuscript for criticism to at least one man having special first-hand acquaintance with the area treated, gained by years of field work in that region. The chapter on the Great Plains Province was parceled out to William C. Alden, M. R. Campbell, and Willis T. Lee. The Southern Rocky Mountain province was read by R. D. George; the Wyoming Basin, Middle Rocky Mountains and Basin and Range province by Eliot Blackwelder, to whom thanks are due for more than ordinary helpfulness. On questions in controversy, favorable consideration was always given to his views, though this acknowledgment is not to be understood as committing him to agreement with all the statements made in these chapters. The chapter on the Northern Rocky Mountains Province was read by William C. Alden and J. T. Pardee; that on the Columbia Plateau by J. P. Buwalda. Virgil R. D. Kirkham contributed valuable criticism and information on the several provinces represented in Idaho, a region in which such recent and first-hand information was specially needed. J Harlen Bretz gave similar assistance on the Columbia Plateau and Puget Trough in Washington. Raymond C. Moore read and criticized the chapter on the Colorado Plateau with great care, as did also H. E. Gregory. Special thanks are due to F. E. Matthes for his careful criticism of the treatment of the Sierra Nevada and for constructive assistance in interpreting the facts about this range. The treatment of the Coast Ranges of California was revised in important respects as the result of the helpful criticism of Bruce L. Clark. However, the men here named are not responsible for any statements not quoted.

The eleven physiographic diagrams used as index maps were prepared specially for this book by Dr. Guy-Harold Smith. While the data of these maps are taken from original sources and represent a store of geographic information not hitherto brought together, the method of delineation here employed is that of Professor A. K. Lobeck, to whom thanks are also due for generous counsel.

All illustrations not made originally by the author or for this book are credited in the legend to the person or organization whose consent was necessary to reproduction. Where the obligation incurred by the author is merely for consent to copy published illustrations or purchased photographs, the credit given in the legend may suffice. In many cases, however, there was gift or loan of photographs, drawings, or plates, involving in some cases much search or effort on the part of the donor. Special acknowledgment for such kindness is due to the following: American Geographical Society for Figs. 95 and 96; Ralph Arnold for Fig. 161; Arthur Bevan for Figs. 56 and 57; Eliot Blackwelder for Figs. 52, 63, 119, 121, 125, 126, 127, and 166; J Harlen Bretz for Fig. 159; R. T. Chamberlin for Figs. 31, 35, and 44; G. E. Condra for Fig. 10; Denver and Rio Grande Western Railroad for Fig. 48; H. W. Fairbanks for Figs. 84, 86, 104, and 158; V. P. Gionella for Fig. 129; W. H. Hobbs for Fig. 68; International Boundary Commission of Canada for Figs. 77 and 78; A. G. Leonard for Figs. 25 and 26; Chester R. Longwell for Fig. 28; G. D. Louderback for Fig. 131; R. C. Moore for photographs of Plains Border; D. T. McDougal for Fig. 137; *National Geographic Magazine* for Fig. 60; Portland (Ore.) Chamber of Commerce for Fig. 154; A. C. Waters for Fig. 100.

CONTENTS

xi

LIST OF MAPS FOR REFERENCE

PHYSIOGRAPHY OF WESTERN UNITED STATES

CHAPTER I

GREAT PLAINS PROVINCE

THE PROVINCE AS A WHOLE

Approximate Boundaries.—The name "Great Plains" has long been in use for a broad belt of highland which slopes gradually eastward from the Rocky Mountains to the Central Lowland. In popular usage the limits of this belt are not defined, nor are the essential characteristics by which it is distinguished from the lowlands on the east. The term "Great Plains" has commonly been associated in the popular mind with monotony of landscape; also with short grass which has in a rough way distinguished the Great Plains from the Prairies or "long-grass country" to the east.

In appropriating the name "Great Plains" to more exact usage, the area has been limited in various ways. Perhaps the line of 20 in. rainfall has been the most used boundary, because in a very rough way that line has been assumed to mark the limit of agriculture without irrigation. In some ways this line is fairly satisfactory but since the introduction of specialized methods of dry farming in arid regions this criterion of "agriculture without irrigation" has lost much of its meaning. If it means raising the ordinary crops of the Mississippi Valley, and in the ordinary way, planting every year with a fair expectation of returns, it is still true that roughly 20 in. rainfall are required in central United States. Farther south increasing heat and evaporation make more water necessary. Conversely, with decreasing temperature and increasing cloudiness toward the north, farming of the ordinary eastern type may often succeed on 15 in. rain. The line of 20 in. rainfall trends west of south from eastern North Dakota to western Texas (Fig. 1). The

1

limit of agriculture of the Mississippi Valley type trends more nearly north and south.   Both lines are exceedingly indefinite and vary greatly from year to year.

Since the contour lines of this region trend nearly north and south, and since the increasing altitude westward is one of the causes of the climatic contrast, the Great Plains have sometimes been delimited on the east by contours.   For this purpose the 1,500-ft. line has been used by some and the 2,000-ft. line

Fig. 1.—Great Plains region, showing lines of equal rainfall and lines of equivalent rainfall.   The solid lines marked 15 and 20 (in.) pass through points of equal rainfall.   The corresponding dotted lines pass through points having a rainfall which is equivalent to 15 and 20 in., respectively, on the Canadian boundary.   (*U. S. Dept. Agr. Bur. Plant Ind.*)

by others.   Still others have used a meridian, the 97th which is not far from the 1,500-ft. contour in Kansas and Nebraska, or the 100th which is, in a general way, not far from the 2,000-ft. contour.   Of course, none of these lines are visible in the field and none of them express distinctions between topographic forms.

Eastern Boundary Here Adopted.—A study of topographic forms makes it possible to draw a nearly north-south line in rough agreement with those already mentioned and separating the characteristic topography of the Central Lowland on the east from other types which characterize the higher plains on the west. Throughout the greater part of its length this line is marked by a low east-facing escarpment, definite at some places, elsewhere ragged and deeply indented or transformed by erosion into a belt of hills. At still other places it is absent. Everywhere east of this line the surface is lower. Locally, at least, this indicates the approximate completion of a younger erosion cycle on the east side. The term "Lowland," as applied to central United States, is justified by comparison with the Great Plains and other provinces, but it is not to be understood that every portion of it lies close to its base level.

In North Dakota (Fig. 3) this province boundary may readily be recognized by an observer standing near the western margin of the Central Lowland, say 50 to 75 miles east of the Missouri River. Looking west, or southwest, the surface is seen to rise gradually but perceptibly like a range of hills or like a gently sloping ridge 300 to 400 ft. high (700 ft. if measured from the valley of the Souris River near the Canadian border). This is the eastward-facing edge of the Missouri Plateau, the northern member of the Great Plains province.[1] The escarpment is distinct for hundreds of miles in southern Canada, or about to the Saskatchewan River.[2] It is likewise clear in the northern part of South Dakota and continues to be recognizable almost to the southern border of that state (see page 61).

In southern South Dakota and Nebraska the Central Lowland merges imperceptibly into the Great Plains, but in northern Kansas (Fig. 2) the eastern margin of the Plains province is a hilly belt to be described under the head of the Plains Border. As far south as central Kansas there is a mild contrast between the smoother or more gently rolling Central Lowland and the higher and more sharply dissected Plains Border. If the Great Plains

---

[1] WILLARD, D. E., "The Story of the Prairies," p. 72, 1907; U. S. Dept. Agr., Field Oper. Bur. Soils, map 33, 1908, Reconnaissance Survey of Western North Dakota; SIMPSON, HOWARD E., The Physiography of the Devil's-Stump Lake Region, North Dakota, pl. X, N. Dak. Geol. Survey, 1911.

[2] Exact descriptions of this feature in Canada are wanting, though it is known to be a significant boundary between regions of different elevation and relief. This contrast is noted by G. M. Dawson in his "Report on the Geology and Resources of the Region in the Vicinity of the 49th Parallel," Montreal, 1875. The northward extent here given is inferred from the description by C. A. Young, Geology and Mineral Resources of Canada, Can. Geol. Survey, *Pub.* 1085, p. 108.

boundary in the Dakotas be connected by a nearly straight line with the eastern edge of the Plains Border in northern Kansas, the line thus drawn will mark essentially the western edge of the glacial drift. The drift does not greatly influence the topography at this place but in various ways it is convenient to use its edge as the province boundary.[1]

In south central Kansas there is another break of 50 or more miles within which the province boundary is unaccompanied by a topographic break (see Great Bend Lowland, page 27).

In southern Kansas, along the boundary indicated on the map, there is a pronounced escarpment 300 to 400 ft. high, ruggedly dissected and locally known as the Red Hills. This escarpment swings westward in Oklahoma and continues southward in Texas, rising above the lowland on Permian shale and capped by the Tertiary of the Great Plains.

Along the streams which cross the Great Plains or head in their margin, this escarpment is generally definite, being 200 to 500 ft. high and locally dissected into badlands. At some places between streams there is a mere steepening of the general eastward slope. Generally in Texas (Fig. 4) the transition between the High Plains on the west and the more or less eroded lower plains on the east is effected within a zone of one to six miles in width.[2] In general, the edge of the High Plains section is more prominent where the Tertiary formations rest on strong scarp-making beds. This is the case in the Red Hills of southern Kansas and again in Texas south of the 35th parallel, where Triassic and Cretaceous formations outcrop in the escarpment and accentuate it.

Altitudes and Slope.—The eastern boundary here traced, nowhere departs very far from the contour line of 1,500 ft., except at the north where it rises to 2,000 ft. The western boundary at the foot of the mountains averages perhaps 5,500 ft. with a range of 1,000 ft. above and below that altitude. This indicates a fall toward the east of about 4,000 ft. Since the

[1] If Nebraska could be treated without reference to the rest of the country this line would not be made a major physiographic boundary. But a workable division of the United States requires that the Central Lowland be delimited from the Great Plains province despite the local weakness in the contrast.

[2] GOULD, CHARLES N., Geology and Water Resources of the Eastern Portion of the Panhandle of Texas, U. S. Geol. Survey, *Wat. Sup. Pap.* 154, p. 9, 1906.

width of the province is nowhere much more or less than 400 miles, the average slope is approximately 10 ft. to the mile.

Sections Distinguished.—With the general altitudes and slopes here given there is large diversity in detail of topographic style. For any adequate description of the Great Plains the province must be divided into 10 sections, and most of these embrace a variety of topographic types. It will be desirable to distinguish the several sections before discussing each more fully. For this purpose it is convenient to begin with the central part of the province, *i.e.*, in Colorado and Kansas, because this portion exemplifies most simply the essential principles in the treatment of the several sections.

The most striking feature here is the phenomenal flatness of the interstream areas near the Kansas-Colorado boundary (Fig. 2). Nearer the mountains there has been more erosion, the flat has been destroyed, and the surface somewhat lowered, so that in parts of eastern Colorado there is an actual interruption of the regional eastward slope and a rise from the west to the flat interstream areas of eastern Colorado and western Kansas. Going east from western Kansas, the upland flats give way to a roughly eroded zone which intervenes between the flat uplands and the Central Lowland.

It is plain that here the central zone is made up largely of remnants of a single great expanse of fluviatile plain or alluvial slope which is known to have spread from the mountains on the west and presumably reached to the Central Lowland. It is equally plain that its eastern margin has been most exposed to erosion, being near the trunk line of drainage and in a relatively humid climate. It is characteristic of plateau dissection to begin at the outward-facing edges, and progress inward as the streams lengthen headward. Thus the eastern margin of the great fluviatile plain has been dissected into the "Plains Border" and this dissected zone is progressively widening westward at the expense of the "High Plains."

The erosion of the western margin of the fluviatile plain has likewise given greater relief to the area known as "Colorado Piedmont." This seems at first a paradox in view of the fact that there is less rainfall here than farther east where the old plain surface is preserved. It has been pointed out[1] that the

---

[1] JOHNSON, WILLARD D., The High Plains and Their Utilization, U. S. Geol. Survey, 21*st Ann. Rept.*, pt. IV, p. 628, 1900.

slightly greater rainfall of eastern Colorado covers the plains with a tight sod whereas the smaller rainfall to the west supports only bunch grasses and other well-separated plants. Against

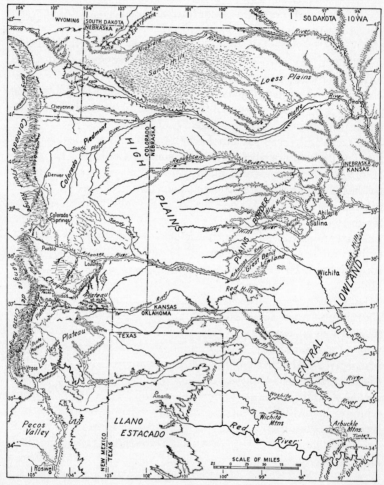

FIG. 2.—Index map; central part of the Great Plains province. (Drawn by Guy-Harold Smith.)

this poor protection the smaller rainfall of the western strip is more effective in erosion than is the larger rainfall farther east. Another and equally important factor in the more rapid erosion of the western part is explained on page 36.

The central Great Plains in Colorado and Kansas are thus seen to embrace three sections: a residual area of almost perfect plains in the middle, known as the High Plains (13 *d* on the general map), with a more eroded area on either side; the Plains Border (13 *e*), on the east; and the Colorado Piedmont (13 *f*), on the west. These are three of the 10 sections of the Great Plains province, all of which are to be discussed later on. With this general scheme in mind, most of the other sections may be easily defined.

The High Plains section extends north about to the Dakota-Nebraska boundary, where it occupies the full width of the province. It ends here in the prominent north-facing Pine Ridge escarpment (Fig. 8, page 17), 1,000 ft. high in the longitude of the Black Hills, but lower to the west and less definite farther east where it follows the south side of the Missouri River. Continued erosion is, of course, shifting this escarpment southward. The High Plains are, therefore, losing ground on the north as they are on the east and west. They were at one time much more extensive.

North of the Pine Ridge escarpment is the Missouri Plateau embracing three sections; an unglaciated section (13 *b*) in the south; a glaciated section (13 *a*) in the north; and the Black Hills section (13 *c*) entirely surrounded by the unglaciated Missouri Plateau. The Missouri Plateau is distinguished from the High Plains by deep erosion. It has not recently been leveled up by new deposition. Hence where its surface locally approaches flatness it is generally the flatness of old age not of infancy, except in the case of river terraces, some of which are wide. A surface of generally rolling terraces with many low scarps indicates old age after a complex history (page 64). At wide intervals are remnants of higher surfaces, from a few hundred feet on the east to a few thousand feet on the west above the general level. Elsewhere, especially near the Black Hills, are badlands which indicate rapid cutting in a new cycle of erosion.

The glaciated section of the Missouri Plateau differs from the section just described only in features due to glaciation. The Black Hills section, a true mountain uplift, is distinguished not only by superior altitude but by its upturned strata, erosion of which has produced a characteristic mountain topography. A half dozen or more similar but smaller mountain groups stand on the plains of Montana east of the Rocky Mountains. None

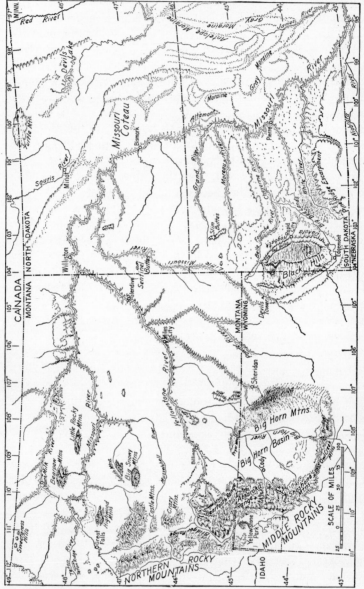

FIG. 3.—Index map; northern part of the Great Plains province.   (Drawn by Guy-Harold Smith.)

of these are considered large enough to be treated as separate sections. They are accordingly treated below as exceptional features of the sections in which they occur.

The High Plains extend south under the name of Llano Estacado, almost to the Rio Grande. West of the southern part are two more sections which sustain somewhat the same relation to the High Plains as does the Colorado Piedmont; that is to say, they are areas in which the fluviatile mantle of the High Plains is missing. The Raton section (13 g) lying in northeastern New Mexico and southeastern Colorado is characterized by its uplifted and canyoned stratum plains, its high dissected mesas, some of them lava-capped, and by other volcanic features (see page 41). South of this is the Pecos section (13 h) consisting of the Pecos and upper Canadian valleys, together making a long trough carved from what was once a part of the High Plains but whose axis is now 500 to 1,000 ft. below the Llano Estacado on the east.

South of the Llano Estacado is a continuation of the same plateau, though declining somewhat in altitude. This southern extension is called the Edwards Plateau (13 i) and includes the Stockton Plateau west of the Pecos River. Its substratum consists of strong limestone strata lacking the fluviatile mantle which is so characteristic of the High Plains. This plateau terminates in a distinct but much dissected escarpment on all sides except where it borders the Llano Estacado on the north and, for a short distance, the mountains on the west. The center of the Edwards Plateau remains a nearly level upland.

East of the southern end of the Llano Estacado and north of the Edwards Plateau is the Central Texas section (13 k), a region of great topographic variety sustaining much the same relation to the Edwards Plateau as the Plains Border does to the High Plains. Over all this part of Texas the strong Edwards limestone (lower Cretaceous) once formed a continuous eastward-sloping cover. The extent to which this protecting stratum has been eroded away is the most essential consideration in distinguishing the larger topographic units in this region. On the west and south the strong limestone cover remains intact in the Llano Estacado and Edwards Plateau. In north central Texas it has been wholly removed and the weaker rocks beneath peneplaned (Osage section of the Central Lowland). On the east the protecting limestone is faulted down along a line running almost

through Austin and Waco.   The down-thrown block continues
to be covered with younger strata.   Both the lower altitude of
this eastern block and the style of topography carved on its

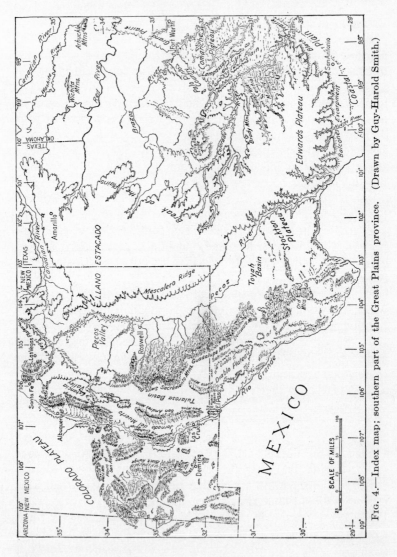

FIG. 4.—Index map; southern part of the Great Plains province.   (Drawn by Guy-Harold Smith.)

younger and softer rocks class it as part of the Coastal Plain.
Hemmed in by the sections thus described is the Central Texas
section in which the cycle of erosion was only in part completed.

Some of the various and strongly contrasted styles of topography within this partly base-leveled section are described on pages 54 to 59 inclusive.

HIGH PLAINS

As already stated, the High Plains (13 *d*) comprise a north-south strip stretching from the boundary of South Dakota almost to the Rio Grande. The most typical part of this section lies south of the North Platte River, *i.e.*, south of Wyoming and Nebraska. The following general discussion refers primarily

Fig. 5.—Typical view of the High Plains in western Kansas. This plain is essentially the original upper surface of the Ogalalla formation. The sod seen in the foreground is the characteristic "short grass" of the High Plains. The trees were planted. (*Photo by Gilbert, U. S. Geol. Survey.*)

to this part, though it is also in the main true of the northern portion except as pointed out later.

Fluviatile Origin.—As stated on page 5, these High Plains are remnants of a former great fluviatile plain which stretched from the mountains on the west to the Central Lowland.[1] The

[1] GILBERT, G. K., Underground Water of the Arkansas Valley in Eastern Colorado, U. S. Geol. Survey, 17*th Ann. Rept.*, pt. II, p. 575, 1896. This region is also discussed more in detail by W. D. Johnson, The High Plains and Their Utilization, U. S. Geol. Survey, 21*st Ann. Rept.*, pt. IV, pp. 612–639, 1900. The fluviatile origin is understood to be dominant but minor portions of the mass were deposited in temporary lakes or by wind. This paper discusses the geology and topography of the High Plains thoroughly, and their settlement and utilization to the date of writing.

fluviatile mantle was laid down by overloaded streams after the manner of alluvial fans, or of flood plains when the streams are building so many bars and shoals that the water is subdivided into many channels, each of which is in turn filled, and the streams shifted. Again, when a stream has raised its channel by deposition, it may break over in one or many channels which may reunite if the flow is sufficient. In these ways the stream becomes "braided." Not only each channel but the entire network is subject to shifting as the old channels are filled. Shallow lakes covering areas which temporarily escape filling

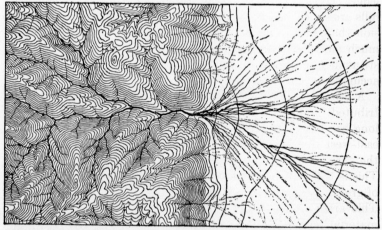

Fig. 6.—Tributary and distributary regions of a fan-building stream. This figure represents a typical stream during the deposition of the "Tertiary mantle" which once covered the greater part of the province. In the mountains the waters were gathered and valleys were cut down; on the plains the water was dissipated and lost and sediment was deposited. (*W. D. Johnson, U. S. Geol. Survey.*)

are incidental and evanescent features of this process. Such a depositing stream may shift laterally for many miles and the deposits of neighboring streams may overlap and merge. Near where the streams issued from the mountains, each stream built its own alluvial fan but farther out the fans merged into a single, broad, alluvial slope. Such deposits were made in this region in late Tertiary time and are frequently referred to as the "Tertiary mantle."

This fluviatile character of the Tertiary mantle is important, for it determines not only the original topography but the internal structure of the mass—in this case the distribution of sand, gravel, and silt. This in turn influences the erosion topography and determines the behavior of ground waters and their utilization.

Character of Sediments.—The evidence of fluviatile origin is found in the nature of the sediments and in their mode of distribution. The material is largely unconsolidated silt with smaller quantities of sand and gravel.[1] Lime is so abundant that any one of these constituents may be found locally cemented into a coherent and rather resistant mass. These masses are the so-called "mortar beds" which, in eroded areas, may make ledges, cliffs, or mesas. Near streams, where erosion is active, hills are so frequently surfaced with gravel as to give the impression that gravel is the main constituent. In reality the silt is much more abundant but where erosion is active the finer constituents are progressively washed away, leaving the gravel to accumulate on the surface.

A critical study shows that the gravel and sand are not distributed haphazard through the mass but are concentrated in long bands having crooked or winding courses with a dominant east-west direction. These branches intersect and reunite like the threads of a great net much stretched from west to east.[2] This is true not only at the surface but at any depth; the bands of gravel, however, occupy different positions at different depths. This arrangement suggests at once that the bands of coarser material represent the channels of the overloaded, braided, and constantly shifting streams which built the fluviatile plain.

The thickness of this unconsolidated material varies from zero to more than 500 ft.; that is to say, it is laid down on an uneven surface. This means that before the rivers began their depositing habit they and their tributaries were at work on the task of base-leveling the area but left the task incomplete, reversed their action, and began to undo the effects of their erosion. Over much the larger part of the Great Plains (south of Montana, at

---

[1] JOHNSON, W. D., *loc. cit.*, p. 635. The predominance of silt is emphasized by Johnson, though the proportions are not everywhere the same. GILBERT, *loc. cit.*, p. 576, states that coarse sand is the chief material in the Arkansas Valley of eastern Colorado, but he states elsewhere that within a belt of undetermined width in this valley the material has been more or less rehandled. Apparently this predominance of coarse sand is in the belt which has been subjected to reassortment during the cutting of the present Arkansas Valley.

[2] JOHNSON, WILLARD D., *loc. cit.*, p. 634.

least, and probably covering part of that state) the fluviatile deposits completely buried the uneven rock surface except for a few high rock hills which now stand island-like above the level of the High Plains.

As may well be inferred, the Tertiary mantle is porous and absorbs the surface waters. Thus erosion is prevented or delayed. Beneath this mantle, shale is the commonest rock. Where streams have cut through the upper formation, springs and seepage are common at the contact.

Fig. 7.—A so-called "buffalo wallow" in the typical High Plains. This is not a true buffalo wallow but a depression due to local settling of the sediments. The sod seen in this view is the characteristic "short grass" of the High Plains. (*W. D. Johnson, U. S. Geol. Survey.*)

Topography.—The surface produced by this alluviation is as flat as any land surface in nature (Figs. 5 and 7). Many thousands of square miles still retain this flatness. In the Llano Estacado or Staked Plains of Texas and New Mexico an area of 20,000 square miles is almost untouched by erosion. North of that, the drainage from the mountains is directly eastward across the belt of the High Plains and the original flat is preserved only between streams.

Among the few and generally insignificant features of relief on the uneroded High Plains are saucer-like depressions, nearly circular basins varying in diameter from a few rods to a mile, ʒnd in depth from a few inches to 30 or 40 ft. The rim is often perfectly definite and formed by the abrupt up-curving of the well-sodded bottom to meet the surrounding plain (Fig. 7). Some of these basins retain temporary ponds after rains and a few of the deeper ones contain water all the time though in varying amount. Two small counties in the heart of the Staked Plains contain from 50 to 60 such temporary lakes besides a few called "permanent." The latter, though the water is warm and ill-tasting, were of great importance to early travelers and wagoners. Later, they became important centers of the cattle industry and some of them have determined the sites of towns, as for example Amarillo.[1] It must not be assumed that basins of this sort, either large or small, even where most numerous, are sufficiently prominent to affect the general aspect of flatness.

In the simplest case these saucer-like depressions represent a mere settling of the surface, probably due to the action of ground water. The faintest original unevenness, not visible to the naked eye, would cause rain water to percolate downward in larger amount where the surface was slightly lower. This would result in compacting the material below and in removing soluble constituents. This process would be cumulative as the basin deepened.[2] Subsurface drainage is of necessity more or less concentrated along the bands of gravel. Accordingly, depressions of the kind described often occur in lines or series.[3] Ordinarily the bottoms of these depressions bear a tenacious sod of buffalo grass or similar short grasses, hence the wind does not aid in deepening them. Where temporary lakes are formed the grass may be killed and in the intervals of drought the basin may be enlarged by wind.

The term "buffalo wallow" is much used on the Great Plains for small circular depressions, though in many cases without

[1] GOULD, C. M., Geology and Water Resources of the Western Part of the Panhandle of Texas, U. S. Geol. Survey, Wat. Sup. Pap. 191, p. 50, 1907; also Geology and Water Resources of the Eastern Part of the Panhandle of Texas, U. S. Geol. Survey, Wat. Sup. Pap. 154, p. 48, 1906.

[2] JOHNSON, W. D., The High Plains and Their Utilization, U. S. Geol. Survey, 21st Ann. Rept., pt. IV, pp. 704 and 710.

[3] HAWORTH, E., Physiography of Kansas, Kan. Univ. Geol. Survey, vol. II, p. 19, 1896.

HAWORTH E., Underground Water of Southwestern Kansas, U. S. Geol. Survey, Wat. Sup. Pap. 6, 1897.

JOHNSON, W. D., loc. cit., p. 710, pl. CXXXIX B.

warrant.   The real buffalo wallow is a shallow depression which (regardless of origin) has been enlarged by the aid of animals. Herds of buffalo once thronged to temporary ponds.   Because of mud carried away after wading and wallowing, and the dust blown away on account of stamping and throwing up soil with their horns, many basins were much enlarged.   The grass being killed, wind erosion was also favored, even when no herd was present.   It will be readily seen that basins thus enlarged would lack the abrupt edge shown in Fig. 7.

Sand dunes occur here and there throughout this section as in most of the other sections of the Great Plains.   In many cases they fringe the leeward sides of rivers, deriving their sand from the channels.   In other cases they are due to the assorting action of the wind on the unconsolidated substratum of the High Plains.[1]   Where the grass is temporarily killed the wind may stir up the soil and carry away the silt to be added elsewhere to the widespread loam or loess, leaving the sand either in place as a residual mantle or urged gradually forward in migrating dunes.[2] Hills of sand, both residual and imported, occupy patches varying in size from a few square miles to a few hundred, occurring throughout the High Plains, but south of Nebraska they form only a very small proportion of the entire area.

Subdivision of the High Plains.—Most of what has been said thus far refers primarily to the High Plains south of the 41st parallel, roughly the course of the Platte River.   North of that line there are important differences which in a more minute subdivision of the United States would determine subsections.

At least four such divisions are determined in extent by the geological formations which underlie them.   Three of these

---

[1] GILBERT, G. K., *loc. cit.*, p. 578, shows that the prominent dune area in the Nepesta quadrangle, east of Pueblo, is of this origin; see also FISHER, CASSIUS A., Nepesta folio 135, p. 3, U. S. Geol. Survey; *cf.* GOULD, C. N., U. S. Geol. Survey, *Wat. Sup. Pap.* 154, p. 11, 1906, and *Wat. Sup. Pap.* 191, p. 35, 1907.

[2] Through almost its entire course across this section the Arkansas River is bordered on the south by a line of sand hills from 2 or 3 miles up to 20 miles in width.   It is assumed by Gilbert, *loc. cit.*, p. 580, that these represent the drift of sand from the Arkansas Channel.   HAWORTH, Kan. Univ. Geol. Survey, vol. II, p. 278, 1896, thinks these sand hills are largely residual. He infers this partly from an occasional covering of coarse gravel and partly from certain evidence that, in so far as they migrate at all, they are moving toward, rather than from, the stream.   This is not a safe generalization.

formations are the Arikaree on the west and north, the loess on the east and south, and the sand hills in the center. The typical High Plains farther south are on the Ogalalla (Pliocene) formation, which is much younger than the Arikaree (Miocene) but older than the sand hills and the loess (Pleistocene).[1] A fourth subdivision in the north is the Goshen Hole lowland in which the underlying Brule clay (Oligocene) has been deeply eroded. The distinctions which concern us here are not those of geologic age but it happens that the sediments deposited in these different periods, being of unlike character and age, are very differently eroded.

FIG. 8.—Pine Ridge escarpment, the northern limit of the High Plains; looking west near the Nebraska-Wyoming state line. High Plains (covered by Arikaree formation) on the left; Missouri Plateau (Brule formation) on the right. (*Darton, U. S. Geol. Survey.*)

Western Nebraska and Eastern Wyoming Upland.—In all the above descriptions the interstream tabular areas of the High Plains, excepting only the dune areas, have been spoken of as flat, the result of the constructional work of former streams. This description must be modified for the northern part of the High Plains, at least for the area outside the loess. The thick sheets of river-laid Arikaree deposits which covered the area west and north of the sand hills are much older than those farther

[1] DARTON, N. H., U. S. Geol. Survey, *Prof. Pap.* 17, p. 14, 1903.

south and have been greatly eroded.[1] This is known not only
by the topography but from remnants of the same formation
more than 1,000 ft. above the present general level.[2] The characteristic topography on the Arikaree formation between streams
in northwestern Nebraska and eastern Wyoming is one of broad,
nearly flat, or only gently rolling tabular uplands between
streams.[3] It is necessary to infer that the erosion surface is an
old one, *i.e.*, a peneplain. Superficially the remnants of the High
Plains between the valleys in northwestern Nebraska differ
little from those of western Texas, but even their very gently
rolling character indicates that they result from erosion, not
from deposition.[4]

It is this older part of the High Plains which ends at the
north in the prominent Pine Ridge escarpment (Fig. 8). How
far this escarpment has retreated southward is not known but
it must be at least 200 miles because remnants of the same
formation are found near the boundary between North and

[1] The Arikaree and Ogalalla are separated by an uncontormity, and it is
not improbable that down-cutting in the northern area went on at the same
time with upbuilding in the southern area, the two processes combining to
produce a continuous plain. The two are similar in origin and character
and at many places have not been accurately separated in the field. Hence
the indefiniteness of the boundary between the subsections.

[2] SMITH, W. S. T., Hartville folio 91, U. S. Geol. Survey, 1903.

[3] DARTON, N. H., U. S. Geol. Survey, *Prof. Pap.* 17, speaks of western
Nebraska as "typical Great Plains" (p. 9) and a former "smooth plain
sloping east" (p. 10) until uplifted in the Early Pleistocene and somewhat
trenched.

[4] The distinction here suggested between the young constructional
surface on the Ogalalla and the old destructional surface on the Arikaree,
is probably too sharp. On so porous a body as the Arikaree, and in a
climate at most only semihumid, run-off is necessarily small. Deposition
may occur wherever a stream is sufficiently weakened by percolation and
evaporation. So degradation and aggradation may be going on at the
same time at different places, producing a plain of gradation. The strips
and patches of newly deposited sediment would rest unconformably on
the older formation and would be assigned a different geologic age. In an
adjacent area, lower altitude or weaker stream action may cause the new
formation to cover the whole surface and be very thick. There would then
be little difference in the topographies of the two areas and the two formations would be very hard to delimit. This difficulty is experienced in
separating the Ogalalla from the Arikaree. When it is stated that the
Arikaree is decidedly older and was eroding while the Ogalalla was forming,
the conditions of such erosion may well have been somewhat as here
described. Hence the superficial contrast between the two is small.

South Dakota.[1] Locally the strata in this escarpment dip south and form a monoclinal ridge or cuesta, justifying the name "Pine Ridge." The shale in the lower part is often fantastically eroded, thus forming a belt of badlands, at places many miles in width.

Goshen Hole Lowland.—A feature of this northern part of the section is the Goshen Hole Basin or Lowland,[2] a great local widening of the North Platte Valley, 50 miles wide on the Wyoming-Nebraska boundary and gradually narrowing eastward in 150 miles to the normal width of the valley. Its bordering bluffs are 700 ft. high at the west end and are, in all essential respects, repetitions of the Pine Ridge escarpment.

This basin indicates that the Platte River has, or has had, in this part of its course a relatively steep gradient, sufficient to admit of down-cutting near the Nebraska-Wyoming line, though at places farther east the fall seems now to be deficient and the stream is probably aggrading. The lateral spread of the basin, like the recession of the Pine Ridge escarpment, is greatly favored by sapping. The hard but easily eroded Brule clay, noted for its badlands, underlies the more gravelly fluviatile deposit. The latter, while largely incoherent, is a protection against erosion because the water enters it instead of running off and eroding the surface.

Sand-hill District of Nebraska.—North of the Platte River and chiefly between the 99th and 103d meridians are 24,000 square miles within which a dune topography dominates[3] (Figs. 9 and 10). Some of these hills are several hundred feet high. Between lines of sand hills "hay meadows" occupy a small part of the area. There are also many lakes[4] in basins which owe their origins to drifting sand. Over several thousand square miles the dunes may be said to be still drifting; elsewhere they are more or less fixed. The area of drifting sand varies

---

[1] DARTON, N. H., U. S. Geol. Survey, *Prof. Pap.* 32, pls. XXXV and XLIV.

[2] For more detailed descriptions see U. S. Geol. Survey, folios 87 and 88; *Wat. Sup. Pap.* 70; and *Prof. Pap.* 17.

[3] DARTON, N. H., U. S. Geol. Survey, *Prof. Pap.* 17, pl. IX, geol. map of Nebraska.

[4] BARBOUR, E. H., Neb. Geol. Survey, *1st Rept.*, p. 67, 1903, states that 100 surveyed lakes have an aggregate area of 1,100 acres. In the two years 1919 to 1920 the brine lakes of western Nebraska produced over $3,000,000 worth of potash, or nearly one-third of the country's output for those years (U. S. Geol. Survey, *Press Bull.* 452, July, 1920).

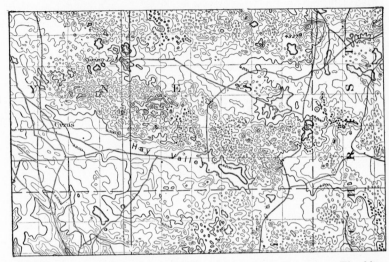

FIG. 9.—Topography of a sandhill tract in western Nebraska. The hilly portions are dune sand. Hay Valley and other flats are on the Arikaree formation. The small squares indicate miles. (*U. S. Geol. Survey, Camp Clarke, Neb., topographic sheet.*)

FIG. 10.—View in the sand hills of western Nebraska. Most of the total area is grass covered like the locality here shown. A minor portion consists of bare and drifting sand. (*Photo furnished by G. E. Condra.*)

with the rainfall from season to season. In rainy summers most of the area is well grassed and supports a considerable grazing industry. Barbour suggests[1] that the drifting of sand in this vast region was due, in part at least, to the great herds of buffalo. Because of close grazing, stamping, etc., the grass, which at best maintained a precarious supremacy over the wind, would be killed in some areas and the drifting of sand from these would aid in overpowering the grass elsewhere. He also cites the Indian habit of burning the grass. The belief is expressed by him that the present covering of grass has come largely since the disappearance of the buffalo and the Indian. Allowing due weight to these considerations, it is to be remembered that the buffalo and the Indian behaved in the same manner over a great extent of territory. The nature of the material at the surface has no doubt been an important factor.

Loess Plains.—East of the Sand-hill district the flatness of the tabular interstream uplands is, on the whole, less perfect than in the southern part of the section, but the existing surface is one of deposition and not of erosion or gradation as in western Nebraska. Here the surface has been recently renewed by a covering of loess whose general thickness in central Nebraska is not far from 100 ft.[2] The older surface beneath was probably much like that farther west beyond the limits of the loess. Its former inequalities were largely evened up by the new cover whose general flatness is exceeded only by that of the High Plains where well preserved. The spreading of this cover was largely the work of winds. No doubt some of the dust was derived from the flood plains and channels of overloaded streams[3] but in this arid region the supply of dust was probably less localized than in the more humid parts of the Mississippi Valley. To the south the loess overlaps the flat uplands of the

[1] *Loc. cit.*, p. 37.

[2] DARTON, N. H., U. S. Geol. Survey, *Prof. Pap.* 17, pp. 15–16. The same writer assigns a thickness of 60 to 90 ft. to the loess in eastern Nebraska, U. S. Geol. Survey, *Prof. Pap.* 32, p. 139. These great thicknesses are no doubt local.

[3] CHAMBERLIN, T. C., Supplementary Hypotheses respecting the Origin of the Loess of the Mississippi Valley, *Jour. Geol.*, vol. V, pp. 795–802, 1897; DARTON, N. H., U. S. Geol. Survey, *Prof. Pap.* 17, p. 16, does not mention wind action as a factor in Nebraska; GILBERT, G. K., U. S. Geol. Survey, *17th Ann. Rept.*, pt. II, p. 576, regards the occasional loess beds of eastern Colorado as probably æolian.

typical High Plains, thinning out in northern Kansas where it merges with the general soil sheet which is itself modified by wind assortment, leaving sand and gravel in some places and spreading dust wherever vegetation prevented wind erosion. This loess sheet in eastern Nebraska is spread alike over the much eroded surface of the older glacial drift of the Central Lowland and the Tertiary mantle of the Great Plains, obscuring the line of contact.

Stream Valleys.—It must not be assumed that the entire High Plains section is free from erosion. The long, transverse streams from the mountains cross this belt in wide, generally shallow, terraced valleys. The North Platte, South Platte, and Arkansas have valley bottoms from one to ten miles wide and generally not more than 100 to 300 ft. below the adjacent uplands, though there are exceptions as in Goshen Hole on the North Platte. It should also be noted that the smooth upland itself slopes toward the great rivers, Platte and Arkansas (see page 35). The Canadian, unlike the rivers named, has cut a well-defined valley nearly 1,000 ft. deep and 5 to 20 miles wide at the top. As the mantle rock is thin here, this valley is deep in the red sandstones beneath (*cf.* Pecos section, page 47).

The terracing of the great valleys is, of course, incidental to down-cutting. No doubt this continues to be the dominant process, but locally and temporarily the streams which cross the Great Plains are aggrading. There are various evidences of aggradation. Great numbers of sand bars strongly suggest it though they do not (as is sometimes assumed) constitute conclusive evidence. Parts of the Platte are thus distinguished by bars and braiding. Borings which indicate a depth of alluvium greater than that to which floods can scour, indicate that filling has taken place.[1]   Evidence of this kind seems to favor a moder-

[1] The following are some of the depths of alluvium reported: Arkansas Valley east of Pueblo, probably 50 to 60 ft.—Darton, U. S. Geol. Survey, *Prof. Pap.* 52, p. 35; Platte Valley in western Nebraska may be filled 70 to 80 ft.—Darton, Scott's Bluff folio 88; Arkansas Valley at Coolidge, Kansas, 35 to 50 ft.—Erasmus Haworth, Kan. Univ. Geol. Survey, vol. II, p. 27.

Allowing for the fact that all depths are probably measured from the surface of the flood plain (10 to 20 ft. above the channel bottoms) and allowing further for the uncertainty in estimates, the thickness of alluvium beyond the depths of possible scour is nowhere known to be great. No important conclusions should be based on such evidence until the fact is more conclusively demonstrated that the thickness of alluvium beneath stream channels is greater than the possible depth of scour.

ate amount of aggradation by streams of the Great Plains but the amounts are not large enough to be very convincing. Natural levees, *i.e.*, flood plains sloping from the stream, are much better evidence, but such features are not prominent in this province. The Platte River in the Camp Clarke quadrangle (western Nebraska) is paralleled for eight miles by a small intermittent tributary on the flood plain indicating that the slope here is away from the main stream, but such instances are few. Actual measurement is, of course, an evidence not to be set aside. In some cases this is afforded by bridges whose original heights above the flood plains are known.[1] On the whole it is not safe to affirm that the streams crossing the Great Plains are aggrading their channels except locally and temporarily.

The headward growth of small tributaries as they invade the sodded uplands of the High Plains is unlike that of stream heads in humid lands. The typical gully is wanting or begins farther down the valley. Instead of it, the side stream (or valley without stream) heads in a "draw," *i.e.*, a nearly flat-bottomed depression which is similar to (no doubt in some cases identical with) one of the smaller saucer-shaped or linear depressions described on page 15.[2] It is plain that sod plays an important part in this manner of initial erosion, apparently defying attack on the surface until the structure has been undermined by ground waters. Original flatness and permeability contribute to the delay by preventing the concentration of surface waters. In the ordinary case, underflow is concentrated along the axis of a valley, the valley being the cause and the underflow the effect. In this case the underflow seems to be primary.[3]

Consequent Drainage.—The consequent character of the streams which originate on the High Plains is evident. They

[1] HAWORTH, ERASMUS, Kan. Univ. Geol. Survey, vol. II, p. 28, states that all bridges over the Arkansas in the area described [western Kansas] were built high enough to permit a man on horseback to pass under. At the time of his writing [1896] many bridges built 8 to 12 years earlier were only three to six feet above the flood plain. He states further that there is "ample evidence that the river channel was formerly 50 to 100 ft. lower" and is now filling.

[2] HAWORTH, E., Physiography of Western Kansas, Kan. Univ. Geol. Survey, vol. II, p. 18, 1896; JOHNSON, W. D., *loc. cit.*, p. 710, pl. CXXXIX A.

[3] JOHNSON, W. D., *loc. cit.*, p. 711; also HAWORTH, E., Underground Waters of Southwestern Kansas, U. S. Geol. Survey, *Wat. Sup. Pap.* 6, p. 19, 1897.

flow in long, parallel, nearly straight courses down the original slope with a noteworthy absence of dendritic tributaries. The Niobrara is typical. It flows east nearly 400 miles without deviating more than 15 miles from the parallel of 42°40'. Such streams occupy very shallow, open valleys and are generally intermittent. The level of springs necessary to support perennial streams is not reached until the fluviatile deposit has been cut through, as the Niobrara finally succeeds in doing near the 100th meridian. As this deposit is relatively porous and rests on impervious shale, springs are quite common along the line of contact wherever the Tertiary mantle is cut through. The point at which the river cuts down through the Arikaree and associated fluviatile deposits into the nearly impervious Pierre shale is east of Fort Niobrara (long. 100°20'). Beyond that point the stream has a different character. The Republican and Smoky Hills Rivers, though heading on the High Plains, cut down quickly to the older (Cretaceous) rock beneath, and became perennial streams.[1] In western Nebraska no stream on the High Plains, north of the Platte, cuts down to the horizon of springs except in Goshen Hole. This is partly because of the greater thickness of the Tertiary mantle toward the north.

The distinctive character of the drainage affords the best means of delimiting the High Plains on the west (Fig. 2). In Wyoming this type of drainage extends west to the Rocky Mountains and is well exemplified by the parallel, east-flowing streams north of Cheyenne. Immediately south of the Colorado boundary there is a south-facing escarpment overlooking the lower South Platte Basin. Tributaries of this stream head in the escarpment and flow south. They are mainly subsequent in origin, at least in their headward portions. For one-half the distance from the Rocky Mountains to the Kansas boundary the Platte Basin is denuded of its Tertiary mantle. Within this area the southern tributaries of the trunk stream flow almost due north. The easternmost of these flows at the foot of a west-facing escarpment, which marks the limit of the preserved High Plains. From the top of that escarpment the drainage is eastward by numerous small parallel intermittent streams consequent

---

[1] HAWORTH, E., Kan. Univ. Geol. Survey, vol. II, pp. 21–42, describes the streams of Kansas individually with reference to rocks crossed, water supply, and topography of valleys.

on the original sloping surface of the fluviatile mantle (Ogalalla formation).[1]

Passing south into the Arkansas Basin, the relations are the same, a northwest-southeast divide separating the feeble east-flowing consequent streams of the High Plains from the tributaries of Sandy Creek which flows southeast to the Arkansas. The southern tributaries of the Arkansas which flow straight north over the denuded Cretaceous, are separated by a fairly definite divide from the characteristic east-flowing streams of the High Plains exactly as in the case of the Platte Basin. The same relations continue south to the end of the Llano Estacado.

Thus the western boundary of the High Plains in Colorado is a line drawn between the heads of the feeble east-flowing streams, which have done little to erode the fluviatile mantle, and the basins of the north- or south-flowing streams on the west where erosion has made large progress. The fluviatile mantle in the Colorado Piedmont portion of the Platte Valley is wholly destroyed. In the corresponding portion of the Arkansas Valley it survives only in patches.

PLAINS BORDER

Eastern Margin of the High Plains.—It has already been pointed out that the High Plains once extended farther east and that they are constantly losing ground by erosion. The area thus lost to the High Plains is being worn down to a lower base level. Between the narrowing High Plains on the west and the broadening Lowland on the east there is generally a strip of rougher country in which the work of erosion in the new cycle is incomplete. Where the strip is narrow, as in Texas, it is not assigned the rank of a separate physiographic section but is treated as a marginal phase of the High Plains. From the Canadian River to southern Nebraska the eroded strip is wide and is recognized as a separate section, the Plains Border (13 *e* on the general map).

The actual edge of the High Plains is a very crenulated line marked at many places by a scarp running in and out among stream heads and known as the "break of the plains." Several factors combine to develop this escarpment. One is the tight

[1] The drainage relations here described are well shown on the geological map of Colorado (1913); also on Darton's Preliminary Geologic Map of the Central Great Plains, U. S. Geol. Survey, *Prof. Pap.* 32, pl. XXXV.

sod cover of the upland which successfully resists erosion. Another is the ground water which readily descends through the porous Tertiary but issues in springs where porous sediments rest on a bed of clay or on the impervious shale. The former is thus sapped and the escarpment carried back and continuously freshened. This process of sapping rather than the simple headward growth of streams is the chief process involved in broadening the eroded border at the expense of the High Plains. It is an important agency which has attracted the attention of all students of the Great Plains wherever the Tertiary mantle has been cut through by erosion.

Fig. 11.—View in the Plains Border. The Tertiary mantle of the High Plains is preserved in the background. (*W. D Johnson, U. S. Geol. Survey.*)

Eroded Cuestas.—Generally speaking, the features here described are absent in Nebraska, partly because of the glacial drift east of the boundary and the thick loess mantle over all. The Plains Border becomes clear in northern Kansas where the outcrops of strata of diverse strength and dipping slightly westward afford conditions for east-facing escarpments. These are not confined to the Great Plains province but characterize the Central Lowland as well. In the latter, however, they are separated by smooth lowlands. One of these Central Lowland cuestas, the Flint Hills just east of the 97th meridian, is very prominent. It is suggested[1] that this ridge may have marked the eastern limit of the stream-laid sediments of the High Plains.

Within the Plains Border three formations of the Cretaceous system give rise to east-facing escarpments, for the most part maturely dissected and appearing as broad hilly belts. The easternmost of these outcrops is that of the Dakota formation (a strong sandstone at the top with weaker shales below) which forms a maturely dissected cuesta 200 to 300 ft. high in lat. 39°, but declining in altitude southward toward the Arkansas River and becoming more and more obscured toward the north by glacial drift and loess. The name Smoky Hills is applied to this belt.[2] West of Salina the name Kearney Hills is applied.[3] The eastern margin of this hilly belt is taken as the boundary of the section and of the Great Plains province. The escarpment is not steep or striking except in the vicinity of streams where it may be very rugged, but broad lowlands are absent west of this line. Twenty-five to thirty miles farther west is a similar belt or eroded cuesta called "Blue Hills" on the outcrop of the Benton limestone, and after a similar interval a third line of hills,[4] formed by the outcropping of the Niobrara chalk which stretches in a broad zigzag belt from Jewell County, Kansas, southwest almost to the Arkansas River.

Great Bend Lowland.—In central Kansas where the Arkansas River turns far to the north in the "Great Bend," all the above-named cuestas turn strongly westward on the north side of the river and die out in the general level of the High Plains. South of the Arkansas the characteristic Tertiary cover and the flat topography of the High Plains[5] go east almost to the 98th meridian and there merge gradually into the Central Lowland. There is thus a break of more than 50 miles in which no province boundary is apparent. The diminishing cuestas which turn southwest on the north side of the Great Bend make bluffs of

[1] DARTON, N. H., U. S. Geol. Survey, *Prof. Pap.* 32, p. 186, 1905.

[2] ADAMS, GEORGE, Physiography of Kansas, Amer. Geogr. Soc. *Bull.*, vol. 24, p. 102, 1892.

[3] HAWORTH, E., Kan. Univ. Geol. Survey, vol. II.

[4] HAWORTH, E., *loc. cit.*, p. 47.

[5] HAWORTH, E., *loc. cit.*, p. 47; by definition the Plains Border is the eroded margin of the Great Plains province. Its limits are necessarily generalized. The large uneroded or little eroded patch south of the Arkansas river is exceptional.

moderate height, but on the south side the valley merges with the broad Tertiary plain.

The term "Great Bend Lowland" is applied to the immediate valley of the river and to an indefinite extent to this plain on the south. This "lowland" is not low with respect to the country north, south, or east of it. It is in reality an eastward extension or outlying part of the High Plains, as indicated both by its mantle rock and its topography. The general level is at least as high as the divides along the same meridian either to the north or south.[1] It is a lowland only in the sense of being but little above the local (temporary) base level of the Arkansas River, which therefore fails to trench it deeply, while streams to the north and south with greater cutting power have carved valleys 300 to 400 ft. deep.[2] Probably one reason for this inability of the Arkansas to degrade its valley in Kansas is found in its crossing of the strong rocks of the Flint-Hills belt after turning south into Oklahoma. This resistant highland is crossed in a narrow valley with local rapids, while the valley above is broad and indefinite and the gradient small.[3]

Red Hills.—This so-called "Great Bend Lowland" finds no natural limit on the south, short of the ragged and picturesque escarpment 300 to 400 ft. high which borders the Great Plains between the Arkansas and Cimarron Rivers. This escarpment is not a single abrupt descent but a deeply eroded belt 10 to 20 miles wide, known as the Red Hills. The descent here combines the "breaks of the plains" with the retreating escarpment of

[1] See Contour Map of Kansas by Henry Gannett, U. S. Geol. Survey, *Bull.* 154, 1898.

[2] HAWORTH, E., in U. S. Geol. Survey, *Wat. Sup. Pap.* 6, points out that in Kansas between the 100th and 101st meridians, the Arkansas seems to run on a ridge of its own construction. Small streams, a short distance away, run from the river instead of toward it.

[3] The so-called "Great Bend Lowland" is sometimes spoken of (following Geo. I. Adams, *loc. cit.*, p. 97) as an arm of the "Prairies" or Central Lowland. This is partly because the topographies of any two plains are superficially similar and there is no break between this and the lowland plains of south central Kansas. It is partly because the valley of the Arkansas River in this "Great Bend Lowland" is agriculturally favored, as are some other large valleys within the Great Plains. It should, however, be borne in mind that physiographic divisions, while very significant in the study of agricultural distributions, are not determined by that criterion and that dividing lines drawn on a basis of agriculture agree only approximately with those fixed by physiography.

the underlying rocks.   The upland level is held locally by beds
of gypsum which, while very soluble in a humid climate or by
circulating ground waters, make a resistant cover in a dry
climate.   The white gypsum, underlain by bright-red sands and
shales, gives gorgeous coloring to the escarpment, already
picturesque on account of its terraced canyons, jutting headlands,
branching divides, and outlying buttes.[1]

Fig. 12.—St. Jacob's Well, Clark County, Kansas; a detail of topography
due to solution near the edge of the Plains Border.   In this vicinity the Tertiary
mantle, where present at all, is underlain by salt-bearing Permian beds.   Subsurface solution permits the surface to collapse, sometimes in well-outlined
sink holes, sometimes in irregular sunken patches making a most disorderly
topography.   (*W. D. Johnson, U. S. Geol. Survey.*)

In the vicinity of this escarpment, the saucer-shaped depressions of the High Plains give place to much deeper and more
abrupt basins due to solution of salt or, in places, gypsum in the
underlying Permian rocks.   Such basins may be miles in extent
and very irregular.   Some of them contain permanent lakes.
Many of them may be so closely grouped as to interlock, causing
a seemingly lawless and tumultuous topography.[2]   Scattered
sand dunes are also present.

[1] Descriptions of the scenery along this escarpment by several writers are
quoted by C. S. Prosser, Kan. Univ. Geol. Survey, vol. II. p. 85.

[2] Johnson, W. D., *loc. cit.*, p. 706.

South of Kansas the outcrops of the several formations appearing in the Red Hills diverge. Those of the main gypsum beds and stronger sandstone form the Gypsum Hills which trend east of south, becoming less and less prominent toward the south. The edge of the overlying Tertiary trends west of south, located generally at the top of a much eroded slope. South of the Canadian River the Plains Border is very narrow and is included in the High Plains section.

COLORADO PIEDMONT

Demarkation of the Area.—Aside from the broad valleys of the Platte and Arkansas the Tertiary cover of the High Plains is almost unbroken along the eastern boundary of Colorado. On account of greater erosion farther west, this cover has mainly disappeared, its remnants being smaller, more scattered, and less flat. Where the mantle is entirely wasted away, the underlying rocks are themselves much eroded. The area which owes its topography to this dissection and denudation is the Colorado Piedmont (13 *f* on the general map). The outline of this section, as shown on the map, reveals at once its close relation to the two chief river systems which are the agents of stripping. Along the axis of the Platte Valley, the denuded area extends far into northeastern Colorado, and along the Arkansas it reaches to the Kansas boundary. On the divide between these rivers the stripping is less perfect, and north of the South Platte the High Plains extend west to the mountains.

The northern boundary of the Colorado Piedmont is almost coincident with that of the state. North of this line the streams of Wyoming and Nebraska flow east in consequent fashion down the original slope of the Tertiary mantle, having an elevation of a mile above sea-level where they cross the Wyoming-Nebraska line. Along the same meridian, the South Platte, 50 miles to the south, is 1,000 ft. lower. Its small northern tributaries head against the south-facing break of the Tertiary upland. In eastern Colorado the edge of the High Plains trends more nearly north and south, and is similarly marked by a divide described on page 24.

For some purposes it is convenient to treat the Colorado Piedmont as extending south to the Raton Mesas and the Park Plateau near the southern boundary of Colorado. This has the advantage of giving a definite and visible boundary, but the surface for 50 miles north of those highlands is more closely allied, both in topography and physiographic history, to the Raton section. It is therefore treated under that head (see page 37), despite the fact that it merges gradually into the Colorado Piedmont.

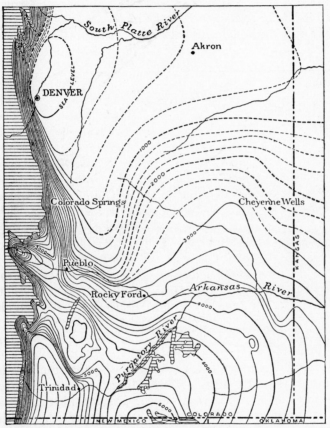

Fig. 13.—Map showing structure of the Dakota sandstone in Colorado. Contour interval 500 ft. Lighter shading indicates higher elevation. (*Reduced from Darton, U. S. Geol. Survey, Bull.* 691.)

Structure and Topography.—Taken as a whole, this section presents an old erosion surface, broadly rolling but locally scarped, such as might be expected to result in an arid climate from a considerable degradation of rocks which are on the whole weak but not uniformly so, and embracing a few strong formations. It slopes east from an average altitude of 5,000 ft. in the great valleys and 7,000 ft. on the central divide.   The altitude of the Colorado-Kansas boundary is uniformly a little below 4,000 ft. except in the immediate vicinity of the large streams.

A more exact description of the topography must take into account the nature of the underlying rock formations.   The distribution of these at the surface is determined by the structure which is briefly as follows:[1] At the mountain foot all strata dip steeply eastward.   The Dakota sandstone, which crops out in the well-known "Dakota Hogback" of the foothills, descends to

Fig. 14.—Flat remnant of Timpas limestone on Carlisle shale, Pueblo County, Colorado.   The growth of pinyon trees on its summit is charactistic.   (*U. S. Geol. Survey.*)

sea-level within a few miles (Fig. 13).   Farther east, all beds rise at a very gentle angle.   There is therefore a structural basin near the mountains, deepest under Denver where relatively young formations are as a consequence preserved.   South of Pueblo a strong upward fold extends southeast, bringing to the surface the same Dakota sandstone which is a mile deep under Denver.   The crest of this fold, because of its distinctive topography, belongs to the Raton section.

On the northern side of this fold, in the immediate valley of the Arkansas, there comes to the surface over large areas an

[1] DARTON, N. H., U. S. Geol. Survey, *Prof. Pap.* 52, p. 56, pl. XXVI, 1906; Structure of the Dakota Sandstone, U. S. Geol. Survey, *Bull.* 691 A, pl. I; U. S. Geol. Survey, *Prof. Pap.* 32, pls. X, XI, and LVIII.

important limestone (Niobrara) which lies far below the surface farther north. This formation appears at the surface in low ridges or lines of limestone hills, or in cuestas with much dissected scarps, occasionally 400 to 500 ft. high (Fig. 14). As compared with the mildly rolling topography on the widespread soft shale elsewhere, the area underlain by the limestone has a decidedly angular or plateau-like topography. For 25 miles above (west of) Pueblo, the Arkansas River runs in a narrow trench, almost

Fig. 15.—Tepee Buttes east of Pueblo, in the Colorado Piedmont section. The one in the foreground shows the concretion or "core" whose resistance to erosion has preserved the butte. (*U. S. Geol. Survey.*)

without flood plain, cut several hundred feet deep in a plateau of this limestone.

Shale is the most abundant rock in the Colorado Piedmont, and on its surface the topography is broadly rolling, but sandstone is interbedded with the shale in the Platte Basin, as limestone is in the Arkansas Basin.[1] The sandstone has a topographic effect similar to that of the limestone but less marked. North of the

[1] For areas underlain by the formations named, see geologic map of Colorado. Strong limestone strata are found in the Benton and Niobrara formations widely exposed in the Arkansas Basin, while strong sandstone strata are found in the formations underlying most of the Platte Basin.

Arkansas River and east of Pueblo are considerable areas where the surface formation is the soft Pierre shale worn down to low relief. The surface in this particular locality has a peculiar interest because of the striking conical hills called "tepee buttes."[1] In this otherwise uniform shale, giant limestone concretions or "cores" occur, some of them 10 ft. in diameter. In the general degradation of the surface these hard concretions protect cones of shale, some of them several hundred feet high. These are the "tepee buttes." A score of such cones may sometimes be seen in a single view (Fig. 15).

On a substratum of shale, small natural lake basins are not uncommon.[2] Most of these are due to wind action, generally to scour, but perhaps in some cases to deposits obstructing drainage ways. Other basins may be explained in part as "buffalo wallows" (see page 15).

Over a large area in the Arkansas Basin, the Tertiary mantle has not been wholly removed, though somewhat eroded. As on the High Plains, the materials of this deposit are subject to wind erosion and assorting (see page 16). The most striking dune area of Colorado is thus produced. It lies some 20 miles northeast of Pueblo, where it covers at least 100 square miles.[3] Other dunes derive their sand from streams, especially from those northern tributaries of the Arkansas which are now rehandling the material of the Tertiary mantle. The prevailing wind is from the northwest, building lines of dunes on the lee sides of many streams.[4] The Arkansas is fringed by such a line on its south side from La Junta (long. 103°30′) eastward across this section and almost across the High Plains (see page 16).

The highest part of the Platte-Arkansas divide, *i.e.*, the part nearest the mountains, was never covered by the fluviatile mantle which surfaced the High Plains,[5] though it was similarly covered by a much older sheet.[6] Parts of these older deposits are now

---

[1] A tepee is a conical tent, used by many Indian tribes.

[2] Stose, Geo. W., Apishapa folio 186, p. 11, U. S. Geol. Survey, 1912.

[3] Nepesta folio 135, U. S. Geol. Survey, 1906.

[4] Gilbert, G. K., Underground Waters of the Arkansas Valley in Eastern Colorado, U. S. Geol. Survey, *17th Ann. Rept.*, pt. II, p. 578, 1896; see also footnote, p. 16.

[5] Darton, N. H., U. S. Geol. Survey, *Prof. Pap.* 32, pl. XLIV.

[6] Monument Creek Formation (Oligocene), U. S. Geol. Survey, *Prof. Pap.* 52, p. 49; and Castle Rock Conglomerate, Castle Rock folio 198, p. 3, U. S. Geol. Survey.

strong conglomerate and make a topography of rather sharp relief. Steep bluffs and mesa fronts 400 ft. high are not uncommon, and the local relief occasionally rises to 700 ft. In addition to this, the greater altitude, 6,500 to 7,500 ft., causes greater rainfall so that there is here much park land and even some good forest. The general appearance of this relatively small district is therefore quite different from that of the section in general.

The two great valleys, Platte and Arkansas, so far as they lie within the Colorado Piedmont, are not mere erosion trenches in an otherwise smooth surface. A north-south section along the 104th meridian shows first a descent of 1,000 ft. from the Wyoming boundary to the South Platte; then a similar ascent of 1,500 ft. to the divide, from which there is again a continuous descent of 1,500 ft. to the Arkansas, followed by a similar ascent to the New Mexico boundary. It is not necessary to assume that these north-south slopes have all come into existence in the present erosion cycle or that they were entirely absent when the smooth fluviatile sheet overspread the plains. Remembering the manner in which that surface was formed, it is quite possible that the confluent sediments of many streams may have made the surface smooth without making it strictly level. It has been estimated[1] that the great streams have cut down their valleys from 400 to 800 ft. since the Tertiary mantle was spread. The balance of the nearly 1,500-ft. difference in level between streams and divide may be ascribed to slopes antedating the erosion.

Résumé of Physiographic History of the Central Great Plains. A long cycle of erosion, probably when the altitude was much less than at present, left the region with a relief of some hundreds of feet. Following climatic changes or crustal movement which caused loss of gradient (in either case a loss of stream power), the area was covered by a smooth fluviatile mantle which buried all but the highest hills.[2] Near the mountains on the west the surface sloped not only east but also north and south from the Platte-Arkansas divide. Then followed climatic change or an uplift on the west which inaugurated a new erosion cycle.

The master streams flowed nearly east over this smooth surface while tributaries descended the smooth slopes from the Platte-Arkansas divide. The general parallelism of these side

---

[1] GILBERT, G. C., U. S. Geol. Survey, 17th Ann. Rept., pt. II, p. 577, 1896.

[2] This mantle is mainly the Ogalalla (Pliocene) formation and is probably the depositional correlative of the last Rocky Mountain peneplain (p. 107).

streams is suggestive of their consequent character and of the smoothness of the slopes which guided them. Farther east (present High Plains) similar consequent streams, originating on the plains, took parallel easterly courses.

The South Platte and Arkansas, being through-flowing streams from the more humid mountains, soon cut down several hundred feet in their upper courses. Streams originating on the plains carried relatively little water, because of the smaller rainfall and the porosity of the substratum. Except where specially favored by steep gradients they have done little work. Those that flow down the lateral slopes of the Platte-Arkansas divide had the original advantage of steeper gradients. The steepness was further increased by the lowering of their mains. Here the Piedmont was denuded, but farther east where the lateral slopes of the Platte-Arkansas divide were insignificant, the original consequent streams flowed straight east, and were so long that the gradients were insufficient to admit of much erosion. W. D. Johnson, in his classical treatment of the High Plains and Their Utilization, accounts for the greater erosion of the Colorado Piedmont by the single factor of vegetation. The initial gradient of streams is not considered. It is noteworthy that in southern Wyoming where the streams flow directly eastward on a low gradient from the mountains, the Tertiary mantle has never been stripped though the vegetation is similar to that of Colorado. In accounting for the stripping of the Colorado Piedmont, a third factor is found in the fact that the original fluviatile mantle thinned out toward the crest of the central divide which was never covered.

In their down-cutting, the main streams and larger tributaries developed broad terraces which were left coated with gravel (and no doubt loam), as the stream cut to lower levels. In the Colorado Piedmont, fragments of such terraces are found a dozen miles from the main streams, the older and higher ones being generally gravelly because later erosion by water and wind has removed their surface loam. The lower terraces, still loam-covered, are the famous irrigated lands of the Platte and Arkansas Valleys.

The eastern edge of the fluviatile mantle has retreated westward, partly by reason of the simple headward growth of east-flowing streams and partly through the agency of springs at its base. For some distance south of the Arkansas River, this retreating edge is closely followed by that of the Permian beds beneath, the incipient peneplains of the Central Lowland crowding close upon the wasting upland. North of the Arkansas River the wasting of the High Plains has left a surface of broken cuestas (Smoky Hills and others).

RATON SECTION

General Characteristics.—It has already been stated that the fluviatile mantle of the High Plains was once approximately continuous to the mountains on the west. The now eroded zone between the mountains on the west and the surviving High Plains extends from the Wyoming boundary to western Texas. Throughout most of these 700 miles the present relief is due to denudation since the cycle of aggradation in which the High Plains were made. A portion of this eroded strip (denuded or never covered) in southern Colorado and northern New Mexico is characterized by greater altitude; also by relief which is not only stronger than elsewhere but of different style and having a longer and more complex history. This is the Raton section (13 *g* on the general map). The prominent features of the topography are high mesas, extensive dissected plateaus, deep canyons, and volcanic mountains of various ages.

No sharp line separates this section from the Colorado Piedmont. On the south, however, it ends in the great Canadian escarpment overlooking the Pecos section. The position of this feature is shown on the geologic map by the edge of the Cretaceous system. West of long. 104° this escarpment is 1,000 to 1,500 ft. high. To the east and northeast it is lower but continues prominent to western Oklahoma.

The section falls naturally into three subdivisions superficially distinguished by their different altitudes, but having more fundamental differences (Fig. 16).[1] Named in order from the lowest to the highest, these are: (1) The Las Vegas Plateau, with its extension the Chaquaqua Plateau,[2] a stratum plain[3]

---

[1] *Cf.* HILL, R. T., Physical Geography of the Texas Region, U. S. Geol. Survey, Topographic folio 3, p. 8, 1899; LEE, WILLIS T., Raton-Brilliant Koehler folio 214, U. S. Geol. Survey, 1922.

[2] The Las Vegas Plateau is properly limited to New Mexico. Its extension or equivalent in Colorado is here called the Chaquaqua Plateau from the name of the largest stream within its borders.

[3] A stratum plain or stripped plain is a degradational plain whose surface is dependent not on base level but on a resistant stratum. Examples of limited extent are common.

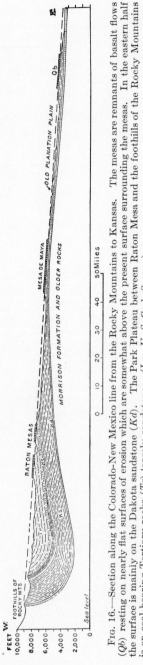

FEET W.

10,000
8,000
6,000
4,000
2,000
0

FOOTHILLS OF ROCKY MTS

RATON MESAS

MESA DE MAYA

MORRISON FORMATION AND OLDER ROCKS

OLD PLANATION PLAIN

Qb

Sea level

0   10   20   30   40   50 Miles

Fig. 16.—Section along the Colorado-New Mexico line from the Rocky Mountains to Kansas. The mesas are remnants of basalt flows (Qb) resting on nearly flat surfaces of erosion which are somewhat above the present surface surrounding the mesas. In the eastern half the surface is mainly on the Dakota sandstone (Kd). The Park Plateau between Raton Mesa and the foothills of the Rocky Mountains is on coal-bearing Tertiary rocks (Tr) largely sandstone. (Lee, U. S. Geol. Survey.)

trenched by canyons and surmounted by volcanic buttes, lava cones, and remnantal mesas; (2) the Park Plateau,[1] a much dissected highland in the western part of the section abutting against the mountains in Colorado and northern New Mexico; and (3) the Raton Mesa group consisting of lava-capped remnants of a still higher plain. The best known of these remnants form a belt extending eastward along the Colorado-New Mexico boundary on the divide between the Purgatoire and Cimarron Rivers. The length of this belt is about 100 miles and its breadth, counting outliers, about 40 miles, but the breadth of any single remnant is much less than that. The group includes also the Ocate lava-capped mesa at the foot of the Rocky Mountains in New Mexico.[2]

Structure.—The topographic forms within this section are intimately connected with the rocks from which they are carved, and the presence of any one formation at the surface is in turn dependent on structure. The dominant structural feature is a synclinal trough beneath the Park Plateau, and a broad anticline or dome

[1] So named by R. C. Hill, Walsenburg folio 68, U. S. Geol. Survey, 1900.

[2] The rough outlines of these subdivisions may be seen on the Willis Geological Map of North America, on which the Las Vegas Plateau appears as Cretaceous locally covered by volcanic rocks; the Park Plateau as earliest Tertiary or latest Cretaceous, and the Raton Mesa group as volcanic. All outlines are shown better on the geologic maps of Colorado and New Mexico.

east of this, beneath the Raton Mesa group (Figs. 13 and 16).[1]
On account of this upward bulge, denudation has exposed older
strata on the east, while much younger and higher strata are
preserved in the syncline near the mountains. Outcrops in the
eastern part of the Park Plateau show westward dips and, where
strong strata are present, east-facing scarps. From the broad
anticline or dome beneath the Mesa de Maya (Fig. 16) a low
arch or anticline trends northwest to the Front Range of the
Rocky Mountains. At intervals along this line the geologic map

Fig. 17.—Fishers Peak, the western extremity of the Raton Mesa, isolated
by erosion. The slopes of the mesa are not everywhere so steep but the relation
between the protecting lava sheets above and the protected shales and sandstones below is everywhere the same. (*U. S. Geol. Survey, El Moro folio.*)

shows the strong Dakota sandstone at the surface, a fact of
prime importance in the explanation of the canyons.

Raton Mesa Group.—The Raton Mesa proper is the highest
and best known representative of the group to which it gives the
name. Its western end is just east of the meridian 104°30′,
near Trinidad, Colorado. This extremity is somewhat isolated
by erosion and known as Fishers Peak (Fig. 17). It is 9,586
ft. above sea-level and nearly 4,000 ft. above the Purgatoire

[1] DARTON, N. H., Geology and Underground Waters of the Arkansas
Valley in Eastern Colorado, U. S. Geol. Survey, *Prof. Pap.* 52, p. 9, pl.
VII. 1906; also U. S. Geol. Survey, *Prof. Pap.* 32, pl. XI.

River. The altitude of the group as a whole declines eastward
for 80 miles, where the lava cap comes to an end near the 103d
meridian, its surface at that place being little above the surrounding level. The several mesas of the group are separated
by gaps within which the lava cap has been removed by erosion.
The large remnant which extends eastward from near the middle
of the group almost to the 103d meridian is known as the Mesa de
Maya (Spanish for "table of mail," or armored mesa). The
name suggests the inevitable impression made by the form of the
table land, namely that it is protected by its covering.

The basalt sheets which cap and protect the mesas rest on
fragments of an old erosion surface or peneplain which bevels the
gently dipping strata. The cap is locally 500 ft. thick and breaks
off in steep cliffs, at places almost vertical. The softer rocks
on which it rests form gentler slopes, locally much eroded.

As the height of the mesas increases westward, the degree
of erosion also becomes greater in that direction. But even near
its western end, basins holding lakes on its surface are not yet
destroyed.[1]

The Ocate Mesa is north of the Mora River in New Mexico and
partially separated by its headwaters from the Sangre de Cristo
Range of the Rocky Mountains. Its altitude is approximately
the same as that of the Raton Mesa proper and it is similarly
covered with and protected by sheets of lava now somewhat
eroded and locally removed. Ocate Crater, 9,000 ft. high,
rises above its southern end.[2]

Park Plateau.—The Park Plateau is 40 miles wide on the
Colorado-New Mexico boundary where it extends from the
Rocky Mountains to the Raton Mesa. With diminishing width
it extends 60 miles northward to Huerfano Park, a deep indenta-
tion of the mountain front. In like manner it extends 30 miles
southward to Ute Park on the upper Cimarron River. In
southern Colorado its altitude is 8,500 ft. on the west side and
7,000 to 7,500 ft. on the east, where it presents an escarpment
of 500 to 1,000 ft. The altitude of its eastern edge does not
vary greatly throughout its length and an escarpment of 500
ft. is fairly well maintained.

---

[1] HILLS, R. C., El Moro folio 58, U. S. Geol. Survey, 1899; LEE, WILLIS
T., U. S. Geol. Survey, folio 214, p. 3, 1922.

[2] HILL, R. T., Physical Geography of the Texas Region, U. S. Geol. Survey, Topographical folio 3, p. 8, 1899.

The rocks of the Park Plateau are, in part, strong sandstones. Though dipping toward the central axis they have been base leveled (Fig. 16). The strength of the rocks beneath this old peneplain has preserved its level on the hilltops while the same peneplain was wholly destroyed farther east and replaced by another at a lower level. Meantime the Park Plateau was dissected. Near the Purgatoire River, which drains most of the Colorado portion and which runs in a narrow valley more than 500 ft. deep, dissection is almost mature. The same is true of the New Mexico portion. Farther north it may be called submature,

Fig. 18.—Spanish Peaks from the northwest with Park Plateau in the foreground. The great dyke is characteristic of this district. The plateau at the left, capped by early Tertiary sandstone, is like many other remnants of the submaturely dissected Park Plateau. (*U. S. Geol. Survey, folio* 71.)

Though not of volcanic origin, the Park Plateau has noteworthy features of igneous origin. Chief among these are the Spanish Peaks (13,623 ft.) which, though lying close to the mountains, belong essentially to the plains. They rise from a plateau of almost horizontal rocks while between them and the mountains runs the usual line of hogback foothills, very picturesquely developed where crossed by the Purgatoire River.[1]

The Spanish Peaks (Fig. 18) are twin mountains of igneous origin, much eroded but having roughly conical forms. Many

[1] HILLS, R. C., Spanish Peaks folio 71, U. S. Geol. Survey, 1901. Excellent illustrations are given of the Spanish Peaks district.

radiating dikes extend far out on the plains. Standing like great stone walls above their surroundings and interfering with the development of drainage, these dikes have retarded somewhat the general wasting of the surface.

Las Vegas Plateau.—The Las Vegas Plateau proper lies south of the Raton Mesas. The Chaquaqua Plateau north of the mesas, corresponding to the Las Vegas Plateau both geologically and physiographically, is treated here as a part of the latter. The surface of both is in the main a stratum plain on the strong Dakota sandstone which is deeply buried beneath other parts of the Great Plains. As the high mesas are approached, the stripping is less complete and the surface rises gradually over higher formations to the lava caps which have protected them. Where the surface approximately coincides with that of the Dakota sandstone the relief is small, but near the Park Plateau on the west, higher formations are encountered dipping appreciably westward. One or more limestone cuestas are thus formed (at least in the Colorado portion) which on account of erosion are highly irregular both in altitude and in general direction. These are often conspicuous by being dark with pinyon and juniper in the midst of a treeless country. The Timpas (Niobrara) cuesta thus presents an eroded escarpment several hundred feet high. Mesas of this limestone are common (Fig. 14, page 32). On a local dome crossed by the Apishapa River[1] the topography thus produced is distinctly rough, having a relief of 600 ft.

Rising above the Las Vegas Plateau are various volcanic features. The high mesas protected by lava flows which preceded the widespread denudation of the Dakota sandstone have already been mentioned. Later lava sheets, preserved in whole or part according to their age, rise little above the general level, some even entering the canyons of the present cycle. A few volcanic cones like Capulin (long. 104°, and 15 miles south of the Colorado boundary) are so recent as to be unaffected by erosion or even weathering.[2] At the other extreme of age are many volcanic necks which stud the plain near the Mesa de Maya.

The principal streams cut deep canyons into the stratum plain. In all cases these canyons are cut into or through the

---

[1] Stose, Geo. W., Apishapa folio 186, U. S. Geol. Survey, 1912.

[2] Lee, Willis T., Extinct Volcanoes of Northeast New Mexico, *Amer. Forestry*, vol. XVIII, pp. 357–365, 1912.

Dakota sandstone which therefore forms the rim or brink.[1]
Running off to the northeast from near the Spanish Peaks, the
Cuchara River flows 15 miles in an open valley over soft rocks
before the stratum plain is reached. Into this it cuts a canyon
500 ft. deep.[2] Southeast of it the Apishapa in crossing the
Dakota sandstone, brought to the surface by the same anticline,
cuts a similar canyon more than 400 ft. deep (Fig. 19). The
Purgatoire River after leaving the Park Plateau flows 25 miles
in an open valley before reaching the stratum plain, then enters a

FIG. 19.—Canyon of the Apishapa River, southeastern Colorado, a characteristic valley in that part of the Raton section which is immediately underlain
by the Dakota sandstone. At the top is the strong Dakota sandstone, whose
surface is a stripped plain. Weaker sandstones underlie the Dakota. Depth,
300 ft. (*U. S. Geol. Survey, folio* 186.)

canyon 70 miles long (measured in a straight line) and 900 ft.
deep in its middle portion. Besides other tributaries it receives
the Chaquaqua in the deepest part of the canyon. Together,
these streams, having destroyed the Dakota cap for a width of
10 or 12 miles, have cut deep into the bright-red rocks beneath,
making what is known locally as the "Red Rocks Country,"
a broad valley with irregular canyon walls, with side canyons
promontories, outlying remnants, and rock terraces.

[1] LEE, WILLIS T., U. S. Geol. Survey, folio 214; Canyons of Colorado.
Jour. Geogr., vol. I, 1902; Canyons of Northeastern New Mexico, *Jour.
Geogr.*, vol. II, 1903. Much information concerning the whole section is
contained in these papers.

[2] Walsenburg folio 68, U. S. Geol. Survey, 1900.

South of the Mesa de Maya, the Dry Cimarron River runs east through a canyon much like that of the Purgatoire in dimensions, style, and geologic relations. The upper Canadian River, flowing south at the front of the Park and Ocate Plateaus, has cut a much deeper canyon, 1,500 ft., but it is still a V-shaped gorge like the Cuchara Canyon, not a broad-bottomed one like

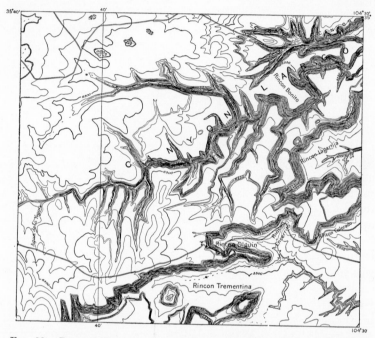

Fig. 20.—Part of Watrous, New Mexico, topographic sheet. The plateau embracing the center of this area, approximately 6,500 ft. high, is determined by the Dakota sandstone and belongs to the Raton section. The contours show that it is a nearly flat surface cut by sharp canyons. A 1,000-ft. escarpment runs diagonally across the area cutting off the southeastern part which is 1,000 ft. lower and belongs to the Pecos section. The vigorous dissection of the upper plateau is due to the proximity of the lower plain. (*U. S. Geol. Survey.*)

the two just mentioned. Tributaries to these southern canyons are not numerous. Few head within the Las Vegas Plateau. Most of the streams named, except the Dry Cimarron, head in the mountains or on the higher and more humid Park Plateau or Raton Mesas. The wonderful Dakota-capped Canadian escarpment which limits the Las Vegas Plateau on the south is not greatly notched by streams (Fig. 20).

Physiographic History.—The physiographic history of this section begins with a cycle of erosion which produced the peneplain whose fragments still survive beneath the lava caps of the Raton and Ocate Mesas. On the surface of this peneplain beneath the lavas are gravel and other subaerial sediments similar to those that cover the High Plains. It is not improbable that the old surface here preserved in fragments was continuous with that of the High Plains, and that in late Tertiary time it covered most of the Great Plains province. It may also be correlated with the last and most widespread of the Rocky Mountain peneplains.[1] According to this view the mountains, subject to degradation, and the plains, subject to aggradation, together constituted a vast graded plain. The whole was then uplifted, during or after which event occurred widespread flows of basalt.

Already at this time the plateau-making Dakota sandstone was stripped along the eastern edge of the section, where it is now found immediately below the basalt cap. The beveled surface beneath the cap truncates younger and younger strata toward the west including the early Eocene. With succeeding uplifts the stripping of the Dakota advanced westward.

Neither the crustal rise nor the lowering by erosion was uninterrupted. The outpouring of basalt on the elevated peneplain was followed by successive rises between which were halts long enough for the development of broad valleys or local peneplains. No doubt all these surfaces were to some extent covered with gravel and finer alluvium as are the High Plains. These in turn were covered by lava flows. Their remnants constitute the lower mesas, Bartlett and others, that cluster round the higher Raton remnants.

The Park Plateau is the most extensive remnant of one of these intermediate peneplains. Its general level (about 7,800 ft. near the eastern margin) is not much below that of the lava-covered mesas farther east, but both surfaces rise toward the west. That of the lava, if projected westward, would pass several hundred feet above the Park Plateau (Fig. 16, page 38). This plateau consists in part of resistant sandstones. In the last great cycle of erosion, during which the Dakota sandstone farther east was in large part stripped of its overlying weaker sediments, these sandstones of the Park Plateau were strong

[1] LEE, WILLIS T., Raton folio 214, p. 13, U. S. Geol. Survey, 1922.

enough to maintain its altitude, though the plateau was dissected to maturity.

The present streams took their courses over the lowest and youngest peneplain, presumably near the end of the Tertiary or later. To some extent these streams were superimposed on alluvium,[1] the so-called "Tertiary mantle," the deposition of which may have been due to change of gradient or to climatic change.[2] Some of the canyons are cut across local uplifts which occurred after the spreading of the Tertiary mantle.[3] The effect of this last folding was small and it must not be confused with the greater folding several thousand feet high which brings the Dakota sandstone to the surface. The most recent volcanic activity south of the Raton Mesas is even more recent than the canyon cutting.

With the stripped plain older in its eastern part than farther west, it may well be that the broad canyons of the Purgatoire and Cimarron are in part the work of an earlier cycle than that to which the Cuchara, Apishapa, and upper Canadian Canyons are restricted. There is some evidence, however, that the breadth of the Cimarron Valley may be otherwise explained. This broad canyon of the Cimarron extends to within 12 miles of the source of the river where the stream is very small. This is anomalous. A study of the valley head shows it to be probable that the present headwaters of the Canadian once belonged to the Cimarron and were diverted by recent volcanic accumulations.[4] This might of itself explain the broad canyon of the very small Cimarron headwaters and the narrow canyon of the much larger upper Canadian.

The higher parts of the Raton section, and especially the steeper slopes, bear scattered trees or even forest, and are therefore not typical in appearance of the Great Plains. Yellow

[1] The extent to which this mantle covered the Las Vegas Plateau south of the Mesa de Maya is uncertain. Even on the north, Gilbert speaks of its western margin as covering only the lower parts of the surface (Pueblo folio 36, p. 2).

[2] JOHNSON, WILLARD D., U. S. Geol. Survey, 21st Ann. Rept., pt. IV, p. 613.

[3] STOSE, GEO. W., Apishapa folio 186, p. 2, U. S. Geol. Survey, 1912. This folio and the Pueblo folio 36 contain histories of neighboring areas or marginal parts of this section. In neither of these quadrangles are so many erosion cycles recorded as in the vicinity of the Raton Mesa group.

[4] LEE, WILLIS T., Jour. Geogr., vol. II, p. 78.

pine, along with other trees, grows above an altitude of 6,500 ft.
On the Ocate Mesa and other highlands, juniper and pinyon
thrive on rocky slopes and gravelly soil as low as 5,000 ft.   Limestone and sandstone ledges and ridges are made conspicuous
by these trees.   The open terraced valleys of the Purgatoire
and other rivers, where they traverse shale between the Park
Plateau and their respective canyons, afford excellent farm
lands.   But grazing, especially sheep raising, is the most widespread industry.   The rural population is largely Mexican.

PECOS SECTION

The Pecos section (13 *h* on general map) is a long trough
lying between the High Plains on the east and the Basin and
Range province on the west.   Its boundaries are marked almost
throughout by steep slopes 500 to 1,500 ft. high, but within
these clearly marked limits the topography varies from flat
plains to rocky canyon lands.   The unity of the section consists
in this, that the whole has been eroded below the once continuous level of the High Plains and of the Raton section.   The
Llano Estacado, surfaced with wash from the mountains on the
west, must once have been continuous across what is now
the Pecos section.

Boundaries.—The section consists chiefly of the valley of
the Pecos River, but embraces also, at the north, a part of the
Canadian Basin.   The average elevation at its north end is
about 5,000 ft. where it abuts against the south-facing scarp
of the Las Vegas Plateau, 1,000 to 1,500 ft. higher.   The western
boundary of this section, north of lat. 34°, is against the lofty
Glorietta Mesa belonging to the Sacramento section of the
Basin and Range province.   At the foot of this highland the
elevation of the Pecos Valley is above 6,000 ft.[1]

Farther south and at a lower level, the Pecos Valley is limited
on the west by the dip slope of the Sacramento Mountains.
Its southern boundary near the 31st parallel is the ragged escarpment, more than 1,000 ft. high, which rises to the Stockton
(Edwards) Plateau.   On the east the valley is bounded by the

---

[1] A general contour map of this region, constructed from data available in
1899, is found in Hill's Physical Geography of the Texas Region, U. S.
Geol. Survey, Topographic folio 3, 1899; see also DARTON, N. H., Topographic Map of the State of New Mexico, U. S. Geol. Survey, 1929.

Llano Estacado, a smooth east-sloping plain which breaks off on its west side in a slope 500 to 800 ft. high.

Topography.—The basin thus enclosed has an uneven rock floor except where covered by alluvium or other quaternary deposits. The general slope is east with the dip of the underlying rocks. The western margin of the Llano Estacado is in fact a very gently sloping cuesta whose west-facing scarp slope is retreating eastward.

The altitude of the Pecos drainage basin at the north is more than 5,000 ft. At the south end, where the river leaves the broad valley to enter its canyon through the Edwards Plateau (Fig. 21), the altitude is little more than 2,000 ft. Most of the valley north of Roswell (lat. 33°30′), and half of it south of that, has an uneven surface resulting from the degradation of rocks of moderate but unequal strength (limestone, sandstone, shale, and gypsum) almost but not quite horizontal. There are many beds strong enough to make scarps and cuestas, terraces and mesas of limited extent, and some of them, especially the limestone strata exposed in the western part, make stratum plains of considerable extent but nothing comparable to the Las Vegas Plateau on the north. Most of the stream channels are dry and the landscape is of desert character. For most of its course above Roswell, the Pecos River has cut a valley 5 to 30 miles wide to an average depth of perhaps 1,000 ft. below the surface here described.

The central part of the Pecos Valley is an alluvium-filled basin. The plain thus constructed stretches for 50 miles north and a greater distance south of Roswell with a width of from 5 to 30 miles. The maximum depth of the alluvium is at least 700 ft., but it is known to rest on an uneven rock surface like that of the valley beyond its limits.[1] A similar plain due to alluviation (or possibly lake-filling[2]) occupies the lower end of the valley just north of the Edwards Plateau. This is the Toyah Basin and comprises most of that part of the section which lies in west Texas.

The immediate valley of the Pecos is bordered on the east by almost continuous bluffs beyond which for a few miles the

[1] FISHER, C. A., Geology and Underground Water of the Roswell Artesian Area, New Mexico, U. S. Geol. Survey, *Wat. Sup. Pap.* 158, p. 6, 1906.

[2] HILL, R. T., Physical Geography of the Texas Region, U. S. Geol. Survey, Topographical folio 3, p. 6, 1899.

eastward-dipping rocks lie at or near the surface. Between this rocky belt on the west and the escarpment of the Llano Estacado on the east is a sloping, alluvium-mantled plain.

Within that part of the Canadian Basin which is included in this section, the highest plateau remnants accord with those of the Pecos drainage basin and of the High Plains to the northeast. But the Canadian Valley is cut much deeper than the Pecos and the plateau surface is more nearly destroyed. Where the two streams are nearest to each other the former is 800 ft. lower. Its basin has therefore a much lower surface and much higher relief. The red sandstone in which it has cut its 1,000-ft. valley has many beds strong enough to make cliffs and rock terraces, but none able to hold its own during widespread stripping. The landscape is therefore one of terraces, mesas, cliffs, and side canyons, many of them cut in the bright-red sandstone. Except in times of freshet, running water is almost limited to the Canadian River, and even that, when low, is interrupted, flowing here over the sand and there through it. The broader terraces are desert plains.

The headwaters of the Canadian River, assembled on the Park Plateau and Ocate Mesa, traverse the Las Vegas Plateau in a shallow valley as far south as Springer, New Mexico, where they drop into a narrow canyon which increases in depth to 1,500 or 1,800 ft. where the plateau suddenly ends in the south-facing Canadian escarpment. The height of the escarpment is somewhat less than the depth of this canyon, so that the stream continues to be entrenched 300 to 500 ft. beneath the lower level. The stream rapidly descends to a level 1,000 ft. below the lower plateau and, with the aid of its side streams, has destroyed that plateau for a width of many miles. The broad area thus dissected is continuous with the narrow valley 1,000 ft. deep, in which the river crosses the High Plains.

Artesian Water.—A large part of the Pecos section possesses little of economic value except pasture, but there is a lack of water for a great grazing industry. The Roswell Basin, however, has a soil similar to that of the High Plains, a topography suited to irrigation, a water supply from the Pecos, and a large supply of artesian water constantly replenished by rains on the nearby mountains to the west. This ground water is recovered both from the alluvium and from the porous strata of the bedrock.[1]

[1] FISHER, C. A., *loc. cit.*, p. 9.

With these resources the Roswell Basin has become an important agricultural and fruit-raising district.

As is generally the case in artesian basins, the supply of water stored in this one is being drawn upon more rapidly than it is being replenished by rainfall. The pressure and flow are therefore diminishing, as is also the area in which flowing wells may be had.

EDWARDS PLATEAU

Boundaries.—At its southern end the Llano Estacado merges imperceptibly into the Edwards Plateau (13 *i*) by the gradual

Fig. 21.—Canyon of the Pecos River in Edwards Plateau. In the arid climate of western Texas, limestone is a very resistant rock. Farther north the Pecos has made for itself a valley 40 to 60 miles wide while the canyon here pictured was being cut. The wide valley was made by stripping softer sediments from the stronger rocks below. (*U. S. Geol. Survey.*)

disappearance of the fluviatile mantle. As a physiographic division, the Edwards Plateau includes the Stockton Plateau west of the Pecos River, the two parts being separated only by the 1,000-ft. canyon of the Pecos (Fig. 21). The similar canyon of the Rio Grande separates the Stockton Plateau from its southern extension in Mexico (not here considered). On its western side the Stockton Plateau terminates against the mountains of the Mexican Highland. Except for this short boundary and the equally short boundary against the Llano Estacado,

the Edwards Plateau is everywhere limited by an out-facing
escarpment. The edge of the Stockton Plateau overlooking
the Toyah Basin to the northwest has already been mentioned;
likewise the northern edge of the Edwards Plateau where it
borders the Central Texas section. Here the edge of the strong,
nearly horizontal limestone which makes the plateau is exposed,
overlying weaker rocks. The eroded and deeply notched escarpment is retreating to the south by sapping. The Balcones escarpment on the south overlooks the Coastal Plain, increasing
gradually in height toward the west from Austin where it is 300 ft.
high, to Del Rio on the Rio Grande, where it is 1,000 ft. high.
This boundary against the Coastal Plain is a line of faulting, not
a single fault but many small ones or, locally, a south-dipping
monocline.[1] The Balcones escarpment, now maturely eroded,
appears from the plain below like a range of wooded hills and is
locally called "the mountains."

Topography.—At the foot of the mountains on the west the
Stockton Plateau is 4,000 ft. high. At the border of the Llano
Estacado the Edwards Plateau is 3,000 ft. high. Where the
Nueces River cuts its valley in the southern margin, the upland
level is 2,200 ft. The level declines eastward to 1,000 ft. near
Austin.

On all sides where this section rises above its neighbors its
edges are more or less dissected by outflowing streams. West of
the 100th meridian where the plateau is wide and the climate arid,
its broad interior is a monotonous grass-covered plain much like
the Llano Estacado. Even here the margins are maturely
dissected. Farther east, where the rainfall is greater and
the plateau is narrower, the dissected margins leave little of the
uncut plateau between them. Nevertheless, remnants of the
original surface are found almost as far east as Austin.[2] This
part of the section is topographically quite unlike the interior of
the western part, though quite like its margin. It is also like
the dissected upland north of the Colorado River, being continuous with it and carved from the same limestone. The reason
for assigning to the Edwards Plateau so great an eastward extension is found partly in the utter lack of any well-marked line

[1] HILL and VAUGHAN, Nueces folio 42, p. 3, U. S. Geol. Survey, 1898.
[2] Austin folio 76, U. S. Geol. Survey, describes the eastern end of the
Edwards Plateau where the Colorado River is adopted as its arbitrary
boundary.

farther west.   The limit here assigned is also recognized in the popular use of the term "Edwards Plateau."

The surface of the entire section is on a single massive and resistant limestone formation which dips gently south and east with the slope of the surface.   It is not a surface made by deposition like that of the Llano Estacado, nor is it a peneplain, but a *stripped plain* or *stratum plain* (page 37), a remarkable example of its kind.[1]   There are in its present topography some features unlike those of a flat surface subject to dissection in its first erosion cycle.   Some of these features are due to the older history; others to the great substructure of soluble limestone, now traversed by innumerable fissures and other passages due to solution.   The character of these underlying rocks and their relation to ground waters are of importance in considering both the topography and the resources of this section.

The flatter parts of the upland differ little from the High Plains.   In contrast with the rugged margin, the soil of the flat interior is fairly deep.   Such valleys as exist are only wide open "draws,"[2] perhaps made by streams which did the stripping, but carrying only storm waters now or none at all.   There are a few shallow depressions or *sinks* which occasionally retain water a short time.   "For miles the level grass-covered plain stretches before the eye like a great sea, the view broken only at long intervals by the tall shaft of a ranchman's windmill."[3] In the draws percolation is large.   Where larger than ordinary, often where several draws meet, there may be a depression or "grass valley" with or without a visible outlet.

Features of Valleys.—As the margin of the plateau is approached, the gully-like heads of stream valleys appear, generally within the draws.   The headward growth of these is guided by the draws, for the supply of water is greater there than elsewhere but the draw gives way abruptly to the gully and does not merge gradually.   The upper courses of these streams cut narrow V-shaped valleys in the strong limestone.   Here most of the water carried is direct run-off; floods from torrential rains are

[1] HILL, R. T., and VAUGHAN, T. W., Geology of the Edwards Plateau and Rio Grande Plain, U. S. Geol. Survey, 18*th Ann. Rept.*, pt. II, p. 207, 1897.

[2] In western United States the word "draw" commonly signifies a shallow valley without a stream.

[3] HILL, R. T., and VAUGHAN, T. W., Geology of the Edwards Plateau and Rio Grande Plain, U. S. Geol. Survey, 18*th Ann. Rept.*, pt. II, p. 206, 1897.

common, but some springs of great size occur where streams in their headward growth have tapped an important water-bearing passage in the limestone. These passages are of all sizes up to large caves.

On account of the great height of the southern escarpment, especially in its western part, the streams rapidly descend some hundreds of feet through the ravine-like valleys here described. At the foot they may cut into a stratum from which unusual quantities of ground water are received. As the supply from this source is constant the habit of the stream changes, being less subject to flood. The effect of the many springs, moreover, is to sap the strong rocks of the canyon walls which thereupon retreat and separate. Thus results the somewhat anomalous form of canyons with almost vertical walls but several miles wide, having flat floors, often covered with fine deciduous forests. Even some agricultural land is present.

On the lower plain beyond the mouths of these canyons, as at intervals within the canyons themselves, all streams run on beds of deep gravel. Where this is deep enough, broad enough, and porous enough, the stream disappears entirely, reappearing where forced to the surface by a less porous substratum. In striking contrast with the intermittent head streams which carry only storm waters, the streams here are fed wholly by water from the ground. They are constant in volume at any one place but are interrupted.[1] In exceptional cases, the same streams higher up in their courses may thus disappear into a bed of fissured limestone as does the west branch of the Nueces below Kickapoo Springs.[2]

As the water-bearing rocks which underlie the Edwards Plateau pass beneath the adjacent Coastal Plain, they become reservoirs of artesian water. In passing from the plateau to the plain they are broken across by the great Balcones fault or group of faults. Along this natural rift, much water is forced to the surface by artesian pressure. Fissure springs or *artesian springs* are thus formed, some of them of remarkable size. The Barton Springs near Austin discharge 25 cu. ft. of water per second.

[1] An "interrupted" stream flows at some places and not at others; an intermittent stream flows at some times and not at others; see Nueces folio 42, p. 1, U. S. Geol. Survey, 1898.

[2] BRAY, WM. M., The Timber of the Edwards Plateau of Texas, U. S. Dept. Agr., Bur. of Forestry, *Bull.* 49, p. 13, 1904.

Some others are much larger. The Comal Springs are the source of a river carrying 328 cu. ft. per second or 212,000,000 gal. per day,[1] more than 5,000,000 bbl.

Vegetation.—The uncut surface of the Edwards Plateau is treeless. Trees, or at least woody plants, occupy most slopes and valley bottoms. According to the moisture received from above and below, these vary from heavy deciduous forests in the lower valley bottoms to sparse and stunted scrub oak, cedar, and chaparral on the higher slopes and farther west. Wherever grass is temporarily weakened, even on the flat uplands, as by overgrazing, which is very common, the humbler forms of tree growth seize upon the ground, as though the luxuriant grass had been holding the ground by inheritance rather than by its greater fitness. When this occurs on the flat upland the effect is an economic loss, because grazing is the leading and only great industry. In the natural state, however, the distribution of forests is ideal, since they serve to prevent soil erosion and increase the percolation of rain waters in the hilly country, while leaving the uplands to grass where erosion is absent and percolation in any case is large.

CENTRAL TEXAS SECTION

General Relations.—North and east of the Edwards Plateau is the Central Texas section from which the plateau-making limestones just described have been in large part removed. As indicated on page 9, the master structural feature of this region is a thick and strong stratum of limestone which dips faintly east and south from the high young plateaus to the Coastal Plain, at the inner edge of which it is faulted down beneath the present base level and remains covered by younger and weaker strata. The country is divided into physiographic sections based on the degree of erosion of this limestone plateau, since it everywhere forms, or has formed, the surface. The section here considered is the area in which this erosion has been carried approximately to or beyond maturity but has not, over any wide area, reached old age, even where the limestone has been extensively removed. Generally where the Edwards limestone itself has been eroded away (within this section), the underlying rocks

[1] HILL, R. T., and VAUGHAN, T. W., U. S. Geol. Survey, 18*th Ann. Rept.*, pt. II, p. 311; pages 207 to 210 describe the several parts of a typical stream descending the escarpment; see also U. S. Geol. Survey, *Bull.* 140, 1895.

are also resistant and the topography is still one of strong relief. The topography of this section varies from place to place according to the nature of the rocks disclosed by denudation and the stage reached in the erosion cycle.

Comanche Plateau.—As the section is defined in the preceding paragraph and on page 9, it embraces a number of clearly distinguished subdivisions which for lack of a technical term may here be called districts.[1]   There is first a belt of submaturely dissected plateau on the east side from Fort Worth on the north to the Colorado River on the south.   This may be called provisionally the Comanche dissected plateau.[2]   This plateau slopes east with the dip of the Comanchean series of limestones (Fig. 22) from an altitude of 1,800 ft. on the west to 800 ft. on the east. The greater elevation of these strata, still farther west, caused them to be eroded away.   Their relatively low level on the east almost protects them from erosion.   South of Waco the east-facing Balcones fault scarp makes its appearance, at first very faintly but increasing in clearness toward the south.   With gradual increase in height toward the west the surface of this Comanche district becomes more and more subject to erosion. As might be expected in an eastward-sloping plateau, the amount of local relief decreases eastward.   Toward the west where valley-cutting is pronounced, a relief of 300 to 400 ft. is not uncommon.   The strong rocks and the semiarid climate cooperate to cause steep valley walls and mesa slopes.   Between the broad valleys of the larger streams are plateau remnants more or less dissected by canyons.   The name "Lampasas Cut Plain" has been applied to the higher and more sharply eroded (western) part of the Comanche dissected plateau.[3]   As the relief decreases

[1] The physiography of this section is so intimately connected with the underlying rocks that a discussion of it is impossible without constant reference to the geologic map.   The necessary data are given on the Willis geologic map of North America, U. S. Geol. Survey, 1911; but in more detail on the geologic map of Texas, issued by the University of Texas, 1916.

[2] It is typically represented in Comanche County east of the 99th meridian and south of the 32d parallel.   The same name, Comanche, is also applied to the great series of strata of which this plateau is composed (Fig. 22). The Comanche series includes the Edwards limestone, the name of which (taken from Edwards County) is associated with the related plateau to the southwest.

[3] HILL, R. T., Physical Geography of the Texas Region, Topographical folio 3, U. S. Geol. Survey, 1900.

toward the east, the angularity is somewhat lost. North of lat. 31° a narrow eastern margin may almost be called a rolling plain. This margin lacks the typical character of the section considered as a whole. It is a local variant of the widespread

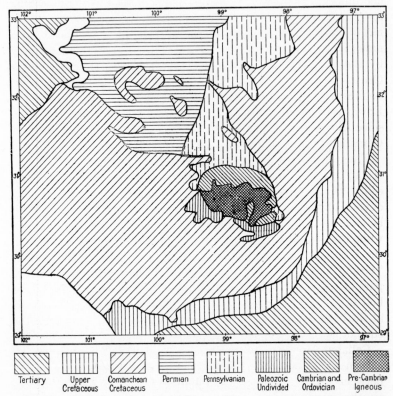

Tertiary   Upper   Comanchean   Permian   Pennsylvanian   Paleozoic   Cambrian and   Pre-Cambrian
           Cretaceous Cretaceous   Undivided   Ordovician   Igneous

Fig. 22.—Geologic map of central Texas. Most of the strongly characterized districts within the Central Texas section owe their character to the underlying rocks. Compare the index map, Fig. 4, page **10** and the general province map, in pocket. The chief geologic distinctions are as follows: Tertiary (Costal Plain, Llano Estacado); Upper Cretaceous (Coastal Plain province); Comanchean Cretaceous (Edwards Plateau, Comanche Plateau, Callahan Divide); Permian (denuded areas); Pennsylvanian (Palo Pinto district); undivided Paleozoic, Cambrian and Ordovician, pre-Cambrian and Igneous (Llano district). (*Reduced from geologic map of Texas.*)

type into which it merges and with which it must be considered in a rational explanation of physical features. This narrow strip is the typical "Grand Prairie." The name Grand Prairie[1] has

[1] Hill, R. T., Geography and Geology of the Black and Grand Prairies, U. S. Geol. Survey, 21*st Ann. Rept.*, pt. VII, 1900.

also been applied to a much broader strip without natural limits, including much of the dissected plateau on the west.

The altitude of the Comanche dissected plateau also decreases toward the north. North of Fort Worth the relief on the Comanche limestone is relatively small and its distinctive character is lost. The change is, however, gradual. There is no abrupt natural limit short of the Arbuckle Mountains. It is rather a matter of convenience that the northern end of the belt underlain by the rocks of the Comanche Plateau is here assigned to the Central Lowland. Employment of the Colorado River as a boundary line between the Central Texas section and the Edwards Plateau on the south is also arbitrary (see page 51), since the change from the flat Edwards Plateau to the dissected Comanche Plateau is gradual.

The eastern and western boundaries of this Comanche district are to a remarkable degree marked by narrow strips of forest called "Cross Timbers"[1] interrupting an otherwise open country devoid of trees except for certain low, bush-like forms. The belt of "Eastern Cross Timbers," nowhere more than 10 miles wide, follows the outcrop of a weak sandy stratum at the base of the Upper Cretaceous as far south as Waco and separates the "Grand Prairie" from the "Black Prairie," the latter being a part of the Coastal Plain. In a similar way the equally narrow belt of "Western Cross Timbers" follows a very sandy outcrop at the base of the Lower Cretaceous and hence marks the western edge of the Comanche dissected plateau.

Callahan Divide.—A second subdivision or district is commonly known as the Callahan Divide, *i.e.*, the belt along the divide between the Colorado River system on the south and the Brazos on the north. Along this line, the plateau-making limestone is locally preserved in broad flat-topped and often steep-sided mesas or groups of mesas 400 to 600 ft. high, while wholly carried away from the upper Brazos Basin and even from a considerable area in the Colorado Basin. This line of plateau remnants (Fig. 22) connects the perfectly preserved Llano Estacado with the dissected Comanche Plateau and it is plain that its striking topography represents a stage of erosion more advanced than that of these plateaus on either side, but less advanced than that of the denuded Permian plains to the north. Where the remnants are broad or closely set, the aspect is like that of the western

[1] HILL, R. T., *loc. cit.*, pp. 73 and 81.

part of the Comanche Plateau, even to the narrow band of "Cross Timbers" at the base.[1] The branch of this forest belt which turns west from the Comanche Plateau and follows in more or less interrupted fashion the northern base of the Callahan mesas may be said to mark the boundary between the Central Texas section and the Osage section of the Central Lowland.

Lowland along the Colorado.—Another district having its own distinctive type of topography is the broad lowland along the Colorado. Here for 100 miles the river flows through a broadly rolling prairie overlooked from the north by the scattered mesas of the Callahan Divide and from the south by the ragged escarpment of the Edwards Plateau. The topography is one of approaching old age. The local relief is several hundred feet, but the slopes are generally gentle. Hard rocks farther down stream prevent the Colorado from cutting much here and its fall is small. This part of the Colorado Basin closely resembles the upper Brazos Basin to the north.

The Llano District.—The southern end of the Central Texas section, centering in Llano County, and being in large part the lower basin of the Llano River, differs strikingly from the other districts in general appearance (see index map Fig. 4 and geologic map Fig. 22). Its most characteristic feature is a central basin with a rolling floor studded with "mountains" 400 to 600 ft. high and surrounded by a plateau rim as high as the "mountain" tops. This rimming bench is in turn surmounted by the frayed escarpments of the Edwards limestone on all sides, except for about 25 miles on the north. The central depression is therefore a basin within a basin; yet so prominent are details as compared with larger relations, that this is always known as a mountainous country.

The central basin, somewhat more than 25 miles wide and 50 miles in length, is carved on granite, gneiss, and schist, which in this case are less resistant than the horizontal Paleozoic strata which make the rim.[2] Some of the "mountains" within the basin are capped by remnants of these strata. Such are flat topped. Others represent hard kernels of the crystalline rock and are maturely dissected. The surrounding bench or rim is in part maturely dissected, elsewhere young. Its width ranges

[1] HILL, R. T., *loc. cit.*, maps.
[2] PAIGE, SYDNEY, Llano-Burnett folio 183, U. S. Geol. Survey, 1912.

from 5 to 25 miles. Back of it is the irregular Edwards escarpment whose height ranges from 200 to 400 ft.

It is impressive to note that the primary cause which differentiated this district from its surroundings was an upthrust and not a sinking. This may be seen in the faults at the edge of the central basin. In practically all cases the upthrow is on the inside.[1] The area was then peneplaned, exposing the crystalline rocks of the uplifted mass before the deposition of the limestone strata which now constitute the neighboring plateaus. When later erosion removed the limestone and laid bare the older peneplain, the crystalline rocks, again exposed, were eroded more easily than the surrounding ancient strata. A topographic basin was thus formed where upheaval had once made a highland. The clean-cut escarpments which now mark some of the fault lines face in instead of out, as the original fault scarps must have done.[2]

Palo Pinto District.—The most noteworthy locality, aside from the Llano district, in which strong rocks are exposed by the stripping away of the Edwards limestone, is a narrow strip on Carboniferous (Pennsylvanian) rocks west of the Comanche Plateau, chiefly north of the Callahan Divide (Fig. 22). It is well exemplified in Palo Pinto County, from which fact this district has been called by Hill the "Palo Pinto Country."[3] It is characterized by steep-sided mesas cut by canyons. These mesas are remnants of strong sandstone beds, while between them on lower-lying shales are rolling mesquite-covered plains.

Physiographic History.—The recent physiographic history of central Texas is strongly suggested by the larger streams. The intricacy of their meanders is striking, but still more so when it is observed that at many places where the meanders are most picturesquely tortuous, there is little or no flood plain. This is true of the Brazos in the Palo Pinto district and in the higher western part of the Comanche Plateau. It is strikingly true of the Colorado as it flows through the rim of the Llano Basin. Generally speaking, it is most striking where the rocks are

---

[1] PAIGE, SYDNEY, *loc. cit.*, p. 10.

[2] As the term "fault scarp" must be reserved for the feature originally produced, the escarpment developed by later erosion is termed a *fault line scarp*.

[3] Physical Geography of the Texas Region, Topographical folio 3, U. S. Geol. Survey, 1900.

hardest, but even where erosion is easier, the lack of broad flood plains at the present stream level is noteworthy.

Such entrenched meanders are, of course, inherited from a time when the stream flowed sluggishly at the level of the present uplands (or rather when the present uplands were lowlands). Evidently the uplift which caused the entrenchment was very recent and was not the one which occasioned the widespread denudation of the surface and the dissection of the Comanche Plateau.

Back of the entrenchment lies an older erosion cycle whose product is the stripped plain of the Edwards Plateau, the same surface which extends for some distance north under the Tertiary cover of the Staked Plains. In the discussion above, the original covering of strong limestone strata over central Texas has been mentioned without reference to its earlier history. Geologic observations indicate that this formation was covered by others and that therefore its present surface is one of erosion and not the original surface of deposition. Here and there are a few small remnants of higher beds; moreover, the topmost beds are not the same everywhere; they are faintly beveled, but on the whole the surfaces of the Edwards and Comanche Plateaus agree remarkably with that of a single strong formation, the Edwards limestone. That this formation should have been so completely denuded with so little degradation of its own surface must be ascribed in large measure to the resistant character of the rock. With its surface as high above base level as at present, this would have been impossible, but even after allowing for nearness to base level during erosion, this surface remains a remarkable example of a stripped (or stratum) plain.

The physiographic history of this region then begins with the erosion of the beds which lay upon the Edwards limestone. At the close of the cycle in which they were carried away, the surface of the entire region from the Coastal Plain west and north to an unknown distance (at least to lat. 33°) was on the limestone which makes the present plateaus. The northern end was later covered by fluviatile wash from the mountains. Later uplift occasioned the widespread stripping away of the limestone itself; its sharp dissection elsewhere; and the approximate development of a new peneplain in some parts of the newly denuded area. It was in the latter part of this last cycle that the phenomenal meanders were developed. This was followed by the uplift which caused the streams to become entrenched.

MISSOURI PLATEAU

Boundaries.—The Missouri Plateau comprises all that part of the Great Plains province which lies north of the High Plains to an undetermined boundary in Canada. Its southern limit is the Pine Ridge escarpment (see index map, Fig. 3, page 8), well shown on the geological map because the higher formations which underlie the High Plains on the south are absent on the north. This high escarpment, maximum 1,000 ft., retreating southward, suggests that the Missouri Plateau is a greatly degraded area (see Fig. 8, page 17). Along its eastern boundary the Missouri Plateau is itself being consumed by the gradual westward spread of the Central Lowland. Here the two provinces, Central Lowland and Great Plains, are separated by the indefinite escarpment described on page 74.

Isolated Mountains.—Scattered through the western third of the Missouri Plateau are a number of small isolated mountain groups, rising 2,000 to 4,000 ft. above the plain. Of these the Black Hills are so large as to merit treatment as a separate section. Some, like the Little Rockies and the Big Snowy (index map, Fig. 3), are diastrophic uplifts similar to the Black Hills and the neighboring Rocky Mountains. Others, like the Highwood and Bearpaw Mountains, are extinct volcanic groups of the same kind as those which border Yellowstone Park on the east. All of them are products of the same forces which made the Rocky Mountains.

The Little Rocky Mountains[1] between the Missouri and Milk Rivers and west of the 108th meridian are typical domed mountains like the Black Hills. The dome is roughly circular in outline and 15 to 18 miles in diameter. Erosion has exposed deep-seated rocks at the center, making rounded crests rising nearly 3,000 ft. above the plain. The steeply tilted younger strata make striking hogback ridges encircling the mountains. The most conspicuous is the "white wall" of Carboniferous limestone, visible for 50 miles, deeply notched or scalloped by the recently revived streams which flow out from the center.

The Big Snowy Mountains, south of lat. 47° and west of long. 109°, differ from the Little Rockies only in such details as result from a broader dome, less steeply tilted strata and less profound erosion, the crystalline rocks not being exposed. This

[1] WEED, W. H., and PIRSSON, L. V., Geology of the Little Rocky Mountains, *Jour. Geol.*, vol. IV, pp. 399–428, 1896.

uplift is in line with the axis of the Little Belt uplift (page 217), though separated from the latter by a structural sag and a strip of plain 10 miles wide. The Larb Hills east of the Little Rockies are a still gentler fold, though rising 1,500 ft. above the plain. Though deeply and maturely dissected, the uplift is sufficiently recent so that the strata of the surrounding plain have not yet been stripped from the dome. The Sweetgrass Hills, 6,000 to 7,000 ft. high, lying near the Canadian boundary and west of the 111th meridian, are ancient intrusives now being exhumed.

The Highwood Mountains south of the Missouri River in long. 110°30′ are a group of extinct volcanoes maturely dissected, their peaks rising 4,000 ft. above the plain. Deeply eroded laccoliths also form parts of the group.[1] These mountains are of special interest because they have preserved near their tops, 3,000 ft. above the present plain, remnants of higher strata which must once have covered the plain.[2] The Bearpaw Mountains, northwest of the Little Rockies, are also old volcanoes, past-maturely eroded, having low rounded crests and wide fertile valleys.[3] The Judith Mountains, north of the Big Snowy, are little more than a group of eroded laccoliths.[4]

There is thus a mingling of characteristics, the diastrophic uplifts being closely related to the great mountain belt on the west, laccoliths being more characteristic of plateaus, and typical volcanoes occurring equally in both.

In a deep reentrant of the mountain front in latitude about 46° stand the Crazy Mountains,[5] a volcanic group at least 30 miles long (north-south) by 15 miles wide, and rising more than 5,000 ft. above the plains. The conventional province boundary allots them to the Mountain province but they are surrounded by nearly flat-lying strata having the topography of the Missouri Plateau. The real mountain front is at the Bridger Range farther west. At the summits of the Crazy Mountains and on

[1] Fort Benton folio 55, U. S. Geol. Survey, 1899.

[2] DAVIS, W. M., "Tenth Census," vol. 15, Report on Coal, pp. 710, 737; also ELDRIDGE, GEORGE H., same vol., p. 745; PIRSSON, L. V., Petrography and Geology of the Igneous Rocks of the Highwood Mountains, Montana, U. S. Geol. Survey, *Bull.* 237.

[3] CALHOUN, F. H. H., U. S. Geol. Survey, *Prof. Pap.* 50, p. 12, 1906.

[4] WEED and PIRSSON, The Judith Mountains of Montana, U. S. Geol. Survey, 17*th Ann. Rept.*, pt. III, p. 576, 1897.

[5] U. S. Geol. Survey, Folios 1 and 56; WOLFF, J. E., Geology of the Crazy Mountains, Montana, Geol. Soc. Amer. *Bull.*, vol. 3, pp. 445–452, 1892.

their long lateral divides is an old topography of rounded forms and mild relief. This old surface is in large part destroyed by revived streams and glacial erosion.[1] Like the Highwood Mountains, this group possesses special interest by reason of the evidence it affords of deep denudation. Here are remnants of strata believed to have covered the adjacent plain, now 5,000 ft. above the surrounding peneplain.[2]

Among the significant features of practically all of the mountain groups here described are rounded crests with steep-sided valleys indicating an old surface of moderate relief dissected by rejuvenated streams. Above the level of 5,000 ft. are woodlands or even good forest interspersed with open grasslands.

Unglaciated Section of the Missouri Plateau

Alluvial Terraces.—The surface of the Missouri Plateau, aside from the isolated mountains already described, may be thought of under four different types:[3] (1) broadly terraced river valleys, (2) interstream uplands imperfectly peneplaned in a series of partial cycles and locally dissected to badlands, (3) high interstream areas widely alluviated by coalescing alluvial fans or flood plains, (4) a combination of the foregoing, glaciated. The last named is treated as a separate section.

By far the most prominent among the terraced valleys is that of the Yellowstone, while second only to it are the valleys of its southern tributaries, chiefly the Bighorn and its branches in the Bighorn Basin. The Missouri, except in its upper course, is a special case with a history of its own (page 76).

The immediate valleys of these and other streams heading in the mountains (the valleys between the present bluffs) are generally narrow and young. Bluffs rising to the first terrace are one hundred to several hundred feet high and at places difficult to cross except by graded roads.[4] The adjacent terrace, or the upland where terraces are absent, may be mildly eroded

---

[1] MANSFIELD, GEO. R., Glaciation in the Crazy Mountains of Montana, Geol. Soc. Amer. *Bull.*, vol. 19, 1907.

[2] UPHAM, WARREN, Tertiary and Early Quaternary Base-leveling, *Amer. Geol.*, vol. 14, p. 237, 1894.

[3] ALDEN, WM. C., Physiographic Development of the Northern Great Plains, Geol. Soc. Amer. *Bull.*, vol. 35, pp. 385–424, 1924. Pl. 11 is a map which may be rendered valuable by anyone who will carefully color the several terraces and formations named in the legend.

[4] ALDEN, WM. C., *loc. cit.*, p. 388.

or carved into badlands. Beyond the present flood plain, especially along the Yellowstone, are terraces, one, two, or three, at vertical intervals of 100 to 600 ft.[1] The width of the valley at the highest terrace level is at places 20 miles. Widths of one to two townships are common. A succession of three recognized levels is found at a sufficient number of places from the Dakotas to the Rocky Mountains to admit of tentative correlation.

Interstream Uplands.—Back of these terrace lands, between the larger rivers, is the widespread surface which was being

FIG. 23.—Rolling plain on the Pierre shale west of Pierre, South Dakota. This is in the Missouri Plateau. The surface is due to deep and extensive degradation. Contrast the surface shown in Fig. 5. (*Photo by E. H. Barbour, U. S. Geol. Survey.*)

eroded while the terraces were being carved and alluviated (Figs. 23 and 26). It consists of smoothly rolling plains or peneplains at different levels, as though cycle after cycle of erosion had but partly destroyed the peneplains of older cycles.[2] The remnants of different age preserved at different levels constitute a crude system of terraces produced by the destructional work of erosion between the great valleys. Generally such terraces are less clear than those of the stream valleys except where the

[1] This statement takes account of only the more prominent and persistent terraces.

[2] An illustration of this near the mountains is given by F. H. H. Calhoun, U. S. Geol. Survey, *Prof. Pap. 50*, p. 9, 1906.

descent from one level to the next is by an escarpment over the outcropping edge of a stronger bed.

The rolling, terrace-like plains here described are the dominant elements of the topography. Erosion has affected them to various degrees, broad valleys sometimes connecting higher with lower levels, obscuring locally the real design. Unconsumed remnants rise above all levels.

There is a good deal of very rough country. Not only in the breaks along the Missouri and Yellowstone is there deep and thorough dissection, in places typical badlands, but in the larger interstream tracts ridges rise in places 500 to 1,500 ft. above the valley bottoms, often with bold cliffs and picturesque towers and pinnacles, especially where the eminences are capped by sandstone.[1]

Near the Rocky Mountains and in certain outlying areas where the beds are inclined, sandstone cuestas appear. Good examples are found on the Salt Creek dome east of the Bighorn Mountains;[2] also in the Wolf and Rosebud Mountains (cuestas) east of the Bighorn River in southern Montana.[3] For some distance west of the Black Hills there is a succession of eroded cuestas.[4] Even in northwestern South Dakota there are parallel lines of buttes trending north-northeast, due to the outcrops of sandstone beds dipping slightly westward.[5]

Broadly Alluviated Areas between Streams.—Surrounded by the type of lands last described (interstream uplands) are certain remnants of broadly alluviated high plains. A space roughly enclosed by the Little Belt, Big Snowy, Judith, and Highwood Mountains is in large part occupied by such plains. They do not differ greatly in aspect from the broadest of the terraces in the valley of the Yellowstone. The underlying material is the same and their altitude differs no more than that of the parallel streams of the present time. Apparently while the great through-flowing streams (Missouri and Yellowstone) were developing wide flood plains there was a considerable area in central Montana drained by weaker streams whose loads were

[1] ALDEN, WM. C., *loc. cit.*, p. 387.

[2] WEGEMAN, C. H., The Salt Creek Oil Field, Wyoming, U. S. Geol. Survey, *Bull.* 452, pp. 40–41, 1911.

[3] See Topographic Map, Rosebud quadrangle.

[4] DARTON, N. H., Newcastle folio 107, U. S. Geol. Survey, 1904.

[5] TODD, J. E., Preliminary Report, Geology of Northwestern Central South Dakota, S. Dak. Geol. Survey, *Bull.* 4, p. 17, 1908.

so excessive that the streams wandered widely, covering the entire area with their coalescing fans or flood plains.

The plains here referred to do not lie higher than the adjacent plains of the type previously described, but there are other smaller remnants of gravel plains that rise as mesas often 500 to 600 ft. above their surroundings. These are the "Flaxville Gravels."[1] Remnants a dozen or more miles in extent are found at various places near the Yellowstone, especially in eastern Montana; also near the Rocky Mountain front from the Canadian border to the Bighorn Basin. The largest remnants are in the glaciated section near the international boundary.[2] The great lateral extent of these deposits indicates that the depositing stream or streams wandered widely, divides being to some extent destroyed by planation and at all events covered.

A large remnant of a still higher gravel-covered plain is known as the Cypress Hills. It lies north of the 49th parallel and for the most part east of the 110th meridian. It stretches 80 miles from west to east and has a flat surface covered with heavy gravel 2,000 ft. above the Saskatchewan River on the north and Milk River on the south, and sloping eastward 12 to 13 ft. per mile. Obviously the gravel was deposited by a stream (or streams) from the mountains. Quite as obviously this points to a time when the streams of the Great Plains crossed the 110th meridian at a level 2,000 ft. higher than that of today.

Divergence of Erosion Levels toward the West.—The difference between present and former levels, as shown by terraces and other gravel remnants, grows less toward the east and greater toward the west. The depth of the Missouri trough in the Dakotas is 300 to 400 ft. The same valley at the Dakota-Montana boundary is 600 to 700 ft. deep. Near the mountain front the Missouri and Yellowstone Valleys and those of their larger tributaries are 800 to 1,000 ft. deep. With this increase of depth toward the west goes a greater erosion of the land near the rivers, with correspondingly greater prominence of sandstone escarpments.

In like manner all terraces and old erosion surfaces converge eastward. In the Dakotas there is a single widespread rolling

[1] COLLIER, ARTHUR J., and THOM, W. T., The Flaxville Gravel, etc., U. S. Geol. Survey, *Prof. Pap.* 108 J, pp. 179–184, 1918.

[2] All areas here mentioned are shown on the map published in the paper by William C. Alden, referred to above.

upland which seems to represent a once continuous surface from which the newer and sharper relief has been carved. Directly east of the Black Hills, this general level is cut on shale (Pierre formation) which contains almost no sandstone beds. On these rocks the upland level where preserved is monotonously rolling (Fig. 23). Farther north, on account of the northwesterly dip, the surface bevels younger strata (Fox Hills, Laramie, and Fort Union) containing some sandstone beds which cause the widely rolling surface to be interrupted by low cuestas.

Here (chiefly north of the Black Hills) a number of monadnocks rise to an almost uniform level 400 to 600 ft. above the peneplain. Sentinel Butte (3,430 ft.) near Medora, North Dakota, is the third highest point in the state. Most of these buttes are flat-topped and protected by strong sandstone. It is known, however, that still higher beds once covered these hills, and that at least 1,000 ft. of rock were carried away in making the peneplain which surrounds them. The altitude of remnants near the Rocky Mountains is much greater, indicating correspondingly greater uplift and erosion. A number of eminences, presumably identical in character, stand out on the plains of Montana. Many lower buttes and mesas, rising 150 to 175 ft. above the plains of Dakota, are capped by a slag-like substance due to the partial fusion of clays by the natural burning of coal beds.[1]

White River Badlands.—The eastern part of this section is remarkable for its badlands. They occur where the widespread peneplain is being actively dissected by renewed erosion. Strips also occur at the edge of the High Plains in the Pine Ridge escarpment. An area east and south of the Black Hills includes the "Big Badlands" between the Cheyenne and White Rivers (Fig. 24) and extends well to the south of the White River and westward along the wasting escarpment of the High Plains. This is the largest single compact area but most of the streams between this area on the south and the glacial boundary on the north are bordered, at least in places, by strips of badlands. The White River runs through the center of the South Dakota area; its tributaries do most of the carving, though those of the Cheyenne participate.

[1] Wood, L. H., Region between Northern Pacific Railroad and the Missouri River, N. Dak. Geol. Survey, *3d Biennial Rept.*, pp. 56 and 62–63, 1904; Leonard, A. G., Topography of North Dakota, N. Dak. Geol. Survey, *3d Biennial Rept.*, p. 132, 1904; U. S. Geol. Survey, *Bull.* 627, p. 10. 1916.

In pointing out the peculiarly favorable conditions for badlands at this place, it should be remembered that badlands are
essentially a type of mature dissection with a drainage pattern
of fine texture, and with steep slopes.   Fine texture (numerous
and closely spaced drainage lines) and steep slopes occur only
where the land lies well above its local base level.   The material
must be easily eroded; otherwise vegetation will cover the surface and prevent minute dissection.   In soft material, steepness
would soon be lost, were it not for continued cutting down of

Fig. 24.—Big Badlands between the Cheyenne and White Rivers, South
Dakota.   The beds here exposed are largely clay (Chadron and Brule).   Remnants of the plateau from which the badlands were carved are seen at the right
and in outlying buttes.   (*Darton, U. S. Geol. Survey.*)

the valleys, which again points to the fact that the land must
lie distinctly above its local base level.   Aridity, although not
essential, is favorable, partly because it is adverse to vegetation
and partly because rain in arid climates is more concentrated
into quick torrential showers which erode much more than do
the slower rains of humid climates.   Aridity also favors the
preservation of forms between stream courses.

These conditions, soft material distinctly above base level
in an arid climate, are well satisfied here.   The original surface
(preserved in occasional mesas or "tables") is 500 to 600 ft.
above the nearby Cheyenne and White Rivers.   The climate is

also sufficiently arid, but the condition which is present in pre-eminent degree is the fitness of the material. The White River formation[1] consists largely of excessively fine clays, poorly consolidated. At intervals are thin beds of sandstone or isolated concretions. Many of the fantastic features of the badlands are due to these harder beds and concretions. Wherever this formation crops out, whether in the Big Badlands, in the Pine Ridge escarpment, the Goshen Hole Basin, or in the edge of the High Plains in northern Colorado, its character is much the same and badlands are more or less developed.

The White River badlands[2] are by no means a monotonous succession of straight slopes making V-valleys and sharp crests. Beside the terracing due to plates of sandstone, many "tables" remain and the larger valleys have flat bottoms or U-shaped cross-sections. Some of the bottoms and all of the "tables" are grass covered, but the steep slopes are bare. The White River itself meanders over a broad flat; its smaller tributaries do the cutting. These are, of course, dry except for a short time after rains. A considerable grazing industry is supported in the broader valleys and the less dissected parts.

Little Missouri Badlands.—All the streams flowing east to the Missouri are attended by strips or occasional patches of badlands, but the only area comparable to that on the White River is found along the Little Missouri. From the southwest corner of North Dakota this stream flows north 120 miles, then turns sharply east for 70 miles to join the Missouri. Throughout this distance it is bordered by badlands forming a belt whose width increases from 6 or 7 miles at the south to 25 or more miles at the bend, and decreases again to 10 or 12 miles on the eastward course. The depth of cutting increases from about 80 ft. at the south to a maximum of over 500 ft. near the bend. Like the White River, the Little Missouri meanders over a broad flat (one-half to one and one-half miles) gouging into the right and left bluffs alternately, dividing and subdividing among sandbars—a much overloaded stream except in times of flood. Even the larger side valleys have flat or broadly rounded bottoms,

---

[1] A good geologic map showing the extent of this formation is found in U. S. Geol. Survey, *Prof. Pap.* 32, pl. XXXV. A similar map for South Dakota is found in U. S. Geol. Survey, *Wat. Sup. Pap.* 227, pl. I.

[2] O'Hara, Cleophas C., Badland Formations of the Black Hill Region, S. Dak. School Mines, *Bull.* 9, 1910.

but the smaller tributaries form a labyrinth of gullies.   Residual mesas and outstanding promontories of the upland increase in size and number with increasing distance from the stream. Nevertheless the dissected zone has fairly definite limits, so that from many points on the brink, if one looks away from the river, nothing is seen but the nearly level upland, while in the opposite direction is a wilderness of chasms, fantastic and picturesque buttes, and divides (*cf.* Figs. 25 and 26).   Generally the divide between the Little Missouri and Missouri Rivers is only 10 to 15

Fig. 25.—Badlands along the Little Missouri seen from the edge of the dissected zone.   This view and the one shown in Fig. 26 were taken from the same point, showing the abruptness of the change from level prairie to badlands. (*Photo by A. L. Fellows, N. Dak. Geol. Survey.*)

miles east of the former.   At that line the tributaries of the Missouri start east in shallow troughs and with little or no cutting power.

The level of the crests between the badland gorges near the river is generally not quite so high as the adjacent upland.[1] This indicates that, before the cycle of badland cutting, the river occupied a shallow valley perhaps 300 ft. deep at the most, and

[1] Wood, L. H., Report on the Region between the Northern Pacific Railroad and the Missouri River, N. Dak. Geol. Survey, 3d *Biennial Rept.*, p. 49, 1904; Leonard, A. G., Geology of Southwestern North Dakota, N. Dak. Geol. Survey, 5th *Biennial Rept.*, p. 35, 1908.

much narrower than the present dissected zone.[1]   Beneath this
old valley bottom the stream has entrenched itself 80 ft. where it
enters North Dakota and 300 ft. near the bend.   At the former
place (southern boundary of North Dakota) the old valley bottom
or present bench is dissected near the river only; at the latter
place the full width of the bench is dissected and a broad strip
of the adjacent upland besides.   Below (east of) the bend, no
older valley bottom is seen and the entire depth of cutting
(550 ft.) is in the upland.

Fɪɢ. 26.—Level plain in North Dakota in which the Little Missouri River has
incised badlands.   This view and the one shown in Fig. 25 were taken from the
same point.   (*Photo by A. L. Fellows, N. Dak. Geol. Survey.*)

From these data it is apparent that the vigorous erosion of
the badland cycle is advancing upstream and has made but a
small beginning where the stream enters North Dakota.   There
is good evidence that in pre-glacial time the Little Missouri
flowed north instead of east from the bend, and was forced into
the latter course by the presence of the glacier in its lower valley.[2]
This accounts for the absence of the bench or old valley in that
part of its course and also for the narrowness of the dissected
zone.

[1] Leonard, A. G., Pleistocene Drainage Changes in Western Nortn
Dakota, Geol. Soc. Amer. *Bull.*, vol. 27, p. 303, 1916.

[2] Leonard, A. G., *loc. cit.*, p. 300.

While the badlands on the Little Missouri have many bare
slopes, the larger part of the area even on the slopes is more or
less grassed.   These badlands as a whole are a grazing country,
not a desert.[1]

FIG. 27.—Extent of glaciation east of long. 112°.   Symbols *K*, *Ia*, and *W*,
indicate Kansan, Iowan, and Wisconsin drift borders.   Mountain glaciation
undifferentiated.   (*Courtesy of Amer. Mus. Nat. History.*)

GLACIATED SECTION OF THE MISSOURI PLATEAU

Extent and Effects of Glaciation.—The description of the
topography of the unglaciated section of the Missouri Plateau
gives a fair mental picture of the surface of the glaciated section

[1] LEONARD, A. G., N. Dak. Geol. Survey, *5th Biennial Rept.*, p. 40, 1908.

ɔefore the advent of the continental ice cap. The chief topographic effect of glaciation was no doubt a smoothing of the
surface, partly by abrading hills but mainly by filling up valleys.
No doubt some valleys favorably situated were deepened, and
locally, as in the Missouri Coteau and other terminal moraines,
a great deal of relief is directly due to glacial deposition, but
the balance would no doubt be largely in the direction of reducing
relief.[1]

Over the larger part of this section (roughly speaking, that
which lies east and north of the Missouri River) the ice advanced
more than once (Fig. 27). The topographic effects of the last
advance are far more important, not only because of the larger
amount of drift deposited, but because of the recency of the
event. Except in the valleys of the larger streams like the
Yellowstone, post-glacial erosion has changed this surface but
little and in the more morainic portions not at all. The older
drift west and south of the Missouri was presumably thin from
the start and the time since its deposition has been so long that
an erosion topography has been fairly reestablished especially
south of lat. 47°.[2]

Near the Rocky Mountain front the edge of the continental
drift sheet turns north, leaving uncovered a strip of plains about
40 miles in width from east to west and 50 or 60 miles long. This
strip was in part covered by glaciers from the mountains and
most of it is here included within the glaciated section.[3]

Missouri Coteau.—The strip of plateau in the Dakotas
bounded on the west by the trench of the Missouri River and
overlooking the Central Lowland on the east, is among the most
remarkable morainic belts of the United States.[4] The drift is
characteristically stony; large boulders abound. The uneroded

[1] *Cf.* Ft. Benton folio 55, p. 5, U. S. Geol. Survey, 1899.

[2] WOOD, L. H., Report on the Region between the Northern Pacific
Railroad and the Missouri River, N. Dak. Geol. Survey, 3d *Biennial Rept.*,
pp. 49–50, 1904.

[3] ALDEN, WM. C., Pre-Wisconsin Drift in the Region of Glacier National
Park, Montana, Geol. Soc. Amer. *Bull.*, vol. 23, pp. 687–708, 1912; also
ALDEN, WM. C., and STEBINGER, EUGENE, Geol. Soc. Amer. *Bull.*, vol. 24,
pp. 529–572, 1913. The limits of the several ice sheets on the Great Plains
are summarized by Alden in the paper already referred to, pl. XI.

[4] WILLARD, DANIEL E., and ERICKSON, M. B., Survey of the Coteau of
the Missouri, Agr. Coll. N. Dak., *2d Biennial Rept.*, 1904; WILLARD, DANIEL
E., "Story of the Prairies," pp. 216–222, 1907.

glacial débris remains as the ice left it, piled in hummocks without order, enclosing basins or "kettles" which contain ponds, swamps, "hay meadows," or merely more boulders. Some of the hills are 100 to 150 ft. high. The variety first promised by the lack of order is soon exhausted and the hummocks and hollows repeat themselves monotonously. Previous to the building of roads and fences the traveler who lost the trail might as well be lost in a forest. Stones were often piled into cairns to mark the roads.

The entire area east of the Missouri River is not thus covered but a large part of it is; generally a strip 15 to 25 miles wide. The terminal moraines are more or less chain-like, the several chains meeting and parting irregularly. Limited strips of rolling ground moraine occur here and there between the bands of terminal moraine.

Taken as a whole, it is a grazing country. There is grass on the stony slopes and hay in the limited bottoms, with excellent water in many of the hollows. The smoother parts are being rapidly appropriated to agriculture.

Aside from features due to glaciation, this strip of plateau is in all respects the same as the rolling upland to the west. If the young trench of the Missouri were filled, the gentle eastward slope would be continuous. East of this upland lies the Central Lowland, degraded to a newer and lower peneplain,[1] the two levels being separated by a slope 5 to 20 miles in width and 300 to 400 ft. high. This is the so-called "escarpment." The greater elevation on the west is not due to strong rocks; the escarpment merely marks the limit of a newer and lower peneplain which began farther east and is spreading westward. The later ice sheet which covered the lowland on the east crept up the slope, but having done so, its energy was exhausted. In successive small advances and retreats, it built its reduplicated terminal moraines. The strip of highlands east of the Missouri River is not therefore to be thought of as due primarily to glacial deposition, though in places there are several hundred feet of drift both on its top and in the valleys which formerly indented its slopes. The moraines are much the most conspicuous element of the landscape but they are merely superimposed on the plateau. The term "coteau" is properly applied to the range of moraines,

[1] The term "peneplain" is used somewhat liberally to signify a surface of low relief (*cf.* footnote, p. 187).

not to the plateau of stratified rocks on which they rest, though this is often spoken of as the Coteau district or belt. The present drainage of the Coteau belt, in so far as there is drainage, is westward; the divide is near the top of the eastward slope.

The entire plateau district east of the Missouri River presents three types of topography. Its eastern slope is relatively smooth ground moraine, already deeply furrowed at places by "coulees," *i.e.*, narrow valleys carrying only storm water. Before glaciation it was doubtless much rougher and less regular. West of this slope is the Coteau proper, almost as the ice sheet left it. This is followed by the slope leading down to the Missouri, covered with a complex of terminal moraine, older ground moraine and outwash plains, all subjected to active erosion.

Physiographic History of the Missouri Plateau

Uplift and Denudation.—The topographic history of the Missouri Plateau is one of long erosion with intermittent elevation. The minimum depth of denudation is inferred from remnants. Residual buttes in the Dakotas are 650 ft. above the peneplain, but 400 ft. more are believed to have been eroded from their tops. Residuals increase in height toward the west. The Highwood Mountains contain remnants 3,000 ft. above the plain which indicate stripping to that extent, and the Crazy Mountains have preserved similar remnants 5,000 ft. above the plain (page 62). It is clear that thousands of feet have been stripped from the western part of the section while perhaps 1,000 ft. have been lost at the east. The fact that relics of various plain surfaces are preserved in the west, up to a height of 1,000 ft. above the general level, or nearly 2,000 ft. above the larger streams, shows that uplift was intermittent, some of the halts being long enough to develop local, or perhaps even widespread, peneplains with correspondingly broad alluviated valleys. The convergence of these various levels at the east indicates that the several uplifts were in the main tiltings, the eastern margin being less elevated than the western.

It appears that in the oldest recorded cycles, major streams followed lines which are now divides. Thus the gravel capping of the Cypress Hills and the Flaxville gravel north of the Milk River mark the positions of ancient valleys. It is well known that a thick layer of porous gravel may protect a surface from erosion while intervening higher areas are cut down to lower levels.

Hypothetical restorations of the profiles of the ancient streams that deposited these gravels leads to the conclusion that in mid-Tertiary time (close of the Oligocene) the Rocky Mountains rose very little above the adjacent plains.[1] Their present prominence, their *front*, is due to differential erosion following a broad uplift of the Rocky Mountain belt without folding, but with decreasing amplitude toward the east. A similar explanation is given for the Rocky Mountain front in Colorado with this difference; that it is customary to regard the degradation of the Colorado Piedmont as having been accomplished in a relatively short time, *i.e.*, since the youngest Pliocene deposits were made.[2]

Drainage History.—Glaciation had important effects on the drainage system of the Missouri Plateau. The approximate agreement of the Missouri in its southward course with the front of the later ice sheet strongly suggests cause and effect. This relation becomes more striking when it is observed that in its southward courses through the Dakotas the Missouri follows the contours of a plateau whose slope is east. Even now, after trenching more than 400 ft. deep into the plateau, the river flows at a level 250 ft. above that of the James, a much smaller parallel stream 125 miles farther east. The difference in elevation would be still greater if the glacial drift were removed from the James Valley.

Evidence[3] indicates that the main streams coming from the west once continued their courses farther east where they joined a trunk stream leading either to Hudson Bay or to the Gulf of Mexico. With the ice blocking the lower courses of these

[1] ALDEN, WM. C., Physiographic Development of the Northern Great Plains, Geol. Soc. Amer. *Bull.*, vol. 35, p. 394, 1924.

[2] To what extent this difference is real, and to what extent due to different methods of approaching the problem, cannot now be known. There is a natural tendency to ask whether there is sufficient reason for allowing so much more time for degrading the Missouri Plateau than the Colorado Piedmont. Some geologists answer in the negative by assigning Pliocene age to the peneplain on the Rocky Mountains in Montana as well as Colorado. Bevan (*Jour. Geol.*, vol. XXXIII, p. 586) expresses this view and cites others. Alden, however, in the paper repeatedly cited, regards the peneplain as *at least* as old as Miocene.

[3] TODD, J. E., History of the Missouri River, *Science*, February, 1914; Preliminary Report on the Geology of South Dakota, S. Dak. Geol. Survey, *Bull.* 1, pp. 9–10, 1894; Hydrographic History of South Dakota, Geol. Soc. Amer. *Bull.*, vol. 13, pp. 27–40, 1901; see also CHAMBERLAIN, U. S. Geol. Survey, 3*d Ann. Rept.*

streams, their combined waters could only follow its edge. Thus the present south-flowing Missouri came into being. Just how far the pre-glacial Missouri followed its present course has not been determined.[1] Nor is it known just what part the several ice sheets played in the change of its course, except that the new valley had already been excavated and partly refilled before the advent of the last ice sheet—the one that built the coteaus. Since the disappearance of the latter the trough has again been deepened, though not to the depth which it had at an earlier time.

All the tributaries from the west down to and including the White were blocked by the ice. Lakes were thus formed. Partial filling of these and the later down-cutting of the river have left the valleys terraced.[2]

Since the change of its course, the Missouri has cut a trough 400 to 500 ft. deep and one to three miles wide between bluffs. The mouths of its tributaries have been lowered and they have been distinctly revived. Their valleys have thus been terraced and local badlands developed. The reason for such a rejuvenation, both of the Missouri and of its tributaries, is probably found in the last general uplift of the western region.[3] Some streams of the Central Lowland have cut similar young trenches, but in none of their basins was there the same combination of factors favorable to badlands.

The cutting power of the Cheyenne River is exemplified by its captures.[4] Its chief northern branch is the Belle Fourche, which encircles the Black Hills on the north. The upper portion of this stream in Wyoming flows northeast in line with the Little Missouri, of which it was formerly a part (see index map,

[1] The limit commonly assigned is Fort Stephenson (long. 101°30′), where the river makes a sharp turn to the south, but Leonard interprets the valley, at least as far south as Bismarck, as pre-glacial; see Bismarck folio 181; also Geology of South Central North Dakota, N. Dak. Geol. Survey, 6*th Biennial Rept.*, 1912.

[2] Todd, J. E., Preliminary Report on the Geology of Northwestern Central South Dakota, S. Dak. Geol. Survey, *Bull.* 4, 1908. This paper discusses the effect of the ice in obstructing valleys, and accounts for all glacial boulders west of the Missouri by icebergs floating in the extensive Lake Arikaree. For mention of individual terraces and suggestions as to their ages, see Exploration of the White River Badlands in 1896, S. Dak. Geol. Survey, *Bull.* 2, 1896, by the same author.

[3] For continued deepening of the trench of the Missouri, see Todd, J. E., U. S. Geol. Survey, *Bull.* 158, p. 150, 1899.

[4] Darton, N. H., Aladdin folio 128, U. S. Geol. Survey.

Fig. 3). From this locality the east-flowing Belle Fourche reaches the Missouri in 300 miles, whereas the Little Missouri makes a circuit of 600 miles to the same point. The higher gradient and more rapid down-cutting of the former enabled it to behead the latter. The captured head stream now turns at right angles to follow the Belle Fourche and, at the point of capture, the reinforced Belle Fourche has already entrenched itself 100 ft. below the abandoned channel. The Grand and Moreau (Owl) Rivers, north of the Cheyenne, enjoy similar advantages over the Little Missouri, which their headwaters now approach within a few miles. Future capture is possible. It is probable also that the main branch of the Cheyenne has extended itself around the Black Hills to the south by a series of captures.[1]

The upper Missouri in north central Montana was also displaced by glaciation. From various evidences[2] it is clear that the Missouri flowed almost directly northeast from Great Falls to Havre and thence eastward through the broad valley now occupied by the Milk River. The valley of the Milk River suddenly changes width at Havre from about one-half mile to two, three, or even four miles. The stream meanders tortuously over its wide flood plain, in a valley which is much too large for it, and which is filled to a depth of 100 ft. or more above the former channel. When the ice sheet moved south to the Bearpaw Mountains, even rising some distance against their northern foothills, the Missouri River which formerly flowed at their northern base was compelled to find another course, which it did by following the valley of an eastern tributary to its head, then cutting a new valley for the rest of the way to the present mouth of the Milk, where the Missouri enters its old valley. The new valley is little more than a gorge, at places almost 1,000 ft. deep.

The region about Great Falls owes much of its interest to glacial interference with drainage. Here the ice crowded the river southward nearly to the Highwood Mountains, compelling it to cut a new channel (Shonkin Sag) which it abandoned when the ice departed and opened a lower way for the water to escape. In the valley above Great Falls, the ice and later the moraine held back a large lake whose bed is now a nearly flat plain.

---

[1] Todd, J. E., Hydrographic History of South Dakota, Geol. Soc. Amer. *Bull.*, vol. 13.

[2] Calhoun, F. H. H., U. S. Geol. Survey, *Prof. Pap.* 50, p. 39, 1906.

Downstream from Great Falls, the old pre-glacial channel was so filled with drift that the present river repeatedly crosses it, locally following the course of the old filled valley and again flowing through an entirely new gorge. A few miles below the city a drift-filled old channel is intersected by the present stream. Here the "Giant Springs," among the largest in the world, issue from the gravel, probably having entered it from the Missouri itself at another intersection farther upstream.[1]

The Missouri River below the city of Great Falls, being out of its old channel, found its new course ungraded. It flows successively over incoherent drift and strong rocks, the former being quickly cut down to grade; the latter producing falls and rapids. In a distance of 10 miles the total fall is 612 ft., one-third of which occurs in five cataracts collectively known as the "Great Falls." The remainder is intervening rapids.[2] Calculations based on the minimum flow of the river indicate that 38,585 hp. might be developed. A part of this is at present developed and utilized.

BLACK HILLS

General Description.—The Black Hills are an isolated mountain range or dome surrounded by the Missouri Plateau. Because of its large dimensions this mountain area is treated as a separate section, though it does not differ essentially from some of the smaller mountain groups on the Missouri Plateau nor from some ranges of the Rocky Mountains.

The doming of the strata affects the surface throughout an elliptical area about 125 miles long and 60 miles wide, the elongation being northwest to southeast, *i.e.*, parallel to the Rocky Mountain front 100 miles away. The "Hills" now rise a little less than 4,000 ft. above the plains on the east (Harney Peak, 7,216 ft. above sea-level) but they have suffered greatly from erosion. Had the uplift occurred all at once and without concurrent erosion, the dome would have risen 9,000 to 10,000 ft. above the plain.[3]

[1] FISHER, CASSIUS A., Giant Springs at Great Falls, Montana, Geol. Soc. Amer. *Bull.*, vol. 19, 1907; the combined flow of these springs has been measured as 638 sec.-ft. Geology and Water Resources of the Great Falls Region, Montana, U. S. Geol. Survey, *Wat. Sup. Pap.* 221, pl. VI, 1909.

[2] FISHER, CASSIUS A., U. S. Geol. Survey, *Wat. Sup. Pap.* 221, p. 76.

[3] DARTON, N. H., Geology and Water Resources of the Northern Portion of the Black Hills, U. S. Geol. Survey, *Prof. Pap.* 65, p. 62; Newcastle folio 107, Fig. 3, p. 6 Contours. on Minnekahta Limestone. U. S. Geol. Survey, 1904.

The effect of erosion has been to uncover the ancient crystalline rocks somewhat east of the center of the uplift and to expose the several formations in concentric elliptical bands, the lowest formation outcropping nearest the center and approximately at the highest altitude, and conversely, the youngest formation outcropping at the outer edge and at the lowest altitude. The truncated edges of the stronger strata form prominent mono-clinal ridges where the dip is steep (for the most part near the

FIG. 28.—Generalized diagram of the Black Hills as seen from the south. In the eastern half of the main uplift all sedimentary rocks have been eroded away, exposing granite and schist in the rough Central Basin. The western half remains covered by nearly horizontal Carboniferous limestones. The uppermost of these (Minnekahta purple limestone) is seen only at the margin of the plateau leaning against the steep edge of the central mass. Outside of that is the almost continuous Red Valley and beyond it the Dakota hogback. Four inward-facing escarpments outside of the Dakota are shown in fragmentary form. (*Newton, U. S. Geogr. and Geol. Survey. Figure reproduced from Pirsson and Schuchert's Textbook of Geology by courtesy of the Editor.*)

circumference) and sloping plateaus where the dip is small (for the most part near the center). Between these are valleys on weak rocks. The Dakota hogback and the "Red Valley" practically encircle the dome and are among the most remarkable examples of their kind (Fig. 28).

Central Basin.—The stripping of the ancient crystalline rocks (pre-Cambrian) exposes them in an ellipse at least 50 miles long and 20 miles wide. This is an area of strong relief containing several peaks over 7,000 ft. high, and many rugged and forested ridges. But between these ridges, especially in the western part, are extensive basins or "parks" of mild relief, forested in patches or covered by open woodland or prairie[1] (Fig. 29). The contrast of these areas with the higher limestone plateau on the west (described below) has caused the entire area of crystalline rocks to be known as the "Central Basin." The main divide is at the edge of the limestone plateau. The streams flowing east from this divide have entrenched themselves but little near

Fig. 29.—Typical landscape on the crystalline rocks of the Central Basin of the Black Hills. In a former erosion cycle this area was reduced to moderate relief with wide park-like valleys (foreground) and residual hills and mountains of which the Harney Peak Range (background) is the largest. The forest on the lower ridge (middle ground) is characteristic. (*Darton, U. S. Geol. Survey.*)

their headwaters, hence the rolling park lands in the western part of the Central Basin remain undissected; but as the same streams proceed farther, their valleys become deeper and deeper, so that the eastern margin of the crystalline area is very rugged.

Limestone Plateau.—Surrounding the Central Basin is a zone in which strong strata capped by limestone are preserved. To picture this zone properly it is necessary to remember that the original dome was relatively flat on top while near the edges the strata are inclined, more steeply on the east than on the

[1] For discussion of forest distribution and origin of the prairies, see GRAVES, HENRY S., U. S. Geol. Survey, 19*th Ann. Rept.*, pt. V, pp. 69–80, 1898.

west. Furthermore, the denuded crystalline area is near the
eastern side.   Hence, on that side the strata being much inclined
are exposed in narrow belts.   On the other side is a broad belt
in which the beds dip gently westward, forming an inclined
limestone plateau, its outer margin only being covered by sandstone.   The eastern edge of this plateau is a prominent escarpment, at places 800 ft. high, overlooking the Central Basin and,
of course, retreating westward.   Its summit is the main divide.
For some distance west of the divide the plateau is young; its
small streams are entrenched little or not at all in wide, park-
like valleys, the general level over broad areas approaching
7,000 ft., or nearly that of Harney Peak.   Farther west, with
increased size and on a steeper slope, the streams cut canyons
400 to 600 ft. deep.

The narrow limestone cuesta on the east corresponding to the
broad limestone plateau on the west is, like the adjacent parts
of the crystalline area, deeply cut by the streams which head
against the western escarpment.

The outer edge of this limestone ellipse is marked almost
throughout by a hogback of the Minnekahta limestone, formerly
called "purple limestone."[1]   This resistant formation is one of
the most important topographic factors in the Black Hills.
Beneath it are red sandstone and shale which cover the outer
and lower margin of the limestone plateau.   The wasting of
these weak beds saps the "purple limestone" and preserves the
steepness of its infacing escarpment, generally about 50 ft. in
height.   This limestone stratum dips steeply toward the Red
Valley, in many places too steeply to permit soil to accumulate.

Red Valley.—As a typical and impressive subsequent valley,
the Red Valley has few equals.   It is carved from the soft shales
of the Spearfish formation whose redness gives color to the whole
landscape.   Forests are absent.   The width ranges from one-
fourth mile to six miles, but is generally not much more or less
than two miles.   Its inner side, several hundred feet high, is
the dip slope of the purple limestone hogback just described.
Its outer side, also several hundred feet high, is the gray scarp
of the Dakota hogback.   Throughout most of its length the
Red Valley is not occupied by streams.   Streams from the central

---

[1] Darton, N. H., U. S. Geol. Survey, 21st Ann. Rept., pt. IV, also all
Black Hills folios; see also Jaggar, T. A., Economic Resources of the
Northern Black Hills, U. S. Geol. Survey, Prof. Pap. 26, p. 16, 1904.

highland cross ridges and valleys alike. Some short intermittent tributaries follow the valley to join the transverse rivers, but between their heads the valley is almost as low and smooth as where streams are present. The Indians called this valley the "race course" for evident reasons.[1]

On the northwestern side of the dome, where the beds are nearly horizontal and the valley is widest, occasional remnants of gypsum interbedded with the shale have preserved steep-sided buttes, the gypsum now appearing as a white cap on top of a brick-red butte.[2]

Dakota Hogback.—The ridge made by the strong Dakota[3] sandstone generally rises 300 to 600 ft. above the adjacent plain, though exceptional points like Mt. Pisgah (6,350 ft.) on the west side are much higher. Where the dip is steep, as on the east side, the ridge is a narrow hogback, steep on both sides. At the ends of the dome, and locally on the west side, the dip is gentle and the ridge becomes an outward-sloping plateau, at places 10 miles wide, generally dissected 300 to 400 ft. deep.

At the northwest end of the main uplift is a smaller one from which all formations above the Dakota have been stripped. The headwaters of the Belle Fourche River cross this uplift in a valley 1,000 ft. deep, cutting far below the strong sandstone into the bright-colored shale which underlies the Red Valley. For some miles from the stream the plateau is maturely dissected and the surface is very rugged.

The topography of the Dakota sandstone, whether hogback or sloping dissected plateau, is so characteristic of the margin of the Black Hills that the conventional boundary of this section is made to follow the line where this formation passes beneath the shale that underlies the surrounding plains.

Cuestas in the Surrounding Plains.—Passing outward from the limit of the Black Hills as here defined, the rocks of the plains are, for some miles, gently inclined. Although generally so weak that they have been reduced to rolling plains, these rocks

---

[1] TODD, J. E., Preliminary Report on the Geology of South Dakota, S. Dak. Geol. Survey, *Bull.* 1, p. 8, 1894.

[2] For an illustration in color see DARTON, U. S. Geol. Survey, 21*st Ann. Rept.*, pt. IV, pl. LXXII, 1900.

[3] The term "Dakota" is properly limited to the uppermost 100 ft. (Upper Cretaceous) of this sandstone. The remaining 200 or 300 ft. (Lower Cretaceous) is properly called the Lakota sandstone; see DARTON, *loc. cit.*, p. 526, 1900.

contain a few strong strata, either limestone or sandstone, which make inward-facing escarpments 50 to 200 ft. high.[1] In a few cases such escarpments, though lying beyond the conventional limits of the Black Hills, help to give the drainage of this section its peculiar pattern (page 85).

Volcanic Mountains.—The northern part of the section has a number of hills or small mountains due to volcanic intrusion and commonly classed as laccoliths.[2] Their locations are seen on the geological map.[3] All are roughly circular and range in diameter from a fraction of a mile to 8 or 10 miles. In degree of erosion they vary from the bare beginning made on Green Mountain (Little Sundance) to the old age of Mato Tepee or Devil's Tower. The former is a small, almost conical mountain in the Red Valley, from whose summit the topmost strata are stripped, but the plug of igneous rock is not yet revealed. Mato Tepee, at the northwest end of the uplift, is what is left of an ancient lava intrusion, either in the form of a laccolith or possibly filling the conduit or throat of a former volcano.[4] This imposing butte is 626 ft. high and consists of vertical angular columns generally 8 to 10 ft. in diameter. Its structure shows it to be a small remnant of a much greater mass.

Physiographic History.[5]—Before the Black Hills dome was uplifted, all the formations named above as outcropping within its limits probably covered the whole area. The raising of an

[1] On the west side is the Greenhorn (limestone) cuesta about 50 ft. high and 1 to 5 miles from the Dakota. This is succeeded at a distance of 2 to 10 (at places, 20) miles by the Niobrara (limestone) cuesta, and this in turn by the Foxhills (sandstone) cuesta 50 to 200 ft. high, and this by the Laramie (sandstone) cuesta, see U. S. Geol. Survey, folios 107, 127, 128, and 150.

[2] RUSSELL, I. C., *Jour. Geol.*, vol. IV, pp. 24–42, points out that in most cases the lava rose more like a plug without spreading between strata. This paper describes all the features due to igneous intrusion in the northern end of the Black Hills dome.

[3] Excellent general maps showing the geology of the Black Hills are found in U. S. Geol. Survey, 21*st Ann. Rept.*, pt. IV (southern half), and *Prof. Pap.* 65 (northern half). See also U. S. Geol. Survey, 21*st Ann. Rept.*, pt. IV, pl. LIX, for entire area. A convenient small-scale map showing the relation of the Black Hills to the Great Plains is pl. XXXV in *Prof. Pap.* 32.

[4] The former interpretation is accepted by N. H. Darton, U. S. Geol. Survey, folio 150. The latter is suggested by D. W. Johnson, Volcanic Necks of the Mount Taylor Region, New Mexico, Geol. Soc. Amer. *Bull.*, vol. 18, p. 319, 1907.

[5] DARTON, N. H., Devil's Tower folio 150, p. 8, gives a summary of events in the recent geologic history of the Black Hills region.

unsymmetrical dome with its apex east of the center no doubt gave rise to radiating streams, those flowing west being longer and having less fall than those flowing east. Now the relative lengths are reversed. The side with the steepest and most active streams was first denuded of its sedimentary rocks. The crystalline rocks beneath wasted more rapidly than the sediments which remained in the limestone plateau. Thus the divide between east-flowing and west-flowing streams was shifted westward with the retreating scarp of the plateau. At the same time, subsequent streams were gradually carving valleys around the entire circumference and developing the monoclinal ridges and valleys. Partly by headward growth and partly by capture (page 78) the tributaries of the Belle Fourche River now practically surround the dome.

When much of this erosion had already been accomplished, the region was partly covered by the lacustrine and fluviatile sediments which now make the Big Badlands. Some stream courses may well have been superimposed on this formation. Its remnants are still found on the floor of the Red Valley on the east. Other remnants lie several thousand feet above the level of the same geologic horizon in the Badlands, thus showing that the dome has since been uplifted by that amount.[1] It follows that the main erosion features were carved when the dome stood much lower than now above the surrounding plain. To the extent that outflowing streams were rejuvenated by level uplift they incised their valleys first on the steep flanks. The effect of such rejuvenation is progressing upstream but has not yet reached the upper courses. It is not surprising then to find the streams in young valleys in their middle courses, while their headwaters occupy old and shallow valleys which have not yet experienced the rejuvenation.

When the eastern part of the Missouri Plateau lay near its base level just before the last general uplift, the Black Hills had almost their present relative elevation. Streams were cutting in the dome, but around its edges they wandered over the plain in intricate meanders planing off the low hills by lateral corrasion, and covering their broad flood plains with gravel. Extensive tracts of such gravel-covered plains remain as terraces at the south end of the dome.[2]

[1] DARTON, N. H., U. S. Geol. Survey, 21*st Ann. Rept.*, pt. IV, p. 558, 1900.
[2] Edgemont folio 108, Early Quaternary Sediments.

With the last general uplift (probably Pleistocene) down-cutting was revived and the streams with their involved meanders were entrenched. This phenomenon is extremely common in the eastern part of the Missouri Plateau. Where the new trench was in soft shale it was soon widened by planing off the spurs. Streams so situated are again meandering on flood plains between widely separated bluffs. This is the case with Beaver Creek and the Cheyenne River on the soft Benton shale west of the dome. But east of Edgemont, the Cheyenne River cuts across the south end of the dome and here it is entrenched in the strong Dakota sandstone. Here the trench is 400 ft. deep, and the meanders, adopted when the stream flowed at the upper level, are preserved almost intact in a gorge at places not much wider than the stream.

RESOURCES OF THE GREAT PLAINS

Mineral Resources.—This province has few minerals of great commercial importance. Bituminous coal and lignite are far the most important. These are widespread and abundant in the Missouri Plateau, the Colorado Piedmont, and the Raton section. The coking coals of the last are especially valuable. They make possible a considerable iron and steel industry. Wyoming's great output of petroleum comes chiefly from the High Plains not far from the Rocky Mountain front. Most of the remainder comes from the Bighorn Basin which for conven-ience is included in the Rocky Mountains, though in reality it is a semi-detached lobe of the Great Plains.

Building materials for local use are abundant but none are shipped extensively unless it be cement, suitable materials for which are widely distributed.[1] The industry is already impor-tant in the Arkansas Valley within the Colorado Piedmont. There are extensive beds of fuller's earth in the Badlands of South Dakota, and a large amount of gypsum both in the foot-hills of the Black Hills and in the same formation underlying the southern High Plains and outcropping on both sides.[2] Immense quantities of salt are known to exist beneath the High Plains and Edwards Plateau and Pecos Basin. Associated with this are potash salts in commercial quantities. These are being worked in the Pecos Basin, but not extensively. The production of potash during the World War from the brine lakes in the

[1] U. S. Geol. Survey, *Prof. Pap.* 32, pl. LXX.
[2] U. S. Geol. Survey, *Bull.* 223, 1904.

Sand-hill district of Nebraska has already been mentioned (page 19, footnote).

In the ancient rocks exposed in local mountain uplifts the precious metals are found. Gold mining in the Black Hills is important.

Water.—The aridity of the climate, except on the eastern margin, makes ground water very important. In the distribution of this, three classes must be considered: (*a*) in the underlying strata of bedrock, (*b*) in the fluviatile mantle of the uplands, and (*c*) in the alluvium of the valleys. The chief artesian water-bearing stratum of the underlying rocks is the Dakota sandstone which outcrops in the foothills of the Rocky Mountains, and of the local uplifts, especially the Black Hills. It is not to be understood that artesian water can be obtained from the Dakota sandstone throughout its whole extent. Where the stratum is sufficiently porous and properly exposed in the foothills to receive water, it may still dip so steeply under the plains that only within a narrow belt near the mountains can it be reached by wells of practicable depth. Around the Black Hills this belt is perhaps 10 to 15 miles wide,[1] but even within this belt the water does not rise to the surface everywhere. Along the Rocky Mountain front the dip of the Dakota sandstone is very steep and the belt within which it can be reached by wells is very narrow. Frequently the pressure or "head" is sufficient to raise the water above the surface of valleys while insufficient to raise it to the surface of the uplands. Thus flowing wells are possible in many valleys of the Arkansas and Platte systems, although impossible on the divides.[2]

Many abundantly flowing wells in the Roswell artesian basin in the central part of the Pecos Valley derive their water from porous strata which outcrop at high levels on the west. This is probably the chief artesian basin of the province.

Beyond the limits of flowing wells, the waters of deep-lying beds may rise in wells partway to the surface, provided the beds are under a watertight cover. Where no such cover is present, the water may descend directly from the surface to the rocks below and be pumped again from them. This is common on the Edwards Plateau, where many wells are drilled into the porous or cavernous limestone.

[1] U. S. Geol. Survey, folios 107, 164, and others.
[2] U. S. Geol. Survey, folios 36, 135, and others.

In the mantle rock on the High Plains (see page 12), the water table may be 100 ft. or more below the upland level.[1] The lower bands or sheets of gravel carry water, but wells encounter these bands at diverse depths. The intervening and overlying silts are relatively dense. Where these beds of alternating character are locally depressed forming a structural basin, the conditions for artesian pressure are present.[2] The downward flexing of beds so deep as to bring the surface of the ground below the surrounding water table causes an upward pressure of the ground water against an impervious bed, very much as water presses upward against the bottom of a boat. When wells are drilled in such a valley, water rises through them just as it rises through a hole in a boat. This condition produces an important type of artesian basin in the High Plains, of which the Meade Basin in southwestern Kansas is the best-known example. Its area is approximately 20 square miles, within which there were at one time more than 200 flowing wells.[3]

The Great Plains are the peculiar domain of the windmill in the United States. This is partly because of favorable climatic conditions,[4] partly on account of the need of water for irrigation, and in large part because of the lack of constant streams to supply water for stock.

Soils.—The general character of the residual soils may be inferred from the physiographic descriptions. They are generally good where the topography is suited to agriculture. An exception might be made of the soil on much of the Benton and Pierre shales wherever they outcrop, from the Missouri Plateau[5] to the Raton section. The purely residual soils of this province are, however, of minor interest.

The soils over a large part of the Great Plains are in part eolian and hence not to be correlated rigidly with the underlying rocks. The loess of Nebraska and adjacent states has been mentioned (page 21), but far beyond the limits of this as shown on the map,[6] broad areas are covered with a surficial sheet which has an admixture of wind-blown material, as is to be expected in

---

[1] JOHNSON, W. D., U. S. Geol. Survey, 21*st Ann. Rept.*, pt. IV.

[2] JOHNSON, W. D., *loc. cit.* p. 701, 1900.

[3] JOHNSON, W. D., *loc. cit.* p. 726.

[4] FULLER, P. E., The Use of Windmills in Irrigation in the Semiarid West, U S. Dept. Agr., *Farmers' Bull.* 395, 1910.

[5] DARTON, N. H., U. S. Geol. Survey, 21*st Ann. Rept.*, pt. IV, p. 580, 1900.

[6] U. S. Geol. Survey, *Prof. Pap.* 32, pl. XLIV.

an arid climate where the wind is a transporting and assorting agent. Such areas (of undetermined limits) occur from the Missouri on the east to northern Montana[1] and the Colorado Piedmont.

Over most of the province the practical interest in purely residual soils is still further reduced by the fact that the chief type of agriculture is by irrigation and is therefore limited to the flood plains and terraces or "bench lands" along streams. The soils on these are alluvial and generally fertile.

The soils of the arid lands are, when watered, generally more fertile than those of humid lands under otherwise similar conditions. This is due to the fact that soluble constituents necessary to the growth of plants are less leached out. To balance this they may be deficient in humus, but so far at least as this province is concerned, the balance is greatly in favor of the arid soils when water is applied.

Native Vegetation.—This province is characteristically one of grasslands, but trees generally appear where the altitude and rainfall (or ground moisture) are exceptional. Most steep slopes above 4,500 ft. in the east (Black Hills) or above 5,000 ft. in the west have at least scattered trees. In the northern part the trees at this level are pines; but in the southern part, where pines begin 1,500 to 2,000 ft. higher, pinyon and juniper take their place at the level named. This lower limit of trees is often spoken of as "dry timber line," but it must not be assumed that trees occupy all higher surfaces. Of steep slopes this would be more or less true, but flat plains may be grasslands up to 1,000 or 2,000 ft. higher.

In the southwestern part of the province, and to a less degree farther north, typical desert plants, cactus, yucca, acacia, etc., mingle with the grasses and are common.[2] The Raton section is a region of transition between this desert landscape and the pure grasslands to the north and east.

Grazing.—This province was formerly almost wholly devoted to grazing and it still continues to be the leading grazing region of the United States. Almost invariably the public range has been overgrazed. There are areas in central Texas where 300 to 500 cattle might once have grazed on a square mile which

[1] Ft. Benton folio 55, U. S. Geol. Survey.

[2] SHREVE, FORREST, A Map of the Vegetation of the United States, *Geogr. Rev.*, vol. III, pp. 119–125, 1917.

will now barely support 50.[1] The damage in many cases is temporary and would be repaired by a period of rest. In other places the loss of the sod cover has caused gullying and loss of soil. In central Texas and the Edwards Plateau it appears that the grass, while able to hold the ground against bushes and cactus so long as undisturbed, is not able to win it again in competition with these when the ground is left bare and open to contest. Here overgrazing has resulted in a great displacement of grass by less valuable vegetation.

Throughout the Great Plains the vigor of the grass varies greatly with the rainfall from year to year. In exceptional years the Sand-hill district of Nebraska is a vast rich pasture. It is in the very dry years, and especially after a series of such, that the topographic function of vegetation is endangered. At such times a former prairie may be converted into an area of shifting dunes, or a sodded upland into badlands.

Agriculture.[2]—East of the Great Plains province, farming is of the ordinary eastern type, generally both as to methods used and as to the crops raised. The western limit of such farming is, of course, not sharp and varies from year to year with varying rainfall. There is no part of the Great Plains which has not its exceptional years with rain enough for crops. Farming in the Great Plains province was formerly limited almost entirely to irrigated districts which are relatively narrow belts along the larger streams. Such farming is a complex business, involving cooperation and large expenditures of money. The returns per acre are also generally much greater and the price of good irrigated land is correspondingly high.

Water for irrigation from wells is very limited and the amount of land thus irrigated must always remain a very small fraction of the whole. Garden, Kansas,[3] has many such wells, but these derive their water from the underflow of the Arkansas River, hence their success has no bearing on the problem of agriculture between streams. In the Roswell Basin of the Pecos Valley (page 49), most of the artesian water which is not wasted,

[1] BENTLEY, H. L., Cattle Ranges of the Southwest, U. S. Dept. Agr., *Farmers' Bull.* 42, p. 7, 1898. At the present time 50 seems a very liberal estimate.

[2] See series of nine maps issued by the U. S. Geol. Survey, showing the Land Classification of the Central and Northern Great Plains.

[3] FULLER, P. E., The Use of Windmills in Irrigation in the Semi-arid West, U. S. Dept. Agr., *Farmers' Bull.* 394, 1910.

is used for irrigating fruit and other valuable crops. For irrigation from ground water this is one of the leading districts of the United States. Also in the Meade ʼBasin (page 88) artesian water is much used in irrigation. The number of undeveloped basins of this character is unknown, but their combined area is in any case a small fraction of the whole. So far as can be seen into the future, the main function of the well and the windmill must be to furnish water for stock and household, and perhaps to irrigate a few acres of garden out of the hundreds of acres employed in dry farming or as a cattle ranch.[1] In recent years there has been a great westward expansion of dry farming, so that at least the eastern margin of the High Plains is now devoted to agriculture. In the northern part of the province where the rainfall is no greater but evaporation is less, almost the entire area is occupied by farms although not all farm lands are cultivated. Cattle raising continues to be important.

Successful agriculture between streams in the western part of the High Plains and west of them to the Rocky Mountains, is largely limited to certain drought-resisting plants. These are all fodder crops which grow and mature with a small amount of moisture. Such farming, like the gardens mentioned above, is subsidiary to the cattle industry.[2]

Transportation.—Despite the lack of obstacles to travel in almost any direction, most of the railroads follow streams. This is partly because of the more uniform grade. The general straightness of the streams and the presence of terraces above flood level make these routes feasible. Moreover, the resources named above lie mainly near the larger streams. But those who cross the Plains should remember that, in so far as they are following the larger streams, the strip of country which they see is not typical of the Great Plains. They see mainly flood plain and "bench lands," in large part irrigated. Only large stock trains and cattle pens along the way suggest the vast, thinly populated, and but little-farmed areas between the favored valleys.

[1] This problem is fully discussed by W. D. Johnson, The High Plains and Their Utilization, U. S. Geol. Survey, 21*st Ann. Rept.*, pt. IV, 1900.

[2] For farming without irrigation, west of the 100th meridian, see Agriculture in the Central Part of the Semi-arid Portions of the Great Plains, J. A. Warren, U. S. Dept. Agr., Bur. Plant Industry, *Bull.* 215, 1911.

CHAPTER II

SOUTHERN ROCKY MOUNTAIN PROVINCE

RELATION TO OTHER PROVINCES

One of the major divisions of the United States is the great barrier of mountains between the Great Plains on the east and the Colorado Plateau, Great Basin, and Columbia Plateau on the west. The entire area is called the "Rocky Mountain System." It is not all mountains but its mountainous and non-mountainous parts are so related that, even in their description and much more in their history, it is necessary to consider them as parts of a larger whole.

Of the four provinces in this division the Wyoming Basin, which lies between the Southern and the Middle Rocky Mountain provinces, is a plateau country merging by narrow passages with the Great Plains on the east and the Colorado Plateau on the south. Thus the mountains of the Southern province are not strictly contiguous with those of the other provinces though certain low anticlines are continuous across the gaps and low isolated mountains stand on the plateau in central Wyoming where the belt of deformation crosses. The Middle Rocky Mountain province is connected with the Northern province only by a single range on the northern border of Yellowstone Park. The park itself is a volcanic plateau. For good reasons it is included in the Rocky Mountain provinces, but, were the lava filling removed, the mountain system would be almost severed at this place by a broad and deep transverse depression. The headwaters of the Yellowstone and Madison Rivers approximately mark the boundary between the mountain provinces.

There is also a difference in character between the Southern and Middle Rocky Mountain provinces, on the one hand, and the Northern on the other. The ranges of the former are, for the most part, linear features, the main crests being on structural uplifts generally flanked by outward-dipping strata making hogback foothills. In the Northern province such division into orographic units is almost wholly wanting. Most of the larger mountain masses are not linear and they have neither axial crest nor monoclinal foothills. They are more like extensive plateaus, deeply and ruggedly carved by erosion.

GENERAL DESCRIPTION

Structure.—The Southern Rocky Mountain province consists mainly of broad, elevated, north-south strips of granite[1] generally flanked by steeply dipping sedimentaries (see index map, Fig. 30 and geologic map, Fig. 31). Usually these latter are lower, commonly making foothills, but locally they cap the mountains. Generally also, the surface of the granite is mountainous, but not everywhere. In South Park, Colorado, it is a plateau 10,000 ft. high. Some of the granite mountains stand above this plateau, others are carved from it by deep erosion. Some of the mountains, notably the San Juan in southwestern Colorado, consist almost wholly of volcanic ejecta.

Structurally these belts are great anticlines deeply eroded. Apparently the flanking strata were once continuous across the crest.[2] Many thousand feet of rock may have been eroded away, though it is not to be assumed that the arch ever rose so high as might be inferred from the steep dips in the foothills. No doubt the dips flattened over the summit as they do now in the Uinta, Bighorn, and other ranges whose sedimentary covers remain.[3] The great lateral monoclines whose tops are seen in the foothills descend far beneath the plains. The granite surface in the mountains may be three to four miles above the buried granite under the plains. The total uplift is the result of repeated rising.

[1] Not all of these rocks are really *granite*, but that is the characteristic rock. Petrographic accuracy is not here important. In this and similar cases the use of the term granite for pre-Cambrian crystalline rocks is so common and so convenient that it is employed here with a mixture of defense and protest.

[2] This is the conclusion of Willis T. Lee, U. S. Geol. Survey, *Prof. Pap.* 95, pp. 27–58, 1915, after studying the field evidence and the history of the discussion on this question; see also RANSOME, F. L., Problems of American Geology; and BLACKWELDER, E., Cenozoic History of the Laramie Region, Wyoming, *Jour. Geol.*, vol. XVII, p. 430, 1909.

[3] This is a common assumption. The extent to which these Uinta structures were produced by lateral compression on the one hand, or by vertical up-thrusting on the other, has been debated from the time of Dutton and Emmons down to the present.

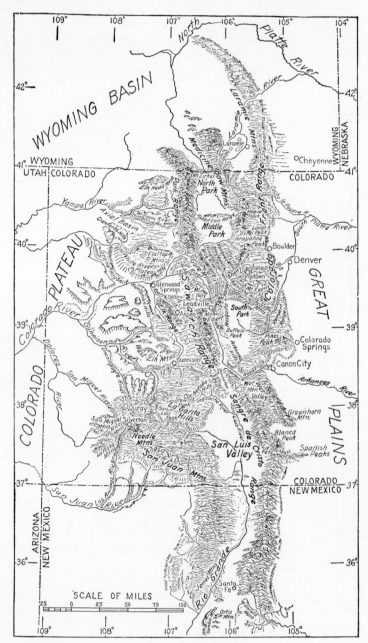

Fig. 30.—Index map of the Southern Rocky Mountain province. (Drawn by Guy-Harold Smith.)

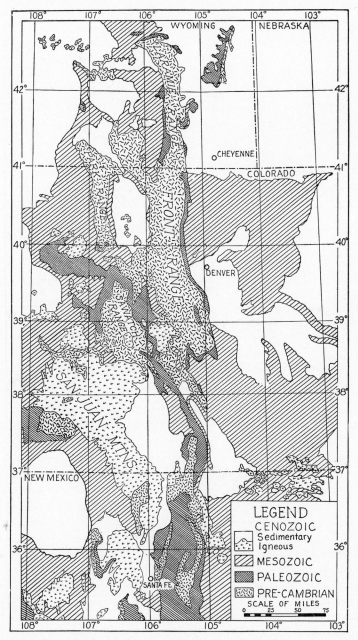

Fig. 31.—Generalized geologic map of the Southern Rocky Mountain province.

Monoclinal foothills are almost as characteristic of these mountains as are granite cores (Fig. 32).   A single formation, the strong Dakota sandstone, makes an imposing hogback which attends more than half of the total mountain frontage in this province.   Only second in extent, and even more impressive because of its color, is the very thick and resistant Carboniferous red sandstone belonging to what is popularly called "the redbeds."   Younger Cretaceous strata make local hogbacks and even the older Tertiary beds, outcropping farther from the mountains, are sometimes turned up slightly.   Locally, these younger beds cover the truncated edges of all older sedimentaries, forming gently inclined planes connecting the Great Plains and the granite plateau.   On such an incline west of Cheyenne,

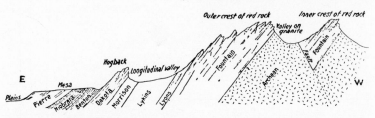

Fig. 32.—Generalized cross-section of foothills near Boulder, Colorado. Except for details due to faulting this section is fairly representative of the mountain border for hundreds of miles.   The great ridge-making formations are the Fountain (red sandstone) of Carboniferous age and the Dakota sandstone of the Cretaceous.   (*U. S. Geol. Survey.*)

Wyoming, the Union Pacific Railroad ascends the mountain side on a moderate grade.

Peneplains on the Granite.—In all parts of this province extensive areas may be found in which the mountain tops rise to an almost uniform level (Fig. 33).   In many cases the summits are still broad and the relief is obviously due to the carving of a surface of small relief.   Such landscapes merge, on the one hand, into undissected uplands of the same height as the mountain tops but of no great relief and, on the other hand, into sharp mountains which rise no higher but among whose crests there is no common level.   Some of the ruggedest mountain areas do not rise above this plateau level and are plainly carved from it. Other ranges or groups of mountains rise several thousand feet above the common level and are plainly what is left of an older generation of mountains.   The widespread common level is obviously a peneplain.

Generally it will be found that the level of peneplain remnants or of accordant crests is lower near the foothills and rises gradually toward the interior. At places, both north and south of Denver, the upland level begins with an altitude of less than 8,000 ft. but may be traced continuously westward to an altitude of more than 10,000 ft. It is obvious that when the peneplain was uplifted it was also mildly arched along a north-south axis.

Fig. 33.—View westward over the younger peneplain to the Continental Divide in lat. 40° near Boulder, Colorado. The view is taken from Green Mountain, an exceptional eminence in the foothills. In the 12 miles between this point and the residual range seen in the distance the level of the ridge crests rises 2,000 ft., *i.e.*, from 7,000 ft. to 9,000 ft. This peneplain is now dissected by valleys having a maximum depth of 1,000 ft. The rock is granite and this belt is always considered to belong to the mountains. (*Photo by J. Raymond Brackett.*)

Allowance must also be made for unequal uplift along the axis itself. When all such allowance has been made, there remain discrepancies in altitude which seem to require that certain higher levels in some localities be ascribed to an older peneplain not wholly destroyed in the making of the newer.

The newer and more widespread surface is commonly called the Rocky Mountain peneplain. It is plainly inappropriate to limit this name to any one peneplain since two have now been recognized in the Rocky Mountains and others may yet be found. The surface thus designated is called here the "South Park" peneplain. The older and higher one was named by Lee the "Flattop" peneplain,[1] from the name of a mountain on which it is preserved.[2]

Peaks and Ridges.—Forty-six mountain peaks in Colorado rise above 14,000 ft., and three hundred more to 13,000 ft., but none to 14,500 ft.[3] They are the culminating points of residual ridges surmounting the South Park peneplain but collectively these higher ridges occupy only a minor part of the area. Most of them rise 500 to 2,500 ft. above the surrounding level. Pikes Peak is exceptional in its relative altitude, rising as it does to 14,147 ft. above a rolling upland which is here but little above 9,000 ft.[4] Yet this same upland, a dozen miles to the north, is itself dissected into mountains called the Rampart Range, their summits being at the same height as the base of Pikes Peak.

Some of these higher mountains have rounded tops with only moderate summit slopes, such as occur on old mountains much subdued (Fig. 43, page 112). Such summit forms may give way abruptly to the oversteepened, often nearly vertical slopes of glacial troughs and cirques. Most of the higher peaks and ridges are thus sculptured by ice (Fig. 42, page 109). On some crests ice work has been carried so far as to obliterate the former erosion topography, leaving only aretes and peaks of the Matterhorn type between broadened cirques and overdeepened valleys.[5]

FRONT RANGES

The name Colorado Front Range is applied to the mountains between the Arkansas River on the south and the Cache la Poudre River near the Wyoming boundary. North of the Cache la Poudre a narrow granite belt extends 150 miles farther under

[1] LEE, WILLIS T., Peneplains of the Front Range at Rocky Mountain National Park, Colorado, U. S. Geol. Survey, *Bull.* 730, 1922.

[2] *Cf.* CHAMBERLIN, R. T., The Building of the Colorado Rockies, *Jour. Geol.*, vol. XXVII, pp. 158–162, 1919.

[3] Publications of the Colorado Mountain Club; "The Mountain Peaks of Colorado," 1923; and "Fourteen Thousand Feet," 1925.

[4] See U. S. Geol. Survey, folios 198 and 203, illustrations.

[5] DAVIS, W. M., The Colorado Front Range, Assoc. Amer. Geogr. *Ann.*, vol. I, pp. 48–50, 53–64, 1911.

the name of Laramie Mountains.   South of the Arkansas River
the front is offset to the west and follows the Wet Mountains.
All these are in the easternmost granite belt and are included
in this discussion of the Front Ranges.

LOCAL DESCRIPTIONS

Laramie Range.—No considerable part of the Laramie Range
rises above the peneplain.   This is 8,500 to 9,000 ft. high near

FIG. 34.—Foothills of the Rocky Mountain Front Range north of Boulder,
Colorado, looking north.   The lower members of the upturned beds are strong
and make the monoclinal ridge or hogback at the left.   The upper beds are weak
and have been planed off by erosion.   This margin of the Colorado Piedmont
section of the Great Plains has been cut down many hundreds of feet since the
last Rocky Mountain peneplain was uplifted.   Before down-cutting it was a
part of the High Plains and approximately at the level of the peneplain in the
mountain area.

the Cache la Poudre River where the name "Laramie" takes the
place of "Colorado Front Range" in local usage.   Elevations
1,000 ft. above the peneplain are exceptional.   Moreover, the
peneplain is not only well developed but well preserved, large
tracts being still uneroded.   Going north into Wyoming, the
altitude declines.   Where crossed by the Union Pacific Railroad
between Cheyenne and Laramie, it is a nearly level upland 8,000

ft. high or 1,500 ft. above the adjacent plains.[1] Here it is known as the Sherman peneplain. At one point the degradational plain on the granite axis merges into the Tertiary plain of the Great Plains, giving some idea of what the whole mountain front was like at a recent geological date. At such a place the traveler may fail to apprehend the real mountain range, since the only "mountains" he sees are the isolated monadnocks, the highest of which are the Sherman Mountains rising 1,000 ft. above the general level.

Some of the sedimentary rocks have resisted erosion better than the granite and now underlie the highest uplands. In the eastern foothills these rocks are crossed in almost impassable gorges by streams which flow over the central upland in wide, shallow valleys. Plainly rejuvenation is going on and has not yet reached the upper courses of these streams.[2]

Medicine Bow Range.—A little south of lat. 40°30′ the Front Range divides into two ranges, the Laramie Range trending almost due north and Medicine Bow trending northwest and terminating about 50 miles north of the Wyoming state line. Between the two is the Laramie Basin (page 141). In Wyoming the Medicine Bow Range has the appearance of a maturely dissected plateau about 10,000 ft. high, surmounted by cirque-carved alpine mountains locally called the "Snowy Range." The range has here a steep eastward front interpreted as a fault-line scarp.[3]

Farther south the range is less high, a "rounded forested ridge,"[4] but its southern end is rugged and alpine like the main Front Range further south. Its local name, "Sawtooth Range," suggests its character. Many peaks have altitudes of between 12,000 and 13,000 ft.

[1] For description and discussion see Darton, N. H., U. S. Geol. Survey, folio 173, 1910; also Blackwelder, E., Cenozoic History of the Laramie Region, Wyoming, *Jour. Geol.*, vol. XVII, 1909.

[2] Blackwelder, *loc. cit.*, p. 438, ascribes these shallow valleys in the upland to a later cycle than the one in which the peneplain was made but preceding the uplift with which the "canyon cycle" began.

[3] Blackwelder, E., *loc. cit.*, p. 440, suggests that the peneplain represented by the summits of the Medicine Bow Range may be of Eocene age since it is distinctly higher than certain nearby remnants which are interpreted as being of the same age as the Sherman peneplain of the Laramie Range.

[4] Beekly, A. L., Geology and Coal Resources of North Park, Colorado, U. S. Geol. Survey, *Bull.* 596, p. 12, 1915.

Boulder District.—Beginning at the north fork of the Cache la Poudre River and extending many miles to the south, a lofty alpine ridge surmounts the well-developed but now dissected South Park peneplain, lying generally near the western border of the granite belt[1] (Fig. 33). Among its notable peaks are Hagues Peak (13,832 ft.), Longs Peak (14,255 ft.), and Arapahoe Peak (13,520 ft.).

FIG. 35.—Flattop peneplain. Looking southeast to Longs Peak, a monadnock made rugged by recent glacial erosion. The plain in this picture is the summit of Flattop Mountain, this being the locality from which the older peneplain takes its name. (*Photo by R. T. Chamberlin.*)

Throughout this distance the level of the peneplain is generally discernible at altitudes ranging from 8,000 ft. near the foothills, to 10,000 ft. around and among the residual older mountains. In this district, notably in and near the Rocky Mountain National Park, many ridges, some of them broad, rise to a fairly uniform level 1,500 to 2,000 ft. above the clearly seen peneplain. These have been interpreted as remnants of the Flattop peneplain, the

[1] FENNEMAN, N. M., Geology of the Boulder District, Colorado, U. S. Geol. Survey, *Bull.* 265, 1905.

CARL A. RUDISILL LIBRARY
LENOIR RHYNE COLLEGE

summit of Flattop Mountain being one of the broader remnants[1] (Figs. 35 and 36).   The highest peaks rise above this level.

Georgetown District.—In the vicinity of Georgetown, west and southwest of Denver, the landscape is dominated by remnants at or near the Flattop level, most of them above 11,500 ft., but the older peneplain, although apparently first discerned in

Fig. 36.—View from Prospect Mountain northwestward across Estes Park. The distant sky line is on the older or Flattop peneplain.   The younger (presumably South Park) peneplain appears distinctly at a lower level.   2,500 ft. below the latter is Estes Park, an erosion valley, modified by ice probably in the older or pre-Wisconsin stage of glaciation.   (*Lee, U. S. Geol. Survey Bull.* 730.)

this district, was never so well developed here as elsewhere.[2] Monadnocks like Mt. Evans (14,260 ft.) rise above this level.

[1] Lee, Willis T., Peneplains of the Front Range at Rocky Mountain National Park, Colorado, U. S. Geol. Survey, *Bull.* 730, 1922.   Lee believes that this peneplain was completed near the middle of the Tertiary (p. 17). Under his plate II B, he states that the summits of the Medicine Bow Mountains, some of which are flat-topped or very even-crested, rise to about the level of the Flattop peneplain.   He would have the South Park peneplain finished at the end of the Tertiary and correlated with Pliocene sedimentation on the Great Plains (pp. 35 and 107).

[2] Ball, Sydney H., Geology of the Georgetown Quadrangle, Colorado, U. S. Geol. Survey, *Prof. Pap.* 63, pp. 30–34, 1906.   Ball wrote his description before any attempt had been made to define more than one peneplain in the Rocky Mountains.   Lee faces the possibility of interpreting the higher remnants as up-warped or up-faulted, but does not adopt this hypothesis.

Farther east and south the general level falls to that of the younger peneplain.

The Georgetown district occupies a central position among the high mountains that stand above the South Park peneplain.[1] The main range of such residual mountains, known only as the Continental Divide, trends southwest from this locality and intersects the Park Range east of Leadville. Extending northwest from the Georgetown district are two high spurs, the Williams River and Vasquez Mountains that indent Middle Park. The Kenosha Hills and Tarryall Mountains branch off

FIG. 37.—View northward along the crest of the Colorado Front Range where it is crossed by the Denver Northwestern Pacific Railroad west of Denver. In the distance at the right is the sloping and dissected younger (presumably South Park) peneplain whose altitude is 8,000 to 9,000 ft. (Fig. 33, p. 97.) The foreground at the left shows the older subdued surface, known elsewhere as the Flattop peneplain, having an altitude of about 12,000 ft. Above it rise monadnocks, Bald Mountain, *B*, not glaciated; and Arapahoe Peak, *A*, strongly glaciated. The effects of recent alpine glaciation are seen also in the foreground and in the cirques at *M*. (*Davis, Assoc. Amer. Geogr. Annals.*)

to the southeast toward Pikes Peak. Most of these mountains have received little physiographic study but the summit of the Continental Divide is described as a gently rolling upland whose edges are notched by cirques and ravines (*cf.* Fig. 37).[2]

South Park District.—South of the residual mountains described and east of the Park Range is the broad expanse of South Park more than 50 miles in diameter. Here the peneplain is well preserved at an altitude ranging from less than 9,000 to more than 10,000 ft. Its northern half is rimmed by the mountains named, but between the Tarryall Mountains and Pikes Peak

[1] This can be seen best on the Topographic Map of Colorado, published by the State in 1913; scale 1:500,000.

[2] RANSOME, F. L., Geology and Ore Deposits of the Breckenridge District, Colorado, U. S. Geol. Survey, *Prof. Pap.* 75, p. 15, 1911.

the peneplain extends eastward with increasing dissection from the Park to the foothills.   On the south there is no sharp limit short of the Arkansas River, though the application of the name South Park is commonly limited to the area north of the Arkansas Hills, a volcanic group.[1]

The undissected upland doubtless owes its preservation in part to its lack of tilting during uplift.   On this account the rejuvenation of its streams instead of being accomplished simultaneously throughout their length, must proceed gradually upstream.   In general the tributaries are not yet affected.   At many places, therefore, the topography of their valleys is mature or old while that of the revived trunk stream nearby is young.[2]

The Arkansas River crosses the granite belt through the Royal Gorge whose exceptionally steep walls rise 1,400 ft. above the stream or 7,000 to 7,500 ft. above the sea.   It is evident that the upland of South Park declines as the river is approached.

Mountains South of the Arkansas River.—South of the Arkansas River the peneplain is a little lower and less perfect than to the north.   Nevertheless, the conspicuous ranges, Sangre de Cristo on the west and Wet Mountains on the east, bear the same relation to the intervening Wet Mountain Valley as the ranges farther north bear to South Park.   The Wet Mountains culminating in Greenhorn Mountain (12,230 ft.) are analogous to Pikes Peak though broader and less high.

The Sangre de Cristo Range is a steep anticlinal uplift, granite cored and flanked by sedimentaries which, at places, overarch the crest.   Its northern part, west of Wet Mountain Valley, does not properly belong to the front ranges.   In lat. 37°30′ between Blanca Peak (14,390 ft.) and Veta Pass (Denver and Rio Grande Railroad), the range is offset 15 miles to the east and becomes the Front Range.   From that point it extends straight south for 140 miles where it ends abruptly, and with it ends the Rocky Mountain System.   At its east foot, a dissected plateau 20 to 30 miles wide slopes eastward from an altitude of fully 8,500 ft.   This plateau (assigned to the Great Plains province)

---

[1] For description of this area see CROSS, W., and PENROSE, R. A. F., Geology and Mining Industry in the Cripple Creek District, Colorado, U. S. Geol. Survey, 16*th Ann. Rept.*, pt. II, 1895.

[2] *Cf.* footnote 2 p. 100.   The question whether these older valleys belong to the peneplaning cycle or were made in an intermediate cycle preceding the great uplift that caused the canyon cutting is not determined.

represents in a general way the position of the South Park peneplain, bu⁺ lowered a few hundred feet by later erosion.[1] For long distances the range rises fully 4,000 ft. above this plain. If remnants of higher peneplains are present they have not yet been recognized.

Features due to alpine glaciers are abundant in the northern part of this range and some evidence of their former presence is found far to the south in New Mexico. Even now two small masses of glacial ice (one of them at least 800 to 1,000 ft. in extent) remain on the protected northeast slope of Blanca Peak in lat. 37°35'.[2] This is probably the southernmost occurrence of surviving glaciers in North America.

West of the south end of the Sangre de Cristo Range and beyond the Rio Grande, almost on the 107th meridian, is a parallel range, the Nacimiento and Jemez Mountains. These rise 3,000 ft. above the plain and are not unlike the Sangre de Cristo in structure and character. Though similar mountains farther south are included in the Basin and Range province, it has seemed best to include these in the Southern Rocky Mountain province because of their close association. This is made closer by the fact that the intervening lava-covered highlands are best treated as a southward extension of the San Juan region of the Rocky Mountains.

RÉSUMÉ OF PHYSIOGRAPHIC HISTORY OF THE FRONT RANGES

Older Cycles.—In its main outlines the physiographic history of this part of the Rocky Mountains is fairly well agreed on. In important respects these Front Ranges are typical of the entire Rocky Mountain division and their history should be given weight in considering the probable history of other ranges.

Physiographic history begins with the great Laramide uplift (post-Cretaceous) which determined the dominant structures. The great flanking monoclines were formed at this time. The height of the mountains thus produced may have been very great. They were in large part peneplaned, probably at least twice, the second cycle being inaugurated by regional uplift of 1,500 to 2,000 ft. without folding. Isolated monadnocks still rise above the older peneplain and extensive ranges remain

---

[1] LEE, WILLIS T., U. S. Geol. Survey, folio 214, p. 13, 1922.

[2] SIEBENTHAL, C. E., Glaciation in the Sangre de Cristo Range, Colorado, *Jour. Geol.*, vol. XV, pp. 15–22, 1907.

unconsumed on the newer. The degree of perfection reached by the older peneplain is of course speculative, but if the drainage of that cycle resembled that of the present, the development of

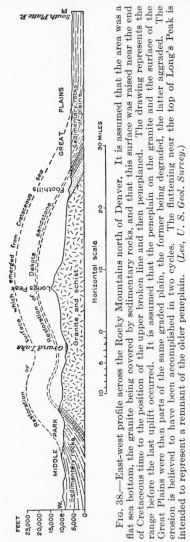

FIG. 38.—East-west profile across the Rocky Mountains north of Denver. It is assumed that the area was a flat sea bottom, the granite being covered by sedimentary rocks, and that this surface was raised near the end of Cretaceous time to the position of the upper broken line and then peneplaned. The drawing represents the range before the last uplift occurred. It is assumed that the peneplain on the granite and the surface of the Great Plains were then parts of the same graded plain, the former being degraded, the latter aggraded. The erosion is believed to have been accomplished in two cycles. The flattening near the top of Long's Peak is intended to represent a remnant of the older peneplain. (*Lee, U. S. Geol. Survey.*)

even an approximate peneplain in the Georgetown district not far from the Continental Divide would imply a rather high degree of development over much of the province.

As the sea in both cycles was probably as far away as at present and a reasonable gradient must be allowed for the streams, these peneplains may well have been formed several thousand feet above the sea. It may be assumed that at the close of the later cycle the greater part of this province and others adjacent were

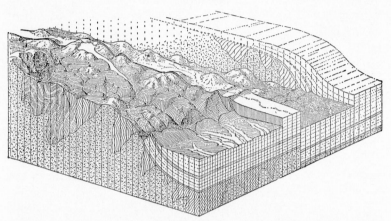

FIG. 39.—Diagram illustrating the history of the Front Range in central Colorado. The block at the rear (right) represents an ancient mountain range of complex structure which has been peneplaned, covered by sediments and again uplifted, arching the newer sediments. The next block represents the same structure reduced to an imperfect peneplain, some of the stronger igneous rocks forming monadnocks and two of the stronger formations among the younger sediments forming low monoclinal ridges. The third blocks is identical with the second except for later uplift. The fourth block (foreground) shows the results of renewed erosion by water and ice. It represents the present surface diagrammatically. Remnants of the imperfect peneplain survive between the canyon-like revived valleys. The monadnocks remain as before, some of them affected by ice erosion. Meantime the Great Plains have been lowered by erosion of their weaker rocks, partly denuding the strong rocks of the mountains, thus giving height to the mountain front and renewed prominence to the hogback foothills. This series of four blocks represents but one peneplain (except the buried one in the first block). The introduction of another cycle would complicate the drawing without making the principles clearer. (*Davis, Assoc. Amer. Geogr. Annals.*)

covered by a continuous graded plain, made by degradation of the mountains and aggradation of the Great Plains. The peneplain in the mountain province is believed to correspond in geologic date with the surface of the Pliocene sediments that now cover the High Plains.[1]

[1] This is Lee's conclusion and agrees essentially with those of Blackwelder and R. T. Chamberlin and with the assumptions underlying Davis' paper already referred to. Ball assigns a Pliocene age to the Georgetown

Canyon Cycle.—The country then rose to about its present height, not this time as a mountain range but as a gentle arch sloping 100 or 200 ft. per mile from the axis to an indefinite base far out on the plains. There was then no mountain "front," no foothills, no mountains in fact, except the residuals of older cycles rising above the upraised peneplain.

Erosion was thus revived, canyons were cut and the plateau itself locally carved into mountains. This erosion is commonly referred to the "canyon cycle," still in progress. This is a much used term in our western mountains, especially where the making of canyons was preceded by a "peneplain cycle." It is correctly inferred that the former has been very short in comparison, but it is a *canyon* cycle only in the mountains where the rocks are very resistant. East of the foothills the rocks are chiefly shales and all easily eroded. In these weak rocks a new peneplain has been developed near the mountains within the same time that was occupied in cutting canyons in the granite to the west[1] (Fig. 34, page 99).

The great down-cutting in the later cycle east of the foothill belt is responsible for the abrupt "front" of the range. Its steepness is dependent on the steep dips of the harder strata upturned there. These were merely stripped and the stripping process still continues.

Glaciation.—Although erosion in the canyon cycle resulted locally in sharp crests and very rugged topography, many (or most) of the main divides rising well above the peneplain retained the rounded forms of subdued mountains (Fig. 43). In the glacial epochs that followed, the lofty divides of rounded form became centers of alpine glaciation and were deeply carved by cirques and glacial troughs (Fig. 41). At places the remnants

---

peneplain, assuming as he did at that time that there was but one Rocky Mountain peneplain.

In a recent paper on the Geologic History of the Front Range by T. S. Lovering, *Proc. Colo. Sci. Soc.*, vol. XII, No. 4, 1929, the opinion is expressed that the older or Flattop peneplain represents in large part a reexposure of the old land surface on which the Cretaceous sediments were laid down.

[1] It is pointed out by Davis, *loc. cit.*, p. 31, that the new peneplain on the Great Plains is itself trenched by valleys of two partial cycles which are still younger. In the mountains the work of these later cycles is a mere continuation of the still young canyon cycle and their effects are indistinguishable. Similar, though not identical, relations are described by Blackwelder in the Laramie Range, *Jour. Geol.*. vol. XVII. p. 441.

FIG. 40.—A normally eroded mountain mass not affected by glacial erosion (*Davis.*)

FIG. 41.—The same mountain mass as in Fig. 40 strongly affected by glaciers which still occupy its valleys.   (*Davis.*)

FIG. 42.—The same mountain mass as in Fig. 41 shortly after the glaciers have melted from its valleys.   (*Davis.*)

of the old subdued surface and the deep valleys and sharp combs of the new may be seen in a single view (Fig. 37).

Drainage.—For long distances the Continental Divide follows the crests of the old monadnock ridges and the drainage is in no way peculiar. The Arkansas River, however, cuts across the entire granite belt in the Royal Gorge. The course of this stream antedates the last uplift and perhaps others before it. The upland is lower near the gorge than elsewhere and there is reason to think that a sag was left here in the original uplift. The river may have followed this sag while the granite was still covered by the strata now outcropping in the foothills,[1] and before the broad valley of the upper Arkansas was cut out. This would make the river consequent on the covering beds and superposed on the granite. It is not certain, however, that what is now the spacious Arkansas Valley on the west was uplifted equally with the Front Range. It is not yet known to what extent the river was thus guided by slopes which the water found rather than made, and to what extent it maintained a preexisting course by cutting down into mountains that rose across it. The full explanation of the Royal Gorge must be sought in connection with that of the upper Arkansas Valley.

PARK AND SAWATCH RANGES

Structure.—Looked at in a broad way, Colorado is crossed by two granite belts which are locally in contact but elsewhere separated by structural depressions. Both belts have subordinate axes *en echelon*. Thus the Front Range is offset from the Pikes Peak mass to the Wet Mountains farther west and again to the Sangre de Cristo, successive anticlines pitching to the southeast. The western belt trends south from Wyoming as the Park Range, but turns southeastward as the Gore Range, and again south, past Leadville, as the Mosquito Range. Meantime the main axis is offset to the west and is found in the Sawatch Range whose southward continuation is buried beneath the San Juan eruptives.

The Sawatch Range ends at the north in the same way that the Colorado Front Range ends at the south. The north end of the Sawatch Range is separated from the Park Range by the structurally depressed Eagle Valley, just as the south end of the

[1] Davis, W. M., Assoc. Amer. Geogr. *Ann.*, vol. I, p. 52.

Colorado Front Range is separated from the Wet Mountains by the structurally depressed Arkansas Valley. A structural sag likewise crosses the axis of the Gore Range 15 miles south of Gore Canyon by which the Colorado River emerges from Middle Park.

Description of Park Range.—North of this transverse syncline the Park Range, extending well into Wyoming, presents the combination of dissected plateau and monadnock peaks and ridges, already described in the Front Range. For a stretch of 15 to 20 miles south of the Wyoming boundary and west of North Park there is a craggy and strongly glaciated alpine ridge rising well above the level of the uplifted peneplain (Mt. Zirkel, 12,200 ft.). North and south of this ridge, crests are accordant, and slopes for the most part moderate. In Wyoming, where the belt is 30 to 35 miles wide, an old rolling surface of broad slopes, averaging perhaps 10,000 ft. in altitude but ranging a few hundred feet above and below that height, is completely dissected by open valleys of a later cycle.[1] Several broad swells (Grand Encampment Mountain and others) rise above 11,000 ft. They seem to be typical subdued mountains. They bear the marks of glaciation, but not vigorous or long enough continued to narrow them to crags.

From the alpine ridge southward to beyond Gore Canyon, *i.e.*, west of Middle Park, the range though not broad is plateaulike with a more or less abrupt descent to the east and declining gently westward.[2] West of both parks the range is attended by monoclinal foothills but at the east foot of the alpine portion abundant moraines occupy three-fourths of the area and obscure the foothills.[3]

About 15 miles south of the Colorado River the range (here known as Gore Range and trending southeast) becomes lofty and serrate though the main crest and even the long northeasterly spurs show a rough approach to uniformity in altitude. Apparently the mountains were carved from a fairly smooth surface declining toward the northeast, first by water, then by vigorous

[1] SPENCER, A. C., Copper Deposits of the Encampment District, Wyoming, U. S. Geol. Survey, *Prof. Pap.* 25, p. 12, 1904.

[2] HAGUE, A., "Fortieth Parallel Survey," vol. II, p. 130; also MARVINE, A. R., "Hayden Survey," 1873, p. 178.

[3] BEEKLY, A. L., Geology and Coal Resources of North Park, Colorado, U. S. Geol. Survey, *Bull.* 596, p. 74, 1915; see also, geologic map of Colorado.

glaciers, the final effect being to reduce the mass to a skeleton without much impairing its height.[1]

Southern Part of Park Range.—A little north of lat. 39°30′ the trend changes abruptly to the south. Here the north-flowing Tenmile River cuts through the mountains. The name Mosquito Range is often applied south of the gap. Not far from its northern end the Mosquito Range is joined by the massive broad-crested Continental Divide from the east (see page 103). Where the two come together the Mosquito Range is itself narrow but

Fig. 43.—High mountain of subdued form, not carved by cirques. This mountain in the Park Range near Leadville, Colorado, gives a fair idea of the forms of most of the higher Rocky Mountains before glaciation. The valley in the foreground was occupied by a glacier whose lateral moraines appear in the picture. (*Capps, U. S. Geol. Survey.*)

its highest peaks are here (Mt. Lincoln, 14,276 ft.). It is also profoundly eroded both by water and ice. There is, therefore, not much room for any remnants of peneplain. Evidence of a general level is, however, not wanting near by. North of Leadville[2] between the higher crests of the Mosquito and Sawatch Ranges is a surface of long slopes and swells of roughly uniform height, the swells being somewhat above 12,000 ft., and even the larger valley bottoms being 10,000 to 11,000 ft. high. None of these plateau-like surfaces in the Park Ranges have yet been definitely correlated with the Flattop or South Park peneplain.

[1] MAEVINE, A. R., *loc. cit.*, p. 188.
[2] EMMONS, S. F., Tenmile folio 48, U. S. Geol. Survey, 1898.

The Mosquito Range is accompanied throughout its length by a fault at its western foot, the mountain range being on the up-thrown and eastward-tilted block.[1]

South of Leadville the range is composed chiefly of sedi-mentary rocks which dip eastward from the fault, the dip slope being relatively gentle and the scarp slope steep. These features suggest block mountains of the first generation, but the faulting may have begun with the Laramide deformation. If so its topographic effects must have been largely erased in the several base-leveling epochs. Some renewed faulting has occurred later but, at least in parts of the range, differential erosion is an important factor.

The altitude and alpine character of the range are well maintained as far south as Buffalo Peak near the 39th parallel. South of that, while continuing to rise 2,000 to 3,000 ft. above the Arkansas Valley on the west, it rises but little above the general level of South Park. Such prominence as it has when viewed from the east, is due in part to stream valleys at its foot.

Sawatch Range.—As previously stated, the Sawatch Range is a great granite-cored anticline pitching to the north. Toward the valleys on the east it presents a magnificent front, but from the west side its impressiveness is less because the adjacent country is very high and broken. The transverse syncline at the north, followed by the Eagle River, has an elevated and rugged surface, the strata being only locally horizontal and everywhere deeply eroded. West of the north end of the range is a considerable area of lofty and deeply dissected plateau included in this mountain province because of its surroundings (page 115).

It is only from favored positions on the west that the granite Sawatch Range is seen to rise prominently above the high divides on the adjacent sedimentaries. The elevation of its crests, 12,000 to 14,000 ft., is appreciated only by remembering that the level of divides in the adjacent country is 9,000 to 11,000 ft. Locally the Sawatch is contiguous with the Elk Range of almost equal height. The latter has a northwest trend, abutting against the Sawatch at the southeast. South of that, the more or less scattered masses of the Sawatch give way without sharp topographic contrast to the laccoliths of the West Elk Mountains.

[1] EMMONS, S. F., Geology and Mining Industry of Leadville, U. S. Geol. Survey, *Mon.* 12, p. 29, 1886.

Southward the range extends to the valley of the Tomichi River which is followed by the Denver and Rio Grande Railroad. The line thus designated separates the great granitic area on the north from the area of volcanic rocks known in a general way as the San Juan region.   Marshall Pass (10,846 ft. high) here separates the Sawatch Range from the Cochetopa Hills, the most easterly range of the San Juan.   A few miles farther east, Poncho Pass separates the Sawatch from the Sangre de Cristo Range.

The topographic elements of the Sawatch landscape are the same as those of the Front Range, alpine ridges and peaks surmounting or alternating with areas having no commanding summits.   This is illustrated at the north end where the Mount of the Holy Cross[1] rises to a height of 2,000 ft. above its spreading, plateau-like spurs.[2]

The Sawatch Range not only has the highest peaks of the Rocky Mountains, but has an exceptionally large number of them (10 above 14,000 ft.[3] and a much larger number above 13,000 ft.).   Many, perhaps most, of these very high peaks are not on the main crest of the range, which is here the Continental Divide. Some of the highest stand many miles east of the main divide on long spurs separated by valleys, cut down almost to the base of the range.   This rambling habit of the lofty crests is an ocular demonstration of the importance of erosion in producing the relief of this range.   To what extent the Arkansas Valley itself was enlarged by erosion is uncertain.   The great lateral valleys which separate the eastern spurs of the Sawatch are primarily the work of water, but especially in the northern part they have been greatly deepened and changed in form by glaciers.   Some peaks, like La Plata Mountain (lat. 39°), owe their present form entirely to glacial erosion.   Others, like Mount Elbert, eight miles to the north, while indented by cirques, retain in part the rounded form which evidently characterized those mountains before glaciation gave them their alpine forms[4] (*cf.* Fig. 40, page 109; also Fig. 43, page 112).

[1] The "cross" consists of snow banks retained in ravines.

[2] For description see Henry Gannett, "Report of Hayden Survey for 1874," p. 420.

[3] "The Mountain Peaks of Colorado" 1923; also "Fourteen Thousand Feet," 1925; publ. by the Colorado Mountain Club.

[4] Davis, W. M., Glaciation of the Sawatch Range, Colorado, Mus. Comp. Zool. *Bull.*, vol. 49, 1905; also Glaciation in the Sawatch Range, Colorado, *Appalachia*, vol. X, no. 4.

MOUNTAINS WEST OF THE GRANITE BELTS

White River Plateau.—A general view of the Southern Rocky Mountain province shows three divergent lobes at the northern end, their axes inclining westward to meet the trends of the middle Rockies. A fourth lobe on the west is directed toward the Uinta Range. There is in fact a continuous anticline connecting this lobe with the Uinta uplift but its crest is very uneven, bulging and sagging by turns.[1] The greatest of these bulges forms the White River Plateau which occupies most of the lobe referred to. The three northern lobes have been denuded of their sedimentary covers but in this western one the underlying granite is barely exposed, partly because the sediments were much thicker.

Structurally the White River uplift is like that of the Uinta Range, steep on the flanks and flat on top. The Uinta also retains a sedimentary cover as does the Bighorn in large part (see also Needle Mountains, page 123). This general structural plan is frequent among Rocky Mountain ranges but is less apparent where the sediments have been largely removed. The White River uplift is only one of a rather large class but the structural type is more perfectly exhibited here than elsewhere.

A mass 30 to 40 miles in diameter has been pushed upward 12,000 to 15,000 ft. without folding.[2] The deformation is all in a belt 6 to 10 miles wide around the edges. It is best observed on the west and south where the Grand Hogback (Mesaverde sandstone), locally 1,500 ft. high, makes a striking boundary between the mountain province and the Colorado Plateau.

Inside this border of tilted beds is a submaturely dissected plateau whose remnants range from 10,000 to 12,000 ft. in altitude. These no doubt represent a peneplain which faintly bevels the almost horizontal beds. Much of the northern part is covered by lava, making the Flattop Mountains. In its physiographic history the White River Plateau differs in no essential respect from other high-lying, plateau-like portions of the Rocky Mountain provinces.

Between the Sawatch Range and the White River Plateau the structural uplift was somewhat less. Here is a kind of saddle in a broad anticline between two rather irregular synclines. One

---

[1] The continuity of this uplift is more apparent on the geologic map of Colorado (1913) than on the Willis map of North America.

[2] WHITE, C. A., U. S. Geol. Survey, *9th Ann. Rept.*, pp. 703, 705, 1887.

of these, on the southwest, is marked by the course of the Roaring Fork; the other appears on the geologic map as a southeastward extension of younger sedimentaries at the western foot of the Park Range. The strata over much of the uplift are nearly horizontal and make a submaturely dissected plateau traversed by the Colorado and Eagle Rivers and the tributaries of the Roaring Fork.[1] The highest divides are above 11,000 ft. and the valley bottoms from 2,000 to 4,000 ft. lower.

Elk Mountains.—The northwest-trending anticline, of which the White River Plateau is the most prominent feature, is paralleled farther south by the Elk Mountain anticline. The two are separated by the synclinal valley of the Roaring Fork which is followed by the Denver and Rio Grande Railroad from Glenwood Springs to Aspen. The Elk Range extends northwest less than 50 miles, its termination being marked by the Huntsman Hills, in some respects resembling the Grand Hogback.

Despite the relatively small extent of the Elk Range, it is one of the most commanding in the Rocky Mountains. A number of summits reach altitudes of about 14,000 ft. The range is deeply cut by gorges and it has the alpine features indicating severe glaciation. Most of the streams head in cirques[2] and occupy glacial troughs to the lower limit of glaciation.

The Elk Range is a great anticline indicating compression from the northeast.[3] Great faulting and overthrusting are also indicated. The center of the range consists of intrusive granite which in certain areas is exposed at the surface by erosion, but elsewhere remains covered by thick and strong sediments.

West Elk Mountains.—South of the Elk Mountain Range is a nearly circular area about 30 miles in diameter, bounded on the south by the Gunnison River. It is characterized by isolated, irregular mountain masses rising to heights of 11,500 to 12,500 ft. above broad valleys or uneven plateaus which are themselves 8,000 to 9,000 ft. high. These are the West Elk Mountains. Most of them are laccoliths, now surrounded by the ragged remains of the Cretaceous strata which once covered them;

[1] Described by GANNETT, H., U. S. Geol. and Geogr. Survey of the Territories, *8th Ann. Rept.*, p. 422, 1874.

[2] EMMONS, S. F., Anthracite-Crested Butte folio 9, U. S. Geol. Survey, 1894.

[3] The structure and, to some extent, the topography of these mountains are clearly and interestingly described by W. H. Holmes, *8th Ann. Rept.*, "Hayden Survey," pp. 68–71, 1874.

but the group in the south central part, which contains West Elk Peak, is carved by great erosion from vast lava flows and tuffs, formerly continuous with those of the San Juan region to the south. The southward slope from these volcanic groups to the Gunnison River is a submaturely dissected plateau sloping 2,000 ft. in 18 or 20 miles. Taken together with a similar but broader and flatter strip south of the Gunnison, it forms a broad plateau-like, east-west belt, 80 miles long from the Sawatch Range to the Colorado Plateau. The Gunnison and its tributaries are actively dissecting this belt which is presumably a former peneplain,[1] perhaps corresponding to the one in South Park. Its altitude is 7,500 to 10,000 ft. Where the Gunnison River leaves the Mountain province it is already incised 2,000 ft. below the general level. In its first 25 miles in the Plateau province it traverses the Black Canyon 2,500 to 3,000 ft. deep.

Much of the West Elk district is plateau-like. However, the relation of its southern half to the San Juan region is such as to make its inclusion in the same province desirable. In the northern half, laccolithic mountains are so closely spaced as to present to the plateau on the west an almost continuous front.

SAN JUAN REGION

South of the Gunnison River (lat. 38°30′) the Southern Rocky Mountain province has its greatest westerly extension in a broad lobe, for the most part lava covered. The name San Juan is applied specifically to the high mountains in the western part, but the same name is also used to designate a much broader and poorly defined region. In a large way the great volcanic area west of the San Luis Valley must be treated as a unit. With it are commonly included the partly isolated mountain groups as far south and west as the La Plata Mountains (lat. 37°20′; long. 108°5′).[2]

SAN JUAN MOUNTAINS

Structure.—The lofty mountains to which the name San Juan is applied in the narrow sense, lie mainly north of lat. 37°45′

---

[1] GANNETT, H., *loc. cit.*, p. 425.

[2] The entire area thus outlined embraces 6,500 to 7,000 square miles. The name San Juan region is sometimes applied to the whole but generally restricted to about 3,000 square miles. CROSS, W., and HOWE, E., Ouray folio 153, U. S. Geol. Survey, 1907.

and west of long. 107°15'.   These consist entirely of lavas and
volcanic tuffs in more or less horizontal sheets.   These rocks
are cut through only by the deepest valleys near the edge of the
province.   Beneath them and beyond their limits are sedimentary rocks dipping away from the mountain center, *i.e.,* to the
north, south, and west.[1]

Topography.—The topography of these mountains is, in the
main, that of a maturely dissected plateau of coarse texture
(*i.e.,* with streams relatively far apart), with a total relief of

Fig. 44.—Crests of the San Juan Mountains northeast of Telluride, Colorado.
The general level of the horizon is above 13,000 ft.   Note the very capacious
cirque in the foreground; also the many steep slopes, crags, and combs due to
glacial erosion.   The rocks are fragmental eruptives and lava flows.   (*Photo by
R. T. Chamberlin.*)

nearly 6,000 ft.   Hundreds of peaks rise above 13,000 ft. and a
few above 14,000 ft.   Valleys from 2,000 to 4,000 ft. deep are
common.   The average altitude in the Silverton quadrangle,
located near the center, is estimated to be 11,500 ft.[2]   The
crests are for the most part rounded and smoothed; some mountains even have flat tops, but this is not the rule.   Glacial
erosion has sharpened some of the peaks and ridges.   Most of

[1] Cross, W., and Howe, E., Ouray folio 153, U. S. Geol. Survey, 1907; for
geology and physiography of these and adjacent mountain groups, see also
folios 57, 60, 120, 130, 131, and 171.

[2] Cross, W., Silverton folio 120

the valleys which head above 11,000 ft. have the U-shaped cross-section of glacial troughs.

Physiographic History.—The structure and forms, above described, indicate that these mountains are carved by erosion from a mass whose surface may have had but little relief. Such a surface may have resulted from the original accumulation of volcanic material, but from various considerations it does not appear probable that the surface before carving was, over any great area, the original surface of accumulation. A brief outline of the constructional history will make this clear:

The geological structure indicates that after the close of the Cretaceous time there was an uplift in this region which caused the strata to dip north, south, and west (east unknown) from the site of the San Juan Mountains. This dome-like uplift was reduced to a peneplain before the volcanic eruptions began.[1] The eruptions came, not in one, but in three epochs, between which and during which there was great erosion, so that a long-continued conflict was waged between erosion and accumulation. After these events, at some time before the glacial period began, the area of the San Juan Mountains was again one of relatively small relief or a rolling peneplain.[2] Even if it were all a true peneplain it is not necessary to suppose that the region lay at sea-level, for the distance to the sea is so great that considerable fall would have been necessary for the streams. At all events this condition was followed by further uplift and two incomplete erosion cycles, producing broad valleys and basins in the adjacent weaker rocks with only canyons in the strong rocks of the mountains. Analogous events farther north in Colorado and Wyoming will readily be recalled (page 108).

Three glacial epochs are recorded in and around these mountains.[3] The first is believed to have occurred during the dissection following close upon the uplift of the peneplain. In the long interglacial epoch that followed, broad valley floors were

[1] CROSS, W., Ouray folio 153, p. 14, and various other papers above cited.

[2] ATWOOD, W. W., Physiographic Studies in the San Juan District, *Jour. Geol.*, vol. XIX, pp. 449–453, 1911; also ATWOOD, W. W., and MATHER, KIRTLEY, Evidence of Three Distinct Glacial Epochs in the San Juan Mountains, Colorado, *Jour. Geol.*, vol. XX, p. 406, 1912. In speaking of the peneplain that preceded glaciation these authors use the words "almost base level" and "extreme old age." The completion of the peneplain they place "probably near or at the close of the Tertiary" (p. 407).

[3] ATWOOD and MATHER, *loc. cit.*

developed around the edges of the mountain uplift and coated with thick boulder beds, derived in part from the glacial deposits. This is the first of the two incomplete erosion cycles mentioned above. It was interrupted by another uplift, and similar broad bottoms were developed 500 to 1,000 ft. lower (the second incomplete cycle). It was only after the completion of these lower valleys that the second glaciation occurred. In the interval of deglaciation that followed, the main valleys were again incised a few hundred feet before the advent of the last glaciers.

Fig. 45.—View westward toward Yellow Mountain and Mt. Wilson, outlying eminences of the San Juan group. Altitudes rise above 14,000 ft. The rocks are mainly volcanic. The topography is fairly typical of the higher, glaciated, parts of the San Juan district. (*U. S. Geol. Survey.*)

In a general way the ice of each epoch fell short of the limit reached by its predecessor. Thus each epoch left its distinctive features. This fact, together with the fact that the deposits of the several epochs are at different levels, gives a distinct importance to the work of each epoch in the greater valleys and around the edges. Within the mountains themselves, the glacial features observed are essentially those produced by the latest ice (Figs. 44 and 45).

Landslides.—The nature of the rocks of these mountains, and their steep slopes, especially since the last glaciation, have been very favorable to landslides. To these factors may be added a considerable rainfall occasioned by the abrupt rise of the mountains above the plateaus to the west. It is believed also that earthquakes have been a factor. The combined effect of these factors has been to make the San Juan Mountains and several of the adjacent groups noteworthy as a region of landslides.[1] They are of scientific interest because of the characteristic topography produced. They are also important economically, because of the problems created in mining. The so-called "rock streams" are peculiar forms believed by some to be slowly moving or creeping after the manner of glaciers.[2]

Needle Mountain Uplift

Structure and General Relations.—South of the San Juan Mountains proper is an almost circular area 20 miles in diameter shown on the geologic map as consisting of pre-Cambrian rocks, largely granite. As the surface of these rocks is essentially as high as the San Juan Mountains and since in the latter the same rocks are buried beneath many thousand feet of lava, it follows that the outcrop of these pre-Cambrian rocks represents a pronounced structural dome. The same rocks beneath the adjacent Colorado Plateau on the west and south, whose surface is 4,000 to 5,000 ft. lower, are buried by thousands of feet of sediments. From this granite upland, therefore, the strata dip away in all directions but especially west and south toward the Plateau province. In a belt 5 to 10 miles wide on the south, Paleozoic limestones are exposed in more or less disturbed and dipping strata. South of that are the east-west hogback ridges and cuestas of Cretaceous strata, which soon flatten out beneath the Colorado Plateau. The strip of dipping and much dissected strong Paleozoic rocks belonging to the Mountain province gives way, somewhat abruptly, to the less dissected plateau on the granite. A similar belt on the west of the granite dome is 10 to 15 miles wide and limited by a north-south line connecting

---

[1] Howe, E., Landslides in the San Juan Mountains, Colorado, U. S. Geol. Survey *Prof. Pap.* 67, 1909; see also, folios and other papers referred to under the San Juan Region.

[2] Chamberlin and Salisbury, "Geology," 2d ed., vol. I, pp. 232–233, 1905; Capps, S. R., *Jour. Geol.*, vol. XVIII, p. 370, 1910; Hole, A. D., Glaciation in the Telluride Quadrangle, Colorado, *Jour. Geol.*, vol. XX, pp. 723–724, 1912.

FIG. 46.—View in the Needle Mountains, horizon at 13,000 ft. or more.   Note general accordance of crest levels.   The rocks are chiefly quartzite and slate.   The close folds are neatly truncated by an old erosion surface.   (*U. S. Geol. Survey.*)

the Rico and La Plata Mountains.[1] The line which separates these mountains from the Colorado Plateau is nowhere far from the edge of the Dakota sandstone which is the essential substratum of the plateau for many miles to the west.

Topography.—The summits of the main Needle Mountain uplift embrace two types of topography. The granite portion is in part a lofty plateau 11,000 to 12,000 ft. high, trenched to a depth of 3,000 to 4,000 ft. by the south-flowing Las Animas River but, over considerable areas, little dissected. Here and there on its surface are remnants of Paleozoic rocks, still in their original horizontal position. The granite plateau is an ancient peneplain now being resurrected and exposed to dissection.[2] That it should still retain in some degree its level character shows the recency of the last uplift.

The northern and eastern margins of the pre-Cambrian mass consist of quartzite. On this and adjacent parts of the granite stand the Needle Mountains, known in the older literature as the Quartzite Mountains,[3] "almost unequaled in this country in altitude and boldness." Their steepness is due primarily to the nature of the rocks from which they are carved. It has been intensified by glaciation but these mountains were no more severely glaciated than the mountains of volcanic rock a few miles to the north in which broader summits and more massive forms prevail.

Minor Mountain Groups on the West

Spurs of the San Juan.—Toward the west the San Juan Mountains present a bold escarpment, deeply embayed by the valleys of the upper San Miguel and Dolores Rivers. West of Ouray (lat. 38°) a bold promontory, of which Mt. Sneffels (14,158 ft.) is the crowning summit, lies between the basins of the Uncompagre and San Miguel Rivers. In the upper basin of the former is the mining district of Ouray; in that of the latter, the Telluride district.

South of the Telluride district between the headwaters of the San Miguel and Dolores Rivers a lofty spur of the San Juan

[1] CROSS and HOLE, Engineer Mountain folio 171, U. S. Geol. Survey, 1910.

[2] CROSS and HOWE, Needle Mountain folio 131, p. 11, U. S. Geol. Survey, 1905.

[3] "Hayden Survey."

has been isolated by erosion from the main mountain mass and is
known as the San Miguel Mountains. Its culminating peak,
Mt. Wilson (14,250 ft.), is one of the highest points in Southern
Rocky Mountain province. It is not known how much farther
west the volcanic cover may have extended. Continued uplift
in the western part of the San Juan district has greatly favored
erosion on this margin, which has resulted in the steep western
face of the mountains.

Smaller Independent Uplifts.—South of the San Miguel
Mountains are first the Rico Mountains, centering in lat. 37°40′,
and then the La Plata Mountains centering in lat. 37°25′. Both
are domed uplifts. The structures of both are complicated by
minor laccoliths, but these are only incidental or subsidiary.[1]
The domes themselves are apparently due to independent causes
and are not unlike the Black Hills of South Dakota (page 79)
though much smaller. Both groups have many peaks more
than 12,000 ft. in height. Mount Hesperus in the La Plata
group is 13,225 ft. high.

EASTWARD EXTENSION OF THE SAN JUAN REGION

General.—The great lava-covered area extending east from
the San Juan Mountains to the San Luis Valley has been little
studied. Much of it has the appearance of a dissected plateau
9,000 to 11,000 ft. high. On the north it merges with, or includes,
the plateau-like Gunnison Valley above whose western part the
mountains rise with a conspicuous northward slope. Between
the main streams the surface rises in indefinite ridges, sometimes
spoken of as "ranges," to altitudes of 12,000 or 12,500 ft. with
some exceptional greater elevations (Stewart Peak, 14,032 ft.;
San Luis Peak, 14,100 ft.). Some of these high divides are
themselves even-crested or plateau-like. From available data
no essential difference can be pointed out between these mountains and the better known San Juan Mountains farther west.
Apparently the mountains farther east have been less sharpened
by glacial erosion. Glaciers were naturally more favored near
the western front which was first encountered by the moisture-
bearing winds.

---

[1] CROSS, W., Rico folio 130, U. S. Geol. Survey, 1905; CROSS, W., and
SPENCER, A. C., La Plata folio 60, p. 10, U. S. Geol. Survey, 1899; see also,
CROSS, W., and SPENCER, A. C., Geology of the Rico Mountains, Colorado,
U. S. Geol. Survey, 21*st Ann. Rept.*, pt. II.

To what extent the accordant summit levels represent the original surfaces of accumulation and to what extent they represent peneplains has not been determined. The main divides may be residual above the lower and more widespread surface.[1] The northern margin of this surface (Gunnison Valley) is said to be a peneplain developed on volcanic rocks which are believed to be of mid-Tertiary age. The question of more than one peneplain in this region has not been studied.

Local.—Of the main divides more than 12,000 ft. high in the eastern part of the San Juan region, the northernmost is the Cochetopa Hills. These are an east-west divide between Tomichi Creek (Denver and Rio Grande Railroad) on the north and the Saguache River on the south. The La Garita Mountains are the divide between the Saguache River and the Rio Grande. The divide between the Rio Grande and San Juan River is a very irregular ridge with many spurs and with considerable areas above 12,000 ft. It continues south into New Mexico with declining altitude, forming a more or less mountainous connection between the San Juan region of Colorado and the Jemez and Nacimiento Mountains of New Mexico.

THE PARKS OF COLORADO

The term "park" as used in the Rocky Mountains indicates any broad depression in which trees are either absent or scattered. In a narrower sense, the Parks of Colorado are certain extensive basins of this character west of the Front Range and east of the Park Range. The San Luis and upper Arkansas Valleys, not commonly called parks, are necessarily included in the discussion of these.

North and Middle Parks.—North and Middle Parks together are conspicuous on the geologic map as an elliptical area of Cretaceous and Tertiary strata occupying a synclinal basin and surrounded by the crystalline rocks of the mountain axes (Fig. 31, page 95).[2] The ellipse ends at the north near the Wyoming

---

[1] ATWOOD, W. W., and MATHER, KIRTLEY, The Grand Canyon of the Gunnison River, Assoc. Amer. Geogr. *Ann.*, vol. V, pp. 138–139 abs, 1915. From the structure of the mountains on the western border of the San Luis Valley it appears that there has been a decided uplift in the latter part of the Tertiary. Siebenthal found Miocene beds dipping east 6 to 15 degrees.— Geology and Water Resources of the San Luis Valley, U. S. Geol. Survey, *Wat. Sup. Pap.* 240, p. 29, 1910.

[2] Best seen on the geologic map of Colorado, Colo. Geol. Survey, 1913.

boundary where the granite cores of the Medicine Bow and Park Ranges meet and merge.   At this transverse bar of granite the syncline, at least 10,000 to 15,000 ft. deep, ends abruptly, its northern end being determined by a great fault.   At the south end the basin ends where the Front and Park Ranges come together near Leadville.

Structurally this large ellipse, 90 miles long and 35 miles wide, is a single basin.   A subordinate east-west anticline[1] near the middle would be of small importance were it not for the volcanic rocks resting upon it, thus forming the "Rabbit Ears Range," a ridge 2,000 to 4,000 ft. high.   This ridge, generally a "rounded swell" surmounted by volcanic mesas and buttes in the western part, separates North Park from Middle Park.

North Park covers nearly 1,000 square miles.   Its floor, bordered by hogback foothills, is generally about 8,100 ft. high between streams.   It embraces some areas, miles in extent, which are essentially flat; but in general the topography is mildly rolling, the larger streams having open valleys about 200 ft. deep.   The North Platte River after gathering the drainage from all the surrounding mountains escapes to the north by a canyon through the granite barrier.   The drainage may well have followed this course since the post-Cretaceous uplift, but the granite barrier was raised by Tertiary faulting.   Whether the stream maintained its course without ponding, or whether a lake resulted, are questions pertaining to earlier cycles rather than the last.   As for the current cycle it is probable that the general explanation of the peculiar drainage of the Wyoming Basin (page 136) applies here also.   On this assumption the present course of the North Platte was chosen on a peneplain made after the faulting, and the river is superposed.

No doubt the granite barrier has determined the local base level of the stream.   Apparently it has approximately held its own while the park has been reduced to a new peneplain. Whether by recent uplift or otherwise, the streams are now slightly incised and a new erosion cycle is beginning.

Of the three parks of Colorado, North Park has the smallest proportion of forest.   Economically, it is a grazing country. General agriculture is possible and it is practiced to some extent

[1] BEEKLY, A. L., Geology and Coal Resources of North Park, Colorado, U. S. Geol. Survey. *Bull.* 596, pp. 82–83, 1915.

but the altitude is not favorable. There are coal deposits which are mined in a small way.

Middle Park is the least typical of the three. Along its eastern and southern margins is an uneven granite surface which may correspond in a rough way to the peneplain in South Park. The rest of the park is broken by two mountain ranges in the south and diversified in the north by volcanic mesas and buttes several thousand feet high. The floor is much dissected.

Middle Park lies in a great eastward bend of the Continental Divide which follows its rim on the north, east, and south.

Fig. 47.—Peneplain on top of Front Range north of Pikes Peak at an elevation of 9,000 ft. Pikes Peak is a monadnock 5,000 ft. high on this peneplain. This same peneplain forms the floor of South Park. Elsewhere (see Fig. 33) it is eroded into mountains. (*U. S. Geol. Survey.*)

Here the Colorado River gathers its headwaters, then crosses the Park Range by Gore Canyon more than 2,000 ft. deep. The relations here are identical with those of the North Platte in North Park and probably indicate a similar history, though it may be that both parks drained to the north before the Rabbit Ears Mountains were made.

When the adjacent mountains were peneplaned, these parks were no doubt parts of the same graded surface which covered the granite areas. Whether they were raised to that level by aggradation or brought down to it by degradation, the present basins are cut below the peneplain and are, in the main, coextensive with the weaker rocks.

South Park.—It is quite otherwise with South Park. It is true that the Laramide uplift left here a structural depression which still retains sedimentary rocks in some parts; also that later a peneplain spread widely over basin and mountains alike (Fig. 47). Here, however, the general level of the peneplain has never been reduced and the park would have no existence, as a basin, were it not for monadnock ridges on its border. It has on the west the Mosquito (Park) Range which, at the south end, is very low or interrupted. On the north are the Continental Divide, the Kenosha Hills, and the Tarryall Mountains. On the South and east there is no continuous rim and no definite boundary unless the park be regarded as limited to the drainage basin of the South Platte. The same type of topography extends east to Pikes Peak and south into Wet Mountain Valley beyond the Arkansas except for later valley cutting by the Arkansas and its tributaries. Most of its area is on the granite peneplain. South Park is, as it were, one story higher physiographically than North and Middle Parks, and its floor is one cycle older.[1]

Upper Arkansas Valley.—Either in the post-Cretaceous uplift or later, or perhaps beginning early and continuing at intervals, the Mosquito Range was made by uplift and eastward tilting from the great Mosquito fault. In the making of this great fault the Arkansas Valley on the west was down-thrown but the early history of the upper Arkansas River and even the time at which it came into being are known only in the most general way. Probably the range on the east was never reduced to the level of the peneplain, which otherwise extended west to the residual ridges and peaks of the Sawatch Range. Whether, to produce this level, it was necessary to grade the Arkansas Valley up or down is not clear. The valley in its present form may be due partly to later crustal movement and partly to erosion by the same stream which, farther down, sawed its way through the Royal Gorge (Fig. 48).

The valley is 60 miles long and floored mainly with gravel. The supply of this during the glacial period was so great that the river became superimposed with reference to the older and less

---

[1] It is not certain that this is true of the entire area. Davis, W. M., The Colorado Front Range, Amer. Assoc. Geogr. *Ann.*, vol. I, p. 43, 1911, suggests that the peneplain may have been developed on weak sedimentary rocks which have since been stripped away. In any case, this could be true of only a small part of the area.

even granite surface in which it is now being incised locally. Near the middle, glaciers from the west crowded the stream eastward on the granite in which it is now cutting Granite Canyon. Above this, eroded gravel terraces occupy most of the width of 6

Fig. 48.—View looking down into the Royal Gorge. Before the last great uplift the Arkansas River flowed at about the level of the top of the present gorge. It followed a broad depression across the South Park peneplain. The final uplift caused the river to entrench itself 1,100 ft. The present plateau level at the top of the gorge represents the floor of the former wide depression which was no doubt a lowland of erosion but perhaps owed its location and part of its depth to crustal movements. (*Photo furnished by Denver and Rio Grande Western Railroad.*)

or 8 miles, but a hummocky surface of moraines and landslides covers much of the valley. In the southern half (where some of the sediments may be older) the gravel plain is 4 to 10 miles wide, most of the material having come from the mountains on the west, thus crowding the river eastward. Through most of this distance the river is now terracing the sediments but at several places it is cutting canyons in the granite.[1]

San Luis Valley.—The San Luis Valley is a structural basin between the Sangre de Cristo Mountains and the San Juan. In northern New Mexico the two highlands are separated only by a narrow rocky valley cut by the Rio Grande through lavas which apparently were once continuous. North of this defile the San Luis Valley stretches more than 100 miles. Its greatest width is nearly 50 miles. Its elevation in the central part is 7,520 ft.; at the base of the mountains about 8,000 ft. The basin is divided into two unequal parts by the San Luis Hills, a northeast-southwest range of volcanic mesas 10 to 20 miles north of the New Mexican boundary. The following description applies primarily to the northern portion.

San Luis Valley is a striking feature when viewed from the neighboring heights. Seen in this general way it looks perfectly flat, the mountains rising abruptly on all sides, and on the east almost precipitously. Viewed from the basin, the floor is seen to slope, not so much to the Rio Grande which traverses the valley, as toward a north-south axis near the east side, marked by the small San Luis River. Near this axis the slope is only three to six feet per mile but the slope increases toward the borders until it becomes 50 to 150 ft. per mile near the mountain foot.[2] The slopes here described are plainly those of alluvial fans. Generally adjacent fans merge into a single inclined plane, but from the gorge where the Rio Grande emerges from the mountains on the west a broad fan spreads out with a radius of at least 25 miles. The greater load of the larger streams from the west has correspondingly broadened their alluvial slopes and shifted the axis of the valley eastward. The streams from the

[1] Well described and figured by M. R. Campbell, Guidebook of the Western United States, U. S. Geol. Survey, *Bull.* 707, pp. 92–93, 1922. Campbell's description at this place and on page 102 would imply that the present course of the Arkansas at this place has survived from a time when the valley was "filled to a great depth with sand and gravel," *i.e.*, presumably, to the level of the highest present terrace. It is further implied (p. 92) that this was at a time when the country lay near sea-level, *i.e.*, before the uplift of the last peneplain. This would assume that the depth of the valley is to be accounted for by crustal movements except for that amount which may be ascribed to erosion of Tertiary sediments.

[2] See map; Siebenthal, C. E., Geology and Water Resources of the San Luis Valley, Colorado, U. S. Geol. Survey, *Wat. Sup. Pap.* 240, 1910. Many facts stated below are from this source.

east are necessarily short, but they are also swift, hence the coarseness of their load and the steepness of their alluvial slopes.

Erosional features are almost totally wanting. The Rio Grande has incised the surface only a few feet. Several smaller streams from the mountains enter it but there are practically no tributaries from the plain.

All the streams flowing from the adjacent mountains into the northern half of the valley are lost by percolation and evaporation from lakes without outlet. One of these, the Saguache which joins the San Luis mentioned above, is second in size to the Rio Grande alone. In view of the high altitude and resulting cool climate and the lack of excessive aridity, this great loss of water by percolation indicates a remarkable porosity of the underlying formations. From this cause the Rio Grande itself in the first 15 miles after entering the valley, loses about one-fifteenth of its flow.[1]

The effect of wind is seen almost everywhere in the piling up of the soil around or in the lee of the scattered greasewood bushes, the most conspicuous native vegetation. In this contest for the mastery between vegetation and wind, the former generally holds a precarious advantage but in certain spots the wind is master and typical dunes cover the surface for miles. As the prevailing winds are from the southwest, the chief area of this kind is on the east side of the valley.

The San Luis Valley necessarily had its inception in the making of the Sangre de Cristo and San Juan Mountains but the present depth of the basin, like the height of most of the Rocky Mountains, is due to repeated crustal movements. At a comparatively late time the San Luis Hills (page 130) were raised across its drainage course, partly by volcanic eruption and partly, it appears, by a fault of more than 1,000 ft. by which the floor of the valley was depressed.[2] This caused a great fresh-water lake which was ultimately filled by alternating beds of sand and clay, the Alamosa formation, from which large supplies of artesian water are now derived. After the basin was filled the alluvium was laid down on top as already described. For the time being this surface cannot be dissected, for the local base level of the valley is determined by the hard volcanic rocks which the Rio Grande must cross in passing out.

[1] Colo. Agr. Coll. *Bull.* 48, p. 30; cited by Siebenthal, *loc. cit.*, p. 55.
[2] SIEBENTHAL, C. E., *loc. cit.*, p. 51.

Of all the great valleys of Colorado the San Luis has the least timber—practically none.   Grass is its most valuable vegetation, though greasewood and sage brush are more abundant.   Grazing is thus greatly favored.   Agriculture, despite the altitude, is favored by the topography and by the supply of water for irrigation.   This water comes both from streams and from wells.

The San Luis Valley is a simple artesian basin in which the strata are alternately porous sand and impervious clay.   The beds of sand come to the surface near the edge and thus receive the water of the streams from the mountains.   In 1904 there were already 3,234 artesian wells with an estimated average flow of 40 gals. per minute.   Much of this water is used for irrigation. It was estimated that this was sufficient to irrigate 25,000 acres or nearly 40 square miles.

CHAPTER III

WYOMING BASIN

Relations to Other Provinces.—The continuity of the Rocky Mountain System is interrupted by the Wyoming Basin (Fig. 49). The floor of this basin is a plateau with a maximum east-west dimension of about 250 miles and a north-south dimension of nearly the same. Its total area is nearly 40,000 square miles. It is bordered for the most part by abrupt mountain slopes, indented by long spurs and studded by isolated mountains. The altitude of the plateau surface is generally between 6,500 and 7,500 ft. Through an opening between the Bighorn and Laramie Mountains this basin floor is continuous with the Great Plains, and by a similar opening east of the Uinta Mountains it is continuous with the Colorado Plateau (page 138).

While the middle Rocky Mountains are topographically separated from the southern, they are not independent. Structurally they should be thought of rather as one continuous system with a local sag in altitude. Within this sag, the mountains are for the most part buried by younger sediments as those of the Caribbean are partly covered by the sea.

STRUCTURE

Mountain Trends.—The form of the Wyoming Basin is dependent on the local trend of the neighboring mountains. This trend in Colorado is almost north-south, but the middle Rockies are much offset to the west. The 108th meridian lies entirely west of the southern Rockies but lies entirely east of the Middle province except for the semi-detached Bighorn Range. This offset is accomplished by a compound curve in the middle of which the trends are almost east and west. The Laramie Range at its northern end curves toward the west and stops. In line with it and farther west are the isolated groups of the Rattlesnake Mountains. A few miles south of these is a line of granite knobs called Sweetwater Mountains, and south of these is a broken

133

array named in order from east to west: Freezeout, Shirley, Seminole, Ferris, Green, and Antelope Hills. These isolated

Fig. 49.—Index map of the Wyoming Basin and Middle Rocky Mountains. (Drawn by Guy-Harold Smith.)

mountains and hills are the tops of partly buried structures which connect the Laramie Range on the east with the Wind River Range on the west.

Connecting the elbow of the Bighorn Range with the end of the Laramie is the "Oil Mountain Anticline,"[1] marked by the out-cropping of older rocks making monoclinal ridges for most of the distance.[2] The most prominent of these may be followed in delimiting the Wyoming Basin from the Great Plains. Aside from these axes are some isolated uplifts standing in no definite relation to others. The Rawlins Hills (page 137) are roughly in line with the Park Range of the southern Rockies and 30 miles beyond its northern end. On the 109th meridian, midway between the eastern ends of the Uinta and Wind River Ranges, is the extensive and much eroded Rock Springs dome.

Subordinate Basins.—The uplifted axes named above divide the province into a number of more or less separate basins. The Laramie Basin has for its eastern and northern rim the curving Laramie Range. On the west is the Medicine Bow Range which, a few miles south of the Wyoming-Colorado boundary, merges with the Laramie and encloses the basin on the south. North of the Medicine Bow, the western rim is neither geologically nor topographically continuous. The entire basin is about 90 miles long and 30 miles wide. Its northern end is the Shirley Basin.

The Carbon Basin[3] lies between the Laramie Basin on the east and the Rawlins Hills on the west, the Park and Medicine Bow Ranges on the south and the Ferris, Seminoe, Shirley, and Freezeout Mountains on the north. It is far from being a simple basin, but it is a strongly characterized and well-recognized district (page 141). Between the Rattlesnake and Wind River Ranges on the south and the Owl Creek Mountains on the north is a long synclinal trough called, as a whole, the "Shoshone Basin." The better known name "Wind River Basin" belongs to its western half.

The term "Great Divide Basin" (page 143) is used chiefly in a hydrographic sense for the area of internal drainage 4,200 square miles in extent, which is roughly limited on the east by the Carbon Basin, on the north by the Green Mountains and

---

[1] WOODRUFF, E. G., and WINCHESTER, D. E., Coal Fields of the Wind River Region, Wyoming, U. S. Geol. Survey, *Bull.* 471, p. 520.

[2] Geologic map of Wyoming, 1925.

[3] This name and Shoshone Basin are taken from the "Reconnaissance Geological Map of Wyoming" by Wilbur C. Knight, University of Wyoming, about 1901.

Antelope Hills, and on the west by the Rock Springs uplift. The structural depression of which this is a part, continues south into Colorado but the districts to which well-recognized names are applied do not cover the entire area. The Washakie Basin, southeast of the Rock Springs uplift, is a structural but not a topographic basin. South of it, in northwestern Colorado, lies the Yampa Drainage Basin, known by the name of its master stream.

Fig. 50.—Canyon cut by the Shoshone River across Rattlesnake Mountain in Bighorn Basin of the Middle Rocky Mountain province.   This stream illustrates the superimposed drainage of the Middle Rocky Mountains and Wyoming Basin.   The mountains were buried and have been exhumed by the erosion of the surrounding weak rocks since the rivers took their courses.   This canyon is now the site of one of the highest dams in the world.   The water thus impounded is used for irrigation in the Bighorn Basin.   (*U. S. Geol. Survey.*)

The Bridger Basin is a structural depression drained by the Green River.   It lies west of the Rock Springs uplift and reaches the limits of the province on the north, west, and south.

DRAINAGE

The drainage of the Wyoming Basin is remarkable.   In passing through or out of the basin scarcely a stream fails to cross one or more mountain ranges.   The Laramie escapes to the east through a canyon across the Laramie Range.   The North Platte after cutting through mountains to get out of North Park, crosses two more ranges, the Seminoe and the end of the Laramie Hills, before reaching the Great Plains. The Sweetwater flows east across the end of the Wind River Range and in and out among the granite hills of the Sweetwater Range before it finally joins the Platte. The Bighorn River which gathers the waters of the Shoshone Basin, cuts through the mountains by a canyon 2,250 ft. deep instead of taking the easy eastward course over the plains to the Platte. The Green River in the western part passes to the south through the Uinta Mountains by a 3,000-ft. canyon. Its eastern tributary, Bitter Creek, flows entirely across the Rock Springs uplift, cutting through great hogbacks in notches 1,000 ft. deep. The Yampa in northwestern Colorado enters the Uinta Range at its eastern end and traverses it lengthwise until it joins the Green in the midst of the mountains. For drainage which is out of harmony with the major topographic features, this province is the most remarkable in the United States.

The Continental Divide follows the Wind River and Park Ranges. Between these there is no connecting crest. Here is the Great Divide Basin from which no drainage reaches the sea. The very indefinite divides which separate it from the Atlantic drainage on the one hand and the Pacific on the other, lie only locally on ridges but elsewhere in the midst of broad expanses of plains.

TOPOGRAPHY OF UPLIFTS

The mountains within the Wyoming Basin are all low. Some of them, like the surrounding high mountains, have granite cores paralleled by hogback ridges. The Sweetwater or "Granite" Range shows nothing but patches of a granite core almost buried by the Tertiary sediments which make the adjacent basin floor. The Rawlins Hills consist mainly of hogbacks or cuestas surrounding and almost concealing a small but steep granite dome. Only a part of this mountain structure rises above the Tertiary floor of the basin, the western part being faulted down and buried.

The Rock Springs uplift, though not now mountainous, is an elliptical mountain uplift, which if there had been no erosion would rise 10,000 ft. above its base.[1] In the wearing down of

---

[1] KEMP, J. F., and KNIGHT, W. C., The Leucite Hills of Wyoming, Geol. Soc. Amer. *Bull.*, vol. 14, p. 310, 1903.

this dome the stronger sandstones have remained as hogbacks on the west where the dip is steep (locally 30 deg.) and as cuestas on the east where dips do not exceed 10 deg.[1] The principal monoclinal ridge (Mesaverde, Cretaceous) is at places 1,000 ft. high and surrounds the elliptical "Baxter Basin" carved out of the softer underlying shales for a width of 15 miles and a length of 40 miles. Outside the first ridge is a succession of hogbacks and cuestas separated by strike valleys. The outermost cuesta, at least as high as the innermost and 5 to 10 miles distant, is of Green River (Tertiary) beds deeply dissected. At places it stands up in table-like plateaus. Elsewhere it forms a belt of gigantic badlands. These decline westward and merge with the floor of the Green River Basin. This cuesta on the east is the Laney Rim (page 144).

A noteworthy uplift is that which connects the Uinta Mountains and the White River Plateau of the Southern Rocky Mountain province (page 115). Extending all the way from one to the other, is an anticline whose axis has been deeply eroded. The continuous and sharply outlined trough thus formed is called Axial Basin.[2] In its western half this trough is followed by the Yampa River. The eastern half is not followed by any one stream but is crossed by several. The continuity of the trough is not that of a single river valley, but that of a belt of weak rocks exposed by unroofing the anticline.

Rising abruptly from the floor of this trough are two isolated mountains, Juniper Mountain (Yampa Peak) and Cross (Junction) Mountain. Except for their small areas they are structurally like the Uinta Mountains and the White River Plateau between which they lie. The Yampa River transects both these uplifts in canyons instead of turning slightly aside to follow the smooth floor of Axial Basin.

Between Axial Basin on the northeast and the White River (the arbitrarily chosen boundary of the Colorado Plateau) on the southwest, is an area of somewhat confused folds which have ₪ot, like the Axial anticline, been reduced to lowlands. On these folds are the Danforth Hills[3] whose highest summits rise 2,000

[1] Schultz, A. R., U. S. Geol. Survey, *Bull.* 381, p. 218, 1910; see also U. S. Geol. Survey, *Bull.* 341, pp. 256–282, 1909.

[2] White, C. A., cited by Bechler, G. R., U. S. Geol. and Geogr. Survey of the Territories, 10*th Ann. Rept.*, p. 363, 1876.

[3] For description see Gale, H. S., Coal Fields of Northwestern Colorado and Northeastern Utah, U. S. Geol. Survey, *Bull.* 415, p. 25, 1910.

ft above the bordering valleys. This district is intermediate in character between the Mountain and the Plateau provinces. Structurally it is a connecting link between the Southern Rocky Mountains and the Uinta Range. It may be assigned to the mountains or to the plateaus according as the chief interest is in structure or in topography. On the whole it is believed to have more in common physiographically with the plateaus.

The Wyoming Basin contains two noteworthy areas of volcanic rocks. The Leucite Hills[1] at the north end of the Rock Springs dome occupy an area about 25 miles north and south by 30 miles east and west. They are chiefly remnants of older cinder cones but their principal physiographic significance is in the fact that lava sheets seem to have been poured out on a surface of low relief, elsewhere destroyed by deep erosion but preserved beneath these lavas at an elevation of 800 to 1,200 ft. above the surrounding valleys.[2] The other volcanic area is that of the Elkhead Mountains at the west foot of the Park Range in northern Colorado. These are likewise flat-topped remnants of sedimentary rocks protected by sheets of basalt at altitudes 2,000 to 3,000 ft. above the plains.

PLAINS TOPOGRAPHY

General Features.—The Wyoming Basin is in large part underlain by Tertiary strata deposited since the great mountain-making movements along with similar strata on the Great Plains that rise to the same height against the eastern foot of the Big-horn Range and others on the Colorado Plateau abutting against the southern foot of the Uinta Range. Over large areas these strata are horizontal but gentle dips are common. The present surface does not represent the limit of filling; everywhere it has been lowered by erosion. The rocks are generally weak but of different degrees of weakness so that in their wasting away escarpments are produced (Fig. 54, page 144).

The topography of the basin floor varies according to the strength of the rocks and the position of the strata. Weak horizontal beds are more or less perfectly peneplaned. Such conditions are found chiefly in the centers of broad structural

[1] KEMP, J. F., and KNIGHT, W. C., The Leucite Hills of Wyoming, Geol. Soc. Amer. *Bull.*, vol. 14, p. 311, 1903.

[2] RICH, JOHN L., The Physiography of the Bishop Conglomerate of Southwestern Wyoming, *Jour. Geol.*, vol. XVIII, p. 608, 1910.

depressions like the Laramie and Great Divide Basins. As the peneplain is not often exactly parallel to the strata, low escarpments are common. Where the strata are parallel to the surface, low flat table lands may remain slightly above the general level. Considerable areas of badlands occur, some of them on the unreduced cuestas, others near streams that are trenching the general level.

On the margins of basins the strata are generally more or less inclined, first gently and then more steeply as the enclosing mountains or local uplifts are approached. The low scarps of the flatter plains thus give way to cuestas, some of them hundreds of feet high and deeply dissected. Where the tilt is sufficient, cuestas give way to hogback ridges. This is generally on the older (Cretaceous) rocks which participated in the Laramide deformation and now make the foothills. They include some strong sandstone strata. Where the strong Cretaceous sandstones are nearly horizontal, as on the west side of the Park Range, there are deeply dissected plateaus.

Influence of Climate.—Some of the prominent features of this province are due to its climate. Among these the Great Divide Basin of internal drainage has already been mentioned. Smaller areas of this kind are not uncommon. Some smaller streams flow east from the Medicine Bow Mountains but fail to reach the Laramie River only 15 to 20 miles away, several of them stopping in lakes which, though without outlet, are practically fresh, indicating that percolation from them to the Laramie River is so rapid as to prevent concentration of their waters.[1] Many streams throughout the province are intermittent. Alkali flats are common. Sand dunes are locally important and even silt dunes occur. The northern part of the Rock Springs uplift has a considerable area in which sand dunes dominate the topography. In the Great Divide Basin the want of vegetation among the alkali flats permits the soil to drift. Where the process is active enough, silt dunes are formed.[2]

There are some hollows of great size, evidently excavated by the wind. One of these, Big Hollow in the Laramie Plains, is nine miles long, three miles wide and 150 ft. deep below the lowest point of its rim. Such excavation is favored by a substratum of

[1] DARTON, N. H., and SIEBENTHAL, C. E., U. S. Geol. Survey, *Bull.* 364, p. 9, 1909.

[2] SMITH, E. E., U. S. Geol. Survey, *Bull.* 341, p. 221.

shale which weathers to a fine dust. Elsewhere curiously carved rocks, many of them being of mushroom form, also attest the strength and efficiency of the wind in this province.

Laramie Basin.—Speaking generally, the floor of the Laramie Basin is a plain of small relief. Its altitude increases from 7,000 ft. at the northern end to 7,500 ft. at the southern end.[1] Its surface also rises gradually toward the mountain borders. Reference has been made above to the failure of some streams from the Medicine Bow Mountains to reach the Laramie River

Fig. 51.—View across the Laramie Plains looking southwest; Little Laramie River in foreground; Medicine Bow Mountains in background. Altitude of the plain at this place about 7,200 ft. (*U. S. Geol. Survey.*)

and to the great hollows excavated by wind. The larger streams, especially the Laramie River, have broad bottom lands which, owing to the altitude, are adapted to hay rather than to cereals. Cattle raising is most important. Agriculture and irrigation are subsidiary to this. The synclinal structure of the Laramie Basin and the character of its rocks make it an artesian basin. It has flowing wells from more than one stratum.

Carbon Basin.—Between the Laramie Basin on the east and the Great Divide Basin on the west, the Cretaceous rocks

[1] DARTON, N. H., and SIEBENTHAL, C. E., Geology and Water Resources of the Laramie Basin, U. S. Geol. Survey, *Bull.* 364; also, Laramie-Sherman folio 173, U. S. Geol. Survey, 1910; and HAGUE, A., "40th Parallel Survey," vol. II, pp. 73–74.

are much affected by minor folds.   Generally the dips are not
steep.   Because of the general degradation by erosion, the strong
sandstone strata make numerous monoclinal and some anticlinal
ridges.[1]   The general elevation is from 6,500 to 7,000 ft.   The
same prevalence of escarpments, rock benches, and dip slopes,
with a general lack of perfect flatness, is witnessed in the drainage
basin of the Sweetwater among the partly buried mountain axes
which connect the ends of the Laramie and Wind River Ranges.

   Shoshone Basin.—The Shoshone Basin embraces in its
middle and eastern portion large areas of good grazing land of
low relief on the rather weak horizontal Tertiary beds.[2]   At

Fig. 52.—Badland topography in the Wind River Basin.   Shows dominance
of the effects of running water even in the driest parts of the district.   (*Photo
by Blackwelder.*)

intervals coal-bearing Cretaceous rocks are upturned against the
marginal uplifts forming hogback ridges and strike valleys.   The
Wind River Basin is roughened by deep erosion which has plainly
been revived since the last peneplain was made.   Most of it is a
barren waste, much of it badlands (Fig. 52).[3]   The Wind and
Bighorn Rivers and a few tributaries have floodplains a mile or

[1] See Veatch, A. C., Coal Fields of Central Carbon County, Wyoming,
U. S. Geol. Survey, *Bull.* 316, pp. 244–245, 1907.

[2] Woodruff and Winchester, U. S. Geol. Survey, *Bull.* 471, p. 520;
Schrader, F. C., Gold Placers on the Wind and Bighorn Rivers, Wyoming,
U. S. Geol. Survey, *Bull.* 580, pp. 128–129, 1914.

[3] Eldridge, C. H., A Geological Reconnaissance in Northwestern Wyoming, U. S. Geol. Survey, *Bull.* 119, p. 17, 1894.

more in width affording valuable farm lands.[1] The revival of
erosion is locally discernible also in the eastern part of the Shoshone Basin as at "Hell's Half Acre" near the Powder River,
an area of 10 to 20 acres, in which the bright-colored Wind River
shales are eroded to a depth of several hundred feet and minutely
and fantastically dissected into badlands.

Great Divide Basin.—The Great Divide Basin, south of the
Antelope-Green Mountain axis and east of the Rock Springs

Fig. 53.—View in the Red Desert east of Rock Springs uplift, an exceptionally
arid part of the Wyoming Basin, having an annual rainfall of less than 10 in.
The sandstone-capped buttes in the distance indicate that the plain is the
result of widespread degradation. (*Photo furnished by Union Pacific Railroad,
U. S. Geol. Survey, Bull. 612.*)

uplift, is mainly on soft Tertiary strata which are nearly horizontal. These strata are in part brightly colored and yield a light
clay soil of red color. The area thus underlain is locally called
the "Red Desert."[2] It embraces most of the Great Divide
Basin and extends south and southwest to the Uinta Mountains.
The Red Desert has a very low relief. Northward toward
the Green Mountains and eastward toward the Rawlins Hills, the
strata incline upward, thus bringing Cretaceous rocks to the

[1] WOODRUFF, E. G., The Lander Oil Field, Wyoming, U. S. Geol. Survey,
Bull. 452, p. 8, 1911.

[2] EMMONS, S. F., "40th Parallel Survey," vol. II, p. 211.

surface. Here is a belt of dissected cuestas.[1] The Great Divide
Basin as a whole is not a single topographic depression but
embraces a number of alkali lakes and playas. The internal
character of its drainage is dependent solely on deficient rainfall.

Washakie Basin.—Between the Great Divide Basin on the
north and the Colorado boundary on the south is the synclinal
Washakie Basin, a structural but not a topographic basin. The
surface is not low, for within the structural depression higher and
younger strata (Green River and Bridger formations) have

Fig. 54.—Terrace and escarpment topography on nearly horizontal Eocene
beds. The area here pictured lies at the western edge of the Wyoming Basin
five miles east of Kemmerer. The topography is typical of the basin floor
where the surface is not quite parallel to the bedding. Many extensive views
are like the one here pictured, but without the escarpment. (*U. S. Geol. Survey.*)

escaped erosion. These now form huge cuestas facing outward
in scarps which rise locally from a few hundred to 1,000 ft. above
the surrounding country. Where the out-facing cuesta is highest
it bears local names, Washakie Mountain on the east, Laney
Rim and Cathedral Bluffs on the north, Table Rock on the
northwest, Pine Bluffs on the west. Cherokee Ridge on the
south is anticlinal and separates this basin from the irregular
Yampa Basin to the south. The great cuestas here described
are at places exceedingly dissected, causing badlands of coarse

[1] SMITH, E. E., U. S. Geol. Survey, *Bull.* 341, p. 221.

texture, broken dip slopes and isolated buttes.[1] The formations exposed in these badlands are famous for the great vertebrate fossils which they contain.

Between the Washakie Basin on the west and the Park Range on the east is a belt 30 to 40 miles wide on Cretaceous and lowest Tertiary strata. These dip slightly westward, their stronger beds making broad cuestas, sharply, and at places deeply, dissected, their weaker beds making longitudinal valleys.[2]

Yampa Basin.—That part of the Wyoming Basin which lies in northwestern Colorado north of Axial Basin is affected both in structure and in topography by mild folding, generally more or less parallel to the axial anticline. Broad areas of small relief are thus separated or interrupted by scarps and dissected cuestas. At least one cuesta is high enough to be locally called the "Williams River Mountains." Its escarpment looks to the southwest over the anticlinal valley of Williams Fork which flows northwestward from the White River Plateau.

Bridger Basin.—A structural and topographic basin drained by the Green River occupies all that part of the province which lies west of the Rock Springs uplift. Except for the 3,000-ft. canyon which the river has cut across the Uinta Range this basin is completely enclosed. Its lowest part is not far from the point where the Union Pacific Railroad crosses the Green River. North of that, the river flows in a broad shallow valley, but to the south, as the basin floor rises toward the Uinta Mountains, the immediate valley of the river becomes a canyon whose depth increases to 1,000 ft. before the mountains are reached. The rise of the plain from the lowest part of the basin floor to the base of the Uinta Mountains is 2,000 to 3,000 ft.

The floor of the Bridger Basin is in large part a plain developed by erosion on soft flat-lying strata. Parts of it near the river are dissected into badlands by renewed erosion. Near the Uinta Range where the slope is considerable and vigorous streams come down from the mountains, badlands of coarse texture are found on a large scale.

Bishop Mountain and Similar Mesas.—North of the Yampa Basin and stretching east and west near the Colorado-Wyoming

[1] BALL, M. W., Western Part of the Little Snake River Coal Field, Wyoming, U. S. Geol. Survey, *Bull.* 341, p. 244, 1909.

[2] BALL, M. W., *loc. cit.;* also, BALL, M. W., and STEBINGER, EUGENE, Eastern Part of the Little Snake River Coal Field, Wyoming, U. S. Geol. Survey, *Bull.* 381, pp. 188–189, 1910.

boundary is a series of widely separated mesa-like remnants of a former plane surface which lay from a few hundred to several thousand feet above the present surface.[1]   Most of these remnants are only two to five miles wide.   Several of them are 10 to 20 miles long.   Most of them are separated a few miles (rarely more than 10 or 12) from the Uinta or Park Ranges.   Their surfaces generally slope north, *i.e.*, away from the neighboring mountains.   Those which border on the Uinta Mountains reach altitudes approaching 10,000 ft. along their southern edges. Those which lie farther north are lower.   The northward slope of the several mesas (and of the plane in which their summits lie) is generally between 50 and 100 ft. per mile.   The lateral slopes leading down in all directions from the flat summits are not precipitous; in many cases they are very gentle and of rolling character, so that the mesa is not a clearly outlined eminence.

All these table lands are capped by coarse gravel from a few feet to a few hundred feet thick, locally consolidated to a conglomerate called the "Wyoming" or "Bishop conglomerate."[2] The interest in these mesas is largely in their contribution to the physiographic history of the Wyoming Basin.   They are fragments of a once continuous graded surface above which the Uinta Mountains rose but slightly.   They are similar in origin and significance to the mesas east of the Front Range of Colorado.

PHYSIOGRAPHIC HISTORY

The chief questions in the physiographic history of this province are: (1) what is the origin of the curious drainage courses, and (2) is the height of the mountains above the basin due to original uplift or to differential erosion.   In other words, are they first-cycle mountains or second-cycle mountains?   The answers to these questions are closely related.

Origin of Drainage Lines.—The Green River was long used as a typical illustration of antecedent streams.[3]   It was assumed

---

[1] See maps of the "40th Parallel Survey"; also geological maps of Wyoming and Colorado.

[2] RICH, JOHN L., The Physiography of the Bishop Conglomerate, Southwestern Wyoming, *Jour. Geol.*, vol. XVIII, pp. 601–632, 1910.

[3] POWELL, J. W., National Geographic Monograph 2, Nat. Geogr. Soc., 1894; WHITE, C. A., Geology and Physiography of a Portion of Northwestern Colorado and Adjacent Parts of Utah and Wyoming, U. S. Geol. Survey, *9th Ann. Rept.*, p. 707, 1887; On the other hand it is noteworthy

that the mountain uplift occurred after the river had its present course. There is now ample evidence that the mountains are older and also that the basins were more deeply filled with Tertiary sediments than at present. Moreover, if the hypothesis of antecedence were accepted for streams crossing the Uinta Mountains, it would still be necessary to account for the streams which cross all the other ranges around and within the basin.

A simple hypothesis to explain the anomalous courses of all the streams is that, after the mountains were made and were being eroded, sediments were deposited in and around the basin to such a depth that they rose above the ranges at the places where streams now cross them. The streams were thus superposed. This is believed to be the only hypothesis adequate to explain the wholesale disregard of present-day mountains by the streams. It does not deny that the mountains may have been repeatedly increased in height. It is known that extensive warping and faulting occurred, at least at or near the close of the Miocene and perhaps also later, but this does not affect the general outlines of the history here given.

Older Erosion Cycle.—The above explanation of the drainage courses implies that the mountains owe several thousand feet of their relative altitude to differential erosion during which they held their own while the weak rocks of the adjacent plains and basins wasted away. Concerning this there is other evidence. Most of the surrounding mountains have been interpreted as carved from an upraised peneplain. It is plain that when these mountains were approaching the local base level the surrounding country must have been at approximately the same level; *i.e.*, the Wyoming Basin must have been essentially full.

Superposition of streams is not uncommon and its effects are widespread but nowhere else in the United States is it found on so grand a scale. It is not intended to assert that all the peneplains traced in these mountains were made at the same time; but probably no serious error is involved in thinking of the whole Rocky Mountain region in relatively late geologic time as a surface of only mild relief, part of it aggradational and flat,

---

that S. F. Emmons in the Reports of the "40th Parallel Survey," Vol. II, pp. 194 and 197, explains the courses of the Green and Yampa Rivers by superposition; HANCOCK, E. T., U. S. Geol. Survey, *Prof. Pap.* 90, pp. 183–189, 1914, gives a critical discussion of the history of the Yampa River and reviews the controversy concerning the origin of the Green River.

the rest degradational and rolling with only local hilly tracts. Such a condition favors the superposing of streams.

Newer Erosion Cycles.—The vast erosion by which the stumps of the mountains were exhumed, the basins reexcavated, and adjacent portions of the Great Plains cut down, was made possible by uplift.   In the main this took place without deformation though uplift along the old axes was probably greater than elsewhere in most cases.   When the great erosion started, the surface of the Wyoming Basin itself was either peneplain or a new plain of deposition; probably in part, one; in part, the other.   During the progress of down-cutting, many local peneplains may have developed on the relatively soft sediments.   Whether any portion of the first widespread peneplain is preserved on the mesas capped by the Bishop conglomerate is uncertain; probably not. Beneath this conglomerate is an old erosion surface, perhaps of the same age as that beneath the lavas of the Leucite Hills (page 139).   All such surfaces indicate the partial reexcavation of the basin.

Evidences of three or four stages in the final denudation are locally preserved in and around the mountains.[1]   The stage of most importance since the uplift is that in which the newer widespread peneplain was produced on the soft rocks, as in the Great Divide, Shoshone, and Laramie Basins.   It is not certain that these well-developed plains in different parts of the province can be correlated as the work of the same stage.   At places these plains are now being trenched by revived streams.

RESOURCES

Taken as a whole the Wyoming Basin is primarily a grazing country.   Considerable parts of it have too little vegetation even to support herds.   Agriculture is possible chiefly around its

---

[1] WESTGATE, L. G., and BRANSON, E. B., The Later Cenozoic History of the Wind River Mountains, *Jour. Geol.*, vol. XXI, pp. 147–151, 1913; BLACKWELDER, ELIOT, Post-Cretaceous History of the Mountains of West Central Wyoming, Wash. Acad. Sci., *Jour.*, vol. IV, p. 445, 1914.   Blackwelder recognizes the following as the chief events of late geologic history: (1) mountains made by folding and thrust-faulting at the close of Cretaceous time; (2) deep erosion; (3) fluvial deposition lasting at least to the Miocene; (4) gentle folding and normal faulting (probably Miocene); (5) almost complete peneplanation (Pliocene); (6) uplift and erosion, excavating the basins and exhuming the mountains.   Four cycles or stages are distinguished in this last period of erosion, associated with three glacial stages in the mountains.

borders, on the flood plains and sometimes on narrow terraces of the streams which descend from the mountains. The Yampa Valley is probably the most favored in this respect.

The chief mineral resource is coal, the amount of which is large. Economically, it is significant that these important coal fields occupy a gap in the Rocky Mountain System. Through this gap the first transcontinental railroad was built.

The moderate folding of the rocks is favorable to the accumulation of petroleum. This has been found in commercial quantities at various places, notably in the Laramie and Great Divide Basins. The same is true of the Bighorn Basin but the great oil developments for which Wyoming is best known are on the margin of the Great Plains.

CHAPTER IV

MIDDLE ROCKY MOUNTAIN PROVINCE

THE PROVINCE AS A WHOLE

As noted on page 92 the Rocky Mountain System is not entirely continuous as a topographic feature. The southern Rocky Mountains are wholly cut off by the Wyoming Basin and the width of the mountain belt is again reduced to a few miles where the Yellowstone lava plateau approaches the Great Plains in southern Montana. This remarkable constriction is one of the reasons for distinguishing the Middle from the Northern Rocky Mountain province. Another reason is their difference in character (pages 92 and 183). The ranges of the Middle province, like those of the Southern, are in the main linear uplifts. Most of them are orographic units, a single range corresponding to a single anticlinal uplift or fault block, though this relation is not universal (see page 158).

YELLOWSTONE PLATEAU

General Relations.—Yellowstone Park is not in the main a mountain country. It has been included in the Mountain province for what seem to be sufficient reasons but most of the area is a high volcanic plateau contiguous with the lower Snake River Plateau on the west. If the Northern Rocky Mountain province were limited to mountains alone, it would be all but severed at this place. The Snowy Range north of the Park and the Absaroka on the east are all that intervene between the Great Plains and the intermontane plateaus (Fig. 49, page 134). A 50-mile stretch of the Yellowstone River where it flows north from the Park separates all the mountains to the north and west from all the mountains to the south and east. It is no doubt true that the lavas of the Yellowstone and Snake River Plateaus conceal minor folds that would connect the mountains to the northwest with those to the southeast, but the lava filling is so deep that, were it removed, a remarkably deep, broad, and straight depression would lie at right angles across the mountain system.

The Yellowstone Plateau is marked off from the Snake Plateau by its superior altitude. The former was an up. when the basalt flowed out over the valley to the west and ca. to rest with surface abutting against the old upland. A desce. of 1,000 ft. or more occurs 10 to 20 miles west of the Park.[1] On the north, east, and south the rhyolite plateau abuts in turn against the Madison, Gallatin, Snowy, Absaroka, and Teton Ranges beside minor uplifts on the south.

Topography.—The altitude of this plateau is generally between 7,500 and 8,500 ft. It is drained chiefly by the headwaters of the Yellowstone River but the Madison River drains its western margin except for the southwest corner which is in the basin of the Snake. The Continental Divide therefore traverses the plateau between ranges of mountains. The divide itself is inconspicuous. Only locally does it even follow a ridge.

The relief consists chiefly of narrow erosion valleys, some of them more than 500 ft. deep, the largest and deepest being that of the Yellowstone River (Fig. 55), in some respects a special case (see page 154). Minor escarpments, some of them several hundred feet high, are seen within the park. Apparently these are in the main due to erosion, guided in some instances by structure.

With few exceptions the courses of the present streams are consequent on the surface of the lava flows. The heads of young valleys are slowly advancing into the plateau and dissecting it, but broad areas remain practically unaffected by erosion. The youthful character of these valleys is impressively shown by comparing them with that of the Yellowstone River above (southeast of) Yellowstone Lake where the old valley, not reached by the rhyolite flows, is several miles wide and has a swampy flood plain.[2]

Physiographic History.—The history of the Yellowstone Plateau begins with the Laramide uplift of the surrounding mountains. The mountains which were formed at that time in and around the park have since been much worn down, but their elevation has been renewed by uplift and eruption. After epochs of sedimentation, erosion, and recurrent eruption, came the great outpouring of rhyolite, leveling up the inequalities.

[1] This line, corresponding to the contrast in rocks, may be traced on the contour map in the Guidebook of the Western United States, U. S. Geol. Survey, *Bull.* 612, sheet 15 d, 1915.

[2] See U. S. Geol. Survey, Topographic map, Lake quadrangle.

FIG. 55.—Canyon of the Yellowstone River. The depth is 700 to 1,100 ft. It is cut in rhyolite, so altered by hydrothermal action as to display brilliant colors. The nearly flat plateau surface is typical of the park. A similar lava surface may be followed westward to the Cascade Mountains without crossing any range of mountains. In the opposite direction within 50 miles of the view here shown are the Great Plains. All that there is of the Rocky Mountain System at this point lies within that 50 miles. (U. S. Geol. Survey.)

Its thickness is probably 2,000 ft.[1] The Yellowstone canyon itself is more than 1,000 ft. deep, cut entirely in the rhyolite. For aught that is yet known the entire depth may be in a single bed poured out in a single flow. It is natural to infer that this great thickness of lava, possibly in a single flow, is one of the chief reasons for the long continuance of the heat which continues to be given off from great depths, partly through the medium of circulating ground waters.[2]

Glacial ice has covered the Yellowstone Plateau at least three different times.[3] The interglacial epochs were long and the larger valleys were greatly deepened between successive ice invasions. At the time of the first ice epoch (early Pleistocene) the Yellowstone River seems to have passed out of the park at a level 1,000 ft. above that of the present stream. The triple nature of the glaciation is of interest historically; to some extent certain terraces correspond to particular glacial stages; the moraines of the several epochs are also distinguished. Nevertheless, in the main, the glacial features of the present landscape are the work of the last (late Pleistocene) glaciation.

The ice here concerned originated as alpine glaciers on the mountains to the north and east, though the climate of the plateau itself may also have been such as to bring it within the zone of ice accumulation rather than wasting. In any case the plateau was covered, at places 2,000 ft. deep, and the ice moved off. Movement was most rapid along lines now marked by the larger streams, the Yellowstone to the north, the Madison to the west, and the Snake to the south. Each of these valleys had its lobe, supported partly from the main center of accumulation and partly from the mountains on either side. The most generally known among these valleys is of course that of the Yellowstone down which, at the stage of maximum advance,

[1] HAGUE, ARNOLD, Geological History of Yellowstone National Park, p. 7, 1912, U. S. Dept. Int., also "Universal Cyclopedia."

[2] The theory that the heat given off through hot springs and geysers is the residual heat of bodies of lava is accepted by Arnold Hague, U. S. Geol. Survey, folio 30 and other papers; also by Walter Harvey Weed, Geysers, p. 3, U. S. Dept. Int., 1912.

[3] ALDEN, WM. C., Yellowstone National Park and Its Environs in the Great Ice Age, "Ranger Naturalists' Manual," 1928. Unfortunately this paper is not available for general circulation. It embodies about all that is known (aside from details) about the movements of ice and its work in the several epochs on the Yellowstone Plateau.

the ice tongue almost 3,000 ft. thick passed for 36 miles from the park before building its terminal moraine. This valley is "a grand and perfect piece of ice sculpture" cut in Archean gneiss.[1]

Yellowstone Lake and Canyon.—The most interesting and spectacular post-glacial change in the park has to do with Yellowstone Lake and the canyon of the Yellowstone River. The lake owes its existence to a dam interrupting the Yellowstone River in its northwest course. The dam may be of lava or it may be of glacial drift or in part of each, the former course of the stream beyond the lake being unknown.[2] It is plain, however, that on the disappearance of the ice the lake discharged westward to the Snake River and thus to the Pacific.[3] At that time the lake level was 160 ft. higher than at present, as indicated by sediments and shore features. It extended north beyond the site of the falls in Yellowstone Canyon. East of Mt. Washburn a small tributary flowed north to the Yellowstone. In its headward (southward) growth this tributary followed a line of weakness in the lava due to decomposition caused by solfataras or a pre-existing canyon filled with soft sediments.[4] The head of this stream ultimately reached and tapped the lake. The escaping waters soon cut deep into the decomposed lava or unconsolidated sediments, thus initiating the present magnificent canyon. The rich colors of the canyon walls are due to the same decomposition which caused the weakness along this line and thus fostered the stream in its headward growth. The down-cutting of the new outlet of the lake soon left the old one dry and thus diverted toward the Atlantic the drainage of about 1,500 square miles which formerly belonged to the Pacific. The falls in the new canyon seem to be occasioned by tracts of fresh rock not yet affected by solfataric action.

[1] WEED, W. H., Glaciation of the Yellowstone Valley North of the Park, U. S. Geol. Survey, *Bull.* 104, p. 13, 1893.

[2] GOODE, J. P., The Piracy of the Yellowstone, *Jour. Geol.*, vol. VII, pp. 262 and 265, 1899.

[3] This perfectly preserved old outlet was first pointed out by Hague, U. S. Geol. Survey, *Mon.* 32, pt. II, p. 194, 1899.

[4] Recent observations by O. T. Jones and R. M. Field (*Amer. Jour. Sci.*, vol. XVII, pp. 260–278, 1929) indicate that the Yellowstone canyon has been cut twice. In the interval it seems to have been filled with lake and stream deposits while the stream was ponded by lava flows farther north. This makes the history of the capture of the upper Yellowstone more complex but does not alter its essential features.

Hot Waters.—Of the features due to heated waters, the fumaroles or steam vents have already been referred to. These are numbered by the thousand and generally represent acid waters.[1] The work of such waters and vapors is seen in the great amount of decomposed rhyolite, especially along the line of the great canyon. Of hot springs there are said to be nearly 4,000. Many of these and all of the geysers are alkaline[2] and carry silica in solution, which they deposit as siliceous sinter or geyserite, encrusting the surface with what guides call "the formation." Other hot springs are calcareous and deposit vast quantities of travertine, the lime being derived from neighboring sedimentary rocks. Many of these, like the Mammoth Hot Springs, have built against the hillside a series of basined terraces over which the hot water descends, cooling as it goes and depositing carbonate of lime, chiefly at the edge of each terrace or bowl where the cooling is most pronounced.

Yellowstone Park with its hundred geysers is by far the greatest geyser region of the world. Nor are the geysers known to be sensibly diminishing, though individuals vary much from time to time. Some become extinct and new ones break out. Both hot springs and geysers are supplied by ordinary ground water heated by steam which rises from the hot rocks below.[3] A variation of the same phenomena is seen in the mud volcanoes and "paint pots." The mud in these cases is chiefly the lava decomposed by solfataric action. Its presence renders the water highly viscous and causes distinctive phenomena.

Scenic Features.—The attractiveness of Yellowstone Park consists chiefly in localized features and phenomena. The broad expanse of plateau largely covered by somber forest is rather monotonous, relieved at places by distant views of the neighboring mountains. Most of its scenic features can be grouped under three heads: (1) lakes, (2) stream gorges, (3) phenomena due to hot waters. In addition to Yellowstone Lake, 7,741 ft. high and 150 square miles in area, the largest at such an altitude in North America, are several others of considerable size and a great

---

[1] Yellowstone folio 30, p. 4, U. S. Geol. Survey.

[2] HAGUE, A., Article on Yellowstone National Park, "Universal Cyclopedia," 1903. The same author discusses the chemistry of the waters in U. S. Geol. Survey, folio 30, and in U. S. Geol. Survey, *Mon.* 32.

[3] HAGUE, A., Geological History of Yellowstone National Park, p. 11, 1912, U. S. Dept. Int.

number of small lakes of glacial origin[1] especially in the mountains. The canyon of the Yellowstone with its precipitous walls 1,000 ft. high, its two falls in which the water falls 422 ft., its brilliant colors and still surviving fumaroles, is justly one of the most noted canyons in the world. The circumstances of its cutting make it much younger both in years and in development than the other gorges in the same plateau.

FIG. 56.—East Front of the Beartooth Range near Montana-Wyoming boundary. The abrupt rise from the Great Plains less than 6,000 ft. high to the subsummit peneplain more than 10,000 ft. high is due to the Beartooth fault whose trace follows the foot of the slope. (*Arthur Bevan, Rocky Mountain Peneplains Northeast of Yellowstone Park. Reprinted by permission from the Journal of Geology, Vol. XXXIII No. 6.*)

MOUNTAINS BORDERING YELLOWSTONE PLATEAU

Beartooth Range.—North of Yellowstone Park and extending east-southeast to the Bighorn Basin is the Beartooth Range, whose western half is also called the Snowy Range. The whole is a broad, anticlinal uplift with a core of Archean gneiss bordered for part of the distance on the north and east by monoclinal foothills on steeply dipping younger strata. Locally these are cut out by the Beartooth fault which gives to the mountains a very abrupt front (Fig. 56). At the west end beyond the Yellowstone River these monoclinal ridges turn north and become

[1] HAGUE, "Universal Cyclopedia," suggests that these small lakes may occupy irregular depressions "in the lava flows," implying that the present plateau surface may be essentially the original surface of flow.

the Bridger Mountains. No doubt similar upturned sedimentaries on the south were dropped down by the faulting which depressed the Yellowstone Plateau and are now covered by volcanic rocks. The gneissic Beartooth Range is separated only by a stream (Clark Fork[1]) from the volcanic Absaroka Range east of the park.

The Snowy Range embraces some of the ruggedest mountains to be found in the province. Their ruggedness comes in part

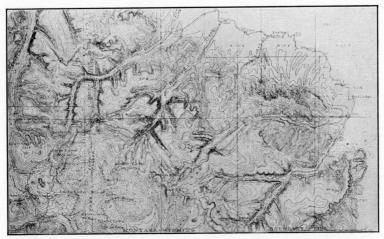

Fig. 57.—Topographic map of a part of the Beartooth Range. Remnants of the younger (subsummit) peneplain are made sufficiently evident by the prevailing light color of the map due to wide spacing of contour lines. Equally clear are the sharp valleys or canyons cut since the peneplain was uplifted. Monadnocks rise above the widespread peneplain to a common level of 12,000 to 12,400 ft. and are interpreted as remnants of an older peneplain. These are less obvious but may be located by following the main divide across the southern half of the map. (*Map by U. S. Forest Service; photo furnished by Arthur Bevan.*)

from steep-sided peaks or ridges rising above the general level and oversteepened by the work of alpine glaciers, but chiefly from dissection by narrow and profound canyons. The greater part of the range is a dissected peneplain not unlike the Salmon River Mountains of Idaho, except for several broad areas called Buffalo Plateau in the bend of the Yellowstone River, where flatness is due to a volcanic cover. Even in these places dissection is approximately mature, but some divides have not yet been narrowed to sharpness and others are broad, rolling areas

[1] Not to be confused with Clark Fork of the Columbia.

relieved by *roche moutonnées*, strewn with boulders, pitted with lakes or furrowed with ravines.[1]

The horizon determined by the crests of the Beartooth Range is among the flattest seen in any high mountains (Figs. 56 and 57). It is generally between 10,000 and 11,000 ft. high or 3,500 to 4,500 ft. above the plains. In the eastern part, within an area 20 miles long and 8 miles wide, many remnants rise above 12,000 ft. (Granite Peak, 12,850 ft.). The summits of these very rugged peaks are also accordant and have been interpreted as remnants of an older peneplain.[2] The aspect is distinctly alpine. Perhaps one-fifth of the surface is bare rock.

During the glacial period the Beartooth Mountains maintained a part of the nevé which supported the ice sheet or Piedmont glacier in the Yellowstone Basin. The mountains themselves had alpine glaciers but were not covered by a general ice sheet. The marks of alpine glaciation are everywhere.

Absaroka Range.—Bordering the Yellowstone Plateau on the east, its western spurs projecting into the National Park, is the lofty mountain mass called the Absaroka Range. These mountains are not separated from the Beartooth except by a canyon. The two ranges are similar in elevation and in the accordance of ridge crests but contrasted in history. The Beartooth is an uplifted lowland while the Absaroka is built by volcanic accumulation, mostly breccias. The name Shoshone Range is sometimes applied south of the Shoshone River but this part is in all essential respects a continuation of the Absaroka. With the termination of the volcanic cover at the southeastern end this range gives way to the lower Owl Creek Range composed of folded sedimentaries and trending east-west (see geologic map of Wyoming).

The total length of the Absaroka is thus seen to be about 100 miles and its width 50 miles. It is therefore far from being a linear uplift if indeed it can be called an uplift at all. It is a dissected volcanic plateau, a complex of accordant divides and

[1] For description see LEIBERG, J. B., U. S. Geol. Survey, *Prof. Pap.* 29, p. 11, 1904.

[2] BEVAN, ARTHUR, Rocky Mountain Peneplains Northeast of Yellowstone Park, *Jour. Geol.*, vol. XXXIII, 1925. Bevan tentatively assigns this upper peneplain to the Oligocene and the surrounding subsummit peneplain to the Pliocene. He differs in this from Alden who thinks it unlikely that the subsummit plateau is younger than Miocene. (Geol. Soc. Amer. *Bull.*, vol. 35, p. 396, 1924.)

isolated sloping plateau remnants, all crests being remarkably even but not broad, generally declining in altitude from an axis near the park boundary.[1] Summits 10,000 to 12,000 ft. high rise 2,000 to 4,000 ft. above Yellowstone Park and 5,000 to 6,000 ft. above the Bighorn Basin. Streams in these mountains have cut narrow and profound canyons. The deepest is nearly 5,000 ft. Glaciation followed, adding the usual alpine features. Few ranges in America surpass the Absaroka in ruggedness and sublimity.

There is ample evidence that a mountain range was raised here near the close of the Cretaceous.[2] Its remnants are now wholly buried. Canyons cut almost to the level of the Bighorn Basin disclose nothing but volcanic accumulation except at the edge of the basin.

Fig. 58.—Intersecting erosion surfaces of the Beartooth and Absaroka Mountains. *AB*, present subsummit plateau observed in both ranges. *MN*, monadnocks of the Beartooth Range whose summits are believed to represent an older peneplain. *XY*, the restored older peneplain, much eroded, and buried beneath volcanic rocks in the Absaroka Range. (*After interpretation by Bevan.*)

Bevan speaks of an old erosion surface beneath the volcanic rocks exposed in the section along Clark Fork[3] which separates these mountains from the Beartooth Range on the north. This old buried surface he correlates with the summit peneplain (*i.e.,* the older peneplain) of the Beartooth Range. The southwestward slope of this peneplain, hypothetically restored, would carry it beneath the volcanic rocks farther south. He also interprets the Absaroka summits as indicating a post-Miocene (*i.e.,* younger) erosion surface, presumably the same as the subsummit peneplain in the Beartooth Range (Fig. 58). There is

[1] The Crandall and Ishawooa topographic sheets, U. S. Geol. Survey, Absaroka folio 52, show the topography in a striking manner. In this folio Hague treats the Absaroka as a dissected plateau.

[2] HAGUE, Absaroka folio 52, p. 3, points out an unconformity above the Laramie in Yellowstone Park. A strong unconformity above the Fort Union is also observed at the eastern foot of these mountains. See FISHER, C. A., Geology and Water Resources of the Bighorn Basin, U. S. Geol. Survey, *Prof. Pap.* 53, p. 33, pl. X-B, 1906.

[3] BEVAN, ARTHUR, *loc. cit.,* p. 574.

nothing to prevent such an intersection of peneplains if the older one be uplifted and tilted, and its lower part be covered with eruptives before the new peneplain is made. The extent to which the present summit level in the Absarokas may be the original surface of the breccias is not fully determined.[1]

BIGHORN MOUNTAINS

East of the Absaroka Mountains, other connecting ranges form a remarkable hook almost enclosing the elliptical Bighorn Basin, 150 miles long and 100 miles wide (Fig. 49, page 134). Strictly speaking this basin is a part of the Great Plains but so nearly severed that it may be treated as an intermontane valley. The Bighorn River enters this basin from the Wyoming Basin on the south by cutting a canyon 2,250 ft. deep through the mountain rim. It leaves this basin again by a 2,000-ft. gorge through the Bighorn Range near its terminus. A few miles farther northwest the mountains end, leaving an open passage 25 miles wide from the basin to the Great Plains. In this capricious performance the Bighorn is typical of Wyoming rivers (see page 136 and compare Fig. 50, page 136).

The highest and most massive mountains along this curved axis are the Bighorn Mountains on the east side.[2] South of the basin and west of the canyon the range is known as the Owl Creek Mountains. A partly isolated mass east of the canyon of the Bighorn River is called Bridger Mountain (not to be confused with the range of the same name in Montana).

Summit Uplands.—The Bighorn Mountains consist essentially of a granite core partly covered by sedimentary rocks, nearly horizontal on the top but generally dipping more steeply on the flanks. These beds approximately cover the northern third and southern third of the range. In these parts summits or uplands of nearly uniform elevation between gorges form a belt 10 to 20 miles wide with an average height of 9,000 ft. at the north and 8,000 ft. at the south. Over considerable areas the slopes of this upland (or hypothetically restored surface) approximately agree with the very gentle dips of the rocks. Such a relation

[1] HAGUE, *loc. cit.*, mentions six epochs of eruption, each represented by a distinct formation.

[2] The name Pryor is given to a small range contiguous with the Bighorn at its northwestern end.

suggests that the uppermost remaining beds, being fairly resistant, may have been stripped, not necessarily at or near base level. On this account there has been less tendency here than elsewhere to explain accordance by peneplaning.

In the middle third of the range the rocks are largely granite. The extensive upland, mentioned above, covers much of this area, but granite ridges rise several thousand feet above the general level of the plateau, properly spoken of here as the sub-summit upland on account of the mountains that rise above it

Fig. 59.—Subsummit upland of Bighorn Mountains in the Cloud Peak quadrangle; looking west over the granite surface at an elevation of 9,300 ft. to Black Butte in the distance. The lakes are morainal. The upland at this place is obviously a peneplain, though perhaps a very ancient one, now stripped. Farther north and south the surface is underlain by sedimentary formations approximately parallel to the surface. (*U. S. Geol. Survey.*)

(Fig. 59). In the discussion of this upland[1] it has not generally been assumed that it represents a peneplain developed just before the last uplift. Rather, it is implied that the nearly horizontal sedimentary strata have been stripped away, exposing the ancient peneplain on which they were deposited. A con-

[1] Darton, N. H., Geology of the Bighorn Mountains, U. S. Geol. Survey, *Prof. Pap.* 51, 1906; Bald Mountain-Dayton folio 141, U. S. Geol. Survey, 1906; Cloud Peak-McKinney folio 142, U. S. Geol. Survey, 1906; Matthes, F. E., Glacial Sculpture in the Bighorn Mountains, Wyoming, U. S. Geol. Survey, 21*st Ann. Rept.*, pt. II, 1900.

spicuous part of the granite plateau is spoken of by Darton[1] as part of an early Cambrian peneplain again exhumed. It is assumed that this later denudation was limited in depth not by the local base level but by the resistance of the granite. As stated in connection with alleged stripped plains elsewhere (page 42), there is no doubt that the upper surface of a resistant rock may maintain a plain above base level within certain limits of height and breadth. Without doubt, when the subdued surface (now the Bighorn subsummit upland) was made, the hard rocks now at the surface tended to arrest erosion and were a factor in determining the final level that was reached. On the other hand, there is no doubt that this subdued surface was developed much nearer base level than at present. No serious error will be involved in thinking of this district as once a part of the late Tertiary surface of low relief which covered the Laramie, Wind River, and other ranges in Wyoming.

In addition to the level tracts underlain by resistant rock there are a few perfect flats of late Tertiary or Quaternary sediments at altitudes of 8,000 to 9,000 ft.[2] It is not to be supposed that such sediments could endure long in so precarious a position.

Secondary Ridges.—Steeply inclined strata on the flanks of the range form ridges of the hogback type. Most of these are low and are classed as foothills, but certain Carboniferous limestones form the so-called "Front Ridges." These are monoclinal ridges rising several thousand feet above the plains, having crests which are locally as high as the summit uplands and generally presenting scarps several hundred feet high toward the mountain axis. They appear on both sides of the range, but are better developed on the east side.

Glaciation.—Nowhere in the United States are glacial cirques and U-shaped valleys better exemplified than in the central portion of the Bighorn Range (Fig. 60). There are many almost vertical cirque walls 1,000 ft. high, and a few exceed 1,500 ft. Lakes in scooped-out granite basins or retained by dams of moraine are numerous. The four conditions pointed out by Matthes as tending toward perfection of cirques are all present

---

[1] U. S. Geol. Survey, folio 141, illustration sheet II, Fig. 10. In U. S. Geol. Survey, *Prof. Pap.* 51, p. 24, this is called a "plain" made by early Cambrian erosion.

[2] DARTON, N. H., *loc. cit.*, pl. XXIII; also Cloud Peak-McKinney folio 142, p. 8, U. S. Geol. Survey, 1906; also illustrations, Fig. 21.

FIG. 60.—Topographic map of Cloud Peak region, Bighorn Mountains, Wyoming. Steep-sided glacial troughs occupy a large part of the area, indenting the old pre-glacial surface of moderate relief. While occupied by glaciers these troughs were elongated headward. Glaciation ceased before the old surface along the crest was entirely consumed by the headward-growing cirques. (*Courtesy of The National Geographic Magazine.*)

here:[1] (1) The pre-glacial valleys were widely enough spaced to allow the development of cirques without mutual interference. (2) Climatic conditions were not sufficiently severe to cause glaciation of the intervening divides and uplands. (3) The rocks are fairly homogeneous so that cirques could develop in one direction as well as another. The jointing is also favorable. (4) There has been little post-glacial crumbling or erosion. As none of the glaciers descended below an altitude of 6,500 ft., the lower ends of the canyons retain their angular pre-glacial forms.

The glacial sculpture of this range is of more than usual interest because topographic features due to glaciation appear side by side with remnants of the old surface on which the ice began to work (see Fig. 66, page 179 and Fig. 67, page 180). It is the habit of alpine glaciers to deepen their troughs and lengthen them headward until, between the cirques on opposite sides of the range, nothing is left of the mountain crest except a crumbling line of crags.[2] For many miles along the Bighorn, crest, strips and patches of the old surface up to several miles in width are preserved. As seen from a distance or on a contour map of large interval[3] these remnants represent a landscape of rounded forms and easy slopes suggesting the advancing age of much subdued mountains. To a closer view the surface is rough and rocky. It has been pointed out that snowfields above the glacier heads tend to produce such forms whose generalized slopes are gentle but whose details are angular.[4] However, there is no reason to believe that this was the major factor in producing the forms here described. It cannot be doubted that these mountains have but recently been raised to their present height and that the surface before the final rise was approaching old age and had but moderate relief.

[1] MATTHES, F. E., Glacial Sculpture of the Bighorn Mountains, Wyoming, U. S. Geol. Survey, 21*st Ann. Rept.*, pt. II, p. 174, 1900. For glaciation of this range see also SALISBURY, R. D., Cloud Peak-McKinney folio 142, 1906.

[2] HOBBS, W. H., The Cycle of Mountain Glaciation, *Geogr. Jour.*, vol. XXXV, pp. 146–163 and 268–284, 1910.

[3] The Cloud Peak topographic sheet of the U. S. Geol. Survey is perhaps the most expressive.

[4] MATTHES, F. E., *loc. cit.*, and personal communication. Matthes calls the topographic work of snowfields *nivation*. Mountain tops like those here in question need to be studied with care to discriminate between the effects of advanced erosion approaching base level and the effects of snow at high levels.

Pryor and Owl Creek Ranges.—The Pryor mountains are a small independent uplift, roughly a continuation of the Bighorn Range, but offset a little to the southwest. They are lower than the range to the south, are covered by the strata which flank the Bighorn, and present the appearance of a dissected plateau composed largely of strong limestone beds.

The east-west range south of the Bighorn Basin, embracing the Owl Creek and Bridger Mountains, 7,000 to 9,500 ft. high,

Fig. 61.—Head of cirque on tributary of Tensleep Creek, Bighorn Mountains. The walls are nearly 1,000 ft. high. The rock is granite. Its well-jointed character appears at the right. The subdued character of the old surface is shown at the right and by the general form of the sky line. (*U. S. Geol. Survey.*)

also has a granite core. Both east and west of Bighorn Canyon the folding of thick strata is very important. These folds indicate a strong compressive force acting north and south. Some of the folds are steeper on the south side. In the Owl Creek Mountain this folding and subsequent erosion has resulted in a series of ridges trending northwest and southeast, or diagonally across the trend of the range.[1]

[1] ELDRIDGE, GEO. H., A Geological Reconnaissance in Northwestern Wyoming, U. S. Geol. Survey, *Bull.* 119, p. 15, 1894; DARTON, N. H., Geology of the Owl Creek Mountains, Senate *Doc.* 219, 59th Congress, 1st Session, 1906.

Bighorn Basin.—The elliptical depression within the bend of the Bighorn Range is included, for convenience, in the Mountain province.   Structurally it is a deep syncline filled with young sedimentary rocks, the upper beds being continuous with those of the Great Plains.[1]   A central ellipse, perhaps 75 miles long and 45 miles wide, has much flat upland with streams in broad valleys several hundred feet deep.   Three residual mountains or groups of such rise 1,200 to 1,500 ft. above the streams.   Badlands are rather common, especially in the southern half.   North of the Greybull River almost half the area is arable but water is not available to irrigate so much.   The chief water supply is from the Shoshone River, made available by the Shoshone dam of the U. S. Reclamation Service[2] (Fig. 50, page 136).

Outside of the central ellipse is a border 10 to 20 miles wide in which the strata that are deeply buried in the center come to the surface in pronounced northwest-southeast folds.   These folds are much eroded, making ridges and terraces with relief sometimes approaching 1,000 ft.   The level pre-erosion surface may well have been high enough to superimpose the Bighorn River on the mountains which it now transects both to enter and to leave the basin.

MOUNTAINS OF WESTERN WYOMING

Wind River Range.—In west central Wyoming, almost surrounded by the elevated plains of the Wyoming Basin, are the Wind River Mountains, one of the highest and most massive ranges of the Middle Rockies.   Almost in line to the northwest is the smaller Gros Ventre Range.   The line of these uplifts bisects the angle between two divergent curved axes.   On one side the Absaroka-Owl Creek Range turns off to the east and on the other the Wyoming and other ranges turn off to the south. All these axes are brought together, sheaf-like, near Yellowstone Park, spreading from there toward the south and east, and in less degree toward the north and west.

The Wind River Range is in several ways remarkably like the Beartooth of Montana; in its broadly exposed granite core, in its

---

[1] For description see FISHER, C. A., Geology and Water Resources of the Bighorn Basin, U. S. Geol. Survey, *Prof. Pap.* 53, 1906; see pls. IV and XI for structure; also HEWETT, D. F., The Heart Mountain Overthrust, Wyoming, *Jour. Geol.*, vol. XXVIII, pp. 536–557, 1920.

[2] FISHER, CASSIUS A., *loc. cit.*, p. 46 and pl. XII.

prominent monoclinal ridges on the northeast with an absence of these on the southwest due to faulting, and above all in its abundant evidence of a former peneplain preserved at an unusually high level.[1] There is also a strong resemblance to the central portion of the Bighorn Range where the subsummit upland is on granite. The broad rolling uplands of the Wind River Range are found mainly in the northern part, more than 12,000 ft. high. Elsewhere are accordant narrow crests between deep glaciated gorges. Monadnocks sharpened by ice erosion rise above the horizon, Fremont Peak to more than 13,000 ft., but there is no suggestion of an older peneplain at their tops.

The older sedimentaries on the northeast side rise too high and are too much a part of the range itself to be called foothills. Paleozoic strata rise to 9,000 or 10,000 ft. and even the Mesozoic "red beds" make a ridge 1,000 to 1,500 ft. above the plains. Still farther out are lower hogback foothills.

Pleistocene glaciers were more vigorous here than in the Bighorn Range, descending to the plains and pushing 10 miles out where they left their terminal moraines. Perhaps for this very reason, or for failure in one of the other conditions named on page 164, cirques are less clearly outlined and less diagrammatically perfect than in the Bighorn Range.

Like most of the Rocky Mountains, the Wind River Range dates from the Laramide epoch. The earliest physiographic feature is the summit peneplain, made sometime in the Tertiary.[2] Later, local plains or late mature topography developed in interrupted cycles but this later history is not known to have involved further deformation. The present altitude of these

---

[1] BAKER, C. L., Notes on the Cenozoic History of Central Wyoming, Geol. Soc. Amer. *Bull.*, vol. 23, abs. pp. 73–74, 1912; WESTGATE, L. G., and BRANSON, E. B., Later Cenozoic History of the Wind River Mountains, *Jour. Geol.*, vol. XXI, p. 143, 1913; BLACKWELDER, E., Post-Cretaceous History of the Mountains of Central Wyoming, *Jour. Geol.*, vol. XXIII, 1915. The U. S. Geol. Survey topographic map of the Fremont quadrangle shows the features here referred to.

[2] MANSFIELD, *Jour. Geol.*, vol. XXXII, p. 485; also U. S. Geol. Survey, *Prof. Pap.* 152, p. 19, gives a table correlating events in western Wyoming and southeastern Idaho as interpreted by Westgate and Branson, Blackwelder, and himself. Mansfield assigns to the Eocene a peneplain in like position farther west. Westgate and Branson assign this peneplain to the Miocene. BLACKWELDER, E., *loc. cit.;* also Wash. Acad. Sci. *Jour.*, vol. IV, pp. 445–446, 1914, tentatively assigns the peneplain to the Pliocene. BAKER, CHARLES L., *loc. cit.*, regards the peneplain as of Miocene age.

mountains above the adjacent plains is due mainly to differential erosion since the last uplift (see Wyoming Basin, page 147).

Gros Ventre Range.—The Gros Ventre Range is a small but distinct mountain uplift separated by a narrow syncline from the Wind River Range and extending northwest to the Tertiary basin which is followed by the Snake River in its southerly course from Yellowstone Park (Fig. 49). Between the Gross Ventre and the Absaroka Ranges to the northeast is a broad syncline retaining in its center remnants of a maturely dissected Tertiary plateau 10,000 ft. high. A narrow synclinal valley separates the Gros Ventre from the Hoback Range to the southwest.

The Gros Ventre Range appears on the geologic map as two or more small spots of granite surrounded by successive bands of strata. This indicates the essential nature of the uplift, an anticline more or less denuded along its axis. Viewed in detail, it consists of several anticlines each steeper to the southwest than to the northeast. The range has this feature in common with the Wind River and Owl Creek Ranges.

Many summits rise to somewhat less than 11,000 ft. Uniformity of altitude is said to be marked[1] and there are several noteworthy flats truncating strata of unequal strength at altitudes between 10,300 and 10,800 ft.[2] It may be inferred that the physiographic history of this range is very similar to that of the Wind River Mountains, though it is not yet demonstrated that the summits, somewhat lower than those of the Wind River Range, represent the same erosion cycle.

Teton Range.—The Teton is a north-south range, 40 miles long, just east of the Wyoming-Idaho boundary and south of Yellowstone Park. Though small in area, this is one of the most majestic ranges of the Rocky Mountains. Its deeply gashed granite crest, snow covered and several thousand feet above timber line, has many peaks above 12,000 ft. and reaches its greatest heights in Grand Teton (13,800 ft.) and Mt. Hayden (13,700 ft.). On the east the range rises very abruptly above the Snake River Valley, a Tertiary basin similar to those of Montana, here expanded into "Jackson's Hole," a valley 12 miles wide with a terraced floor and enclosed on the south by glacial moraines. The western slope of the range descends less steeply

[1] SCHULTZ, A. R., Geology and Geography of a Portion of Lincoln County, Wyoming, U. S. Geol. Survey, *Bull.* 543, p. 16, 1914.

[2] BLACKWELDER, E., *loc. cit.*, p. 199.

to the Teton Basin, a slightly lower valley continuous with the Snake River lava plain of Idaho. Both slopes are deeply carved by water and ice. The details of the alpine crest are characteristically the work of glaciers. Several of these still remain.[1]

Lying in a region of closely folded rocks, the Teton Range is an almost undeformed fault block uplifted on the east.[2] The deep-lying granite was thus brought up beside weak sedimentary

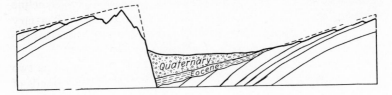

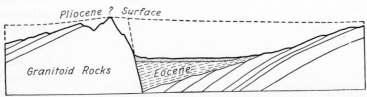

Fig. 62.—Diagram of the East front of the Teton Range to explain two possible origins of the escarpment: *a* as a modern normal fault scarp; *b* as a fault line scarp discovered entirely by erosion. In both cases the broken line represents an old erosion surface of small relief. In *a* this surface is older than the fault and older than the Quaternary sediments. In *b* the old erosion surface was developed after the faulting. When the mass was uplifted, the weak Eocene beds on the east side were cut down and the fault block of granitoid rocks again stood out as a mountain. Western United States contains scores of mountains and valleys whose interpretation involves a choice between these two cases. (*After Blackwelder.*)

rocks whose degradation increased the relative height of the mountain front. So much is true whether the fault scarp be now in its first erosion cycle or the second. Alternative explanations are set forth in Fig. 62.

There is reason to believe that this range, like many others, was approximately base leveled (probably late in Tertiary time) and that as the result of later widespread uplift, erosion

[1] Hague, W., and others, Yellowstone folio 30, p. 3, U. S. Geol. Survey. For description see also St. John, Orestes, U. S. Geol. and Geogr. Survey of the Territories, *Ann. Rept.*, pt. I, pp. 411–416, 1877.

[2] Blackwelder, E., A Reconnaissance of the Phosphate Deposits in Western Wyoming, U. S. Geol. Survey, *Bull.* 470, p. 460, 1910.

carved out the present relief.[1]   Two small summit flats survive, but the narrowness of the crest and the vigor of erosion on so steep a front were unfavorable to survival.   According to this hypothesis the Teton Range is a perfect example of a mature block mountain of the second generation, the most impressive of its kind in America because of the vast erosion involved and the majesty of the exhumed mass.   Throughout the middle Rocky Mountains and Wyoming Basin the assumption that the relief is largely due to differential erosion in a second (or later) cycle and not due directly to diastrophism is favored by the widespread agreement between strength of rocks and present altitude.

MOUNTAINS OF THE IDAHO-WYOMING BORDER

General Relations.—South of the Yellowstone and Snake River Plateaus a belt of parallel mountain ranges extends south nearly 200 miles, or almost to the Uinta Range.   The belt has a maximum width of about 80 miles, divided almost equally between Wyoming and Idaho.   At the north these ranges veer toward the west and disappear beneath the lavas of the Snake River Plain.   On the east they are bordered by the broken plains of the Green River, formed on horizontal Tertiary strata. With altitude diminishing southward, the mountains, except the westernmost range, disappear beneath the horizontal rocks of the plain near the southern boundary of Wyoming.

The western limit of this group of ranges is the somewhat arbitrary boundary between the Rocky Mountain province and the Great Basin.   The attempt has been made to draw this line in such a manner as to leave on the east the closely crowded mountains whose forms are determined chiefly by close folding, thrust-faulting, and erosion, and on the west what seem to be block mountains due perhaps to normal faulting, more widely spaced and often separated by Quaternary-filled valleys.[2]

---

[1] BLACKWELDER, E., Post-Cretaceous History of the Mountains of Western Central Wyoming, Wash. Acad. Sci. *Jour.*, vol. IV, pp. 445–446, abs., 1914; also *Jour. Geol.*, vol. XXIII, 1915.

[2] Such a line would follow the Bear River northward at the west foot of the Bear River Range, passing east through the Bear River Gap to Soda Springs, thence north along the eastern edge of Blackfoot and Willow Creek lava fields.   This leaves the Aspen and the Idaho-Wyoming Ranges as the westernmost members of the Middle Rocky Mountain province. This is essentially the line indicated by George R. Mansfield, U. S. Geol. Survey, *Prof. Pap.* 152, pl. XV, 1927.

Structure and Topography.—The region is one of close folds, some of them overturned, and thrust faults dating from the Laramide epoch. Of several great thrust faults one, the Bannock thrust[1] in Idaho, is perhaps the greatest in the United States. It has been traced 150 miles. The overthrusting toward the east cannot be less than 12 miles, is probably 35 miles, and may be more.

To name and describe these ranges singly would involve too much detail.[2] Structural sections are much like those of the folded Appalachians. Even in form and history the two systems have much in common, though the crests of these mountains are less even and simple than those of the northern Appalachians. Ridges and knobs of fairly uniform height between 9,000 and 10,000 ft. are not uncommon at the north and in the Snake River and Caribou Ranges which rise on opposite sides of the strike valley of the Snake River. The Wyoming and Salt River Ranges east of the state boundary have even greater altitudes, 10,000 to 11,000 ft. at the north, but they rise only moderately above the Wyoming Basin whose floor is here 7,500 ft. high.

South of the 42d parallel the relief diminishes. Only here and there do monoclinal ridges rise 700 ft. above the horizontal Tertiary beds that floor the surrounding and intervening plain. The surface, aside from the Bear River Range on the west, is more largely plateau than mountain. The plateau portions are continuous with the plains of the Wyoming Basin by way of the gaps in the low monoclinal ridges. The Bear River Plateau, west of the state boundary, is deeply dissected but its rocks are not folded. The surface rises westward over the gently dipping Tertiary beds to a height of 8,000 ft. Here the plateau ends in an escarpment looking westward over a valley to the Bear River Range. The northern end of this plateau lies east of Bear Lake. Here the Tertiary (Eocene) sediments have been in part stripped away and the old pre-Eocene topography is again revealed,

---

[1] RICHARDS, R. W., and MANSFIELD, G. R., The Bannock Overthrust, *Jour. Geol.*, vol. XX, pp. 681–709, 1912.

[2] VEATCH, A. C., U. S. Geol. Survey, *Prof. Pap.* 56, 1907; SCHULTZ, A. R., U. S. Geol. Survey, *Bull.* 543, 1914; MANSFIELD, GEO. R., U. S. Geol. Survey, *Prof. Pap.* 152, 1927. These papers give excellent maps of different parts of the area. The belt as a whole stands out clearly on the geological map of the United States; also on the U. S. Geol. Survey contoured map of the United States. Mansfield's paper gives a discussion of the physiography.

probably, as yet, but little modified. This part is called the "Bear Lake Plateau."[1]

The valleys of the Idaho-Wyoming border, except at its southern end, occupy a much smaller fraction of the total surface than in the Appalachians. For the most part they follow the strike of the less resistant strata. Even the larger ones are nearly 6,000 ft. above the sea, but the common grains thrive where irrigated, and there is much good pasture on the hillsides.

Physiographic History.—It is plain that the original folds of all these mountains were approximately peneplaned. This erosion cycle ended with the Snowdrift peneplain, patches of which still survive on some of the higher crests. Topographically they correspond to the summit upland in the Wind River and other ranges in Wyoming.[2] Successive uplifts since that event have raised the old land surface to a height somewhat less than that of the Wind River summits. The first uplift after the Snowdrift cycle was followed by five interrupted erosion cycles previous to the current post-glacial valley cutting. With some allowance for local variations these may probably be correlated with the four cycles described for the Wind River and other ranges farther east. In both regions the first cycle following the general peneplain advanced little beyond maturity on the stronger rocks. Some broad valleys were produced but no broad flats. In eastern Idaho this cycle was interrupted by an epoch of aggradation (the Salt Lake [Pliocene] beds). On these sediments the Bear River may have taken its superposed course across the mountains, if this was not accomplished earlier. The remaining cycles, except the last, advanced locally to late maturity, making some broad valleys and local terraces, each at a lower level than its predecessor, but no extensive plains. In the current cycle, streams are again entrenching themselves in canyons or narrow valleys.

Meantime the Tertiary sediments have steadily been wearing down and back. Probably their general surface was continuous with that of the summit peneplain when the latter was made. The present height of mountains above plains is due in some measure to arching of the peneplain but probably much more to degradation of the plains.

[1] Mansfield, Geo. R., *loc. cit.*, p. 13; see also Blackwelder, E., Post-Cretaceous History of the Mountains of Central Western Wyoming, *Jour. Geol.*, vol. XXIII, p. 203, 1915.

[2] See footnote p. 148.

WASATCH MOUNTAINS

Location and Boundaries.—For nearly 200 miles the Wasatch and Bear River Ranges, trending north-south, form the western front of the Rocky Mountain province. The southern end of the Wasatch is near the pass south of Mount Nebo traversed by the San Pete Valley Railroad running east from Nephi. South of this are the high plateaus of Utah, an elevated belt in line with the Wasatch Range and often incorrectly represented as a continuation of that range. At the north the Bear River Range terminates with equal clearness within the great bend

Fig. 63.—West front of Wasatch Range at Ogden, Utah. A great fault is assumed to have its trace at or near the foot of the mountain. The internal structure of this great fault block is complex. It is not related in any simple way to the outlines of the mountain mass. (*Photo by Blackwelder.*)

of the Bear River which in its northwesterly and westerly course is followed by the Oregon Short Line.

On the west these ranges descend with remarkable abruptness to the Bear River, Great Salt Lake, Jordan River, and Provo Lake (Fig. 63). Through most of its length the western base is less than 5,000 ft. above the sea (Great Salt Lake, 4,200). The eastern slope is less steep and less straight, and descends to a much less definite base. At two points only is the eastern face abrupt. Generally the range gives way on the east to dissected or dissecting plateaus. South of the Uinta Mountains (lat.

40°40′) this dissected plateau, 8,000 ft. or more in elevation, is a part of the Colorado Plateau province. North of that, the sag between the Wasatch and Uinta Mountains is structurally a part of the Mountain province. It is occupied in part by Kamas Prairie, an intermontane basin less than 10 miles in diameter, and in part by great laccoliths.[1]

Topography.—The crest of the Wasatch proper is generally above an altitude of 10,000 ft., but the Bear River Range is a little lower. East and southeast of Salt Lake City are long lines of peaks exceeding 11,000 ft. in height (Timpanogos, 11,957 ft.). The crests of the Bear River Mountains at the north show evidence of the old peneplain, so common farther north, but this is not noted in the Wasatch proper.

The most striking element in the topography of this range is its abrupt, wall-like western front.[2] At intervals of a few miles this steep face is interrupted by canyons branching headward, subdividing the slope into ridges. It might normally be expected that the valleys in approaching the mountain base would broaden and that the dividing ridges would decrease in height and breadth. Instead of this the sharp V-form of the canyons is kept up generally to the very foot of the mountain, often with increase of gradient near the base. The intervening ridges, instead of dying out gradually on the plain, frequently end in triangular facets[3] somewhat steeper than the general mountain slope. These are features which have been assumed to indicate recent or continued faulting and are more fully discussed under the Great Basin (page 335).

The eastern slope of the range lacks all these characteristic features of the western slope. It is not everywhere longer, partly because the eastern foot of the range is higher than the western, and partly because the steep slope above the western base does not continue to the summit. The eastern slope is

---

[1] BOUTWELL, J. M., Geology and Ore Deposits of the Park City District Utah, U. S. Geol. Survey, *Prof. Pap.* 77, p. 43, 1912.

[2] BLACKWELDER, E., New Light on the Geology of the Wasatch Mountains, Utah, Geol. Soc. Amer. *Bull.*, vol. 21, pl. 39, 1910. This is perhaps the most striking of the many published views of this slope. The same paper contains instructive diagrams showing the structure of the range; see also, LOUGHLIN, G. F., A Reconnaissance in the Southern Wasatch Mountains, Utah, *Jour. Geol.*, vol. XXI, pp. 436–452, 1913.

[3] DAVIS, W. M., The Mountain Ranges of the Great Basin, Mus. Comp. Zool. *Bull.*, vol. XLII, p. 153, Fig. 11, 1903.

deeply dissected into rugged mountains and affords no suggestion of an inclined plane or even of a former rolling surface.[1]

Glaciation.—For a distance of 35 miles between the latitudes of Salt Lake City and Provo the range was glaciated.[2] As the crest is here nearer the east side, the longest glaciers (about 10 miles) were on the west side where they descended to about 5,000 ft. above the sea, or 1,000 ft. lower than the limit of the less vigorous glaciers on the east side. Even on the west side most of the glaciers did not reach the plain. Some of the valleys, notably that of the American Fork, are typical glacial troughs in their upper portions while the lower portions remain acutely V-shaped.[3] As the grade of the stream does not appear to have been seriously disturbed it seems that in this case the change of form was brought about by oversteepening the sides rather than overdeepening the axis, a point which has led to much discussion. The deposits of these glaciers are of special interest because of their relation to the sediments of Lake Bonneville[4] and the correlation thus made possible between the glacial epochs and those of Lake Bonneville. The usual features due to alpine glaciation are present. Cirques are generally small and imperfect, the altitude of their floors being 8,500 ft. or over.[5]

Drainage.—The insignificance of the Wasatch Range in the control of drainage is remarkable. Three large streams which head in the Uinta Mountains on the east, discharge into Great Salt Lake on the west. The Bear River accomplishes this by a great detour to the north. The Weber River cuts through the range in a canyon and emerges at Ogden. The Provo River crosses in a canyon to Provo Lake, continuing to Great Salt Lake under the name of the Jordan River. The Denver and Rio Grande Railway approaching Provo from the east follows a similar transverse valley. It was at one time common to account for all such streams as antecedent but the proximity of the Wyoming Basin, in and around which are many superposed streams, suggests that all these streams may be superposed (*cf.* page 136).

[1] DAVIS, W. M., The Wasatch, Canyon, and House Ranges, Utah, Mus. Comp. Zool. *Bull.*, vol. XLIX, p. 17, 1905.

[2] ATWOOD, W. W., Glaciation of the Uinta and Wasatch Mountains, U. S. Geol. Survey, *Prof. Pap.* 61, 1909.

[3] *Idem*, p. 75.

[4] GILBERT, G. K., U. S. Geol. Survey, *Mon.* 1, p. 310.

[5] DAVIS, *loc. cit.*, p. 17; also Fig. 1, p. 17.

Structure and History.—The fact of greatest topographic significance is a great fault or fault zone at the western foot of the range.   Upward movement on the east side of this fault was probably greater than the present height of the mountains above Great Salt Lake.   The block thus uplifted did not consist of undeformed strata but had previously been closely folded and thrust-faulted and then greatly eroded.   The strike of the folded beds is in general east of north.   In so far as ridges result from erosion of a folded mass, these ridges should be related to the strike.   The fact that the remarkably straight western base of the range cuts across the strike of the folded rocks whose harder strata do not even make spurs beyond the straight base line, is probably the chief reason for believing that this and similar ranges are the result of faulting.[1]   The Wasatch has these features in common with many of the basin ranges (page 336).

It is uncertain to what extent the present mountain form, especially the steep west face, is influenced by the great thrust faults.[2]   These nearly parallel fault planes divide the mountain mass into four or five great slabs dipping east.   Locally the effect of this is to superpose stronger rocks on weaker and to expose the former at the top of the mountain slope, so that the effect of sapping is added to the other processes which tend to produce a steep slope.[3]   Such relations are very prominent near Ogden where the west face is unusually steep (Fig. 63).   Complications of this kind are not known to exist in the Bear River Mountains.

UINTA MOUNTAINS

The Uinta Range lies mainly in northeastern Utah just south of the Wyoming boundary.   It is the largest east-west range in the United States and perhaps the largest in the western hemisphere.   It is approximately 150 miles long and 30 to 40 miles wide and it has many peaks and crests more than 12,000 ft. high.

[1] As noted on p. 338 the presence of the features here mentioned does not necessarily prove that an escarpment, due ultimately to faulting, is in its first cycle of erosion.

[2] BOUTWELL, J. M., Stratigraphy and Structure of the Park City Mining District, *Jour. Geol.*, vol. XV, p. 455ff., 1907.

[3] BLACKWELDER, E., New Light on the Geology of the Wasatch Mountains, Utah, Geol. Soc. Amer. *Bull.*, vol. 21, p. 534, 1910; LOUGHLIN, G. F., Reconnaissance in the Southern Wasatch Mountains, Utah, *Jour. Geol.*, vol. XXI, pp. 436–452, 1913.

Structure.—The structure of this range in its simplest form is that of a flat-topped anticline. It consists of an elevated, nearly horizontal platform between abrupt monoclines (Fig. 64). The term "Uinta structure" is used to describe this type.[1] Dips in the central platform rarely exceed 5 or 6 deg. while in the flanking monoclines the average dip may be as high as 45 deg. The greatest uplift is near the northern edge, the gentle dips of the summit platform being generally toward the south. To a remarkable extent the surface of this range is parallel to the exposed beds.

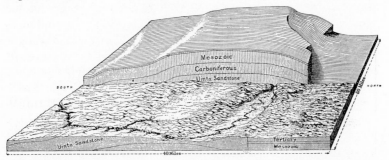

Fig. 64.—Structure of the Uinta Mountain Range. In the diagram the vertical scale is about twice the horizontal. A thickness of about 18,000 ft. of rock is shown to have been eroded from the original structure to make the present relief. (*After Powell.*)

The lowest formations seen are pre-Cambrian quartzites. These now form the actual plateau, having been exposed by the erosion of an average thickness of 18,000 ft. of strata which once covered the central portion, but which appear now only on the flanks. Of these steeply dipping formations on the north and south, some, generally among the lower systems exposed near the central mass, are very resistant and form high monoclinal ridges. The younger systems (Mesozoic) lying farther from the central mass are, for the most part, less resistant and have been worn down lower. Their worn-down edges are in large part covered by horizontal Tertiary formations. These last constitute an eroded plateau rising high against the flanks of the mountains, locally above 9,000 ft., thus greatly reducing its relative elevation.

[1] POWELL, J. W., Geology of the Eastern Portion of the Uinta Mountains, U. S. Geol. and Geogr. Survey of the Territories, p. 11, 1876.

The mountain uplift itself is one of the greatest known. It has been computed that the monoclines are 30,000 ft. high.[1] The relatively small elevation above the adjoining plains is due in part to the stripping of the arch by erosion and in part to marginal burial by horizontal sediments.

A local modification of the above described structure arises from the substitution of a great fault for the monocline on the north side near the Green River. The effect of this is to eliminate the monoclinal ridges. At the east end of the range the uplift is smaller in amount and less simple. Here the main uplift is attended on the south by a subordinate one, giving rise to the Yampa Plateau. This uplift is included with the Uinta Range in the Middle Rocky Mountain province.

Topography.—The topography of the Uinta Range is closely related to the structure. The broad central tract has numerous peaks more than 12,000 ft. high and numerous ridges at slightly lower altitudes. All these summit elevations are on the resistant pre-Cambrian quartzite. The strongest of the monoclinal ridges is likewise of quartzite (Mississippian). The main divide is near the structural axis not far from the northern edge of the summit upland. From this line streams, subequally spaced, flow north and south in deep canyons, breaking through the hogbacks in great notches known as "gateways."

The one feature which is totally out of harmony with the structure is the course of the Green River, which flows across the range from north to south in a devious canyon 3,000 ft. deep. In the center of the uplift the Green River receives the Yampa which has itself followed a course almost as defiant of structure as that of the Green.[2]

Glaciation.—West of the meridian of the Upper Green River (about 109°40'), the range was severely glaciated. For a span of 80 miles almost the entire surface of the central upland was covered by glacial ice.[3] The topographic maps of this area show a number of ridges similar in height and appearance to the main crest. Generally these are narrow and sharp and are

---

[1] POWELL, J. W., *loc. cit.*, p. 11; WHITE, C. A., *9th Ann. Rept.*, U. S. Geol. Survey, later computed the rise at 28,800 ft.

[2] See references under Wyoming Basin, p. 146.

[3] ATWOOD, W. W., Glaciation of the Uinta and Wasatch Mountains, U. S. Geol. Survey, *Prof. Pap.* 61, 1909. In addition to the text, this paper contains valuable maps and illustrations.

FIG. 65.—Head of a cirque in the Uinta Range. As this is near the crest of the range the rocks are horizontal. The general direction of the crest is east-west, its borders being scalloped by cirques such as this. Compare Fig. 66. (*U. S. Geol. Survey.*)

FIG. 66.—Crest of the Uinta Range scalloped by cirques. The remains of an older surface are sufficiently extensive to show its subdued and gently rolling character. (Compare Fig. 60, page 163.) For the nature of the cirque walls, but vaguely shown here, see Fig. 65. (*U. S. Geol. Survey.*)

surmounted here and there by peaks of the Matterhorn type. Locally the ridges have rolling summits a fraction of a mile to several miles wide, similar to those in the Bighorn Mountains.

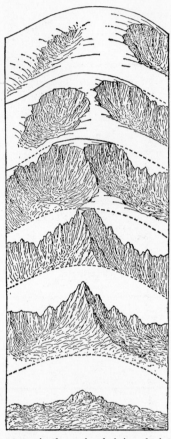

Fig. 67.—Successive stages in the cycle of alpine glaciation. Subdued mountains having relatively smooth slopes are gradually consumed by the headward growth of cirques, beginning in water-carved valleys. (Compare Fig. 42, page 109; also Fig. 79, page 207.) The earlier stages are common. The intermediate stages are beautifully shown in the Bighorn Mountains (page 162). Later stages (mountains of the Matterhorn type) are exemplified in the Bitterroot, Cascade, and other severely glaciated ranges. It is probable that the last stages here pictured are exemplified in some of the larger basins of the Uinta Range, formed by the coalescence of neighboring cirques. (*After Davis.*)

These ridges are so disposed as to divide the entire area into more or less independent basins. Atwood has enumerated and described 124 of these basins, ranging in area from 1 to 30 or more square miles.[1] The floors of these basins, while generally far from smooth, have small relief as compared with the abrupt ridges which rise several thousand feet above them. The basins are plainly glacial cirques. The larger ones may result from the coalescing of several, perhaps many, cirques in the process of glacial erosion. It is possible that all stages of the

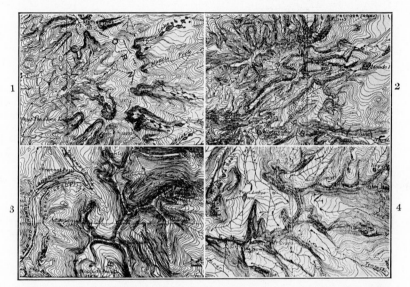

Fig. 68.—Series of four maps illustrating progressive consumption of a mountain crest by cirque erosion. (1) Cloud Peak Quadrangle, Wyoming, an early stage; (2) the same, a later stage; (3) Leadville quadrangle, Colorado, early maturity; (4) Philipsburg quadrangle, Montana, complete dissection, a *fretted upland*. (*Hobbs, Geographical Journal, vol.* 35.)

glacial cycle[2] may be found exemplified in these mountains (*cf.* Figs. 67 and 68).

In the nearly horizontal and well-jointed quartzite beds of the summit area, glacial quarrying was favored. Here are found the largest cirques or the most extensive coalescence of cirques by the destruction of intervening divides. All the canyons are

[1] *Idem,* map, pl. IV.

[2] DAVIS, W. M., Assoc. Amer. Geogr. *Ann.,* vol. I, p. 58, credits E. Richter with the first systematic statement of the cutting down of divides by alpine glaciers, Geomorphologische Untersuchungen in den Hochalpen, *Petermann's Mitteilungen,* Ergenzungsheft 132, 1900; see also HOBBS, W. H., The Cycle of Mountain Glaciation, *Geogr. Jour.,* vol. XXXV, pp. 146–163 and 268–284, 1910.

U-shaped. Many of them contain moraines. Hanging valleys, lakes in rock basins, and lakes behind morainic dams are characteristic features.

History.—The great Uinta fold seems to have been made near the close of the Cretaceous. With its growth began the enormous erosion which ultimately removed 7,000 cubic miles[1] from its summit. Along with this erosion went the accumulation of the surrounding Tertiary beds. From the uniformity of crest levels it is assumed that a peneplain was produced.[2] The simplest conception is that the wearing down of the summit and the filling up at the base proceeded together until the central mass stood little if any above its local base level. Complete burial may be assumed in the pass where the Green River was superposed. Later regional uplift caused a few thousand feet of the new and poorly consolidated sediments to be carried away, thus increasing the relative altitude of the mountains and making canyon cutting possible. The actual course of events may have been much more complex, but these with subsequent glaciation are the essentials.

[1] POWELL, *loc. cit.*, p. 201.
[2] ATWOOD, *loc. cit.*, p. 10.

CHAPTER V

NORTHERN ROCKY MOUNTAIN PROVINCE

DISTINCTIVE CHARACTER

In that part of the Rocky Mountain System that lies north and west of Yellowstone Park and within the United States the separation of mountains into distinct ranges is indefinite. Large tracts bearing distinct names may be separated by broad valleys, or only by canyons, or it may be that no one knows where the separation should be. The separate units may have any shape, some being as broad as long. Throughout more than half of the area the term "range" is misleading. Most of the mountains are not arranged in lines, hence have no trend and no dominating crest, only a multitude of minor crests running in all directions between the streams of a mature drainage system. Neighboring divides are in general of nearly uniform height. In a wide view so many of these crests fall into nearly the same plane that the sky line in many cases is almost horizontal though the valleys may be very steep and from 1,000 ft. to a mile in depth. Recent faulting or differences in rock structure or unequal erosion may cause one divide or peak to rise above its neighbors, but the uniformity is more striking than the exceptions. The larger part of the area looks like an approximate peneplain raised to a level from 6,000 to 9,000 ft. above the sea and sharply dissected almost or quite to maturity.

The continuity of the mountain landscape thus described is broken by occasional wide valleys with nearly flat or, it may be, hilly floors from 2,000 to 5,000 ft. below the mountain crests. The width of such valleys may be 5 or 10 miles or even more and their length much greater. Generally, but not always, such depressions are floored with weak Tertiary sediments in contrast with the strong igneous or metamorphic rocks that make the mountains. These are the much discussed Tertiary lake basins (page 219).

Montana has a dozen or more Tertiary lake basins and its mountains are thus divided into more or less circumscribed

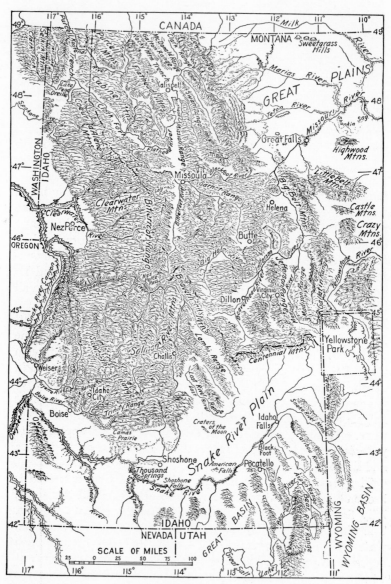

Fig. 69.—Index map of the Northern Rocky Mountains. (Drawn by Guy-Harold Smith.)

patches sometimes loosely spoken of as ranges.   In Idaho, the entire mountain area, except at the northern end and close to the eastern border, is almost uninterrupted by valleys having sufficient continuity to subdivide the mountain mass into ranges, properly so called.

MOUNTAINS OF IDAHO

The mountains of Idaho are in several ways the most typical representatives of the Rocky Mountains north of Yellowstone Park.   Here the distinctive characteristics, the accordance of

Fig. 70.—View on the Lolo Ridge over the Coeur D'Alene Mountains, showing the plateau character.   This sketch represents the most widespread character of the mountains in Idaho.   (*U. S. Geol. Survey.*)

crest levels, and the lack of linear ranges are seen in their best development and over the largest area (Fig. 70).   Here also is the largest area underlain by rocks almost uniformly resistant. Moreover, much of the discussion concerning the physiographic history of the wider area has been carried on with primary reference to the mountains of Idaho.

Boundaries.—The outer boundaries of this great mountain area are for the most part clearly marked topographically and significant historically.   In general the western and southern boundary is the edge of the Columbia and Snake River lava plains where they abut against the mountains or (in the northern part) invade the marginal valleys.   The altitude of the line thus defined is nearly 6,000 ft. in eastern Idaho but declines toward the west and north to about 3,000 ft. where the Salmon River emerges from the mountains.   The northern limit of the area to be described here is set arbitrarily at Clark Fork.   Beyond that, to the north, the mountains are less continuous though there is no sudden change in character.   Toward the east the area extends to the eastern foot of the Continental Divide.   On this side the Bitterroot Mountains, a distinct north-south range raised by faulting, are exceptional in character but are included here because of contiguity.

Rocks.—Twenty thousand square miles of this area are the exposed surface of a great granite batholith, structureless except for local development of foliation.[1]   The northern end of the area is mainly on the rocks of the Belt series (Algonkian), immensely thick and almost uniformly resistant.   There are minor areas of undifferentiated pre-Cambrian and also of lavas. The rocks of the southeastern part of the area are folded and metamorphosed paleozoics with some mesozoics.   Erosion here has been so conditioned by structure that definite northwest-southeast ranges have resulted.   Elsewhere valley cutting has been about as easy in one direction as another.

Local Names.—As might be expected where natural limits are lacking, names are applied to the several parts of this vast mountain area in an arbitrary and often confusing manner.   The names Salmon River, Clearwater, and Coeur D'Alene Mountains seem originally to have designated the mountains drained by the respective rivers whose names they bear.   According to such a plan the main ridge separating two drainage basins would bear two names, one for each side.   To avoid this it is customary now to limit the name Salmon River Mountains to the area south of the main Salmon River, sometimes extending to the Snake River Plain, sometimes excluding the peripheral mountains which are drained in the opposite direction.[2]

[1] ELDRIDGE, GEO. H., A Geologic Reconnaissance across Idaho, U. S. Geol. Survey, 16*th Ann. Rept.*, pt. II, p. 220, 1895, accounts for the nearly north-south trend of certain minor constituent "ranges" by differential erosion on account of foliation.

[2] In the area of folded paleozoic rocks are three well-marked ranges drained, in part, by south-flowing streams. These are the Beaverhead Range or Continental Divide on the Montana border (for the use of this

In like manner the name Clearwater is applied to the mountains between the Salmon River and the North Fork of the Clearwater, extending east to the Bitterroot Range and, north of that, to the valley of Clark Fork.   As both the Clearwater and the Salmon have very short northern tributaries, the mountains in each case lie largely in the drainage basins of the streams whose names they bear.   The name Coeur D'Alene is applied to the mountains, or district, extending north from the Clearwater as far as Clark Fork and Lake Pend Oreille.   For no obvious reason it is extended eastward almost 100 miles into Montana on the south side of the Flathead-Clark Fork Valley.   The whole area is sometimes covered by the name Bitterroot Mountains.   This name in its more restricted sense stands for a definite linear range rising above the Clearwater Mountains on the west and the Bitterroot Valley on the east, and extending from Lolo Pass in lat. 46°40′ to Nez Perce Pass in lat. 45°40′.[1]

Summit Levels.—Anywhere in this great area (excluding the Bitterroot Range) the major crests within a single broad view are of subequal height, indicating that before the cutting of the valleys the whole region was one of small relief.   With proper reservations, this former surface may be called an upraised peneplain.[2]   Wherever this term is used it is understood to mean the surface which would be restored by again filling the valleys.

Despite the accordance of neighboring crests, the restored surface, *i.e.*, approximately the level of the ridge tops, is not level but warped.   The altitude of the crests is greatest in the southeastern part near the Montana boundary in lat. about 44°30′.

---

name see J. B. Umpleby, U. S. Geol. Survey, *Bull.* 528, p. 23, 1913), the Lemhi Range, and the Lost River Range.   The Boise Range on the west and the Trinity on the south are other examples of such peripheral ranges. The Sawtooth Range is a conspicuous divide between the headwaters of the South Fork of the Salmon River and those of the Boise and Payette.

[1] The application here given to the names Bitterroot and Clearwater Mountains is taken from Lindgren, U. S. Geol. Survey, *Prof. Pap.* 27, 1904. For the extent assigned to the Coeur D'Alene see F. C. Calkins, U. S. Geol. Survey, *Bull.* 384, p. 14, 1909.

[2] The word "peneplain" signifies "approximately a plain."   Unfortunately there is no single term for the more common case of a surface of moderate or small relief, *i.e.*, "approximately a peneplain."   There is, therefore, a constant tendency to use the word peneplain with more and more allowance for relief, especially when the surface referred to no longer exists but is hypothetically restored by filling up the valleys (*cf.* Sierra Nevada, p. 413).

The greatest up-warp is along an east-west axis continuous at the east with the Centennial Range (the east-west portion of the Idaho-Montana boundary) and extending westward into Oregon, crossing the Snake River at the place where the Columbia Plateau is highest and the canyon deepest (page 250).

From southeastern Idaho where the crest level is at 10,500 ft., the level declines both north and south. In 50 miles to the north it falls 2,000 ft., the altitude being 8,500 ft. in the vicinity of

Fig. 71.—A portion of Poverty Flat, Salmon River Mountains, Idaho; elevation 9,600 ft., bordered by canyons with a maximum depth of 5,000 ft. This flat is a remnant of the old peneplain indicated by the even crests of the mountains in the background. (*U. S. Geol. Survey.*)

Salmon near where the Salmon River turns westward from its northerly course. It continues to decline northward in the Clearwater Mountains where it is little above 7,000 ft. even on the east side. The Coeur D'Alene Mountains rise to 7,000 ft. only on the Continental Divide. The elevation of the Salmon River Mountains also decreases toward the west from the point of maximum height mentioned above. In long. 114° near Challis, it is 9,600 ft.[1] (Fig. 71). In the Sawtooth Mountains it is about 9,000 ft., though exceptional peaks rise much higher. In the Boise Mountains it is less than 7,000 ft.

[1] Altitudes taken from J. B. Umpleby, U. S. Geol. Survey, *Bull.* 528, p. 24; and *Bull.* 539, p. 14.

The level of crests almost within sight of the province boundary on the west may be given at 5,000 ft. in the north, 6,000 ft. in the middle, and 7,000 ft. in the south. Just what becomes of the hypothetical old surface as the margin is approached, is not always easy to say. It may be bent down or faulted down and covered later by the lavas of the Columbia Plateau, or it may descend to the level of the plateau and be continuous with the summit levels of that province.[1] In any case it is much eroded.

Locally there are considerable areas of nearly flat surface at the summit level. Poverty Flat near Challis contains 25 square miles at an elevation of 9,600 ft.[2] A few quartzite hills rise perhaps 100 ft. above the general surface which bevels the inclined strata. In a very general way the breadth of the summits is greater in the middle of the Salmon River Mountains than near the edges or farther north. In the Clearwater Mountains some of the divides are still broad but the Coeur D'Alene district has only sharp ridges. Toward its western edge the old level is difficult to trace.

The continuity of the crests and the forbidding character of the gorge-like valleys is well indicated by the location of the two great trails, the Lolo and the Nez Perce, leading westward from the passes of the same names located, respectively, at the north end and south end of the Bitterroot Range. Both trails follow ridges. Lewis and Clark in 1805 crossed Idaho by the Lolo trail after failing to force a passage down the Salmon River Valley.[3]

Local prominences rise above the general level, either unconsumed hills on an old erosion surface or perhaps (in some cases) due to recent faulting. Several areas contain peaks above 11,000 ft. Most points above 8,000 ft. in elevation were centers

[1] LINDGREN, W., U. S. Geol. Survey, 20*th Ann. Rept.*, pt. III, p. 78, states that "the whole mountain region should probably be regarded as a vast plateau separated from the Snake River Plains by fault lines." In U. S. Geol. Survey, 18*th Ann. Rept.*, pt. III, p. 629, he describes the even granite crests as declining gradually from 9,000 ft. to 4,000 ft. and then descending with a steeper slope below the Tertiary rocks of the plateau; RICH, JOHN L., *Econ. Geol.*, vol. XIII, 1918, states that the old erosion surface in the mountains is continuous with that on the plateau. This involves the physiographic history of the region to be referred to later.

[2] UMPLEBY, J B., U. S. Geol. Survey, *Bull.* 539, p. 15, 1913.

[3] LINDGREN, W., U. S. Geol. Survey, *Prof. Pap.* 27, p. 9, 1904; and UMPLEBY, J. B., *Bull.* 528, p. 17, 1913.

of Pleistocene glaciation.   In the Sawtooth and other high divides this was severe.   Glacial features descend to 7,000 ft. in the Wood River Basin on the southern margin, and to lower and lower levels farther west, reaching down to 5,000 ft. in the valleys on the western side of the mountains.   This difference in elevation is to be expected, in view of the fact that the snows, accountable for the glaciers, came from the west.

Valleys.—Most of the valleys are narrow gorges, those of the main streams being 3,000 to 5,000 ft. deep, often too narrow and rugged to follow and so steep as to be difficult or impossible to cross.   As late as 1904 the Salmon River was crossed by only one wagon road in 130 miles.[1]   The central portion of the Clearwater Mountains is described as "a labyrinth of forested ridges, sloping gradually at first toward the canyons and then dropping off in precipitous descents."   Here and there are narrow gravel terraces, fragments of valley trains due to glaciation.   Other terraces, cut in the rock, are likewise generally narrow and interrupted and more familiar in the northern part of the area than elsewhere.   Still others, in the northern part, are of sediments believed to have been deposited in lakes caused by the obstruction of the valleys by the lavas that built the Columbia Plateau.   The arrest of down-cutting would at the same time cause the streams to cut laterally and make rock terraces.[2]

A few exceptional features of drainage deserve notice.   The Sawtooth Range divides the headwaters of the Boise and Payette Rivers on the west from those of the Salmon on the east.   The former are deeply incised and rapidly cutting down; the latter for some distance have perhaps the gentlest gradients in the region.   This contrast should be thought of in connection with the westward tilt of the old surface whereby the profiles of west-flowing streams were steepened and those of east-flowing streams flattened.   The Salmon, moreover, follows a very circuitous course to reach the Snake which is not far off by way of the Boise.   The west-flowing streams are therefore constantly capturing new territory and shifting the divide eastward.[3]

[1] LINDGREN, W., *loc. cit.*, p. 14.

[2] On the terracing of these valleys, involving in some cases four or five terraces, see HERSHEY, OSCAR H., Some Tertiary and Quaternary Geology of Western Montana, Northern Idaho and Eastern Washington, Geol. Soc. Amer. *Bull.*, vol. 23, pp. 517–536; also abstract in same volume, p. 75, 1912; see also LINDGREN, W., *loc. cit.*, pp. 26–27.

[3] LINDGREN, W., U. S. Geol. Survey, 18*th Ann. Rept.*, pt. III. p. 629, 1907.

Basins.—Though the valleys of this region are generally of the canyon type some of them broaden locally into basins from 5 to 15 miles wide, several of these basins being almost as wide as long. Most of these are floored with Quaternary deposits and several of them partly filled with Tertiary sediments. Among the best known of these valleys are the Idaho Basin,[1] probably in part diastrophic, lying east of Boise Ridge, and containing Idaho City; Smith Prairie on the South Fork of the Boise, 30 miles east of Boise, 8 to 10 miles in diameter; and

Fig. 72.—Beaverhead Range from the southwest. The range is on the Idaho-Montana boundary. The plain in the foreground is the floor of the Lemhi Valley (page 222). The smooth crest of the range represents the summit peneplain and the base of the range is marked by a fault which may antedate the peneplain. In that case the valley is due to post-peneplain erosion as explained on page 195, Fig. 73B. (*Photo by Atwood.*)

another on the Payette, 20 miles north of Boise, 5 miles by 10 and probably due to erosion. The Salmon River above Shoup (where the deep continuous gorge begins), runs through a series of such basins separated by canyons.[2] The first is at the east foot of the Sawtooth, perhaps a Pleistocene lake bed 40 miles long and 6 or 8 miles wide, with an altitude of less than 5,000 ft. and bordered on the west by enormous moraines from the Sawtooth. At Challis on the same river is a similar basin 10 to 15 miles in diameter, with arms extending 10 to 15 miles up tributary

[1] LINDGREN, W., *loc. cit.*, p. 625.

[2] Most of these basins are mentioned by Geo. H. Eldridge, U. S. Geol. Survey, 16*th Ann. Rept.*, pt. II, pp. 220–223, 1895.

streams. Its rich alluvial lands are on a floor of Quaternary gravel. A similar basin occurs at the junction of the Pahsimeroi and Salmon.   Prairie Basin, 15 to 20 miles west of the Salmon River and just south of the 45th parallel, is an intermontane valley believed to be deeply filled with glacial deposits.

At Salmon and extending up the Lemhi Valley is a larger basin, flat and fertile, with an area of 250 to 300 square miles. This basin is cut deep in Tertiary rocks which themselves partly fill a much greater and deeper valley.   The steep-walled valley is drained to the northwest by Lemhi Creek, but the valley is continuous to the southeast with that of Birch Creek, the steep walls of the former being continuous with those of the latter. The divide between these two streams (lat. 44°30′) seems to have been determined by the up-warp of the old surface now indicated by the crest levels (see page 222).[1]

The long troughs just mentioned are due ultimately to diastrophism, though the country has since passed through at least one erosion cycle and the present valleys are mainly erosional. The origin of some others of these basins is undetermined. A few seem to be satisfactorily explained by erosion alone but the nearly uniform character of the rocks limits the application of this explanation.   Some of the basins are plainly associated with crustal movements, yet a nearly circular basin is not apt to be caused in that way.   It may well be that different basins have different origins.   Yet the analogy of the Tertiary lake basins of Montana, which are due mainly to diastrophism, favors the supposition that crustal movement had much to do with these (see page 221).

Physiographic History

Order of Events on First Hypothesis.—Necessarily the intrusion of the great batholith and the elevation both of it and of the rest of the region antedates any land forms now in existence. Deep erosion and ultimate peneplaning followed.   To trace the exact course of events leads quickly into controversy, the main

---

[1] It is assumed by J. B. Umpleby, U. S. Geol. Survey, *Bull.* 528, pp. 23 and 26, that the entire valley once drained to the southeast and that the northwest-flowing Lemhi has resulted from the warping of the former surface.   V. D. Kirkham, on the other hand, finds evidence that the early Tertiary streams flowed north almost from the edge of the Mountain province; Idaho Bur. Mines and Geol. *Pamphlet* 19, p. 11, 1927.

point at issue being whether the peneplain was made before the existing basins or later. The former supposition is the older and perhaps more common assumption. On this assumption the order of events was as follows: (1) The region was uplifted before any existing land forms were made. (2) It was reduced by erosion to low relief called, for convenience, a "peneplain." (3) The peneplain was elevated, much as at present, and dissected by the present valleys. Whatever marginal flexures or faults now outline the mountain province were made presumably during this elevation though possibly started earlier.[1] (4) Floods of lava built the Columbia Plateau on the west, rising against the mountain spurs and invading the valleys, damming the outflowing rivers, causing lakes in which sediments were deposited. The retarded streams, either above the sites of such lakes or, later, wandering over the sediments that filled their basins, cut laterally into the steep valley sides making occasional rock terraces which may have been veneered with river gravels. (5) In time the streams carved gorges in the lava plateau, again lowering their downstream courses and restoring their cutting power in the mountains. (6) Most of the deposits made in the mountain valleys during the interruption were cleaned out and erosion of the bedrock again started. (7) Glaciation of the higher mountains caused valley trains, at places 300 ft. deep. (8) In post-glacial time the valley trains have been largely removed and erosion of bedrock is again in progress, although it is believed that not much headway has been made in deepening the valleys since the lava flows occurred.

Origin of Basins.—The assumed history of the broad basins may best be given separately. If made by faulting or warping, these events may have accompanied the uplift of the peneplain. If made by erosion[2] they were (according to this hypothesis) made after the uplift. In either case some of them were deeply, although perhaps not wholly, filled with Miocene sediments which in some cases were deformed by still later folding, after which their surface was much lowered by erosion while the surrounding mountains of hard rock retained their height. It is primarily the Miocene age of these sediments which led to the assignment

[1] MANSFIELD, GEO. R., reviews the history of the Snake River Valley, so far as known, in U. S. Geol. Survey, *Prof. Pap.* 152, pp. 359–361, 1927.

[2] UMPLEBY, JOS. B., Geology and Ore Deposits of Lemhi County, Idaho, U. S. Geol. Survey, *Bull.* 528, p. 26, 1913.

of the peneplain to the Eocene, though the conclusion is supported by analogy from British Columbia and by the relations of the Miocene lavas of the Columbia Plateau to the valleys of the mountain border on the west.[1]

Order of Events on Second Hypothesis.—It is not to be supposed that this hypothetical history presents no difficulties. If the broad basins were made by erosion the question is raised how a few valleys came to be so exceptionally wide while the great majority are still gorges. If the Miocene sediments in one of these basins were made and folded since the peneplain, why has the peneplain itself escaped serious deformation? These questions and others are raised by Blackwelder, who presents an alternative hypothesis.[2] This assumes (1) that the broad valleys, whatever their origin, existed before the peneplaning, (2) that they were filled with weak Tertiary sediments, (3) that the peneplain was developed on all rocks, strong and weak alike (except for its imperfections), and (4) that differential erosion after uplift again revealed the basins by partly or wholly removing the weak sediments. According to this hypothesis the age of the peneplain is probably Pliocene.

Between the two hypotheses here presented no dogmatic decision is now possible[3] but evidence in favor of a Pliocene peneplain, at least in the southern part of the mountain area, continues to accumulate. The disagreement would be much reduced by assuming that the divides in northern Idaho represent

---

[1] LINDGREN, W., The Idaho Peneplain, *Econ. Geol.*, vol. XIII, p. 486, 1918.

[2] BLACKWELDER, ELIOT, The Old Erosion Surface in Idaho, a Criticism, *Jour. Geol.*, vol. XX, pp. 410–414, 1912.

[3] No attempt is made here even to mention all the pertinent points that have been raised. The whole discussion down to 1924 is satisfactorily summarized by George R. Mansfield in *Jour. Geol.*, vol. XXXII, pp. 472–487, 1924. He does not undertake a final decision but does not find the later hypothesis proved for the area in which he worked, *i.e.*, southeastern Idaho. The following papers, beside personal communications, are cited:

UMPLEBY, J. B., *Jour. Geol.*, vol. XX, pp. 139–147, 1912.
BLACKWELDER, ELIOT, *ibid.*, pp. 410–414.
UMPLEBY, J. B., *ibid.*, vol. XXI, pp. 224–231, 1913.
ATWOOD, W. W., *Econ. Geol.*, vol. XI, pp. 697–740, 1916.
BLACKWELDER, ELIOT, *ibid.*, vol. XII, pp. 541–545, 1917.
ATWOOD, W. W., *ibid.*, pp. 545–547.
RICH, J. L., *ibid.*, vol. XIII, pp. 120–136, 1918.
LINDGREN, W., discussion, *ibid.*, pp. 486–488.
LIVINGSTON, D. C., discussion, *ibid.*, pp. 488–492.

an older peneplain than the one recognized farther south. It is in northern Idaho that the (presumably) Miocene lavas of the Columbia Plateau invade the mountain valleys like an encroach-

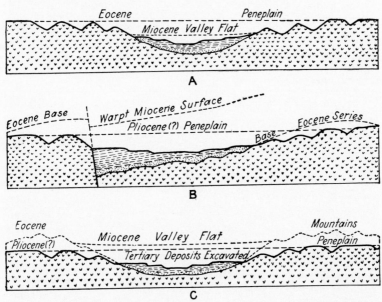

Fig. 73.—Hypotheses of Tertiary peneplanation in Idaho. (*After Blackwelder.*)

A. An Eocene plain cut across folded Cretaceous and older rocks. Later, broad and deep valleys were excavated and then partly filled with Oligocene and Miocene sediments. In still more recent time streams have partly dissected the filling (essentially Mr. Atwood's conception).

B. An early Tertiary surface, either plain or hilly, on which a thick series of Tertiary sediments was deposited. Afterward the region was gently folded and faulted so that the Tertiary beds were left alternately above and below base level. In post-Miocene times a period of comparative quiescence permitted the cutting of a plain over the entire district, but some of the weak Tertiary deposits were preserved because they were far below base level. In consequence of a later uplift streams rapidly excavated and planed the Tertiary deposits down to a new base level and at the same time carved canyons and ravines in the harder rocks adjacent.

C. A broad, deep valley was excavated early in the Tertiary period and then more or less completely filled with Oligocene and Miocene deposits. The region was thereafter reduced to a peneplain, but a part of the Tertiary deposits were so far below base level that they could not be removed. Subsequent rejuvenation of the region permitted the streams to trench the Tertiary beds quickly and reduce them to a new plain, while the harder rocks adjacent were carved into mature topography with occasional remnants of the peneplain. On this hypothesis deformation of any kind is eliminated.

ing sea, affording the strongest evidence for the greater age of the mountain topography. Quite independently of this fact Kirkham finds in the topography itself evidence of two peneplains in the northern area, both distinctly older than the one whose remnants survive farther south.[1]

RESOURCES OF THE IDAHO MOUNTAINS

The resources of the Salmon River, Clearwater, and Coeur D'Alene Mountains consist of their minerals, forests, water power, grazing lands, and soils. The precious metals have been mined with more or less success for many years. No very great

FIG. 74.—View north over the Coeur D'Alene Mountains near Wardner, Idaho. This is an important mining district. The mountains are seen to be the result of dissection of a plateau-like uplift. (*U. S. Geol. Survey.*)

camp has been developed, although the Coeur D'Alene district furnishes one-third the lead of the United States. The mountains are well forested except the highest peaks or ridges. The lumber industry is fairly active in the mountains surrounding

[1] KIRKHAM, V. D., personal communication. In *Pamphlet* 19, Idaho Bur. Mines and Geol., pp. 11–13, Kirkham adds his testimony to the Pliocene age of the peneplain on the borders of the Snake River down-warp.

C. P. Ross concludes from his field studies that the region between the Salmon River and the Snake River Plain was virtually peneplaned both before and after the period of Tertiary vulcanism, presumably Miocene, the earlier peneplain being sharply incised by valleys before the volcanic eruptions (Wash. Acad. Sci. *Jour.*, vol. XVIII, p. 268, 1928). For older peneplains see ANDERSON, A. L., Cretaceous and Tertiary Planation in Northern Idaho, *Jour. Geol.*, vol. XXXVII, pp. 747–764, 1929.

Coeur D'Alene and Pend Oreille Lakes. The intermont basins have considerable areas of fertile soil. So also have the river valleys like those of the Wood and others on the southern margin which broaden in the mountains as they approach the Plateau province. In these areas both climate and soil favor the common crops and orchard fruits of northern United States. The volume of the streams is sufficient to irrigate large areas and afford vast water power. The abundant grasslands supply hay and pasture. Sheep are herded in great numbers in some valleys.

These resources are attractive but, except for the forests, they concern but a small fraction of the vast area which is mainly a wilderness. In 1904 Lindgren wrote of the Clearwater Mountains as viewed from Bald Mountain near the western edge, it is "a wild and lonely country with not a settlement or even miner's cabin in the first 80 miles, while to the west, 4,000 ft. below, is the undulating plateau of Camas and Kamiah prairies checkered with fields of waving wheat or wild grass." Most of the area is embraced in government forests and, so far as can be foreseen, should form one of the chief permanent forests of the United States.

BITTERROOT MOUNTAINS

Topography.—The Bitterroot Range is part of the compact mountain mass of Idaho mountains and inseparable from the Clearwater, but, being a linear range, in some ways distinct in character, it requires separate description. The mountains between Lolo Pass on the north and Nez Perce Pass on the south (page 187) rise rather abruptly from 1,000 to 3,000 ft. above their neighbors on the west and 5,000 to 6,000 ft. above the Bitterroot Valley on the east. An altitude of about 9,000 ft. above sea-level is fairly constant among the higher peaks and crests, but the height increases toward the south where Trapper Peak rises to 10,175 ft. The "saddles" or passes between these peaks are generally between 7,000 and 7,500 ft. high.

These mountains, while not remarkable for great height, are among the most characteristically alpine of the United States. Everywhere the effects of alpine glaciation are prominent. What with precipitous cirque and valley walls at high levels, swamps in U-shaped valleys, and a close-set jungle of pine and underbrush in the gorges, the region is all but impassable. A single safe but very difficult horse trail crosses the range, or did in 1904.[1]

[1] LINDGREN, W., U S. Geol. Survey, *Prof. Pap.* 27, p. 41.

The contrast is striking between the snow fields and serrated peaks of the Bitterroots on the one hand and the monotonous, heavily timbered ridges of the mountains to the west not 2,000 ft. lower.   The general accordance of summit levels in the Bitterroots is very marked[1] and suggests that they have been carved from an uplifted surface which was not far from a plane.

On the western side of the range the summit levels of the Bitterroot descend within a few miles, generally not more than 10 or 15, to the general level of the crests of the Clearwater Mountains, which in its eastern part is generally between 7,000

FIG. 75.—View southwest from Hamilton, Montana, showing the floor of Bitterroot Valley and the smooth front of the Bitterroot Range.   See Fig. 76 for explanation.   (*U. S. Geol. Survey.*)

and 8,000 ft., rarely more than the latter.   The western side of the Bitterroot Range is marked by deep, strongly glaciated, U-shaped valleys which merge into the V-shaped canyons of the Clearwater at the lower limit of glaciation.   Between these valleys are serrate spurs whose pointed crags have a rough agreement in altitude.

Eastern Slope.—The eastern slope of the range is in a large way almost a plane, inclined at an angle ranging from 18 to 26 deg.[2]   It has the appearance of having once been a perfect

[1] *Idem*, pls. VII B and VIII A.

[2] LINDGREN, W., *loc. cit.*, pls. I, II, III, and IV; see also U. S. Geol. Survey, topographic map of the Hamilton, Montana, quadrangle.

inclined plane, scored later by 20 or more consequent streams which now descend the slope in nearly parallel gorges (Fig. 75). The upper portions of these gorges are, as might be expected, thoroughly glaciated and often typically U-shaped.[1] The lower unglaciated portions are V-shaped and apparently very young.

Both structural and physiographic evidence indicates that this eastern slope is a fault scarp (or fault-line scarp) whose present inclination is essentially that of the fault plane itself (Fig. 76). This plane is exposed in a horizontal belt four miles wide, the height of the slope being 4,000 to 6,000 ft. It is not

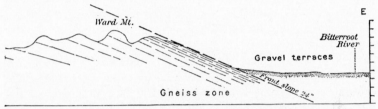

Fig. 76.—Diagram of the front of the Bitterroot Range. It is generally agreed that the foot of the range marks the position of a great fault, and that the mountain front corresponds more or less closely with the fault plane. If the scarp be in its first cycle of erosion the down-throw is necessarily on the east, the last movement being so recent that the lower part of the slope is almost untouched by erosion. If it be assumed that the fault scarp is in its second cycle the fault may have been a thrust, by means of which weak Tertiary beds on the east were brought into contact with the strong gneiss on the west. It must then be assumed that the weak beds were eroded, and the gneissic block stripped, so rapidly that the lower part of the slope is not yet altered by erosion. (*After Lindgren, U. S. Geol. Survey.*)

to be assumed that the range is a simple tilted block with a dip slope to the west. That would scarcely be consistent with a fault dipping east at so low an angle. It is more likely raised above the Clearwater Mountains by faulting as it is from the valley on the east.[2] The language here used, following custom, assumes that the mountains and the fault scarp are in their first cycle of erosion. Consideration must also be given to the hypothesis that the fault is old and the topographic features in their second cycle (see Fig. 76). In that case it is quite as

---

[1] This is a technical expression, not to be taken too literally. The typical glacial trough is wider at the top than at the bottom. Its cross-section does not have the parallel sides of the letter "U." Davis has suggested the term "catenary" (the form of a loose chain held by the ends) but it has not come into general use.

[2] LINDGREN, W., *loc. cit.*, p. 49.

likely that the fault is a thrust with upthrow on the East.   It is so mapped and interpreted by Flint.[1]

The upper portion of the eastward-sloping mountain face was necessarily exposed first, whether by faulting or erosion. Consequent streams began there and were elongated downstream as the displacement or erosion increased.   Hence it is in the upper portion that the valleys are oldest and deepest.   The effect of this excess of cutting in the upper portions, emphasized by glacial erosion, has been to carry the main divide westward and down the west slope of the mountain block.   This explains why the highest peaks of the Bitterroot are not on the main divide but on the spurs east of it, in one case as much as 10 miles.

The lower ends of the valleys descending the east slope are so young as to indicate that the valley is still deepening.   Near the foot of the slope these valleys are separated by facets of the faulting plane, but little eroded.   Moreover, some of these valleys have a higher gradient near the foot than farther up.

MOUNTAINS OF THE CANADIAN BORDER

GENERAL STATEMENT

Internal Boundaries.—From the Great Plains on the east to Puget Sound on the west, the International Boundary traverses a maze of mountains almost unrelieved by broad valleys. Several ranges on the east are exceptional in their linear form and jagged crests, but west of that the type is mainly that described on page 183, although continuity is not so remarkable as in central Idaho.   There has been much confusion in dividing this great mass and in naming its several parts.   Daly has undertaken to introduce system and order[2] and he seems to be generally followed except in the use (in the United States) of the term "Rocky Mountains."

As these mountains cannot be divided into structural units and all have nearly the same character, certain valleys have been selected as lines of division.   These valleys are chosen for their continuity rather than their breadth, although several of them

[1] FLINT, RICHARD FOSTER, A Brief View of Rocky Mountain Structure. *Jour. Geol.*, vol. XXXII, pp. 410–431, 1924.

[2] DALY, REGINALD A., The Nomenclature of the North American Cordillera between the 47th and 53d Parallels of Latitude, *Geogr. Jour.*, vol. XXVII, pp. 586–606, 1906; also Geology of the North American Cordillera at the 49th Parallel, Can. Geol. Survey, *Mem.* 38, 1912.

are locally expanded. At least two of these are continuous beyond the basin of any one stream, their several parts being drained in opposite directions. Such continuous topographic depressions are called *trenches*. The continuity of such trenches is in part structural but was made more perfect by glacial erosion which lowered the divides between streams that are in headwater opposition. Four great valleys, two of them classed as trenches, are of the first rank.

The Rocky Mountain Trench, only 60 miles from the Great Plains, is probably the greatest of its kind in the world (see Fig. 69, page 184). It extends 800 miles northwestward from Flathead Lake in Montana and is drained by eight different streams. Alternate streams flow northwest and the others southeast. With a different character the depression is continued directly south another 150 miles by the Flathead and Bitterroot Valleys. The Kootenai River in its southward course occupies the trench at the International Boundary.

Sixty-five miles to the west along the 49th parallel is the similar Purcell Trench, which here carries the waters of the Kootenai northward. These two trenches intersect about 200 miles north of the International Boundary. In line with the Purcell Trench extended southward is the valley which contains Lakes Pend Oreille and Coeur D'Alene.[1]

The headwaters of the Columbia River are in the Rocky Mountain Trench which it leaves at about the 52d parallel, flowing south in an almost straight line to the Columbia Plateau in Washington, crossing the International Boundary about 50 miles west of the Purcell Trench. For the purpose here in hand this part of the Columbia's valley is called the "Selkirk Valley."[2] Eighty miles west of the Selkirk Valley is the broad valley of the lower Okanogan, west of which are the Cascade Mountains.

The great valleys and trenches here named outline the larger units of the Northern Rocky Mountain province near the Canadian border. Daly would use the term "Rocky Mountains"

[1] The southward extensions of the Rocky Mountain and Purcell Trenches are suggested by F. C. Calkins in U. S. Geol. Survey, *Bull.* 334, 1909.

[2] An almost straight north-south valley occupied by the lower Kettle River and Christina Lake just west of the 118th meridian would cut off an eastward detour of the Columbia River which embraces the Rossland Mountains just north of the 49th parallel. Daly points this out (*Mem.* 38, p. 40) but prefers to use the actual course of the Columbia River to separate the main mountain groups.

for the ranges between the Great Plains and the Rocky Mountain Trench and no others.[1]　West of them are the Purcell Mountains extending to the Purcell Trench, and west of them the Selkirk Mountains extending to the Selkirk Valley.　The term "Columbia Mountain System" is proposed by Daly for the mountains between the Selkirk and Okanogan Valleys.　Pardee states that these mountains are known as the Okanogan Highlands.　This would bring the naming of this group into harmony with that of the other three, each of which bears the name of the trench or valley on the west.[2]

In addition to the four valleys of the first order, seven others are designated as boundaries.　Together, these divide the province into 12 north-south strips each with its own name. Most of the strips are marked by a north-south line of higher mountains, called a "range."　The difference between these mountains and those of central Idaho is not so great as might be inferred from this statement.　Most of the dividing valleys are gorge-like.　Except for the two main trenches, the spaces between the "ranges" are occupied, mainly, not by valleys, but by other mountains a little lower and of essentially the same character. Everywhere, except on the eastern margin, accordance of summit levels prevails.

Rocks and Structure.—The exact physiographic history of these mountains and their relation to structural deformation are not wholly clear, but the following facts are apparent from Daly's maps and cross-sections.[3]

The strong metamorphosed beds of the Belt series east of the Purcell Trench are moderately folded and closely faulted along north-south lines.　From the Purcell Trench almost to Clark Fork (just west of the Idaho-Washington boundary) the closely compressed and highly metamorphosed paleozoic rocks are almost vertical and north-south faults are not noted.　West of that, abundant intrusives and volcanic rocks have complicated or obscured the folding so that outcrops are in irregular patches

[1] This is not necessarily inconsistent with the use of the term "Northern Rocky Mountain *province*" to designate a wider area, since any large area may receive its name from certain characteristic features within it.　It is doubtful, however, whether a geographic name whose application has once been broadened by custom can again be restricted to a narrow meaning.

[2] PARDEE, J. T., Geology and Mineral Resources of the Colville Indian Reservation, U. S. Geol. Survey, *Bull.* 677, p. 14, 1918.

[3] DALY, R. A., *loc. cit.*, vol. III, maps.

instead of north-south belts. None the less, meridional valleys prevail through the entire extent, though they are more widely spaced in the western part where north-south structural elements are not now apparent.

East of Purcell Trench, where faulting abounds, there is no evident correlation between past crustal movements and present altitude. Roughly speaking the ranges are outlined by faults

FIG. 77.—Looking east over the heavily wooded mountains of the Nelson Range west of the Purcell Trench, north of the 49th parallel. These mountains have been carved from an elevated peneplain and overridden later by the Cordilleran ice sheet. The rocks are conglomerates, quartzites, schists, and other strong rocks greatly deformed and standing at high angles. (*International Boundary Commission, Department of the Interior, Canada.*)

but they seem to be independent of upthrow and downthrow. The relation to folding is equally obscure. At least one mountain is synclinal and a number are monoclinal but the rocks (west of the front ranges) are so nearly equal in resistance that no extensive correlation has been made out between altitude and resistance of beds to erosion. The larger number of prominent streams follow fault lines. To what extent they took these courses by following structural depressions and to what extent they have subsequently followed faults as lines of weakness is undetermined.

Physiographic History.—The great majority of geologists would interpret the forms of these mountains as involving at least two cycles of erosion, one to make the imperfect peneplain and another to carve the valleys after uplift. It may readily be assumed that uplift was unequal and that near the eastern margin (Clarke and Lewis Ranges) it was so great that all vestiges of the peneplain have been destroyed (*cf.* Figs. 77 and 78). It is well known that a two-cycle history involves adjustment of drainage to rock structure, streams following the weaker rocks so far as possible. Throughout most of the area the differences in resistance are so small that the absence of adjustment does not greatly embarrass the theory. In the front ranges, however, such contrasts are significant. The imperfection of adjustment there is not satisfactorily explained.[1]

As opposed to the two-cycle explanation Daly presents the hypothesis that the mountains were made by a single uplift and have never been peneplaned but that, in the process of wearing down, the more rapid degradation of the higher parts has resulted in approximate equality of ridge heights. The essentials of this hypothesis are: (1) that on account of isostasy and concurrent erosion, mountains are raised with increasing difficulty beyond a certain level; (2) that wasting becomes increasingly rapid with increase of altitude. Above the level where trees stop and glacial cirques form it is believed that the destructive agencies are at least several times more efficient than immediately below that level.[2]

This theory assumes that the present mountains are the remains of those which were raised by the folding and faulting, presumably in the Laramide revolution. Minor uplifts are assumed but do not affect the theory. It is also assumed that streams have in the main inherited their courses from those originally chosen along structural depressions.

Since, with respect to accordance of summit levels, this area is part of a vast region extending far to the south where the hypothesis of peneplaning is satisfactory and no other has been

[1] *Idem*, pp. 603 and 609.

[2] DALY, R. A., The Accordance of Summit Levels among Alpine Mountains, *Jour. Geol.*, vol. XIII, pp. 110–125, 1905; also Can. Geol. Survey, *Mem.* 38.

considered, it seems best to use the assumptions and the terminology of the two-cycle hypothesis in describing the Canadian border.

RANGES EAST OF THE ROCKY MOUNTAIN TRENCH

Ranges in Glacier National Park.—The Lewis Range is the front range in northern Montana, extending south to the Blackfoot River (lat. 47°). Its best known portion is the 50-mile stretch between the Canadian border and the Great Northern

Fig. 78.—Looking east across Flathead Valley fault trough to the Clarke Range just north of the International Boundary and of Glacier National Park. Dissection by glaciers is the principal process suggested by the mountain forms. Contrary to the general rule in the Northern Rocky Mountains there is here no general level to which crests rise and no suggestion of an even-topped mass from which the mountains have been carved. (*International Boundary Commission, Department of the Interior, Canada.*)

Railroad. Here Glacier National Park embraces the mountains east of the upper Flathead Valley, a strip about 20 miles wide which includes also the Clarke Range eight miles west of the Lewis and so closely related that the two are only locally distinguished.[1] Both ranges have craggy peaks reaching altitudes

---

[1] Willis called this range Livingston because of its continuity with the Canadian range of that name. For various reasons (see Can. Geol. Survey, *Mem.* 38, p. 28) Daly has substituted the name Clarke. Lewis and Clarke in their expedition of 1803–6 are believed to have been the first white men to visit these ranges.

from 8,000 to more than 10,000 ft., or 2,000 to 3,000 ft. above the tree line (Fig. 78). The peaks are separated by U-shaped passes as low as 5,500 to 6,500 ft. above the sea. The ranges themselves are here separated by a deep and continuous valley draining north and south from the middle. The level of Waterton Lake (4,186 ft.) on the north-flowing stream is lower than that of the Great Plains (5,000 ft.). Flathead Valley on the west is still lower (3,500 ft. at the Canadian boundary).

This double line of mountains is remarkable both for its structure and for its erosional features. The whole is a synclinal block, each limb cut off by a steep outer face, the two ranges being formed by the upturned edges of the strata, dipping generally from 5 to 30 deg. toward the central trough. The entire block constituting the mountain ranges has been pushed eastward by one of the greatest thrust faults known. The Algonkian dolomites, quartzites, and slates, which constitute the mountains, have been pushed out over the Cretaceous shales which underlie the plains. The thrust plane is almost horizontal, being nowhere seen to dip more than 10 deg. It can be traced for seven miles[1] in the direction of thrusting, but the extent of the thrust was much greater because the overthrust block has wasted by erosion. There is clear evidence that the thrust was at least 15 miles and it may have been much greater.[2] The vertical component of this faulting is several thousand feet.

This great thrust block, consisting of moderately dipping strata, is given a steep easterly face by sapping. As the underlying weak Cretaceous shales are eroded away, the stronger rocks above break off and the escarpment retreats. The mountain front is deeply scalloped by narrow bays heading in branching canyons whose walls, some of them nearly 5,000 ft. high, rise close to the crest of the Lewis Range. Intervening promontories rise boldly 3,000 to 4,000 ft. above the Great Plains. There are also outlying remnants.

The scenery of these mountains is closely related to its structure. The so-called "architectural effects" in scenery are commonly associated with beds alternately hard and soft, and either horizontal or dipping but moderately. The effect is

---

[1] WILLIS, BAILEY, Stratigraphy and Structure of the Lewis and Livingston Ranges, Montana, Geol. Soc. Amer. *Bull.*, vol. 13, p. 307, 1902.

[2] CAMPBELL, M. R., The Glacier National Park, a Popular Guide to Its Geology and Scenery, U. S. Geol. Survey, *Bull.* 600, p. 12, 1914.

heightened if the beds are distinctly jointed. These conditions are quite as significant in the erosive work of ice as in normal erosion. It is largely to a favorable combination of such conditions that the mountains of Glacier National Park owe their exceptional scenery.

Vigorous alpine glaciation (Fig. 79) has left craggy peaks of great height and steepness, cirques with almost vertical walls several thousand feet high, U-shaped valleys, knife-edge aretes,

Fig. 79.—Scene in Glacier National Park showing Grinnell Lake and Glacier. The gentle dip of the rocks is well shown. The glacier occupies a cirque whose walls were made almost vertical and caused to retreat by plucking at the base. The same is true of the two nearly vertical drops in the valley, one partly hidden by the ice, the other behind the lake. The pyramidal form of the mountains at the left is very characteristic, their steep faces being the sides of glacial troughs. The ridge behind the glacier, known as the Garden Wall, is a typical alpine comb or "arete" left between expanding cirques on both sides. (*Cf.* Fig. 60, page 163.) The lake basin was gouged out by the glacier at a time of greater extent. (*Copyright by Fred H. Kiser.*)

lakes in rocky basins, and lakes held by morainic dams. The features of the Clarke Range are similar but the crags are less steep. A considerable number of glaciers remain to the present time. Although much reduced in size their work of sculpturing the mountains is still in progress and may be studied to advantage.[1]

Nothing here suggests an ancient physiographic history or a second cycle. Not only are there no remnants of a former plane

[1] ALDEN, WM. C., Glaciers of Glacier National Park, U. S. Dept. Int., 1914.

surface; there is even no accordance of summit levels, although Willis believes that such accordance might appear along lines of strike by undoing the effects of recent warping.

The upper Flathead Valley is a straight, open valley five to eight miles wide, underlain in part by Miocene beds and partly filled by glacial deposits. It is drained by a copious south-flowing stream which, 40 miles south of the International Boundary, turns west through the next range of mountains to enter Flathead Lake in the Rocky Mountain Trench.

Galton and McDonald Ranges.—Between the upper Flathead Valley on the east and the Rocky Mountain Trench on the west is a belt of continuous mountains generally 6,000 to 7,000 ft. high. The highest summits are in two parallel lines near the east and west margins, known respectively as the Galton and McDonald Ranges. Both lines are on fault blocks but the relation of faulting to the relief is questionable.

These ranges resemble those to the east in their linear form but they lack some of the alpine features. The crests are generally accordant as in most of the mountains to the west and only a few of the highest points rise above the forests. The difference in scenery is in part due to rocks. Both are of pre-Cambrian sedimentaries[1] largely metamorphosed, but much greater contrasts of hard and soft beds are found in the Clarke and Lewis Ranges than anywhere to the west. The Galton-McDonald belt was plainly reduced to low relief (for short, a peneplain) in a former cycle. It is conceivable that the same peneplain covered the mountains to the east and that their present character is due mainly to greater elevation with the resulting increased erosion by water and ice.

Southward Extensions.—The description here given of ranges east of the Rocky Mountain Trench apply primarily to the mountains north of the Great Northern Railroad. Similar structures extend in range-like form, either continuous or *en echelon*, southeastward to the Blackfoot River in lat. 47°. The altitudes are similar and the effects of alpine glaciation are often striking although not equal to those in Glacier Park.[2] In line

---

[1] The U. S. Geol. Survey's geologic map of North America classifies them all as Algonkian. On the maps of the Canadian Geol. Survey, *Mem.* 38, most of them are classified as Cambrian.

[2] CHAPMAN, ROBT. H., Notes on the Structure of the Rocky Mountains in Lewis and Clarke Timber Reserve, Montana, *Trans.* Amer. Inst. Min.

with the Galton and McDonald Range is the Swan Range and west of that the Mission Range, apparently a fault block tilted east and carved into peaks and ridges of accordant height. The Cordilleran ice cap, having covered the low northern end of this range, thinned toward the south and came to an end leaving the high southern end free from the ice sheet (Fig. 80). It was high enough, however, to support alpine glaciers of its own.[1]

The Rocky Mountain Trench at and south of the International Boundary has a floor of small relief covered with glacial drift

Fig. 80.—Diagram of Mission Range, Montana, looking east. The higher southern end nourished vigorous alpine glaciers which plowed their troughs to the foot of the range. With diminishing altitude toward the north these features are less marked. The Kootenai-Flathead lobe of the Cordilleran ice sheet scoured the northern end of the range. Its terminal moraine lies against the range at the north but declines in altitude southward and swings across the plain enclosing Flathead Lake. Between glacial troughs the range is normally eroded. (*After Davis.*)

and alluvium. Tertiary sediments partly fill the valley around Flathead Lake. These cover a fault block (or blocks) downthrown on the east but upthrown (as shown in Daly's sections) with reference to the mountains on the west.

Mountains East of the Purcell Trench

Purcell Mountains.—The Purcell group embraces three of the minor ranges which cross the 49th parallel. The height of their accordant crests generally approximates 7,000 ft. Being thus below tree line they are monotonously covered with forest except for a few masses not reduced to the general level (maximum altitude 7,518 ft.). Because of approximate uniformity of strength of rocks the scenery is lacking in detail. They have

---

Eng., vol. XXIX, pp. 153–156, 1899. The cross-section given by Chapman shows folding and many faults; see also Bevan, Arthur, The Rocky Mountain Front in Montana; Geol. Soc. Amer. *Bull.*, vol. 40, pp. 427–456, 1929.

[1] Davis, W. M., The Mission Range, Montana, *Geogr. Rev.*, vol. II, pp. 267–288, 1916; also Features of Glacial Origin in Montana and Idaho, Assoc. Amer. Geogr. *Ann.*, vol. X, pp. 75–147, 1920. These two papers give a good general description of the physiography of the Flathead Valley and adjacent mountains.

none of the "architectural features" which characterize structures of alternating hard and soft beds, and which are so well
exemplified in the front ranges.   Moreover the features due to
alpine glaciation occur only on several high masses, most of the
rest having been overridden by the Cordilleran ice cap at least
as far south as the transverse gorge of the Kootenai (Fig. 81).

Cabinet Mountains.—South of the Kootenai Gorge are the
Cabinet Mountains which were not broadly covered by the ice
cap but whose lowest pass, the north-south valley in which is
Bull Lake, was occupied by a southward-moving tongue of the
Cordilleran ice.[1]   The topography of the Cabinet Mountains is
more like that of the Coeur D'Alene than like the rest of the
Purcell group.   In the middle portion of this range south of the
Kootenai Gorge is a considerable area of quartzitic rocks, together
with some granite rocks, never reduced to the prevailing summit
level (maximum altitude 8,500 to 9,000 ft.).   This high area
supported its own local glaciers and is now typically alpine.

Flathead Mountains.—Northeast of the Cabinet Range,
between it and the Rocky Mountain Trench, is the Flathead
Range which, like the Cabinet, is separated only by a gorge from
the Purcell Mountains proper.   The Flathead Mountains are
similar to the Purcell but more reduced.   Between them and the
Cabinet Range is a distinct depression with mildly hilly surface
dotted by many lakes, the result of the Cordilleran ice sheet which
covered the valley after passing over the Flathead Mountains.

Selkirk Mountains

The Selkirk Mountain System, very prominent in Canada,
extends south of the International Boundary a little more than
one degree of latitude to the Columbia Plateau.   It comes to an
end in the detached group of granite hills west of Lake Coeur
D'Alene.[2]   This system between the Purcell Trench and the
Columbia Valley is subdivided into three ranges by the valleys
of the Priest River and Clark Fork.[3]

The structure of the eastern half differs from that of the
mountains on either side.   Here, in addition to granite, are

---

[1] PARDEE, J. T., The Glacial Lake Missoula, *Jour. Geol.*, vol. XVIII,
p. 382, 1910.

[2] CALKINS, F. C., U. S. Geol. Survey, *Bull.* 384, p. 13, 1909.

[3] Sometimes called the Pend Oreille River after leaving Lake Pend
Oreille.

Paleozoic and perhaps older formations of great thickness and strength, conglomerates, quartzites, dolomites, schists, and phyllites, greatly compressed and metamorphosed. Vertical planes abound, some of them due to upturned bedding, some to schistosity.

Such is the substructure of the easternmost or Priest Range. Even in this the crests, now well above 7,000 ft., were reduced to accordant levels. On account of their altitude they failed to be covered by the Cordilleran ice cap but themselves became centers of alpine glaciation and were thus carved into the most rugged forms to be found between Glacier National Park and the Cascade Mountains. The Kaniksu Range on the Washington-Idaho boundary west of Priest Lake has the same structure but lacks the altitude and resulting alpine features.

The mountains west of Clark Fork, though members of the Selkirk system, are more like those of the Columbia system on the west and need not be described separately.

THE COLUMBIA SYSTEM

If the division of mountains on the Canadian border were made on the basis of structure instead of topographic continuity the area between Clark Fork and the Columbia would be allotted to the Columbia system instead of to the Selkirks. From long. 117°10′ westward, abundant intrusive and volcanic rocks have in large part masked the old north-south structural features which are believed to have prevailed and which still appear where the metamorphosed sediments are preserved and exposed. Considerable areas are occupied by batholiths now denuded of their former cover of sedimentaries whose north-south corrugations are believed to have imparted to the streams their meridional courses.[1] The north-south alignment of mountains continues west to the limit of the province, the chief valleys being those of the Columbia, Sanpoil and Okanogan.

[1] PARDEE, J. T., Geology and Mineral Resources of the Colville Indian Reservation, Washington, U. S. Geol. Survey, *Bull.* 677, p. 43, 1918. This paper is one of the chief sources of information on the area here described. Other papers dealing with smaller areas are:

UMPLEBY, J. B., Geol. and Ore Deposits of the Republic Mining District, Wash. Geol. Survey, *Bull.* 1, 1910; Geol. and Ore Deposits of the Myers Creek Mining District, Wash. Geol. Survey, *Bull.* 5, 1911; Geol. and Ore Deposits of the Oroville-Nighthawk Mining District, Wash. Geol. Survey, *Bull.* 5, 1911; see also DALY, R. A., Can. Geol. Survey, *Mem.* 38.

All these mountains are relatively low and of gentler slopes than those farther east.   Few ridges rise above 6,000 ft. and the areas above 5,000 ft. are not large.   The Cordilleran ice sheet was almost unbroken until it approached the Columbia River on

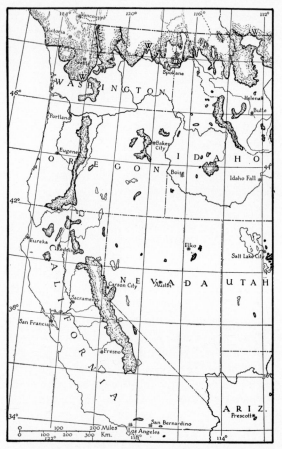

FIG. 81.—Extent of glaciation west of long. 112°.   Symbols *Ia* and *W* indicate Iowan and Wisconsin drift borders.   Mountain glaciation undifferentiated. (*Courtesy of Amer. Mus. Nat. History.*)

the south.   Moraines and lakes are prominent, though naturally in so mountainous a country the thickness of the drift varies greatly.   Valleys are terraced with the remains of valley trains and lake deposits.   Only in the irregular driftless margin on the south are soils derived from the underlying rocks.

There is here the same appearance of a summit peneplain as noted elsewhere but subsequent erosion has resulted in gentler slopes, probably because of lower stream gradients. Whatever the age of the peneplain elsewhere, Pardee found no surface in this area older than middle Tertiary.[1] Tertiary basins are found here both older and younger than the peneplain.

The mountain tops are generally forested but the valleys are grassed, being generally too dry for trees. Soils are fertile, and wheat and other field and garden products grow in the valleys. On the west side, even the lower uplands and mountains are sometimes cultivated, the rainfall there being sufficient for dry farming. Several mining districts produce the precious metals.

Near the Okanogan River and especially west of it the mountains or hills are distinctly lower although still of the same character, except for a valley flat several miles wide which declines to levels below 1,000 ft. Ten miles west of this river the Cascade Mountains rise abruptly to summit levels of about 8,000 ft.

MOUNTAINS OF SOUTHERN MONTANA

The mountains of Montana south of lat. 47° are divided into relatively small masses, mainly by the Tertiary basins to be described more fully later. The rocks lack the uniformity observed farther north and west, being of all ages from pre-Cambrian to Tertiary. In practically all of these ranges or mountain masses accordance of summit levels is prominent, although some carry peaks or ridges that were never reduced.[2]

MOUNTAINS BETWEEN BITTERROOT AND DEER LODGE VALLEYS

A large area south of Clark Fork and west of Anaconda has been studied chiefly because of the Philipsburg mining district near its center.[3] Between the parallel Bitterroot and Deer

[1] PARDEE, J. T., *loc. cit.*, p. 43. His statement is made with reference to the southern half only and is not meant to imply disbelief in the Eocene age of the peneplain elsewhere. Umpleby, working in the Republic district a few miles farther north, assumes the peneplain to be Eocene; Wash. Geol. Survey, *Bull.* 1, p. 12.

[2] ATWOOD, W. W., in his paper on Physiographic Conditions and Copper Enrichment, *Econ. Geol.*, vol. XI, pp. 697–740, 1916, describes topographic features and gives his interpretation of the physiographic history of this part of Montana; also many pictorial illustrations.

[3] EMMONS, W. H., and CALKINS, F. C., Geology and Ore Deposits of the Philipsburg Quadrangle, Montana, U. S. Geol. Survey, *Prof. Pap.* 78, 1913. This paper is the chief source of information on this district.

Lodge Valleys is that of Flint Creek. On the rocks of the Belt series west of this valley are the Sapphire Mountains which have the familiar dissected-plateau character with a summit level below 8,000 ft., few points rising above 8,500 ft. On the granite batholith and metamorphosed paleozoics east of the valley is the Flint Creek Range in which the level of accordant summits appears but locally, much of the crest rising above that level and showing the features of alpine glaciation. Transversely across the south end lies the Anaconda Range, the Continental Divide, with the city of Anaconda at its northeast end. Its rocks are granite and Algonkian sediments. Almost the entire crest is ruggedly alpine with many peaks above 10,000 ft., hence far above the horizon of the peneplain in neighboring mountains.

MOUNTAINS IN THE BEND OF BIG HOLE RIVER

South of the Anaconda Range is a roughly circular mass of mountains 30 to 40 miles in diameter within the bend of the Big Hole River. These mountains have been little studied and no official name is authorized.[1] Their rocks are granite and metamorphosed Paleozoics and they rise to altitudes above 9,000 ft., hence presumably embrace many ridges and peaks that were never reduced to the general level.

THE BUTTE-HELENA DISTRICT

The area to be described under this name extends west from the upper Missouri to Deer Lodge Valley (upper Clark Fork). It extends north to the valley of the Blackfoot (lat. 47°) and comes to a point at the south between two Tertiary troughs occupied, respectively, by the Jefferson and Big Hole Rivers. In large part this is the area of the Boulder batholith (commonly called the Butte granite, technically quartz monzonite) but there are also eruptives and some metamorphic sediments.

The Continental Divide traverses almost the entire length of this district, turning back to the northwest from its southern end, yet there is no linear range. The divide west of Helena is on the "deeply dissected plateau country" which is here a "broad, grassy, soil-covered axis" less than 7,000 ft. high.[2] North and east of Butte it is "a mountainous area having no commanding

[1] The name "Big Hole" is applied to the divide connecting these mountains with the Beaverhead Mountains on the Idaho-Montana boundary.

[2] BARRELL, JOSEPH, Geology of the Marysville Mining District, Montana, U. S. Geol. Survey, *Prof. Pap.* 57, p. 3, 1907

summits,"[1] but with a general level 7,000 to 8,000 ft. high. Here on the east slope of the Continental Divide is an old surface of deeply decayed granite remarkably free from rugged peaks, but the 1,000-ft. descent to the west into the valley of the Silver Bow Creek (city of Butte) is so steep that the railroad accomplishes it only by skirting the face of the escarpment for eight or nine miles. This scarp indicates a fault, one of the many in Montana which have been concerned in the making of the Tertiary valleys. Here there is reason to believe that faulting is still in progress.[2]

Here and there are exceptions to the general prevalence of flat summits or accordant ridge crests. The most conspicuous is found in the Highland Mountains, a small group 16 miles south of Butte. Here are alpine peaks rising to 10,000 ft.

The area here described is one of the greatest mining regions of the world. Butte has been the world's greatest copper camp. Helena and other centers have been prominent in the precious metals.

The east-west strip north of Clark Fork and south of the Blackfoot River, extending west to their junction, has in its eastern part, on Cretaceous rocks, a somewhat uniform summit level between 6,000 and 7,000 ft. high. West of the 113th meridian the upturned edges of Paleozoic limestones and quartzites give the mountains a more linear form and greater ruggedness. This is the Garnet Range.

THE THREE FORKS DISTRICT[3]

South of the Butte district and west of the Yellowstone River are the basins of three north-flowing streams that unite near Three Forks to form the Missouri. The intervening divides are known, respectively, as the Gallatin, Madison, and Jefferson Ranges, each range bearing the name of the stream on its west side.[4]

[1] WEED, W. H., Granite Rocks of Butte, Montana, and Vicinity, *Jour. Geol.*, vol. VII, p. 737, 1899; Butte Special, U. S. Geol. Survey, folio 38.

[2] CAMPBELL, M. R., Guidebook of the Western United States, U. S. Geol. Survey, *Bull.* 611, pp. 106–107; WEED, W. H., Shifting of the Continental Divide at Butte, Montana, Geol. Soc. Amer. *Bull.*, vol. 16, p. 587, 1905.

[3] For general description and discussion see Three Forks folio 24, U. S. Geol. Survey, 1896.

[4] These streams were reached by Lewis and Clarke in their westward journey in 1805. On receiving the news of Jefferson's reelection to the presidency they named the three streams in honor of the President, Secretary of State (James Madison) and Secretary of the Treasury (Albert Gallatin). See CAMPBELL, M. R., U. S. Geol. Survey, *Bull.* 611, p. 100.

Almost anywhere in these mountains a dominating level of summits may be observed, although it varies in altitude from place to place ranging from 7,000 to 10,000 ft. Higher masses (generally residual) also rise above it. The valleys, except the Tertiary basins, are generally canyons but in the southern part of the Madison Range these young valleys, carved since the last uplift, have not wholly destroyed the older, smoother, soil-covered surface with moderate slopes and small relief.[1] The surface of the Gallatin Range is exceptional, being largely of volcanic breccia. Whether its accordant crests are constructional or erosional is not determined.

The broad lowlands of this district are in Tertiary basins partly filled and then terraced during and since the glacial period. The present level of the rivers at their confluence is a little above 4,000 ft. Terraces at places rise as much as 1,000 ft. above the streams.

The structure of this region is very complex and the streams while trying to conform to some of its features, have had to defy others. The manner in which they have come to flow in their present courses has not been worked out in detail. Some of the major folding (presumably of the Laramide epoch) is along nearly north-south axes. In this it agrees with the main lines of Laramide deformation farther north. These lines are cut across by a great belt of Archean gneiss resembling the cores of many of the principal ranges produced in the Laramide epoch. This gneissic belt trends west-northwest, being apparently an extension of the Beartooth Range north of Yellowstone Park. Its direction is in harmony with that of all mountain structures to the east and southeast. This area, located at the intersection of north-south axes with nearly east-west axes, was therefore deformed in both directions, perhaps at the same time.

The upper portions of both the Gallatin and Madison Rivers, south of the transverse gneissic axis, follow anticlinal valleys. Such courses are assumed only after long-continued erosion and best of all on upraised peneplains. Both streams may have followed the slope of the peneplain, tilted toward what is now the Three Forks Basin, a center of depression in late Tertiary time. In case of the Madison, at least, the warping of the peneplain and aggradation of the Tertiary basin may have caused the crys-

---

[1] MANSFIELD, GEO. R., Unusual Type of Lateral Hanging Valley, Geog. Soc. Phila. *Bull.*, vol. IX, 1911.

talline barrier to be buried by sediments on which the river might be superimposed.

The Madison and Gallatin Mountains are in no proper sense linear ranges. Together they occupy an area that is almost square. The Archean axis lies across both ranges with no depression between them except the canyon of the Gallatin River. The Jefferson Range is separated by a sag in the gneissic axis and is distinctly linear, the trend of its long southward extension being perhaps controlled by the strike in the region of folded and metamorphosed paleozoic rocks.

The extensive anticlinal valley, 50 miles long and 5 to 10 miles wide, followed by the Madison River south of the crystalline belt, is deeply filled with Tertiary sediments. These are already much wasted by terracing but erosion is limited in rate by the necessity of cutting down the strong Archean barrier which determines the local base level. Meantime the stream meanders broadly, building sand bars and islands out of the excess load received from the easily wasted sediments. Among these islands the river flows in many channels, a typically braided stream.

This basin and others branching out from the junction at Three Forks afford perhaps the largest area of rich agricultural land in Montana. The terraces are valuable for grazing. Alder Gulch in the Jefferson Range was once a thriving gold camp, giving rise to Virginia City, the capital of Montana until 1874. Before that time the district had yielded about $60,000,000, and it continues to produce in a small way.

MOUNTAINS EAST OF THE MISSOURI RIVER[1]

In central Montana the Rocky Mountain front makes a wide detour to the east to surround the Belt and Little Belt Ranges. These, with the Castle Mountains, form a semi-detached mountain

[1] The following are the chief sources of information on this area:

WEED, W. H., Geology of the Little Belt Mountains, Montana, U. S. Geol. Survey, 20*th Ann. Rept.*, pt. III, 1899.

Fort Benton folio 55, U. S. Geol. Survey.

Little Belt folio 56, U. S. Geol. Survey.

WEED, W. H., and PIRSSON, L. V., Geology of the Castle Mining District, Montana, U. S. Geol. Survey, *Bull.* 139, 1896.

PARDEE, J. T., Geology and Water Resources of Townsend Valley, Montana, U. S. Geol. Survey, *Wat. Sup. Pap.* 539, 1925.

BEVAN, ARTHUR, The Rocky Mountain Front in Montana, Geol. Soc. Amer. *Bull.*, vol. 40, pp. 427–456, 1929.

area nearly 100 miles in diameter cut off from the main mass to the west by the valley of the Missouri River, a wide Tertiary trough at the south, but only a canyon in hard rock at the north.

The whole is an uplifted area exposing ancient (Algonkian and Cambrian) rocks in the center and bordered on the north, east, and south by upturned Paleozoic and Mesozoic beds which descend beneath the Great Plains. Looked at more closely the structure shows two broad anticlines or elongated domes, the Belt and the Little Belt, with northwest-southeast trend, separated by Smith's River flowing northwest, as does the Missouri, first through a Tertiary basin and then through a gorge in the hard rocks. Both uplifts are flat arches, the beds in the Little Belt being almost horizontal on top and dipping 8 to 10 deg. on the flanks. Steeper local dips are due to laccoliths and other intrusions. A poorly defined structural axis, whose position is fairly well indicated by the main divide, has a northwest-southeast direction but curves eastward toward the Big Snowy group (p. 61) being quite out of line with the Rocky Mountain Front.[1]

Both ranges show a widespread dominance of accordant crests from 7,000 to 8,000 ft. high. Isolated peaks or rounded knobs may rise 1,000 ft. above the general level. Most of these are residual but in the Little Belt some are unroofed laccoliths. Sharp valleys cut deep below the nearly level horizon but do not completely dissect the old surface.

The upturned rocks on the margin make monoclinal foothills. Being of unlike resistance the strong hogback-making formations are crossed by streams in narrow gorges, while broad strike valleys follow the outcrops of weaker beds. In crossing the wide belt of Carboniferous limestone it is common for streams to disappear or to become interrupted, reappearing later as giant springs where less soluble rocks are reached.

Castle Mountain, south of the Little Belt, is a small independent uplift but in large part a volcano. Its nearly level forested crests rise to 8,400 ft. and are surmounted by an unreduced remnant of the old volcano, the "Castle," which was a center of alpine glaciation.

The valley of the Missouri River west of the Big Belt has a terraced floor of Tertiary and Quaternary sediments 5 to 10 miles wide extending almost continuously from Three Forks to north of Helena, a distance of 60 miles. The Tertiary sediment

[1] BEVAN, ARTHUR, *loc. cit.*, p. 450.

is at least 1,200 ft. deep.[1] The down-folding or faulting that made this trough accounts for the western front of the Belt Mountains.

The central alluvial surface is but little below 4,000 ft. Further down-cutting waits on the deepening of the gorge downstream. Meantime the stream flows through braided channels and meanders over a broadening fertile flood plain.

TERTIARY BASINS

General Relations.—Depressions commonly called "Tertiary Lake Beds" exist throughout the northern Rocky Mountains.[2] In the area now to be considered they have peculiar importance, generally outlining the mountain units. They contain most of the population and in many cases control the drainage.

Located among mountains with an average height of perhaps 6,500 to 7,500 ft., the floors of these valleys are generally from 3,000 to 5,000 ft. high. In width they range from several miles up to 10 or 15 miles. Some continuous depressions are nearly 100 miles long but more or less subdivided by transverse swells. The lower parts of all contain Tertiary sediments, frequently Oligocene at the bottom. Miocene is generally represented, with perhaps a coating of Pliocene. Pleistocene stream gravels are widespread. The filling is frequently deep, being 3,000 ft. in at least one place.[3]

In general these beds are either horizontal or dip but slightly; at places they are moderately folded or faulted. An unknown amount of their mass has been eroded away to form their present surface. This surface is a series of gently sloping terraces with eroded edges, leading down to generally broad bottom lands along the axial streams.

[1] CAMPBELL, M. R., U. S. Geol. Survey, Guidebook, *Bull.* 611, p. 120, mentions a well of that depth near Helena.

[2] The locations of most of these basins are roughly shown on the geologic map of North America, 1906. A later and presumably more accurate sketch for Montana only is given in Campbell's Guidebook of the Northern Pacific Route, U. S. Geol. Survey, *Bull.* 611, 1915, facing p. 134. A still later sketch given by Pardee in U. S. Geol. Survey, *Wat. Sup. Pap.* 539, 1925, is here reproduced as Fig. 82. This last outlines the main depressions (presumably Tertiary) with or without sediments. Pardee also gives a larger scale and more exact map of the basins north and west of Butte in U. S. Geol. Survey, *Bull.* 531, pl. XIV, opposite p. 244.

[3] PARDEE, J. T., U. S. Geol. Survey, *Bull.* 531.

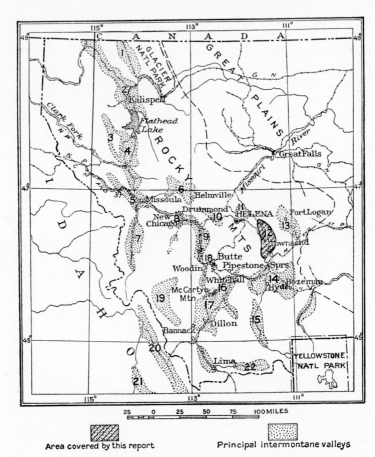

Area covered by this report   Principal intermontane valleys

Fig. 82.—Index map showing location of Tertiary basins in Montana and
Idaho. (*Pardee, U. S. Geol. Survey, Wat. Sup. Pap. 539.*)

1. Flathead Valley; 2. Kalispeli Valley; 3. Little Bitterroot Valley; 4.
Mission Valley; 5. Missoula Valley; 6. Blackfoot Valley; 7. Bitterroot Valley;
8. Flint Creek Valley; 9. Deer Lodge Valley; 10. Avon Valley; 11. Prickly
Pear Valley; 12. Townsend Valley; 13. Smith River Valley; 14. Gallatin Valley;
15. Madison Valley; 16. Jefferson Valley; 17. Beaverhead Valley; 18. Silver
Bow Valley; 19. Big Hole Valley; 20. Lemhi Valley; 21. Pahsimeroi Valley;
22. Centennial Valley.

Around some of these basins the upland summits seems to indicate a former peneplain bent down and passing beneath the sediments in a dish-like form.[1]   Others are as plainly faulted down, while still others might have been produced wholly by erosion. Except for post-glacial faulting on the east side, the upper Madison Valley northwest of Yellowstone Park appears to be of this kind.   Some of the basins are crossed by ridges of the underlying hard rocks through which the main streams now flow in narrow gorges, due probably to superimposing when the Tertiary filling was deeper, possibly in some cases to antecedence.   All these basins have, no doubt, been deepened from time to time by repeated crustal movements which raised the mountains more than the valleys.

The earlier history of these basins involves the controversy mentioned on page 193 regarding the relative age of peneplain and basins.   With respect to later history the facts are more plain.   At a time not far from the close of the Tertiary and the beginning of the Quaternary, many of the basin floors (perhaps all) were local peneplains whose levels endured long enough to enable some side streams to reduce their floors to the same temporary base level.[2]   Rejuvenation of streams followed, either by reason of crustal warping or by change of drainage to a more advantageous direction, and the valley floors were terraced.

The number of terraces in at least half of the valleys is three, and these may perhaps be correlated.   The highest, in places,

---

[1] PARDEE, J. T., Geology and Ground-water Resources of Townsend Valley, Montana, U. S. Geol. Survey, *Wat. Sup. Pap.* 539, p. 38, 1925; see also citations by Geo. R. Mansfield, Tertiary Planation in Idaho, *Jour. Geol.*, vol. XXXII, p. 476, 1924.

[2] PARDEE, J. T., *loc. cit.*, p. 42; ATWOOD, W. W., Physiographic Conditions and Copper Enrichment, *Econ. Geol.*, vol. XI, p. 712, 1916, interprets the physiographic history of southwestern Montana in four cycles of erosion. He represents most of the Tertiary basins of Montana and Idaho as draining south into the Snake River until dammed by the Snake River lavas.   On this supposition the Continental Divide at that time lay far to the east. Later the Missouri River is stated to have worked headward from near Great Falls and to have tapped the basin near Helena.   He finds that this capture, with similar captures by Clark Fork and other streams, in course of time resulted in reversing the drainage of most of the basins.   This conception of a former southward drainage across the Centennial Range to the Snake River is not in accord with the findings of V. D. Kirkham who has made a study of the eastern counties of Idaho; Idaho Bur. Mines and Geol., *Pamphlet* 19, 1927.

carries glacial drift, now largely wasted away, of an early Pleistocene glaciation.   The second terrace (at least along the Missouri)
was made and dissected at an interglacial stage.   The third is in
part floored with outwash gravel from glaciers of the Wisconsin
stage of glaciation.[1]

Description of Individual Basins.—Among these Tertiary
basins the following are prominent.   Lemhi and Pahsimeroi
Valleys in Idaho lie respectively west of the Beaverhead and
Lemhi Ranges, trending south-southeast.   Both are crossed by
the axis of greatest uplift of the Idaho peneplain.   The divides
between north-flowing and south-flowing streams appear to
be determined by that uplift whose axis is in line with the Centennial Range to the east.

Bitterroot Valley, 65 miles long and 9 miles wide, separates
the Bitterroot from the Sapphire Mountains.   The Bitterroot
River with its flood plain two to three miles wide between
Pleistocene terraces falls from an altitude of 3,900 ft. at its south
end to 3,150 ft. at the north.   There the valley is constricted
and for a few miles the sediments are absent because the hard
rocks rise above their level.   The valley broadens again along
Clark Fork with a northwest trend.   Curiously enough the
river leaves this trough for a more southerly course at the northeast foot of the Clearwater Mountains.

During the advance of the Cordilleran ice sheet the valley
of the Clark Fork was crossed and obstructed by the ice near
the Montana-Idaho boundary.   The resulting flood in its own
valley and those of its tributaries is known as Lake Missoula.[2]
The water was 1,000 ft. deep over the present site of Missoula
from which place the lake spread star-like, occupying all connecting valleys south of the ice front and below a level of 4,200 ft.
A prompt discharge of this impounded water by the breaking of
the ice dam is sometimes appealed to as a possible source of
the great volume of water necessary to cause the scablands of
eastern Washington (page 258).[3]

The wide Flathead depression north of the Clark Fork and
west of the Mission Range is obviously of structural origin.   Its

[1] PARDEE, J. T., U. S. Geol. Survey, *Wat. Sup. Pap.* 539, p. 43, 1925.

[2] PARDEE, J. T., The Glacial Lake Missoula, *Jour. Geol.*, vol. XVIII,
pp. 376–386, 1910.

[3] HARDING, H. T., Possible Supply of Water for the Creation of the
Channeled Scablands, *Science*, vol. 69, pp. 188–190, 1929; BRETZ, J. H.,
Geol. Soc. Amer., 42d ann. meeting, abstract, 1929.

level is low (Flathead Lake 2,885 ft.) but any Tertiary sediments that may be present are concealed beneath the moraines of the Cordilleran ice sheet and the silt deposited in glacial Lake Missoula.[1] A lobe of the Cordilleran ice sheet passed down this valley truncating the spurs of the Mission Range[2] and building a great recessional moraine which now holds back the waters of Flathead Lake. Northwest of the lake the structural depression continues as the Rocky Mountain Trench and is not known to contain Tertiary sediments. The upper valley of the North Fork of the Flathead farther east is an independent depression, floored with Tertiary beds, from which the river escapes by a narrow transverse valley to the larger depression on the west.

Deer Lodge Valley is a north-south Tertiary trough west of Butte followed by the headwaters of the Clark Fork. Forty miles north of Butte the trough turns to the northwest, followed by the river. South of Butte the depression extends nearly if not quite to the Beaverhead-Jefferson trough. It is very narrow here but still floored with Tertiary beds. Branching off to the east and extending to and beyond Butte is the valley of the Silverbow, a part of the same depression. Parallel with the northern end of the main depression and only 15 to 20 miles away is the northwest-southeast Avon Basin at the northeast foot of the Garnet Range. It is believed that a large fault with downthrow toward the valley separates this basin from the mountains to the northeast.[3]

The Missouri River from its origin at Three Forks to a point east of Helena follows approximately the course of a similar depression, the Townsend Valley,[4] which connects through a narrows with the similar Prickly Pear Valley east of Helena. Tertiary beds cover a width of 8 to 10 miles and are at least 1,200 ft. deep. The river seems to have been superimposed at both ends of this basin, coming in from the south across a spur of the Big Belt Mountains and escaping at the north by a gorge through the barrier that connects the Big Belt and Lewis Ranges. These

---

[1] A recent well south of Polson, drilled for oil, appears to penetrate 500 ft. or more of Tertiary sediments beneath 500 or 600 ft. of drift, perhaps faulted down between rocks of the Belt series (Note by W. C. Alden).

[2] DAVIS, W. M., Assoc. Amer. Geogr., *Ann.*, vol. X, p. 94, 1920.

[3] PARDEE, J. T., U. S. Geol. Survey, *Bull.* 531, p. 231.

[4] This basin has been more studied than any of the others. The work of J. T. Pardee, U. S. Geol. Survey, *Wat. Sup. Pap.* 539, 1925, has already been referred to.

valleys are apparently due mainly to down-warping[1] though faulting on the east side played a part. A major earthquake in 1925 had its epicenter just south of this valley, probably on the prolongation of the same fault.[2] This valley has the above mentioned three terraces typically developed and a fertile flood plain three to six miles wide on which the stream meanders broadly, pending the deepening of the gorge by which it leaves.

At its south end this depression joins the great down-warped areas south of Three Forks and west of Bozeman. An area full 40 miles in length from east to west, and of irregular width almost as great, constitutes the lower basins of the Jefferson, Madison, and Gallatin Rivers. Its long, terraced slopes, adapted to grazing, rise to an altitude of 5,500 ft. Most of the alluvium is between 4,000 and 5,000 ft. high. It is broadest (6 to 8 miles) along the Gallatin River. Here Bozeman is the metropolis of one of the leading agricultural districts of the Rocky Mountains.

An axis of crystalline rocks separates the Three Forks Basin from the north-south basin followed by the Madison River in its upper course. This depression, 8 to 10 miles wide and 40 miles long, may be due mainly to erosion. Its substructure is anticlinal. The post-glacial faulting observed on the east side is not known to be connected with deformation old enough and great enough to account for the basin.

Above a barrier west of Three Forks, the Jefferson River with its headwaters the Beaverhead traverses a Tertiary basin 100 miles in length, expanding into the wide, terraced plain of which Dillon is the center. This is more or less connected with the Big Hole Basin at the northeast foot of the Beaverhead Mountains.

East of the Missouri River the basin of the Smith River separates the Big Belt Range from the Little Belt. Also the Yellowstone River, flowing north from the National Park, is believed to follow a valley of the same origin.

---

[1] PARDEE, J. T., U. S. Geol. Survey, *Wat. Sup. Pap.* 539, describes clearly a down-warped surface which he interprets as a pre-Oligocene peneplain but does not specifically say that it extends beyond the borders of the basin.

[2] PARDEE, J. T., Montana Earthquake of June 27, 1925, U. S. Geol. Survey, *Prof. Pap.* 147, pp. 7–23, 1926.

CHAPTER VI

THE COLUMBIA PLATEAU

THE PROVINCE AS A WHOLE

CHARACTERISTICS AND BOUNDARIES

The Columbia Plateau embraces about 100,000 square miles in Washington, Oregon, and Idaho. It is, in the main, built up of nearly horizontal sheets of lava, the surface of which is flat or rolling, but there are many variations from this simple character. The province is bounded on the west by the Cascade Mountains and on the north and east by the Rocky Mountain province. On these three sides the surface abuts against higher land and the boundaries of the province are evident. On the south it is bordered by the Great Basin which has much in common with this province. The southern boundary as here drawn leaves the characteristic "basin ranges" (page 330) to the south. On the south side of this rather arbitrary boundary are most of the detritus-covered desert plains, while on the north side volcanic rocks underlie the thin soils. The location of a line drawn by any of these criteria is necessarily inexact.

UNDERLYING ROCKS

Igneous Rocks.—The rocks of this region are mainly lava flows. Basalt is much more abundant than acid lavas, especially in the better populated and more traveled parts of the province, but acid lavas (lighter colored, sometimes red or purple) underlie the margins of the Snake River Plain and parts of eastern Oregon. The basalt occurs in flows (extrusive sheets) from 10 ft. to more than 200 ft. thick. In the deeper canyons as many as 12 to 20 such sheets have been counted in a single exposure. These sheets have the common features of present-day lava flows, scoriaceous upper surfaces, evidences of quick cooling at the lower contact and of slower cooling in the interior, where they are often jointed in beautiful hexagonal columns.

225

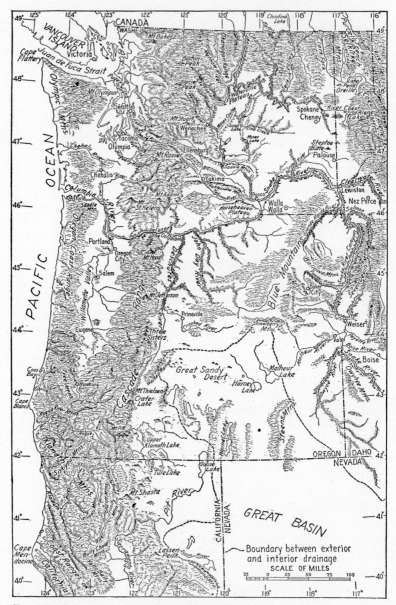

Fig. 83.—Index map of Columbia Plateau and parts of adjacent provinces.
(Drawn by Guy-Harold Smith.)

All are black or nearly so. In some instances soil formed and trees grew on the surface of a flow before being buried by the next flow.[1] Interbedded with the basalts are local beds of volcanic dust and lapilli.

At places the great canyon of the Snake on the western boundary of Idaho cuts through more than 4,000 ft. of basalt flows. To this thickness may be added another 1,000 ft. known to have been eroded from the plateau which the canyon trenches; at

Fig. 84.—Wall of the Grand Coulee, Washington; height 800 ft. At least 10 separate lava flows can be distinguished in this view. (*Photo by H. W. Fairbanks.*)

other points in the great canyon, the lower part of the wall consists of granite and schist.

Lake and Stream Deposits.—More abundant than the fragmental volcanic rocks but still vastly inferior in amount to the basalts are sand, gravel, and clay. Some of these deposits represent alluvial fans from the wash of adjacent mountains or other stream-laid sediment. Others are deposits in lakes.

[1] I. C. Russell gives excellent descriptions of the many features of this rock which indicate the circumstances of its accumulation.—U. S. Geol. Survey, *Wat. Sup. Pap.* 4, pp. 43–45, 1897; see also U. S. Geol. Survey, *Bull.* 199, pp. 60–65, 1902.

It is to be remembered that the lava flows came at intervals, sometimes of hundreds, possibly even thousands, of years judging from the thickness of soils formed in the meantime. Moreover, no one flow covered the whole area. As accumulation shifted, streams and stream deposition also shifted. In certain areas lakes persisted for long periods, their boundaries changing from time to time as new flows occurred. In these lakes, thick deposits were made of sand, gravel, silt, and clay, interbedded with sheets of basalt.

In eastern Washington and western Idaho there is a large district, 175 miles long and 75 miles wide, in which such interbedded sediments are abundant. This is due to the fact that lava flows coming from the west obstructed and ponded the normal drainage from the mountains on the east.[1]

A large area in southwestern Idaho and eastern Oregon was occupied by one or more lakes or was receiving continental deposits for several geological periods.[2] Into these depressions lavas were occasionally poured, but the total thickness of lake sediments is large in proportion to that of intercalated lava. The geologic map shows a large area in which the lake beds appear at the surface. This represents only approximately the extent of the lake, for it is to be remembered that it changed its outline repeatedly during the period of volcanic flows. In a very general way it may be said that the proportion of lake sediments to lava is greatest near the center of this area and less near the edges. In two other basins thick sediments accumulated upon the lavas. These are the basins of the John Day River in northern Oregon and the Columbia River in southern Washington.[3]

All the sediments here described, together with the beds of lapilli and volcanic dust, are of interest and importance because of their relations to artesian water in a country where water is so scarce as to constitute the limiting factor which determines development and population.

[1] RUSSELL, I. C., U. S. Geol. Survey, *Wat. Sup. Pap.* 4, p. 55; PARDEE, J. T. and BRYAN, K.: Geology of the Latah Formation, U. S. Geol. Survey, *Prof. Pap.* 140 A, 1926; KIRKHAM, V. R. D., and JOHNSON, M. M., The Latah Formation in Idaho, *Jour. Geol.*, vol. XXXVII, pp. 483–504, 1929.

[2] LINDGREN, W., Boise folio 45, U. S. Geol. Survey; BUWALDA, JOHN P., Gas and Oil Possibilities of Southwestern and South Central Idaho, Idaho Bur. Mines and Geol., *Pamphlet* 5, 1923.

[3] SMITH, GEO. O., Ellensburg folio 86, U. S. Geol. Survey.

Physiographic History

The Surface Beneath the Lava.—The physiographic history of this province begins with the ancient surface before the lavas were erupted. This is known to have been locally rough, even mountainous, partly by the fact that some of the old peaks rose above the lava flood which was at least several thousand feet deep. Such peaks are for the most part outliers of the Rocky Mountains of Idaho and are therefore most numerous in eastern Oregon and Washington. There are no similar outliers on the side toward the Cascades because that range, instead of being older than the lava flows and only partly submerged, was a part of the flooded region, being raised into mountains later (page 417).

Other evidence of the rough character of the now buried surface in the district referred to, is found in the great canyon of the Snake River which cuts through the basalt and deep into the granite below. Here the upper surface of these older rocks is very irregular. At places the granite rises in the canyon walls 2,000 to 2,500 ft. above the river, though still covered by 1,000 to 2,000 ft. of basalt. At intervening points it sinks below the river level, showing that the basalt flows at this place inundated a mountainous country, converting it into a plateau.[1] Some of the old mountains were high enough to stand out as islands in the basaltic sea. Some of the buried mountains have very steep slopes. This locality is between the mountains of Idaho and their outliers, the Blue Mountains of Oregon. Its relief was therefore no doubt much greater than that of localities farther from the mountains. In the Sumpter quadrangle, Oregon, in the Blue Mountain section, it is known that the pre-lava surface was "practically a plain."[2]

Manner of Eruption.—The great outpourings of lava which inundated this rough surface (in the Miocene, Tertiary) have frequently been spoken of as fissure eruptions. It is assumed that lava would issue from open fissures in vastly greater quantities than from craters and, partly on this account, would retain its heat and fluidity longer, so that it would come to rest on a

[1] Lindgren, W., Gold and Silver Veins of Silver City, De la Mar and Other Mining Districts in Idaho, U. S. Geol. Survey, 20*th Ann. Rept.*, pt. III, p. 78, 1899.

[2] Pardee, J. T., and Hewett, D. F., Mineral Resources of Oregon, vol. I, no. 6, p. 24, 1914.

very extensive area with an almost horizontal surface. Among the reasons for ascribing the lavas of this province to fissure eruptions are: (1) their vast extent and nearly horizontal surface, except as deformed later, and (2) the general absence of the kind of fragmental products which generally result from crater eruptions.[1] It should, however, be remembered that over large areas in the Snake River Plain local centers of eruption are found in sufficient numbers to make the hypothesis of fissure eruptions

Fig. 85.—Lava cone, Snake River Plains near Arco, Idaho. The very gently sloping cone is of basalt, and represents one of the sources of the lava in the surrounding plain, with which its slopes merge. Fragments of fresh basalt may be seen between the sage bushes in the foreground. Contrast Fig. 87. (U. S. Geol. Survey.)

unnecessary. It should be expected that in case of fissure eruptions, the lower and older beds would be crossed by dikes representing the passage through which later lavas reached the surface. Such dikes are found in abundance in certain localities,[2] but they are not numerous in the walls of the great canyons. No doubt such fissure eruptions were important in the province as a whole although not in the Snake River Plain. No doubt also, the dis-

[1] Lindgren, W., loc. cit., p. 94.

[2] Lindgren, W., The Gold Belt of the Blue Mountains, 22d Ann. Rept., U. S. Geol. Survey, pt. II, p. 597. Similar occurrences in the Cascade Mountains are mentioned by Russell, Wat. Sup. Pap. 53, p. 30, and G. O. Smith, U. S. Geol. Survey, folio 86, p. 2.

charge from fissures graded into more and more localized eruptions producing in some cases lava and cinder cones.[1] Eruptions of lava may occur quietly throughout a great distance or be more or less localized. When sufficiently localized, craters and cones make their appearance. On the recent lava plains of the Snake River there is abundant evidence that lava has issued from local orifices now marked by low mounds of black basalt never more than 200 or 300 ft. high, and with slopes so gentle that their bases may be 8 to 10 miles in diameter.[2] These are analogous to the low domes that form on ice where water issues from a hole and freezes. Indications of crater eruptions of both solid and liquid materials producing cinder cones, lava cones, and lava plains, are all found in eastern Idaho. The different types of eruption merge into one another, as do also the resulting topographic forms.

The variety of phenomena attending eruption in this province was very great and as the time elapsed since the last activity has been short, the products of eruption are well preserved. Russell found this region a particularly fruitful field for the study of the various phenomena attending eruption.[3]

It is well known that basaltic lavas are very fluid. The vast extent of certain nearly horizontal beds in this region also indicates a higher degree of fluidity. It was believed by Russell that at the time when the Columbia lavas ceased to accumulate, the flooded portions of Washington and Oregon may be thought of as a "monotonous plain."[4]

It is to be remembered that the several flows came at intervals, some of which were hundreds or even thousands of years, so that soils were often formed on one sheet before it was covered by the next. A fair picture of the landscape in these intervals may be obtained by assuming that the flows have not yet ceased on the Snake River Plain, but that the present time is merely an

[1] STEARNS, HAROLD T., Craters of the Moon National Monument, Idaho, *Geogr. Rev.*, vol. 14, pp. 363–372, 1924. A recently discovered fissure through which eruption has taken place is described by Stearns in this paper; see also Idaho Bur. Mines and Geol., *Pamphlet* 14, 1928.

[2] RUSSELL, I. C., U. S. Geol. Survey, *Bull.* 199, p. 63, 1902, LINDGREN, W., U. S. Geol. Survey, *18th Ann. Rept.*, pt. III, p. 626; KIRKHAM, V. R. D., Idaho Bur. Mines and Geol., *Pamphlet* 19, 1927; note especially pl. I-D and IV, map.

[3] See Summary in U. S. Geol. Survey, *Bull.* 217, pp. 37–38; also *Bull.* 199.

[4] U. S. Geol. Survey, *Wat. Sup. Pap.* 53, p. 30; see also *Bull.* 199, p. 66.

interval between eruptions.   The gravel and finer alluvium now brought down by the "lost rivers" and accumulating as fans or widespread wash near the mountains are the counterpart of many of the interbedded sediments between the basalts.   Others of these beds correspond to the sediments now accumulating in ephemeral lakes.   Elsewhere were large permanent lakes not often invaded by lava flows.

Crustal Deformation since the Lava Flows.—Most of this province in Washington and Oregon is believed to have been depressed since the lava flows occurred.   This conclusion is reached as follows:[1]

The lava is known in at least one place to be 4,000 ft. thick. There is nothing at its base to suggest that it was laid down in water.   All the evidence indicates that it flowed over dry land above sea-level.   This means that, without allowance for sinking while the flows continued, the surface of the last sheet must have been at least 4,000 ft. high; and if the surface was level, as Russell assumes, the whole plateau must have had that height. If allowance be made for erosion the altitude must have been still greater.   Outside of the Blue Mountain section, where later rising is indicated, the lava surface east of the Cascades in Washington and northern Oregon rarely exceeds 3,000 ft.   The reasoning outlined above would require that the original level should have been at least 1,000 ft. higher.   The great area surrounding the junction of the Snake and Columbia and lying less than 1,000 ft. above the sea, where the upper surface of the basalt is to be found beneath 1,600 ft. of lake sediments[2] may well have sunk more than 4,000 ft.

Whether or not the argument for this amount of sinking is conclusive, it is reasonable to assume that sinking has occurred, since the lava cover where its thickness is one-half mile (a fair estimate of the average) would exert a downward pressure of 200

[1] RUSSELL, I. C., Geology and Water Resources of Nez Perce County, Idaho, U. S. Geol. Survey, *Wat. Sup. Pap.* 53, pp. 52–54, 1901; LINDGREN, W., The Gold Belt of the Blue Mountains of Oregon, U. S. Geol. Survey, *22d Ann. Rept.*, pt. II, p. 598, 1901.

[2] SMITH, G. O., Ellensburg folio 86, p. 2, U. S. Geol. Survey.   A well just south of Lewiston, Idaho, penetrated basalt to a depth of more than 2,000 ft. below sea-level.   The report does not state that the base of the basalt was reached.   In a similar way the base of the basalt is known to be at least 2,700 ft. below sea-level at Attalia near the mouth of the Snake River.—V. R. D. Kirkham, personal communication.

tons on each square foot. It should also be remembered that the withdrawal of 50,000 to 60,000 cubic miles of molten rock from beneath the surface must necessarily be compensated in some way.

On the other hand the surface has locally risen both relatively and absolutely. Such uplifts of the lava surface in and around the Blue Mountains in eastern Oregon reach altitudes of 6,500 to 7,000 ft. In the main this is a gentle warp with dips not exceeding 3 deg., but in the John Day Basin on the western margin there was sharper folding, some dips reaching 30 deg. The Cascade Mountains, although not a part of this physiographic province, represent an uplift of the lava surface.

In the Yakima district, at the east foot of the Cascades in Washington, there is evidence of two epochs of folding since the time of eruption. The older folds seem to have been base-leveled before the later uplifting occurred (page 267). This evidence of a complex history in the western margin of the plateau is not matched by any similar evidence farther east where, for aught that is known to the countrary, the present lava surface may be almost the original surface of the flows (page 238).

Establishment of Drainage Lines.—The courses of streams in this province must be interpreted in the light of the crustal movements mentioned above. The Columbia River flows south from Canada into northeastern Washington where it receives the Spokane from the east and then turns sharply northwestward and describes a semicircle with a diameter of 100 miles around the "Big Bend Country." Turning again to the west on the Washington-Oregon boundary, it cleaves the Cascade Range from crest to sea-level. In describing the Big Bend the river falls from an altitude of 1,000 ft. at the mouth of the Spokane to about 300 ft. at the mouth of the Snake. On the flanks of the Cascade Range the Columbia traverses the highest part of the plateau in Washington, altitudes on both sides of the river being more than 3,000 ft. A nearly straight course might be chosen from the mouth of the Spokane to that of the Snake without encountering any altitudes above 2,300 ft. It is plain therefore that the Columbia pays small heed to the general slopes of the plateau. No doubt when the Columbia skirted the edge of the plateau in the Big Bend it did so as a consequent stream, following the lowest available course to the sea. With the same option offered now it would follow the chord of the arc and save at least 700 ft. of canyon cutting.

A more striking illustration of the same principle is found in the Snake River. From Wyoming it enters the extreme east end of this province, where, for many miles, its several branches run over the surface of a flat plateau 5,000 ft. above the sea. At Idaho Falls the stream drops 30 ft. into a canyon whose depth gradually decreases, leaving the stream again on the plateau surface. Seventy miles farther down stream at the American Falls (long. 113°), the stream drops 50 ft. into a canyon. Except for a stretch of 50 miles in the lake beds of western Idaho where the land adjacent to the river is dissected, the canyon which begins at the American Falls continues almost without interruption to the junction with the Columbia. The Snake is thus exceptional in the great proportion of its course between canyon walls. The height of these in southern Idaho varies from 50 ft. (at the American Falls) to about 800 ft. The plateau level falls from 4,742 ft. at Idaho Falls to 2,125 ft. at Weiser (lat. 44°) on the western border of the state. Thus far the Snake is plainly a consequent stream, first on the lava cover, then on the lake beds.

From the bend west of Weiser to its mouth (see Fig. 83, map), the Snake describes a great semicircle similar to the Big Bend of the Columbia and equally unaccountable from the standpoint of present-day slopes and altitudes. In its northerly course it traverses a mile-deep canyon where the plateau is nearly 7,000 ft. high between the Blue Mountains on the west and the Northern Rocky Mountain province on the east. The depth of the valley decreases to 2,000 ft. at the Washington boundary and to several hundred feet before the junction with the Columbia is reached.

It is evident that the course of the Snake River was antecedent to the last uplift of the Blue Mountain district. If the great canyon were now filled up, the Snake would have its choice of two courses, either of which would be at least 2,000 ft. lower than the one now followed. One of these options would take it west across central Oregon to the valley of the Deschutes. The other has been chosen as the route of the Oregon Short Line. It crosses through the center of the Blue Mountains, its highest pass being a little more than 4,200 ft. above the sea. This level is known to have changed both by diastrophism and erosion since the drainage lines were chosen, but it remains true that at that time the northward course on the state border was lower than any

westward course.[1] With reference to that elevated portion
of the plateau the river is now antecedent.

While the great streams of the region are antecedent to some
of the main structural and topographic features, there are other
cases in which stream courses are plainly guided by such features.
Thus the Snake River, after flowing north on the Washington-
Idaho boundary to Lewiston, turns squarely to the west, receiving
the west-flowing Clearwater at the bend. These two streams
in their westward course flow at the foot of a steep monocline
(locally a fault), 2,000 ft. high.

Obviously the Clearwater in its lower course and the Snake
below their junction are guided by constructional slopes due to
crustal movements and are therefore consequent streams. The
question arises, why the Snake from Weiser to Lewiston was able
to maintain its course through a rising barrier while the vigorous
Clearwater and the combined stream below the junction were
controlled by structural slopes. Three explanations are possible:
a. The monocline on the north may antedate the streams, *i.e.,*
it may be older than those uplifts which are now traversed by
antecedent streams; *b.* The Snake may at first have continued
its northerly course and been diverted by the rise of the plateau
on the north. If so, its old channel and valley have since been
completely effaced; *c.* There is a third possibility, namely, that
the streams were guided westward by some initial inequality
of level, incident to lava accumulation, and that the monocline
developed later along the same line.[2]

The Grand Ronde River in northeastern Oregon flows northeast
but encounters the Blue Hills structural dome in southeastern
Washington and turns east into the Snake River. Questions
raised by the course of this river are similar to those just considered. If it be assumed that all structural deformations of
the lava cover occurred at the same time (an unwarranted
assumption), it follows that some streams were vigorous enough

[1] LINDGREN, W., U. S. Geol. Survey, 22*d Ann. Rept.,* pt. II, p. 597.

[2] RUSSELL, U. S. Geol. Survey, *Wat. Sup. Pap.* 53, p. 71, uses language
which implies diversion from a former northward course but does not inti-
mate that any evidence of such a former course remains. Something like
the third explanation given above is implied in his footnote on page 70,
where he suggests that a canyon once cut "would mark out a line of weakness
which would determine where maximum deformation would occur in case
the beds should be warped or displaced by a tangential thrust acting at right
angles to the course of the canyon."

to hold their antecedent courses while weaker streams were being diverted.

Most of the medium-sized streams which head in the mountains follow consequent courses down their slopes. The map shows this distinctly for the Blue Mountains and the Owyhee in southwestern Idaho. It is exemplified by the streams of eastern Washington which flow westward from the mountains of Idaho.

Fig. 86.—Snake River Plain; looking across the young canyon of Snake River. Note the blocks of basalt in the foreground at the left. No soil layer appears in the canyon wall. (*Photo by H. W. Fairbanks.*)

It also appears in the numerous coulees (canyons without streams) which traverse central Washington in a southwesterly direction (page 258).

Division into Sections

Different parts of the province differ greatly in altitude and degree of dissection, and in the general style of topography produced. On this account the province is divided into five sections. For want of adequate surveys and maps it is not now possible to indicate the boundaries of these sections with exactness.

The *Snake River Plain* in southern Idaho is a typical young lava plateau, one of the best of its kind in the world (Fig. 86). It slopes toward the Snake River from a maximum height of nearly 6,000 ft. at the northeast to less than 4,000 ft. on the 115th meridian. (See map, page 184.)

Farther west the surface is lower and more eroded. This is because weak sedimentary rocks (lake beds and others) either underlie the surface or are interbedded with lava above the level of streams, hence favoring dissection. The topography where affected by these conditions is distinctly different from that of the Snake River Plain and the area may be appropriately treated as a separate section. As shown on the map and described on pages 244–248 the *Payette section* is much more extensive than these sedimentary beds. The term Payette section may be used for the present to designate a geographic region of varied character, partly as described, partly mountainous, partly lava plain. An undetermined share of this belongs to the Snake River Plain.

In northeastern Oregon, is the *Blue Mountain section.* It consists of a nucleus of old mountains not covered by the floods of lava. Later uplift has raised the mountains and domed the lava surface to a height of 7,000 ft. As these higher parts of the lava surface have been roughened by erosion they are here included in the Blue Mountain section.

West and north of the Blue Mountain section is the *Walla Walla section*, the largest of the province. It embraces some 40,000 square miles and is far from homogeneous. For detailed description it must be divided into units of lower order. From levels of 2,000 to 4,000 ft. at the base of the surrounding mountains the surface slopes toward the center where the Snake River joins the Columbia at an altitude of less than 300 ft. Thence the Columbia flows west through the Cascade Mountains to the Pacific. Most of the lavas that underlie this and neighboring sections are distinctly older and more eroded than those of the Snake River plain. These are often called the Columbia lavas, using the word in a narrow sense to distinguish them from the Snake River lavas.

South of the Walla Walla section and west of the Payette is an area, the *Harney section*, having much in common with the Great Basin but lacking the characteristic "basin ranges." It is a very arid country covered in part by detritus which the streams are unable to transport. Most of the drainage is to lakes without outlet.

SNAKE RIVER PLAIN

Fresh Lava Surface.—The lava-covered basin of the Snake River in southern Idaho constitutes a long eastward extension of the Columbia Plateau province (Fig. 69). The axis of the Snake River depression has been flooded with black Pleistocene basalt which overlies the lighter acid lavas (Pliocene) which form the substratum of the margins. The basalt covers practically all of the populated districts of the section and has been much more studied than the older acid lavas of the margin. This is the part, therefore, that forms the basis of most of the descriptions. Physiographically the basalt-covered center does not differ greatly from the margins on the older acid lavas.

East of long. 115°,[1] the topography is very simple. It is that of a lava plain, much of which is so new that weathering has made but little progress. The very thin soil only partially hides the black basalt. Over areas some miles or even dozens of miles in extent, the lava flows are practically unweathered, scoriaceous, scraggy, and very difficult to cross. Some of these flows may have occurred only a few centuries ago. In southwestern United States they would be called by the Spanish term *malpais*. One such field of extremely fresh lava occupies 100 or more square miles traversed by the Oregon Short Line, beginning a few miles west of American Falls (long. 113°). Northeast of that another large area is crossed by the railroad west of Blackfoot (long. 112°30'). Between the 113th and 115th meridians the northern margin of the plateau contains large areas which have but recently been the scenes of volcanic activity. One of these districts has been set aside as the Craters of the Moon National Monument.[2] These and other lava tracts, while more strikingly fresh than the vast plain, are no more level; in fact they retain the original roughness of the scoria which commonly disappears with weathering long before stream erosion begins.

---

[1] A few miles east of the 115th meridian the Snake River leaves its general westerly course and flows nearly north for 20 miles. At the south end of this jog it receives the Salmon Falls Creek from the south and at the north end it receives the Malade River from the east. This locality is interesting in itself because of the Thousand Springs and Salmon Falls, but it is especially worth fixing in mind as marking the approximate eastward limit of the area within which the lake beds are important.—RUSSELL, U. S. Geol. Survey, *Bull.* 199, pl. I; LINDGREN, U. S. Geol. Survey, 20*th Ann. Rept.*, pt. III, pl VIII.

[2] STEARNS, HAROLD T., *Geogr. Rev.*, vol. XIV, pp. 363–372, 1924.

Altitudes and Slopes.—The vast plain is sensibly flat. In reality the margins on the older, lighter colored lavas slope toward the belt of basalt which occupies the middle. The latter is slightly higher near its median line. Here also are most of the low basaltic mounds which mark points of extrusion. A transverse section of the basaltic belt suitably chosen and passing through one of the larger mounds, might show a total relief of 300 to 600 ft., half of it being due to the mound itself, the other half to the lateral slopes of the plain.[1] For a considerable distance the Snake River flows near the southeastern edge of the basalt formation. Along its northwestern edge are local sinks or ephemeral lakes in which the streams from the mountains on the north come to an end and disappear.

At its northeastern end the Snake River Plain is over 6,000 ft. high. The river is 5,000 ft. high only near the Wyoming border. Before reaching the mouth of the Malade (long. 115°) the plateau surface has fallen to less than 3,300 ft. Slopes of 10 to 30 ft. per mile from margin to axis are common. As some well-constructed mountain railroads have grades of 200 ft. per mile, it will be seen that the slope of these plains is generally not apparent.

Buttes and Lava Cones.—The appearance of a great sea of lava is intensified by the occasional buttes which rise abruptly from its surface as steep islands above the water.[2] Some of these are of older and different volcanic rock (rhyolite, andesite, etc.) and represent the summits of much eroded, older volcanic mountains rising above the flood which covered their bases and submerged their lower neighbors (Fig. 87). Of this character is Big Butte rising 2,350 ft. above the plain, also Middle and East Buttes northwest of Blackfoot. Very different in appearance from these steep buttes of older rock are the many broad low domes, mentioned on page 231 (Fig. 85), produced by the up-welling of the liquid basalt.

Streams from the Mountains.—The rivers which descend from the bordering mountains are for the most part unable to transport their loads of sediment to the Snake. Those entering from the south manage, after a fashion, some intermittent, some perennial, to deliver their waters to the main stream, but they

---

[1] KIRKHAM, V. R. D., Geological Reconnaissance in Eastern Idaho, Idaho Bur. Mines and Geol., *Pamphlet* 19, pp. 4 and 9, 1927.

[2] RUSSELL, I. C., U. S. Geol. Survey, *Bull.* 199, p. 16; also pl. V, opp. p. 34; KIRKHAM, V. R. D., Idaho Bur. Mines and Geol., *Pamphlet* 19, p. 9, 1927.

have veneered a broad strip of the basalt plateau with their
detritus which appears on the geological map as Quaternary
deposits. The Snake itself (both North and South forks) has
the same habit in its upper course above Idaho Falls.

The rivers from the mountains on the north must traverse
the plain for a much longer distance than those from the south
before reaching the Snake River. As noted above, the Snake
River follows the south side of the basaltic belt. That belt
itself, being highest in the middle, constitutes a barrier which

Fig. 87.—East Butte, Idaho, an old rhyolitic volcano surrounded by basalt.
The Snake River downwarp was first covered by acid (generally light-colored)
lavas which came from such volcanoes as this. Later the axis of the valley was
flooded with basalt, surrounding some of the old volcanoes and no doubt burying
others. (*Russell, U. S. Geol. Survey.*)

would turn aside the streams coming from the north. None of
these northern streams brings its waters to the goal. It is probable that the Malade would, at least in wet seasons, if the water
were not used for irrigation. Two of these streams are known,
respectively, as the Big Lost and Little Lost Rivers. These and
others diminish in volume after issuing from the mountains,
and give out, sometimes at one point, sometimes at another,
occasionally filling playa lakes. The aridity of the climate
would of itself cause these streams to disappear before going very
far from the mountains, but their exhaustion is hastened by per-

colation due to the jointing and scoriaceous character of the lavas and to the porosity of the interbedded sediments.[1]

Dendritic Tributaries.—Because of the lack of surface water as well as on account of its extreme youth, the Snake River Plateau above American Falls has scarcely yet begun its cycle of erosion. West of that place the Snake flows to the mouth of the Malade through a canyon. A beginning has been made,

Fig. 88.—Wood River Valley; looking north from Hailey. This and other streams reach the Snake River Plain from the mountains on the north. Their valleys just before reaching the plain afford some of the best agricultural land in Idaho. The view here shown is just within the limits of the Mountain province. The water of Wood River, when not all used for irrigation, may occasionally reach the Snake. Its companion streams farther east, Lost River, Little Lost River, and Birch Creek, disappear in sinks on the plain. (*Lindgren, U. S. Geol. Survey.*)

but not much more than a beginning, in the development of dendritic tributaries. At places the walls are notched by ravines and canyons between which are flat remnants of the plateau.

Snake River Canyon and Falls.—After falling 50 ft. at American Falls, the Snake River flows in a moderate trench to Twin Falls where it drops 180 ft. Two miles below this at Shoshone Falls it drops another 210 ft. Below this it runs in a canyon 700

[1] RUSSELL, I. C., U. S. Geol. Survey, *Bull.* 199, p. 25.

ft. deep. At Salmon Falls near the mouth of the Malade the stream again descends 25 ft.

All these falls are of the Niagara type, due to differences of resistance among lava beds in a nearly horizontal position. Like Niagara, they are all receding up stream, thus lengthening headward the deep gorges below the falls. It has even been affirmed[1] that the canyon of the Snake in southern Idaho has been excavated more largely by this process of recession than by the downward corrasion of the stream.

FIG. 89.—Blue Lake Alcove, looking south into Snake River Canyon, Idaho. This is a short canyon, only two miles long, caused by the recession of a spring. If a stream be substituted for the lakes, this view becomes representative of the Snake River Canyon in its narrower parts, and of its larger tributaries. (*Russell, U. S. Geol. Survey.*)

Spring Waters in Snake Canyon.—The large and relatively steady flow of the Snake (estimated at 8,000 sec.-ft. in January and 40,000 sec.-ft. in June[2]) is noteworthy in view of the small and inconstant supply from its tributaries. This is largely supplemented by the spring water which falls into the gorge from the more porous beds outcropping in the canyon walls. In part this is the water of the "lost rivers" from the mountains on the north. Almost all of it issues from the north wall of the canyon. The so-called "Thousand Springs" opposite the mouth of the Salmon River (long. 115°) afford a spectacular case of

[1] RUSSELL, I. C., U. S. Geol. Survey, *Bull.* 199, p. 125.

[2] Silver City folio 104, U. S. Geol. Survey.

such supply of ground water (Fig. 90). Within one-half mile along the canyon wall a constant volume of water estimated at 500 sec.-ft. or more, enters the river. Most of this water issues from a layer of cellular or scoriaceous basalt 185 ft. above the river. The volume which enters in less noticeable style is no doubt many times as great.[1]

FIG. 90.—The Thousand Springs, Snake River Canyon, Idaho. These springs issue from the north wall of the canyon and are fed by water from the mountains farther north. Most of the water follows a single layer of cellular, scoriaceous basalt from which it issues at a height of 185 ft. above the base of the precipice. The water is used to irrigate the alluvial plain within the canyon. (*Russell, U. S. Geol. Survey.*)

Soils and Vegetation.—Except on the fresh lava flows the Snake River Plateau is beginning to be covered with a thin residual soil formed from the basalt. Near the mountain borders and in the embayments there is a local covering of alluvium, often coarse or gravelly. The most noticeable soil cover, however, is a fine yellow dust soil which covers large areas, including the slopes of some of the volcanic buttes. From its physical character and its occurrence on rocks of different kinds, Russell ascribed

[1] For description see RUSSELL, I. C., *loc. cit.*, p. 27.

to this formation an aeolian origin.[1]   The alluvial soils of the stream valleys are the chief resource for agriculture.

Sage brush is the one nearly omnipresent form of vegetation. On the better or deeper soils, or where favored by greater moisture, bunch grass is also abundant.   Over the larger part of the area it appears but sparsely, interspersed with the sage brush. Some higher portions of the plateau near the mountains are covered by open forest.   Elsewhere trees are represented chiefly by the cottonwood which lines the banks of the Snake River where the breadth of the canyon permits.

Agriculture and Grazing.—Throughout the stretch of river here described, farming is carried on in a limited way by using the waters of the Snake to irrigate the canyon bottom.   The water of the Thousand Springs is largely used to irrigate a considerable tract of bottom land.   As early as 1902 Russell estimated that 8,000 acres were being irrigated from springs in the Snake Canyon between Shoshone Falls and the mouth of the Malade, a distance of about 50 miles measured along the river. The valleys of the lost streams emerging from the mountains on the north also afford some excellent agricultural land.   Most of this should, however, be allotted to the Mountain province.

Most of the Snake River Plain is now and, so far as agricultural science can be foreseen, must always continue to be, a grazing country so far as it can be used at all.   Cattle and sheep are the chief resources.

PAYETTE SECTION

Distinguishing Features.—A large area west of the 115th meridian differs from the Snake River Plain as described above in three important respects:

1. Its altitude is less.

2. Lake beds underlie the surface, either immediately or interbedded with sheets of lava.

3. Because of the weakness of the sedimentary rocks the surface is partly dissected by stream valleys.

The area thus designated borders the Snake River and its principal tributaries on both sides and extends well into Oregon. Patches of young basalt plain like that farther east occur within this area but they occupy a smaller fraction of the total and are separated by valleys that cut down into the lake beds.

[1] RUSSELL, *loc. cit.*, p. 21.

Altitude and Slopes.—The plateau level near the Snake River declines in altitude from about 3,500 ft. on the eastern side of the Payette section to 2,600 ft. on the Oregon border and less than 2,200 ft. near Weiser. The northern margin of the plateau rises approximately to 4,000 ft. and the southern margin to 6,000 ft. above sea-level. This is the altitude of the divide between the Snake River Basin and the basin of internal drainage to the south.

Fig. 91.—North wall of Snake River Canyon in the Payette section south of Boise, Idaho. The so-called "canyon" is here greatly widened. The land in the foreground is a terrace. The rocks are lake beds with intercalated basalt sheets. One of the latter caps the mesa. (*Russell, U. S. Geol. Survey.*)

The presence of the lake beds and the relatively low levels along the Snake River both point to subsidence along a great arc extending from near Yellowstone Park to the point where the Snake River enters its great canyon on the Oregon border. Structurally this subsidence is indicated by the dips of the older lavas on the margins of the province. In general these lava flows dip toward the axis. In the eastern part they pass beneath the Snake River basalt and in the western part beneath lake beds which are interbedded with the Snake River basalt. The amount of subsidence increases from east to west, its maximum, many thousand feet, probably being in eastern Oregon. The lowest part of the trough thus produced was filled with water in which sediments accumulated. At intervals during the same time, the dry land portion of the trough was being filled by basalt which also occasionally covered or partly covered the accumulated sediments.

Topography on the Lake Beds.—The topography on the lake beds, occupying perhaps 5,000 square miles, is that of a partly dissected plateau. It is a country of mesas separated by abrupt valleys with or without streams. Near to the main streams dissection has made much progress although no large areas could be called mature. With increasing distance the topography more and more resembles that of the lava plains.[1]

The Snake and its larger tributaries, Boise, Payette, and Owyhee, have terraced valleys several hundred and locally 500 to 1,000 ft. deep and varying in width from one to ten miles. Some of the older terraces are nearly 600 ft. high and somewhat eroded. The later and lower ones, like the valley bottoms, are nearly flat.

Owyhee Mountains.—South of the Snake River and close to the Oregon boundary, rise the Owyhee Mountains, a north-south range about 30 miles long, rising above 8,000 ft. and entirely surrounded by the plateau surface. Although well removed from others of its kind, this range is in general appearance much like the "basin ranges"[2] and would be counted among them except for its isolated position. Granite and older eruptives are exposed in its central axis. This range may or may not have been an island in the lava sea. At all events it was a center of an upward bulge after the surrounding lava plateau was formed. The plateau therefore slopes from these mountains in all directions, having at their foot an altitude of about 5,000 ft. It is furrowed by canyons, partly because of greater rainfall and favorable slope near the mountains, partly because some or all of the lavas are older than the Snake River basalts.[3] Farther west and north, the widespread lavas, generally called the Columbia River lavas, are distinctly older than those of the upper Snake Basin, which by contrast are called Snake River lavas. At all events there is not in southwest Idaho and adjacent states any

---

[1] For descriptions of the topography on these lake beds see W. Lindgren, U. S. Geol. Survey, 18*th Ann. Rept.*, pt. III, p. 629; also folios 45, 103, and 104.

[2] LINDGREN, W., U. S. Geol. Survey, 20*th Ann. Rept.*, pt. III, p. 77, 1899.

[3] Silver City folio 104, U. S. Geol. Survey.

such great expanse of remarkably flat lava plains as is found in the upper Snake Basin. Aside from the area underlain by lake beds much of the surface of the Payette section is underlain by acid lavas similar to those of the margins of the Snake River section, being of similar age and topography.

Agriculture and Grazing.—The Payette section, especially in its larger valleys, supports a larger population than the lava plains to the east. Grazing is the most widespread industry. The county which contains Boise, the state capital, is one of the chief sheep counties of the United States. Where agriculture is possible it is very profitable. Farming is practically limited to the valley floors and terraces of the chief streams. On the old lake beds agriculture is not favored either by the character of the soil, the water supply, or by the topography (dissected plateau).[1] The summer flow of these streams is all used for irrigation. In these cases the cultivated areas may still be enlarged by storing the winter run-off for summer use. The valley of the Boise is the chief farming country in this part of the province. The irrigable area in the valley of this river alone is estimated at 357 square miles but it is not probable that the stream carries enough water to irrigate this entire area.[2]

The waters of the Snake have been relatively little used. West of the 116th meridian the bottom lands become important but until the river reaches the Oregon boundary its immediate valley is narrow and the fall of the stream relatively small, hence it would be difficult to divert its waters to the higher terraces. That part of the Snake River that marks the state boundary south of Weiser, a stretch of 30 miles, has broad bottom lands confluent with those of the four large tributaries which enter here, the Owyhee and Malheur from Oregon, and the Payette and Boise from Idaho. This section therefore affords the chief farming district of Idaho.

The commonest crop is alfalfa which is grown largely for winter feed. Farming here is thus seen to be closely related to the grazing industry. Some grain is also raised and there are large orchards of apples, pears, and prunes.

Ground Water.—A resource of considerable importance is found in the springs both hot and cold. From such springs and

[1] Boise folio 45, U. S. Geol. Survey.
[2] LINDGREN, W., and DRAKE, N. F., Nampa folio 103, U. S. Geol. Survey. 1904.

from wells near them, Boise has a municipal water supply both hot and cold.[1]   Springs at Vale, Oregon, on the Malheur River, furnish water at 198°F., the hottest in the region.   Various other places have hot springs.

Artesian water, if not flowing, at least rising by natural pressure, is available over practically the whole farming district described above.   Probably 1,000 square miles are thus favored.[2]   The water comes from the mountains through the more porous members of the lake beds.   The layers which confine it under pressure are the clay beds of the same formations.

Mining.—The only mining in the part of the province here described is in the Owyhee Mountains.   Here are important mines of gold and silver.   Placers have been worked in a small way in the Boise Valley.   The towns of this province, notably Boise, have profited by the mining industry of the adjacent Mountain province.

BLUE MOUNTAIN SECTION

Character.—Northwest of the Payette section is a mountainous area, chiefly in northeastern Oregon but extending a short distance into southeastern Washington.   As stated earlier, some of these mountains antedate the lava flows and stood as islands rising several thousand feet above the lava sea.   However, since the entire district, mountains and lava alike, has been further elevated since the eruptions, and since the lava plateau around the older mountains has been much dissected, it is thought best to include the elevated and roughened lava margin in the Blue Mountain section.   Defined in this way the Blue Mountain section in Oregon becomes contiguous with the Northern Rocky Mountain province in Idaho, the two highlands being separated only by the deep canyon of the Snake River, 15 miles wide at the top.

Mountains Older than the Plateau.—Of the central and older mountains it is stated that, "in its general aspect the region consists of closely folded Paleozoic and early Mesozoic strata, shattered by large masses of intrusive rocks, partly covered by Neocene lavas."[3]   This is also the character of the mountains on

[1] RUSSELL, I. C., Notes on the Geology of Southwestern Idaho and Southeastern Oregon, U. S. Geol. Survey, *Bull.* 217, p. 24, 1903.

[2] RUSSELL, I. C., U. S. Geol. Survey, *Bull.* 217, p. 25, 1903.

[3] LINDGREN, W., The Gold Belt of the Blue Mountains of Oregon, U. S. Geol. Survey, *22nd Ann. Rept.*, pt. II, p. 577, 1901.

the opposite side of the Snake River on the border of the Northern Rocky Mountain province. Lavas rise on the shoulders of these ranges to a height of nearly 7,000 ft.

Among the best known mountains on the Oregon side are the Wallowa Mountains[1] just north of the 45th parallel. They are described as an island 25 miles in diameter in the sea of basalt.[2] They rise 9,000 ft. above sea-level and 3,000 ft. above the dissected plateau surface. These are only one of half a dozen mountain groups or "ranges," all of the others being included under the general name of Blue Mountains. The best known of these are the Elkhorn Range west of Baker City, the Greenhorn Range some 35 miles farther southwest, and the Strawberry Mountains, a high group between the East fork of John Day River and the 44th parallel. All of these groups are surrounded by, or consist partly of, the elevated and dissected surface of the lava plateau.

Mountains Carved from the Plateau.—Embracing the Strawberry group is a belt of uplifted plateau surface 10 to 30 miles wide lying just north of the 44th parallel, stretching east to within 40 miles of the Snake River and west to within 50 miles of the Cascades. Through much of its length it rises to between 6,000 and 7,000 ft. Its superior altitude gives it a larger rainfall than that of the adjacent plateau. It is therefore much dissected and, for the same reasons, forested, its area being largely occupied by the Malheur and Deschutes National Forests.

A similar upraised strip of the plateau surface trends northeast from north central Oregon to the southeast corner of Washington.[3] It forms the northwestern and northern border of the Blue Mountain section. The portion of this uplift which lies in southeastern Washington is a dome more than 5,000 ft. above the sea and 4,000 ft. above the structural troughs on the east and north through which the Snake River flows, 25 miles away. The top of this dome is dissected to maturity and near the Grande Ronde River to a still later stage. Near its base the dome is less dissected. Despite the elevation of the dissected plateau,

[1] Called also Eagle or Eagle Creek Mountains, also Powder River Mountains.

[2] LINDGREN, W., U. S. Geol. Survey, 20*th Ann. Rept.*, pt. III, p. 92.

[3] See contour map of the United States, U. S. Geol. Survey, 1913, 40 miles to the inch. Compare also the following maps in the Atlas of American Agriculture: pt. I, sec. E, Natural Vegetation; pt. II, sec. A, Precipitation and Humidity; pt. II, sec. I, Frost and the Growing Season.

the dips of the lava sheets rarely exceed 3 deg.[1]   The surface
is largely occupied by National Forests.

Snake River Canyon.—The strip of basalt plateau whose
level surface formerly filled the passage between the Blue Mountains and the Salmon River Mountains of Idaho, was 20 or more
miles in width.   The Snake River traverses this belt from south
to north and in cutting its canyon a mile deep and 15 miles wide
has destroyed most of the plateau surface for a distance of 50
miles.   If this work of erosion could be undone, the restored

Fig. 92.—Lava plateau in western Idaho near the 45th parallel, looking west
to the Wallowa Mountains of Oregon.   The intervening canyon of Snake River
is hidden from view.   Its tributary, Crooked Creek, in the foreground, is rapidly
cutting down, as indicated by the convex slopes.   Note the trees on north-facing
slopes.   Elevation about 7,000 ft.   (*Lindgren, U. S. Geol. Survey.*)

surface of the basalt plateau between the Wallowa Mountains
and the Seven Devils would be more than 6,500 ft. high.   The
level of the stream falls in this stretch from 2,100 ft. at Weiser to
about 700 ft. at Lewiston, Idaho, where its course turns west
across Washington.   The greatest depth of the canyon is therefore 5,000 to 6,000 ft., or about the same as the maximum depth
of the Grand Canyon of the Colorado.   Its width also is not
very different, being about 15 miles at the broadest.   Where
cut through sheets of basalt, the canyon walls spread out and

[1] For description see Russell, I. C., Geology and Water Resources of
Nez Perce County, Idaho, U. S. Geol. Survey, *Wat. Sup. Pap.* 53, p. 59, 1901.

show many of the imposing architectural features which enter so largely into the descriptions of the cliffs and canyons of the Colorado Plateau.

The slopes of the canyon here consist of alternating cliff and terrace with great talus slopes. The horizontal lines thus afforded are crossed by vertical gashes and intricately branching ravines, leaving outstanding towers and a confusion of corrugated ridges. It is a great mistake to assume that the impressiveness of a great canyon is measured by the mere steepness of its sides. Only the color of the Colorado Plateau is lacking, the somber blackness of the basalt cliffs being relieved only by the grey of the bunch grass on the rock terraces and talus slopes, and by scattered trees above the altitude of 4,000 ft. The rocks exposed in this canyon are mentioned on page 227. Where basalt overlies the granite and schist, the lower part of the canyon cut in the older rock is precipitous. In the basalt above, the canyon widens out.

The canyon of the Salmon River is second in grandeur only to that of the Snake. It parallels the latter in western Idaho before turning west to join the great canyon of the master stream. The canyons of the Grande Ronde in northeastern Oregon and of the Clearwater which issues from the Idaho mountains still farther north and joins the Snake at Lewiston, are similar to that of the Salmon.

Forests.—Most of this area above 4,000 ft. at the south or 3,500 ft. at the north, is covered with pine forest. This applies to plateau and mountains alike. The summits of the highest mountains, Seven Devils and Wallowa, are bare above 7,500 ft. Their topography indicates glaciation to a moderate degree.

WALLA WALLA SECTION

The Section as a Whole

All that part of the province that lies north and west of the Blue Mountains is here treated as a single section, the largest in the province. There is much diversity among its several parts but the propriety of ranking them as sections is doubtful. Its several parts, or districts, will be described separately although without assigning definite boundaries in all cases.

The Snake River joins the Columbia near the center of this section. Here the plateau surface is less than 500 ft. high. Its further decline westward is interrupted by several upwarps through which the river follows its antecedent course in canyons about 1,000 ft. deep.[1] The entire section slopes toward this low valley from the north, south, and east, the margins of the section being 2,000 to 3,000 ft. high.

Most of the underlying rock of the Walla Walla section is basalt but two considerable areas in the western part are underlain by lacustrine sediments like those of the Payette section. There is general agreement among geologists that the lava flows are mainly Miocene but different parts of the section differ so greatly in their erosional histories that various ages have been assigned ranging from Eocene[2] to the close of the Pliocene.[3]

It is noteworthy that the youngest lava flows observed are on the east side and the evidences of greatest age and erosion on the west side, but a generalization to the effect that the western part is older than the eastern would not now be justified. Mainly on the basis of studies in the eastern part, Bretz believes the general surface of the basalt to be essentially the original surface of the lava flows incised only here and there by valleys that cut deeper than the mantle rock.[4] Smith and Willis, approaching the area from the west, believe that the surface of the basalt is a peneplain.[5] There is no inherent improbability in the assumption that different parts of the section may have had different physiographic histories but if this be true the two histories remain to be worked out and distinguished.

---

[1] These canyons, the first of which is the Wallula Gateway, have an interesting relation to the great floods which made the scablands described on p. 258.—BRETZ, J HARLEN, The Spokane Flood beyond the Channeled Scablands, *Jour. Geol.*, vol. XXXIII, pp. 97–115 and 236–259, 1925.

[2] SMITH, G. O., Mt. Stuart folio 106, U. S. Geol. Survey, 1904; *cf.* LINDGREN, W., Silver City folio 104, U. S. Geol. Survey, 1904.

[3] RUSSELL, I. C., U. S. Geol. Survey, *Wat. Sup. Pap.* 53, pp. 54 and 55, 1901; UMPLEBY, J. B., U. S. Geol. Survey, *Bull.* 528, p. 48, 1913, speaks of these lavas as dating from late Oligocene or Early Miocene to about the close of the Pliocene.

[4] BRETZ, J H., The Channeled Scablands of the Columbia Plateau, *Jour. Geol.*, vol. XXXI, p. 623, 1923; BRETZ, J H., Glacial Drainage on the Columbia Plateau, Geol. Soc. Amer. *Bull.*, vol. 34, pp. 576 and 581, 1923; PARDEE, J. T., Geology and Mineral Deposits of the Colville Indian Reservation, U. S. Geol. Survey, *Bull.* 677, pp. 14 and 47, 1918. The area here concerned lies north of the Columbia River and near the Cascade Mountains.

[5] SMITH, G. O., and WILLIS, BAILEY, Contributions to the Geology of Washington, U. S. Geol. Survey, *Prof. Pap.* 19, pp. 28, 52, etc., 1903.

Eastern Margin

Extent and Altitude.—Southeastern Washington with the adjacent margin of Idaho and a small part of Oregon northwest of the Blue Mountains constitutes a district that is fairly homogeneous. The area here contemplated extends west almost to a line connecting Spokane with the Columbia River at the point where it first touches Oregon.

The term "Palouse Country" or "Palouse Hills" is often used for the part of this area north of the Snake River, most of it being in the Palouse River Basin, the river itself being in another district. The slope is west and northwest from altitudes of

Fig. 93.—Topography of the Palouse district near Pullman, Washington. (*Russell, U. S. Geol. Survey.*)

3,000 or 4,000 ft. at the foot of the Coeur D'Alene Mountains in Idaho and the Blue Mountains in Oregon. Correspondingly, the annual rainfall decreases from about 25 in. on the east to 10 in. on the west. Generally speaking, the elevation near the foot of the mountains stops just short of the lower level of forests, which is about 3,500 ft. in this vicinity. The district as a whole is often called the "Wheat Belt" as it is preeminent among the wheat-raising districts of the arid region.

Topography.—The district has a rolling surface of broad rounded wave-like swells, rising generally 20 to 80 ft. above valleys, which contain neither streams nor channels (Fig. 93). Here and there in the northern part are isolated buttes of older rock, outliers of the Idaho mountains, rising abruptly above the lava plateau. The type of these is Steptoe Butte, an isolated quartzite mountain rising 1,000 ft. above the plain in the heart of the wheat country midway between Lewiston, Idaho, and Spokane, Washington. From its summit the vast wheat fields are seen stretching away in all directions over the rolling hills "like a stormy sea." Only the eastern shore of this sea can be seen. It is made by the mountain border in Idaho with its jutting promontories like those of a sunken coast. "Each level-floored inlet and embayment is yellow with grain and each headland dark with pines."[1] The explanation of this rolling topography is bound up with that of the soil as noted below.

Soils.—The soil of southeastern Washington has excited much interest. It is very fine textured and deep, at places 50 to 75 ft., with an almost total absence of any kind of stones. Its fine texture causes it to be exceedingly retentive of moisture. It absorbs moisture so rapidly that there is no direct run-off from the greater part of the area. Russell speaks of slopes of 25 or 30 deg. which are not marked by rills or gullies either in the natural state or when plowed and left fallow for a year.[2]

In former years this was frequently cited as an example of a residual soil derived from basalt and, as such, contrasted with the less fertile soils derived from more siliceous igneous rocks. Russell explained it as a residual soil whose great thickness is due to the ready decomposition of basalt. On this assumption the hills and valleys were made in a recent humid epoch (presumably Pleistocene). The run-off is not now sufficient to supply the valleys with streams, hence the channels have become obliterated. In agreement with this supposition it was pointed out that all the valleys are drained, the axis of each sloping downward to the next in the orderly fashion of an erosion topography, and that some of the valley bottoms are wide and flat.

On the other hand this soil has the physical characteristics of loess. There is ample evidence that it is an accumulation of wind-borne dust, probably from the more arid region to the west and southwest. Not only does this supposition agree with the loess-like character, but it has also been shown that the chemical composition is not what could be expected from the decomposi-

---

[1] Russell, I. C., A Reconnaissance in Southeastern Washington, U. S. Geol. Survey, *Wat. Sup. Pap.* 4, p. 39, 1897.

[2] U. S. Geol. Survey, *Wat. Sup. Pap.* 53, p. 47.

tion of the underlying basalts. It is also pointed out that many of the hills are steeper on the northeast (leeward) side and that the soils are commonly deeper on that side and that ridges trending transverse to the prevailing wind sometimes have cusps pointing leeward. These may be dune features but it is known that the cores of these hills consist of various kinds of sediment, part of which at least is not wind-borne.[1] The agency of wind in making the surface deposit or "soil" which veneers the hills, may be accepted as proved. To account for the prevailing absence of dune-enclosed basins it is fair to assume that during the accumulation of the æolian deposit, surface waters were also at work.[2] Locally (and generally buried) there is a true residual soil grading downward into basalt.[3] Elsewhere are occasional sedimentary deposits like those of the "lake beds" farther west.

This wheat country is crossed or bordered by the canyons of the Snake, Clearwater, and Salmon Rivers. On the east these canyons are 2,000 ft. deep, their slopes showing a succession of basalt ledges separated by terraces or talus slopes, all soil-covered and bearing bunch grass except the faces of the ledges. In the bottoms of these canyons are occasional narrow strips of flood plain, affording excellent fruit farms. West from the Idaho boundary the canyon of the Snake becomes progressively shallower, the plateau along its margin being dissected by tributary canyons cut down to the level of the master stream. Farther south around Walla Walla and in Oregon, are some broader valleys irrigated from streams that head in the Blue Mountains.

Water Supply.—Wheat farming on the uplands is without irrigation. This is one of the most notable "dry-farming" districts of the United States. The soil absorbs the rain and melting snow so readily that there is practically no surface run-off.

[1] BRYAN, KIRK, The "Palouse Soil" Problem, U. S. Geol. Survey, *Bull.* 790, pp. 21–45, 1927.

[2] For the arguments in favor of residual origin, see RUSSELL, I. C., A Reconnaissance in Southeastern Washington, U. S. Geol. Survey, *Wat. Sup. Pap.* 4, pp. 59–64, 1897; for a statement of the æolian hypothesis see CALKINS, FRANK C., Geology and Water Resources of a Portion of East Central Washington, U. S. Geol. Survey, *Wat. Sup. Pap.* 118, pp. 45–49, 1905.

The field observations made by these two writers agree in the main except as to the gradation of the soil into the underlying rock which was affirmed by Russell, while the opposite was observed by Calkins.

[3] BRETZ, J HARLEN, The Channeled Scablands of the Columbia Plateau, *Jour. Geol.*, vol. XXXI, p. 623, 1923.

To prevent loss of moisture by evaporation the ground is kept constantly plowed.   Crops are raised in alternate years only.

Water for domestic purposes is hard to obtain and often of poor quality.   The deep and firm-textured soil, exceedingly retentive of moisture, gives up water very slowly to surface wells which are sunk from 30 to 50 ft. deep.   Moreover, the soil of a semiarid country quickly yields soluble salts which make well waters unpalatable.   In many communities water has been hauled 10 to 15 miles in tank wagons and stored in cisterns for domestic use.[1]

In a portion of the wheat belt, artesian wells have been successful and the conditions seem favorable over a strip extending westward perhaps 15 to 25 miles from the mountains.[2]   The head is small and flowing wells are found only in the deeper valleys, but deep wells yielding good water under moderate pressure will doubtless come to be the chief supply of this district. The water comes from porous sediments between the basalt sheets.   For reasons stated on page 228 these sediments become less and less abundant with distance from the mountains.   It is probable, however, that in no large portion of the Columbia Plateau will this resource be found entirely wanting.   The depth of such wells in eastern Washington ranges from seventy-five to several hundred feet below the bottoms of the larger valleys. Deeper wells will doubtless be drilled in the future.   Many springs issue from these porous sediments exposed in the canyon walls in eastern Washington.

The Coulee District

Altitude and Slope.—Adjoining the district here described as the eastern margin, is a roughly circular area extending north to the Spokane and Columbia Rivers, west to the Columbia and south to the Snake.   This is here called the "Coulee district" for reasons stated below.   It differs in important respects from the eastern margin.   For the most part it is lower, being not more than 1,000 ft. high at the south and southwest.   Its major slopes and drainage are southwestward, almost directly away from the Spokane-Columbia trench on the north near which it is 2,300 to 2,500 ft. high.   A strip 10 to 20 miles wide on the north-

[1] RUSSELL, I. C., U. S. Geol. Survey, *Wat. Sup. Pap.* 4, p. 13, 1897.
[2] RUSSELL, I. C., *loc. cit.*, p. 78, says "a strip 10 to 15 miles along the eastern border of Washington."

west side, the Waterville Plateau, just within the bend of Columbia River, is exceptional, being distinctly higher than the rest.

Rainfall and Vegetation.—The rainfall of the Coulee district is less than farther east, as might be expected in a region where

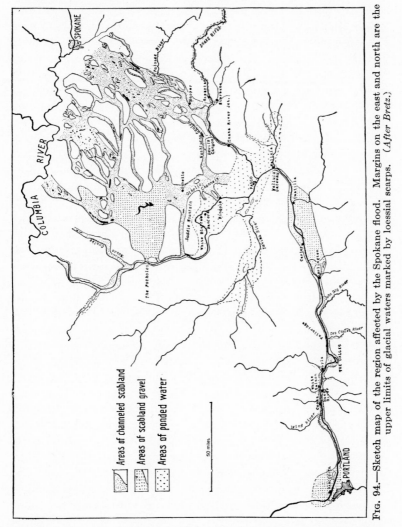

Fig. 94.—Sketch map of the region affected by the Spokane flood. Margins on the east and north are the upper limits of glacial waters marked by loessial scarps. (*After Bretz.*)

precipitation is so closely related to altitude. It ranges from 5 in. at Pasco, where the Snake and Columbia Rivers join, to 18 in. at Spokane. The Waterville Plateau is an exceptionally wide tract of plateau summit. Being in the immediate rain shadow of the Cascade Mountains it receives less rain than Spokane whose altitude is lower.

In general aspect and vegetation much of the area is almost desert. There are some large areas of drifting sand and very scant vegetation. The drier parts have no trees, not even cottonwoods, along the streams. Sage brush is the dominant form of life. At places bunch grass grows between the sage bushes. The higher the surface the greater the proportion of grass. Along the higher northern edge bunch grass almost excludes the sage brush. Here wheat culture extends westward to the Waterville Plateau which is similar in productivity to the Palouse district on the east.

Coulees and Scablands.—This district is distinguished by a type of erosion topography in some respects unique, not known to be exemplified elsewhere in the United States or equaled elsewhere in the world. The parts thus characterized are known as scablands.[1] These are strips of bare or almost bare basalt, roughly eroded and generally channeled by canyons known as coulees. As each strip of scabland throughout its width has been eroded to a lower level than that of the remaining original surface, and as the vertical-walled channels within each strip are numerous and intersecting, the term coulee is not always applied to one particular gorge but is sometimes used to designate an entire strip of scabland. The strips themselves merge here and divide there, forming a net-like pattern, enclosing remnants of the original plateau surface. This is true of all except Moses Coulee, the most western of all, which is isolated midway between Grand Coulee and the Waterville Plateau. The total area of scablands is at least 2,000 square miles or one-fifth of the district here considered.

In general these coulees traverse the district from northeast to southwest. They represent approximately the normal drainage lines of the present day but more accurately the lines of Pleistocene drainage. Most of them now carry water rarely if at all. These coulees and scablands result from erosion by

[1] Bretz, J Harlen, The Channeled Scablands of the Columbia Plateau, *Jour. Geol.*, vol. XXXI, pp. 617–649, 1923; also *Geogr. Rev.*, vol. XVIII, pp. 446–477, 1928. For discussion of some of the theories involved see Wash. Acad. Sci. *Jour.*, vol. XVII, pp. 200–211; Bretz, J Harlen, The Dalles Type of River Channel, *Jour. Geol.*, vol. XXXII, pp. 139–149, 1924; Alternate Hypotheses for Channeled Scablands, *Jour. Geol.*, vol. XXXVI, pp. 193–223 and 312–341, 1928.

glacial streams of great volume and steep gradient escaping from the ice-covered area to the north.[1] As the plateau in its larger aspect was smooth but in detail rough, these great streams spread widely, dividing, subdividing, and reuniting in web form and stripping the mantle rock from broad belts (Fig. 94). Within the web or between the great strips are remnants of the original surface, preserving the loess cover and the mature drainage pattern of the Palouse country.

The entire coulee system begins abruptly at the limit of glacial advance a few miles south of the Spokane and Columbia Rivers. Its limit is equally sharp on the west and south where the out-flowing waters were received by the master streams, Snake and Columbia, running in valleys ample enough to carry all the water to the sea, not without floods but without further crossing of the uplands. The Palouse River follows the easternmost belt of scablands beyond which no drainage issued from the ice-covered area, and scablands are wanting. Toward the northwest the coulees become more widely spaced. The Waterville Plateau has none.

Where the Ellensburg beds overlie the basalt, scablands are absent, the conditions for their development not being fulfilled (page 261). There are also about 1,000 square miles of surface covered by gravel spread out and laid down by the streams that made the coulees. This area is adjacent to the lower course of Crab Creek, south of the Great Northern Railroad. The surface is relatively low and streams converging here lost not only their cutting power but much of their transporting power.[2]

The old channels in these scablands reveal a peculiar lack of grading (Fig. 95). All stream beds, here or elsewhere, are more or less subject to local scouring in time of flood. Thus deep holes are made but generally filled again between floods when the deeper water is relatively quiet. On the other hand the floods here referred to seem habitually to have excavated basins, not in loose material but in the solid basalt which is, however, broken into blocks by closely spaced vertical joints. One such rock basin, south of Moses Lake, is 75 ft. deep below its down-stream

---

[1] It has been suggested that a sudden draining of glacial Lake Missoula may have furnished the water necessary for this work (see p. 222).

[2] A map of scabland areas and gravel deposits is given by Bretz accompanying his paper on Channeled Scablands of Eastern Washington, *Geogr. Rev.*, vol. XVIII, pp. 446–477, 1928.

rim.[1] Such basins are repeated at intervals along the same channel and the channels are many, generally separated by tabular masses of basalt. Thus a peculiar topography is produced which is more or less characteristic of the 2,000 square miles of scablands.

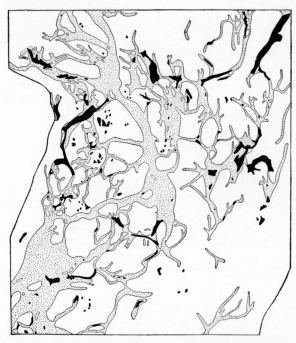

Fig. 95.—A part of the Drumheller Channels in the scablands of Washington. The whole area lies within the channel floor of the great spillway of the Spokane flood. Deeper local channels are stippled. Rock basins are shown in black. Note branching and intersection of channels. (*After Bretz. Reproduced by the courtesy of The American Geographical Society from The Geographical Review, vol.* 18.)

For the interpretation of such features it is fortunate that we have at the present time a single illustration of similar features being made elsewhere. This is at The Dalles of the Columbia, just above the entrance to the gorge through the Cascade Range.[2] Were the water removed from this channel a topography would be revealed showing all the striking features

[1] U. S. Geol. Survey, Corfu topographic sheet.

[2] In the paper referred to above, the *Jour. Geol.*, vol. XXXII, pp. 139–149, 1924, J Harlen Bretz describes the peculiar features of the Columbia Channel at The Dalles and points out their homology with those of the scablands.

of the scablands, including a rock basin whose bottom is 90 ft. below the rim on the downstream side. In the production of such features Bretz notes three essential factors; (1) a stream of large volume, (2) high gradient, and (3) close vertical jointing. In most streams one or more of these factors are wanting. Even in this district not all the basalt that was washed bare is thus channeled but "there are hundreds of miles of channels of this character on the plateau, none of them along present major streams and many of them without even intermittent streams."

Grand Coulee.—The well-known Grand Coulee differs in some respects from those described. In this the main canyon is so large and continuous that the interlacing of channels and other scabland features is not prominent. This difference in character results from a difference in history.[1] All the smaller coulees farther east were made in a pre-Wisconsin glacial epoch when the escaping waters were not concentrated into one great stream but crossed the plateau in nine or ten main courses, interlacing but never combining into a single stream. At that time the Grand Coulee, although independent of the others, had much the same character but apparently became incised much more deeply across the higher part of the plateau. In the last, or Wisconsin, glacial epoch, the Columbia River east of the Grand Coulee was not covered by ice, but west of that a glacial lobe from the Okanogan Valley crossed and blocked the Columbia Gorge, damming back its waters until they rose to the level of the former Grand Coulee. Then they followed that depression to the lower course of Crab Creek by which they rejoined the Columbia. The glacial waters of this epoch, although not so abundant as in the former epoch, concentrated all their energies along a single course. The stream, moreover, was probably larger then than now.

The present Grand Coulee north of Coulee City is a canyon, 800 to 900 ft. deep and one and one-half to four and one-half miles wide. Its nearly vertical walls are of basalt, of which a dozen or more sheets may be seen at some places (see Fig. 84, page 227). The basalt thins toward the mountains on the north,

---

[1] RUSSELL, I. C., A Geological Reconnaissance in Central Washington, U. S. Geol. Survey, *Bull.* 108, 1893;

CALKINS, FRANK C., Geology and Water Resources of East Central Washington, U. S. Geol. Survey, *Bull.* 118, p. 18, 1905;

BRETZ, J HARLEN, Glacial Drainage on the Columbia Plateau, Geol. Soc. Amer. *Bull.*, vol. 34, pp. 573–608. 1923.

exposing the granite which made the pre-basalt surface. The floor of the coulee is nearly flat but the old channel is locally clogged with glacial and wind-borne material forming shallow basins which retain alkali lakes.

Farther south the plateau level declines and the valley is less deep but the gorge reappears at intervals by a drop of the former stream bed over a basalt cliff, the site of a former waterfall. A feature of this kind three miles south of Coulee City is extraordinary. Here the vertical plunge of the stream was 400 ft. to the level of the present lake which fills a pothole of unknown

Fig. 96.—Head of lower Grand Coulee, looking south from the brink of the old cataract. Pothole Lake at the right. (*Photo by E. J. Evans. Reproduced by courtesy of The American Geographical Society from The Geographical Review, vol. 18.*)

depth. A similar fall is found several miles to the east. It indicates that the stream had several parallel channels or that the current was concentrated along more than one axis in a channel four miles wide.

Like Shoshone and other falls in this province, these were of the Niagara type, retreating up stream and leaving gorges in their wake. There are few features in the United States possessing at the same time the lonely grandeur, the historical significance and the accessibility of these extinct Niagaras which have been so little visited and remain so little known.[1]   South.

[1] The first mentioned fall three miles from Coulee City is in a state park and reached by excellent highways.

of this point a series of lakes occupies the axis of the valley, the water percolating from one to the next. The northern members are therefore fresh. The last of the series is Soap Lake whose water is so strongly alkaline as to feel slippery to the hands.

South of Soap Lake and the Great Northern Railroad the course of glacial drainage was not confined by canyon walls. It followed the present drainage lines of Crab Creek, a stream of feeble and precarious flow. Moses Lake lies along this line but is fed mainly by springs, its waters escaping by seepage and evaporation. It remains sufficiently fresh for stock.

Moses Coulee.—Ten miles west of the Grand Coulee and isolated from the rest is Moses Coulee. Although smaller it is much like its eastern neighbor even in the matter of cataracts. One of these drops 400 ft. over three distinct ledges in less than a mile. Like all the others it had a pre-Wisconsin history and like the Grand Coulee it was used again by waters escaping from the last glacier.[1] By this course the water from the Okanogan lobe joined the Columbia.

Pleistocene Submergence.—It has long been believed that the lower parts of this section were covered by water in late Pleistocene time. It is now recognized that the land was temporarily below sea-level though the water was kept fresh by the outward current. Submergence extended almost to Lake Chelan on the north and perhaps 50 miles up the Snake River from its mouth. The highest points known to have been submerged are now more than 1,200 ft. above the sea.[2] The physiographic effects were not large but some of the coulees are known to have been partly filled and their bottoms made flat. Scattered boulders borne by icebergs constitute the principal evidence.

Resources.—In the eastern part of this district the topography and soil between coulees do not differ from those of the eastern margin of the district. Farther west the loess is less and less in evidence; drainage systems are less mature and the typical landscape of the Palouse country disappears. Except for the scab-

---

[1] BRETZ, J HARLEN, Geol. Soc. Amer. *Bull.*, vol. 34, p. 578, reproduces a photograph of Moses Coulee showing the wide channel of Spokane age sharply trenched by the canyon made in the last glacial epoch.

[2] *Ibid.*, The Late Pleistocene Submergence in the Columbia Valley, *Jour. Geol.*, vol. XXVII, pp. 489–506, 1919. The work of Russell and other former workers in this field is cited.

lands, wheat culture is extended westward until increasing aridity makes it impossible. Near the northern edge, however, where the altitude is greater and rainfall sufficient, the same type of farming extends to the Cascade Mountains. Elsewhere grazing is the chief industry but limited by lack of water. Within reach of water this district shows all the familiar and regrettable effects of overgrazing. Farther from the water holes the bunch grass is preserved. It is probable that the water-bearing beds in the lacustrine formation or between the basalt sheets would afford water enough for wells to make most of the area available for grazing. There is not much reason to expect flowing wells[1] but the water could easily be pumped by windmills. As may be judged from any good map, there is not much human population.

Yakima District

Between the Columbia and the Cascades is an area drained largely by the Yakima River. As Yakima is also its largest and most widely known center of population the area is described here as the Yakima district.

Transverse Ridges.—The distinctive character of this district is largely due to its geologic structure. From the great north-south axis of the Cascade uplift, subordinate anticlines extend eastward, at least eight in number, between the Wenatchee River on the north and the Columbia on the south. These anticlines form ridges rising from 1,000 to 3,000 ft. above the intervening valleys, the floors of which are in general not much more than 1,000 ft. above the sea. In a general way these ridges trend east (Fig. 97), some of them reaching to the Columbia and several of them still farther. Their axes are, however, not strictly parallel. In more than one instance two or three of them merge at their eastern extremities thus enclosing structural basins which are at the same time topographic and drainage basins.

In general the ridges are even-crested and smooth-sided, the consequent streams on their sides having only young valleys. Most of them are not high enough to be forested but bear, instead, an abundant growth of bunch grass with some sage brush. They very much resemble the Waterville Plateau. The southernmost of these ridges, between the Yakima and Columbia

---

[1] Calkins, Frank C., Geology and Water Resources of a Portion of East Central Washington, U. S. Geol. Survey, *Wat. Sup. Pap.* 118, p. 90, 1905.

Rivers, is a broad upland called "Horseheaven" on account of
its abundant grass. A little wheat has been raised here by dry-
farming methods, but the yield per acre is small.

Structural Valleys.—The intervening valleys are in all essential
respects arms or isolated portions of the arid plain on the east.
The rainfall is usually not more than 12 in. Sage brush is the

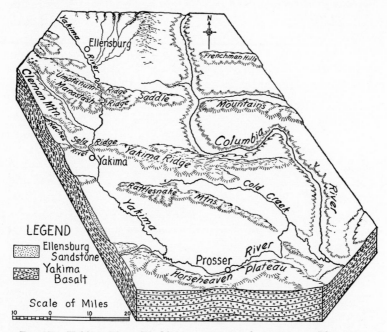

Fig. 97.—Yakima River, Washington, an antecedent stream. The east-west
ridges are due to crustal movement. The river had previously adopted its
southerly course and maintained it by cutting down as fast as the ridges rose.
(Drawn by Guy-Harold Smith.)

chief native vegetation. The Yakima River in crossing these
valleys from north to south is locally bordered by cottonwood
trees.

The underlying rock in most of these valleys is the Ellensburg
formation consisting of sand, gravel, silt and volcanic ash. This
fills the basins to a depth of at least 1,200 ft. in some places. It
thins out toward the ridges which are made almost wholly of
basalt.

The Yakima River.—The Yakima River after descending the
east slope of the Cascade Mountains north of lat. 47°, turns

south and crosses five of these ridges and the intervening valleys before turning again east at the north foot of the Horseheaven Plateau. It follows the edge of this plateau to the Columbia.

The Yakima crosses not only the transverse ridges but also the intervening troughs in a young valley. It cuts through the ridges in gorges from 1,000 to 3,000 ft. deep, choosing its points of crossing without regard to sags in the crests which might in several cases have been found nearby. The channel is also incised in the valley bottoms, some more, some less, because they are of unequal elevation. Throughout its course are beautiful entrenched meanders, not only where the stream crosses the lowlands but in the deep gorges traversing the uplands.

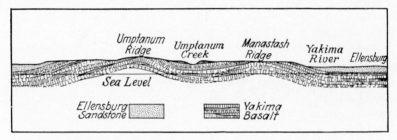

Fig. 98.—North-south section at the eastern base of the Cascade Range in Washington. The ridges are represented as anticlines which were base-leveled and again uplifted. (*G. O. Smith, U. S. Geol. Survey.*)

Physiographic History.—The physiographic history of these features is interpreted as follows by Smith and Willis:[1] The flows of basalt and the deposition of the Ellensburg sediments (late Miocene) occurred before the elevation of the Cascade Range. The rise of that range at the close of the Miocene was accompanied by gentle transverse folding. Thus ridges were formed which extended east from the mountains just as the present ridges do. The whole Cascade region, along with these lateral ridges, was then reduced to a peneplain. Although the anticlinal ridges were thus destroyed, their places were represented on the geologic map by strips of basalt, laid bare by denudation. In the intervening synclines the sediments were preserved. The peneplain formed at this time is known as the Cascade peneplain.

[1] Smith, G. O., and Willis, Bailey, Contributions to the Geology of Washington, U. S. Geol. Survey, *Prof. Pap.* 19, 1903; also Smith, G. O., Ellensburg folio 86, U. S. Geol. Survey, 1903.

Later the Cascade peneplain was uplifted to the height of the present mountain tops. At the same time the transverse folds on the east side were renewed along axes almost agreeing with those of the former uplifts. It is the result of this last folding which we observe in the present ridges. Their smooth tops and sides represent the peneplain, and the small streams which are beginning to furrow their sides are consequent on the last uplift.

Whatever may have been the nature of the drainage during the earlier events here recounted, it is certain that the Yakima River was following its present course before the final uplift, while most of its tributaries are just where they should be if determined by that uplift; *i.e.*, they are consequent. The Yakima is an exceptionally good example of an antecedent stream, the evidences of this character being repeated in each ridge crossed.

Reflection will show that if the surface of the ridges is recognized as a peneplain, it is impossible to account for the present features by a single uplift. This peneplain has been traced westward into the Cascade Range and it also extends eastward until it can no longer be distinguished from surfaces of other origins.[1]

Artesian Water.—Where the anticlines coalesce and make closed basins, the structure is favorable to artesian water. The chief development has been in the basin which contains the city of Yakima, *i.e.*, in the valleys of Atanum and Moxee Creeks. The artesian water in this basin comes from porous beds near the base of the Ellensburg formation.

Irrigation and Agriculture.—This is the chief irrigated district of Washington,[2] and the Yakima and Naches Rivers are the leading streams. The Kittitas Valley (containing Ellensburg) is chiefly engaged in producing hay and other field crops and vegetables. The Atanum-Moxee Valley (containing the city of Yakima) is one of the best known fruit districts of the United States and is also famous for its hops. Farming is chiefly on the broad areas of fertile alluvial soil. This is in large part a reworked volcanic ash, one of the most abundant constituents of the Ellensburg formation. The residual soil on the basalt

---

[1] See p. 252 for doubt expressed on this point.

[2] For information on agriculture, irrigation, and soils see SMITH, G. O., Geology and Water Resources of a Portion of Yakima County, Washington, U. S. Geol. Survey, *Wat. Sup. Pap.* 55, 1901; also Ellensburg folio 86, 1903.

and sediments of the ridges is fertile and productive where sufficiently thick. Farming in many of these valleys has been greatly fostered by the construction of storage reservoirs by the U. S. Reclamation Service on the headwaters of the Yakima, Naches, and their tributary streams from the Cascades. This has increased the area of irrigable land by several hundred thousand acres. The climate is too arid for successful dry farming except where ground water and soil conditions are peculiarly favorable as on a few alluvial terraces.

North Central Oregon

Distinguishing Features.—The area between the Cascade Mountains on the west and the Blue Mountains on the east is not sharply distinguished in character from the districts described above. Its underlying rocks are the same. North central Oregon is somewhat higher than south central Washington and has more rainfall, though not so much as the Palouse country.

The drainage is north to the Columbia and is sufficiently vigorous to cut steep-sided channels and gorges in the basalt. To a greater extent than in eastern Washington the minor streams in this district head in the mountains and therefore carry more water. From the Walla Walla on the east to the Deschutes on the west at least five streams from the mountains reach the Columbia. As many more travel the greater part of the distance before uniting with one of the five. It is by the character of the drainage that this district is distinguished and delimited from the Harney section on the south. Like the rest of the Walla Walla section it drains to the sea. Local base level is sufficiently low and the gradient sufficiently steep to make possible the headward growth of tributaries and the cutting of sharp valleys. The Harney section has internal drainage and the salt lakes that mark its local base level lie so high that streams can do but little cutting.

The Deschutes River.—The largest and most interesting stream in this district is the Deschutes, which flows north to the Columbia at the east foot of the Cascades. It flows through a plateau composed chiefly of basalt. From Cline Falls to its mouth (144 miles) it flows in an abrupt canyon 500 to 2,000 ft. deep. Its fall is large, being 13 ft. per mile for the last 100 miles, and about twice that amount for the next 100 miles above. In many ways the Deschutes is a remarkable stream. Its waters are clear and fresh and it has the distinction of having the most uniform flow of any river in the United States which does not flow from a great lake. It is very unlike a desert stream. At its junction with the Columbia, its maximum recorded discharge is only six times its minimum.[1] With most rivers this ratio rises into the hundreds. In its middle course, for 50 miles above the mouth of the Crooked River, the Deschutes never varies in height more than 8 to 10 in. This striking phenomenon is due to the fact that its bed is cut in sheets of cellular basalt.[2]

Fig. 99.—Canyon of the Crooked River, six miles below Prineville, Oregon. It must not be understood that the term canyon necessarily designates a valley no wider than the stream. Both in the Columbia and the Colorado Plateaus the type here shown is quite as common as that of the Grand Canyon of the Colorado, or that of the Yellowstone, or the Royal Gorge of the Arkansas. The flood plain within this canyon affords the only farming land of the district. For some distance above Prineville its width is four or five miles. (*Russell, U. S. Geol. Survey.*)

Into this porous substance all flood waters disappear, and are stored. In times of drought the deficiency is made good from this reservoir.

This uniformity of flow together with its high gradient makes the Deschutes particularly valuable as a prospective water-power resource. It has been estimated[3] that 600,000 hp. can easily be developed on this stream and its chief tributary without interfering with the use of the stream for irrigation. This plan provides also for the irrigation of a half million acres.

[1] Grover, N. C., U. S. Geol. Survey, *Wat. Sup. Pap.* 344, p. 12.

[2] Russell, I. C., U. S. Geol. Survey, *Bull.* 252, p. 20.

[3] Lewis, John H., Deschutes River, Oregon and Its Utilization, U. S. Geol. Survey, *Wat. Sup. Pap.* 344, p. 83.

The chief tributary from the east is the Crooked River (Fig. 99). For more than 100 miles (in a direct line) it follows a devious westerly course, most of the way in a canyon. It is fed largely by springs. Below Prineville where the canyon is four to five miles wide the waters of the stream are all used for irrigation.

Topography.—On its eastern side this district merges with the Palouse Hills and has the same character, the soil being loess or volcanic ash and the topography between streams being

Fig. 100.—Typical mound topography of the southwestern portion of the Columbia Plateau. View near Maupin, Oregon. These mounds are of volcanic ash resting on basalt. None exceed 6 ft. in height or 75 ft. in diameter. Their composition is identical with that of the sheet of volcanic ash which in some localities covers the surface uniformly. (*A. C. Waters and C. W. Flagler.*)

determined partly by wind. Toward the west the valleys become more canyon-like, or coulee-like, partly because of greater aridity and partly because the soil cover is less thick, and streams, even intermittent streams, cut into the basalt. The depth of valleys tributary to the Deschutes River reaches a maximum of 1,000 ft. In the more desert parts, as in the immediate valley of the Columbia River, the angularity of the streamless valleys is marked. To a smaller extent than in the Palouse country, the surface between streams exhibits the same rolling topography as that which prevails on the loess.

The soil in the Deschutes Basin is in part residual, but no large area is free from an admixture or a thin cover of æolian or ashy material. Volcanic ash is present, at least as an admixture, growing more abundant toward the south. It is not improbable that the surficial mantle is to be accounted for mainly or wholly by deposition from volcanic eruption rather than by æolian distribution.[1] In this part of the lava plateau, and to some extent in others, are numerous small circular or oval mounds (Fig. 100). Those of this district range from 15 to 75 ft. in diameter and from one to six feet in height. Such mounds occur in various parts of the United States (page 445) and doubtless have various origins. In the Columbia Plateau they seem to be the remains of a thin sheet of volcanic ash, otherwise stripped away from the underlying basalt.[2]

Agriculture.—Over large stretches the soil is very thin, as in the Warm Springs Indian Reservation, west of the Deschutes below the mouth of the Crooked River. Here the soil is rarely more than two feet thick and there are areas where the fresh basalt is exposed.

East of the river the soil is much thicker. A strip east of and parallel to the Deschutes below the mouth of the Crooked River is known as the "Haystack Country" and "Agency Plain." This is in all essentials similar to the great wheat belt of eastern Washington. Most of it remained as public land until 1903 when it became known that this area was suited to dry farming and the growth of wheat. It was then rapidly taken up.[3]

The need of water for domestic purposes in this district is about as pressing as in eastern Washington. Tank wagons often haul water 12 to 15 miles. There is reason to hope for success with artesian wells in some parts. Many of the springs which enter the Crooked River near its source are warm (60 to 87°) indicating that the water has come from a depth of perhaps one-half mile. Although this does not assure success with artesian wells it is a favorable indication.

---

[1] WATERS, A. C., and FLAGLER, C. W., Origin of the Small Mounds on the Columbia River Plateau, *Amer. Jour. Sci.*, vol. XVIII, p. 212, 1929.

[2] WATERS, A. C., and FLAGLER, C. W., *loc. cit.*, p. 215. This paper names 13 theories to account for these and similar mounds and cites representative papers from the literature of the subject.

[3] LEWIS, JOHN H., *loc. cit.*, p. 77.

HARNEY SECTION

General Character.—In central Oregon, south of the drainage basin of the Crooked River, is an area of some 8,000 square miles, 4,000 ft. or more in height, allied on the one hand to the Columbia Plateau and on the other to the Great Basin. Like the former it owes its general form and much of its elevation to nearly horizontal beds of basalt. Like the latter it has internal drainage, its scanty streams being lost in the loose mantle rock or ending in alkaline lakes. Throughout most of the area the bedrock is deeply covered with uncompacted material. In its eastern part, around Malheur and Harney Lakes, where drainage centers, this loose material is alluvial detritus. Elsewhere it is made up wholly or in part of broken-up pumice, ranging in size of grain from dust to lapilli. Popularly it is called "sand." Throughout several thousand square miles, known as the "Great Sandy Desert," this material covers the surface to a great depth, locally as much as 70 ft.[1]

Rocks and Topography.—Nearly the entire section is underlain by sheets of basalt approximately parallel to the surface and apparently not much eroded. For aught that is known the present rock surface may be the original surface of the flow. A few large patches of lava are, in fact, so recent as to be bare and unaltered. After the last flows, except those just mentioned, came explosive eruptions which yielded great quantities of ash, covering the larger part of the Harney section and extending beyond it on the west and north.

The area in which this material is deep and the surface level is the Great Sandy Desert. It is a poorly defined area elongated from northwest to southeast, 150 miles long and 30 to 50 miles wide, crossing the Harney section and extending beyond its limits. Russell says of its topography "so nearly uniform is the surface that one might drive throughout its length without meeting any greater obstruction than the rigid sage brush and without finding a single watering place for men or animals."[2]

The central and western parts of this section are dotted with volcanic cones so numerous that Russell counted 50 from one commanding summit. Most of them are not more than 200

---

[1] Russell, I. C., Preliminary Report on the Geology and Water Resources of Central Oregon, U. S. Geol. Survey, *Bull.* 252, p. 16, 1905.

[2] *Loc. cit.*, p. 13.

ft. high. Some of these are very young. Others are the remains of older and much eroded volcanoes. Several low escarpments are apparently due to erosion but aside from these and the volcanic hills and mountains the central and eastern parts of the section have little relief.

Vegetation.—The character of the Great Sandy Desert is not to be ascribed wholly to want of precipitation. This is, indeed, small but the aridity is intensified by the porous character of the mantle rock into which all surface waters disappear. East of the desert, in the vicinity of Harney and Malheur Lakes, bunch grass is abundant and the grazing industry has been important. The valleys of three small streams that enter the lakes are important irrigated districts.

The general level of this section is not much above 4,000 ft. At this level the moisture is insufficient to support trees. At a slightly higher level junipers are able to grow. These are, therefore, found on some of the buttes. Pines become possible at about 5,000 ft. Above that level they clothe the Cascades of southern Oregon.

Drainage System.—The two shallow lakes, Harney and Malheur, survive throughout the year, although suffering great changes in extent from season to season. They are bordered by swamps, showing that the soil here is of different character from that of the desert to the west. The direction of drainage is from Malheur Lake to Harney, which affords the final evaporating surface for the drainage system. Its water is therefore very alkaline while that of Malheur Lake is relatively fresh.

Until recently this entire drainage system constituted the headwaters of the Malheur River which flows east to the Snake. Then a lava flow crossed the main stream forming a dam, behind which the water rose and spread. Had its level risen 10 to 15 ft. more it would have overflowed the dam. Meantime, however, it had spread so widely that evaporation was equal to the total supply. In this case exterior drainage was changed to interior drainage, not by a change of climate but by a change of topography. The climate is the same now as before, and the same above the dam as below it.

CHAPTER VII

COLORADO PLATEAU PROVINCE

THE PROVINCE AS A WHOLE

Distinguishing Features.—The name here applied to a vast province of 130,000 square miles was first given to a much smaller area in the Grand Canyon district. The larger area is often appropriately spoken of in the plural as the "Colorado Plateaus." Its several parts, some of them strongly differentiated, have certain features in common which distinguish the entire province from its neighbors.

The first distinguishing feature is approximate horizontality of its rocks. In the contiguous provinces the strata are folded. Tilted beds in this province are limited to a few great monoclines and the borders of a few local uplifts. There is no lack of steep slopes but, except on recent volcanic features, they are due to erosion guided in some cases by structure. In all the larger features the relation between structure and erosional history is obvious. There is no other province in America where such relations are more impressive.

The second distinguishing feature of the province is great elevation. Aside from canyon bottoms, no considerable portion of it is lower than 5,000 ft. Between this and 11,000 ft., there are plateaus of all altitudes, some of them being higher than the nearby mountain ranges. Except where bordered by high mountains on the north and east, this province generally overlooks its neighbors from a bold escarpment.

A feature which distinguishes the entire province is its remarkable canyons, not one but hundreds. These are favored by (1) elevation of the plateau above its base level; (2) strength of rocks and aridity of climate, both causing steep slopes to waste slowly; (3) the bordering mountains and strips of lofty plateau which provoke rainfall and thus furnish water to the through-flowing streams. Lastly (4) it must be remembered that canyons are features of youth. Considered with reference to the current

274

erosion cycle, the great canyons of this province are about at their maximum of grandeur.

A characteristic feature developed in horizontal strata in an arid climate is the retreating escarpment. A series of beds

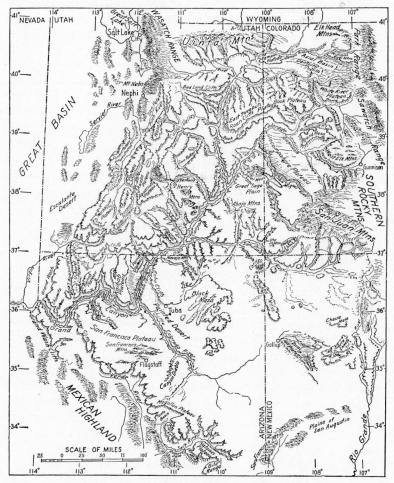

Fig. 101.—Index map of the Colorado Plateau province. (Drawn by Guy-Harold Smith.)

100 ft. thick or 1,000 ft. thick may have been stripped away for miles; yet the remaining portion may have suffered little or no loss of height. Our common conception of erosion involves the wearing down of a surface somewhat uniformly rather than a

wasting at the edges by which a mass of horizontal beds is reduced in extent without greatly eroding the surface of the part that remains. As pointed out by Dutton,[1] this latter process seems to be dominant on arid plateaus. It is clearly expressed in some of the major features of the province and also in countless minor plateaus and mesas that give character to the region. The process cannot be discussed here in detail but it is closely connected with the removal of talus. To one unacquainted with arid lands, the general insignificance of talus as compared with the importance of cliffs is one of the surprising features of the topography in this province.[2] (Note the absence of talus in Fig. 111, page 304.) In regions like the Colorado Plateau it is not to be assumed that the retreating escarpment is a single straight vertical face. This would offer a small area of attack and the cliff would retreat but slowly. It is rather a fringe, shredded by many canyons and hundreds of tributaries. The forces of weathering attack not only from the front but from the flanks and rear, and spread destruction both ways from every crack. A common result is an isolated mass left standing for a while in front of the line. None the less, in a large view the cliffs form a good line and the frayed margin is narrow as compared with the well-preserved plateau.

Variety among Parts.—The constituent plateaus, more or less sharply separated and receiving local names, are numbered by the dozen. Some rise, table-like, above their neighbors on all sides; others abut, step-like or terrace-like, against their higher neighbors; a few are basin-like, limited on all sides by infacing cliffs. They differ also in the degree of dissection by streams, ranging from widespread flats or rolling lava plains to deeply and maturely dissected mountains of erosion. As a consequence of differing altitudes and stages in the erosion cycle, the several plateaus differ greatly in temperature, rainfall, and vegetation. At one extreme are hot wind-swept deserts; at the other are cool, lake-dotted, dense forests; between these are open forests, park and grass lands.

More than half of the area of this province has trees of some kind but good forests are much more restricted. Yellow pine occurs above 7,000 ft. where the rainfall is sufficient. In favored

[1] DUTTON, U. S. Geol. Survey, *Mon.* 2, pp. 62–63, 1882; see also FENNEMAN, N. M., U. S. Geol. Survey, *Bull.* 730, p. 126*ff*, 1922.

[2] GREGORY H. E., U. S. Geol. Survey, *Prof. Pap.* 93, p. 130, 1917.

spots are good forests or, it may be, park lands where patches of pine and aspen alternate with grasslands. Below 7,000 ft. pinyon and juniper may fairly cover the surface or, with lower altitude and greater aridity, be widely scattered. The higher portions of the province, embracing most of the western and southern margins, are comprised in national forests but such reserves are by no means all forest covered.[1]

Subdivision into Sections.—The primary basis of subdivision is altitude and extent of dissection. Some of the section boundaries follow the great escarpments, others are vaguely located between areas of unequal dissection.

The greatest crustal uplift was in the southwestern part of the province, *i.e.*, in the *Grand Canyon district;* but here also was the greatest denudation. It is not, therefore, at present the highest part of the province, although locally rising above 9,000 ft. This section is almost coextensive with the area of exposed Carboniferous rocks but includes areas where these are covered by volcanics.

From the Grand Canyon district the strata dip north along the western side of the province, indicating that the uplift at the north was less. For this reason (aided locally by a lava cover) a north-south strip in central Utah escaped the prodigious wasting which occurred farther south, hence the remnants here stand higher than in any other part of the province. These remnants on the west side, some of which rise above 11,000 ft., are known as the *High Plateaus of Utah.* The ascent of 5,000 to 6,000 ft. from the Canyon district on the south to the summit of the High Plateaus is made by a series of rock cliffs and terraces among the most remarkable in the world. These great cliffs are retreating escarpments and mark the present stage of denudation in its progress toward the north.

Continuous with the strip of High Plateaus on the western border of the province is a 50- to 100-mile strip running east along the northern border and abutting against the Uinta Mountains on the north. It consists of north-dipping beds limited on the south by a great escarpment. The higher southern margin is called *The Tavaputs Plateaus.* The whole section is known as the *Uinta Basin,* most of its interior portion being lower than the edges both structurally and topographically. It was preserved from wasting by the same circumstance which saved

---

[1] See U. S. Dept. Agr., map of National Forests.

the High Plateaus, namely that the greater uplift was to the south, and the denudation which began at the place of greatest uplift has not yet reached far enough north to consume this strip.

The remaining boundaries within the province are less definite. South of the Uinta Basin, between the High Plateaus on the west and the Rocky Mountains on the east, is a great area which by preeminence justifies the name of *Canyon Lands*. Tertiary and youngest Cretaceous beds, in so far as they covered this section, have been stripped back to their present limit in the escarpments already mentioned. These continue to recede while canyons, already numerous and at places intricate, continue to increase in depth and number.

Canyons are not everywhere closely spaced, especially in southwestern Colorado and the adjacent part of Utah (see page 315) but they constitute the chief characteristic of this great region. Canyons tributary to the San Juan extend this dissection a short distance into Arizona. Farther south, in both Arizona and New Mexico, the plateaus are less deeply and minutely canyoned. This is the *Navajo section.* It extends south in Arizona to the Little Colorado and its headwaters, the Puerco, and in New Mexico to the Zuni uplift. South and southeast of that dome, volcanic features are so numerous as to give character to the landscape and require separate treatment. This is the *Datil section.*

GRAND CANYON SECTION

Definition and Extent.—The Grand Canyon district has already been defined as that southwestern part of the province in which uplift was so great and denudation so deep as to expose Carboniferous rocks (see Fig. 110, page 300), the oldest rocks of the province, at altitudes of 7,000 to 9,000 ft. These same beds descend nearly to sea-level beneath the High Plateaus to the north. A similar descent to the east beneath the Navajo section is accomplished mainly by the great East Kaibab monocline and the Echo Cliffs monocline (Fig. 102), just east of the Little Colorado. At the southeast the surface beds of the Grand Canyon section dip gradually beneath the volcanic cover of the Datil section. Locally within the Canyon section the Carboniferous limestones are covered by lavas, but elsewhere, despite the local contrasts, there are certain topographic features that prevail throughout this section and are absent from the rest.

PLATEAUS NORTH OF THE CANYON

General Plan.—The section is cut in two by the Grand Canyon, north of which the country is again subdivided by great north-south faults. In part these are southward extensions of the

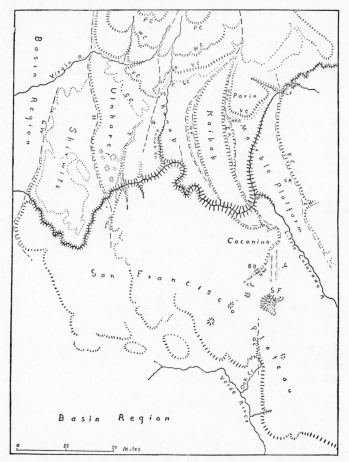

FIG. 102.—Sketch map of the Grand Canyon district. *GW*, Grand Wash escarpment; *H*, Hurricane escarpment; *T*, Torroweap Valley; *WK*, West Kaibab fault and monocline; *EK*, East Kaibab monocline; *SC*, Shinarump Cliffs; *VC*, Vermilion Cliffs; *WC*, White Cliffs; *PC* Pink Cliffs; *EC*, Echo Cliffs; *SF*, San Francisco Mountain. (*After Johnson.*)

same lines which subdivide the High Plateaus. In any case they belong to the same system, the members of which are narrowly spaced at the north but diverge toward the south where they occupy a belt 150 miles wide. The several plateau units marked off by these fault scarps differ in altitude, topography, and climate. In general they rise step-like from west to east, each step being roughly 1,000 ft.

Shivwits Plateau.—Farthest west is the Shivwits Plateau. Its western boundary (and that of the province) is the Grand Wash fault (Fig. 102) one of the great faults of the region, with a throw near the river of 7,000 ft.,[1] the escarpment being about 4,000 ft. The throw diminishes toward the north and gives out near the state boundary. On the line of this fault, the Shivwits Plateau overlooks the Grand Wash, a dry drainage course of the Great Basin. From the top of this escarpment more than 6,000 ft. above the sea, the plateau slopes gently eastward 30 miles to the foot of the Hurricane fault scarp. In topography and appearance the Shivwits is similar to the Uinkaret Plateau, next to be described.

Uinkaret Plateau.—Near the Colorado River, the Hurricane fault and its escarpment measure about 1,800 ft. The throw increases toward the north and becomes 6,000 ft. near the state line where it takes the place of the Grand Wash fault as the province boundary. This great fault is the western boundary of the Uinkaret Plateau.

The surface of this plateau, 8 to 10 miles wide and reaching north 50 miles to the "Chocolate Cliffs" (page 303) is dissected by shallow open valleys in the Kaibab limestone. Above this nearly level surface rise mesas and table lands, capped and protected by the remnants of ancient lava flows. Mount Trumbull, rising nearly 2,000 ft. above the plateau, consists of several lava masses. There are also young volcanic cones, perhaps 160 in all, some of which are as fresh as the lavas ejected by Mauna Loa within a century. At least one of the lava flows entered the canyon since it was cut to its present depth and has since been trenched by the river to a depth of 100 ft., but this was by no means the latest of the lava flows.

Kanab Plateau.—The Uinkaret Plateau ends on the east at the Toroweap fault scarp (700 ft.) which extends north from the canyon for 18 miles with diminishing altitude. East of that line is the Kanab, the broadest of the plateaus and least pronounced in its features. Its desert surface of small relief is divided midway by Kanab Creek, the only northern tributary

[1] Lee, Willis T., U. S. Geol. Survey, *Bull.* 352.

which comes down from the High Plateaus of Utah into the Grand Canyon. Even it can scarcely be said to do this, since its middle course in the Kanab Plateau is dry most of the year. It is a good example of "interrupted" stream.

Kaibab Plateau.—East of the Kanab is the Kaibab, the highest, most beautiful, and most interesting of the plateaus of the Grand Canyon region. Its altitude is from 7,500 to 9,300 ft. It rises above the Kanab by a combination of fault and monocline. On the other side the descent is made by the East Kaibab monocline by which the limestone beds descend again 2,500 to 4,000 ft. to form the platform in which the Marble Gorge is cut. Between these great displacements, 35 miles apart where the Kaibab is highest, and converging toward the north, the uplifted block forms the Kaibab Plateau.

Unlike the monotonous surface of the Kanab, that of the Kaibab is maturely dissected by rounded valleys of gentle slope not more than 300 or 400 ft. deep. Despite the ample rains of summer and snows of winter, the valleys on top of the plateau are streamless. Even the channels of the streams which cut them have been erased. Near the edges of the Kaibab the valleys deepen into ravines and carry streams. The upland is clothed with forests of pine, spruce, and aspen, opening here and there into grassy parks. Except in the higher parts where the spruce forms thickets, flowers bloom in profusion from June to September. Some springs are found and there are many ponds of fresh water in basins, probably due to the solution of the Kaibab limestone. This fact, like the absence of streams, points to subterranean drainage, a suggestion which is supported by the number of great springs which discharge into the canyon from the sides of this plateau.[1]

San Francisco Plateau

Extent.—The name Colorado Plateau was first applied to the district south of the great canyon. It was thus given the same rank as the Kaibab and others on the north side. Usage soon broadened the application of the name Colorado Plateau to cover both sides of the river. The name San Francisco Plateau, now applied to all that portion of the Grand Canyon section which lies south of the river, is taken from San Francisco Mountain, near Flagstaff.

[1] NOBLE, L. F., U. S. Geol. Survey, *Bull.* 549, p. 26, 1914.

Unlike the area north of the river, this large district is fairly homogeneous, except for the lava-covered area to be mentioned later. The great faults of the northern area stop either at the river or a few miles to the south; hence there are no sharp contrasts of altitude in short distances. Aside from the mountains the altitude ranges from 6,000 to 7,000 ft.

Topography and Drainage.—In a large way the slope of this plateau agrees with the regional dip of the rocks, which is north toward the High Plateaus and east toward the Echo Cliffs

Fig. 103.—Black Bill Park west of San Francisco Mountain at an elevation of 7,000 ft.; a characteristic view in the higher parts of the volcanic district of the Colorado Plateau in Arizona. The underlying rock is volcanic, covered locally with alluvium. The mountains in the background are volcanoes. At and above this elevation pines cover the surface, either in a scattered way, making "parks," or in good forests. (*U. S. Geol. Survey.*)

monocline (see page 278). The larger valleys lead northward toward the Colorado almost from the brink of the escarpment that makes the province boundary on the south. But this simple plan is modified by the great Kaibab uplift from which the rocks dip and the surface slopes south as well as east and west. Here the southward slope, though interrupted by the canyon, is resumed at its south wall and the local drainage is from the river.

The dominant style of the topography in the northern part of the San Francisco Plateau, like that of several of the plateaus north of the canyon, is a rolling surface with few steep slopes. This is due to approximately mature dissection by wide open valleys from 100 to 400 ft. deep. Where these lead toward the Colorado Canyon, their lower courses may be deeper and even canyon-like, but between the Little Colorado and Cataract Canyon, embracing all that part of the Grand Canyon which is best known, the smaller valleys on the south side lead away from, instead of toward, the Colorado. The southern rim of the canyon is, therefore, merely notched by these shallow valleys, whose heads are being continually cut away by the broadening of the canyon. The southeastern part of this section has much smaller relief than the rest, being at places nearly flat.

Below the level of the rolling surface, a few abrupt canyons have been cut by streams which may once have been larger but which exist now only as occasional floods of muddy water after torrents of rain. Canyon Diablo, a southern tributary of the Little Colorado, is a typical example well seen from the Santa Fé Railroad. Cataract Canyon of the same type is the chief one draining toward the Colorado.

Volcanic Features.—An area of 2,000 to 3,000 square miles centering near Flagstaff is covered by lava flows (Fig. 103 page 282) and dotted by several hundred volcanic cones. The highest of these is San Francisco Mountain, 12,700 ft. above the sea or 5,000 ft. above the plateau. None of the cones or lava flows are old and some bear no evidence of being made longer ago than yesterday, beyond the fact that they are cold (Figs. 104 and 105).[1] The topography of this part of the plateau is that of a large number of small lava flows of different ages, the older ones eroded, the edges of the younger often marked by abrupt and rocky slopes preserving the exact form in which the moving lava congealed.

A detail near the edge of this district which has excited much interest is Crater Mound, once known as Coon Butte. It is a funnel-shaped crater three-fourths of a mile in diameter and 600 ft. deep. Its rim rises from 120 to 160 ft. above the surrounding nearly level plain toward which it slopes and the beds dip with a steep gradient. The otherwise horizontal sandstones and limestones are turned up at angles of 10 to 80 deg., averaging perhaps 30 deg.

This crater derives its special interest from the fact that there is a total lack of any volcanic ejecta in or around it. There

[1] JOHNSON, D. W., A Recent Volcano in the San Francisco Mountain Range, Geogr. Soc. Phila. *Bull.*, July, 1907.

Fig. 104.—Surface of recent lava flow, Sunset Crater, near Flagstaff, Arizona. The hill in the background, having an altitude of more than 7,000 ft., is sparsely covered with yellow pine.   (*Photo by H. W. Fairbanks.*)

Fig. 105.—Young basalt cone on the eastern edge of the San Francisco volcanic field.   (*U. S. Geol. Survey.*)

are, however, large blocks of limestone on the surrounding plain which may represent the material blown out by a single steam explosion to make the great crater. Further interest attaches to this crater because of the suggestion that it may have been caused by the impact of a great meteorite. Many small meteorites have been found in the vicinity but no portion of the great meteorite supposed to be buried within the crater has ever been found, although a number of deep holes have been drilled in search of it. With either origin it is unique and deserves the attention given it.[1]

Climate.—The altitudes of the Grand Canyon section are reflected in the climate. The valley of the Little Colorado, less than 5,000 ft. above the sea, has less than 5 in. of rainfall per year, high temperatures, and a very strong diurnal range. Flagstaff, nearly 7,000 ft. high, is 10° cooler (average annual temperature 46°) and has an annual rainfall of 22 in., the greatest in Arizona.[2] A similar climate is observed on the Mogollon Plateau, the high edge of the province southeast of Flagstaff.

Between the Kaibab Plateau and the bottom of the Grand Canyon the range of climate is as great as from the mountains of Colorado to the Mohave Desert.[3] Winter snows are often 10 ft. deep on the Kaibab, while snow rarely falls in the lower half of the canyon and freezing is rare at the bottom. Summer heat is often intense.

The higher and more humid parts of the Canyon section are covered by open forests. This is true of the Kaibab Plateau and even of the border of the Grand Canyon south of the Kaibab. It also includes the higher levels around San Francisco Mountain (Fig. 103) and the edge of the province to the southeastward for 200 miles. This last is "from all points of view the finest forest in the southwest."[4]

[1] GILBERT, G. K., *Science*, vol. III, pp. 1–13, 1896; MERRILL, GEO. P., Smithsonian Miscellaneous Collection, vol. 50, pp. 461–498, 1908; Astron. Soc. Pac. *Pub.*, vol. 32, pp. 259–264, 1920 (includes a bibliography); FAIRCHILD, H. L., *Science*, vol. LXIX, pp. 485–487, 1929, gives an interesting history of the controversy, strongly favoring the meteoric hypothesis.

[2] ROBINSON, H. H., The San Franciscan Volcanic Field, Arizona, U. S. Geol. Survey, *Prof. Pap.* 76, p. 18, 1913.

[3] NOBLE, L. F., U. S. Geol. Survey, *Bull.* 549, p. 25, 1914.

[4] GANNET, HENRY, U. S. Geol. Survey, *19th Ann. Rept.*, pt. V, pp. 47–48; see also PLUMMER, F. G., Forest Condition in the Black Mesa Forest Reserve, Arizona, U. S. Geol. Survey, *Prof. Pap.* 23, 1904.

GRAND CANYON

Between the mouth of the Paria River (Echo Cliffs) and the Grand Wash, the Colorado River runs through the Grand Canyon. It is not to be understood that this is the only canyon of the Colorado. From the junction of the Green River with the upper Colorado (formerly called the Grand) to the Grand Wash, the Colorado flows 500 miles between canyon walls. Within this distance "there are only three points at which it is possible to reach the river with a wheeled vehicle. At a few other places pack animals may be taken to the water's edge."[1] Upstream from the Echo Cliffs the name Glen Canyon is applied as far as the Henry Mountains, north of which is the Cataract Canyon. From the Echo Cliffs to the Little Colorado (66 miles) is the Marble Gorge, a part of the Grand Canyon, two-thirds of a mile deep and exceptionally narrow.

Dimensions.—The length of the Grand Canyon below the Little Colorado, ignoring minor crooks and turns of the river, is about 200 miles. A straight line from end to end is 125 miles long. It is commonly described in divisions corresponding to the plateaus on the north; the Kaibab division 50 miles, the Kanab division 50 miles, the Uinkaret 25 miles, and the Shivwits 75 miles. In traversing this distance, the river falls from a level of 2,640 ft. to 1,000 above the sea. As the actual length of the river is 218 miles, the average fall is a little more than $7\frac{1}{2}$ ft. per mile or fifteen times that of the Ohio.

The canyon varies in depth from 3,500 ft. to 6,000; the latter depth is in the Kaibab division. West of that it has a depth of approximately one mile at the western edge of each fault block described on page 279.

The width of the canyon at the top ranges from a little less than 5 to more than 15 miles. The walls are, therefore, far from vertical as is sometimes mistakenly conceived. If such were the case, the Grand Canyon would be relatively uninteresting. Contrary to first impressions its grandeur and impressiveness are in large part dependent on the sculpture of its sides, which necessarily involves widening (Fig. 106). Parts of the less beautiful and little visited Marble Gorge conform more nearly to the primitive conception of a wonderful canyon. The narrowest point of the Grand Canyon below the Marble

[1] U. S. Geol. Survey, *Wat. Sup. Pap.* 556, p. 101, 1925.

Fig. 106.—A portion of the dissected north wall of the Grand Canyon showing the characteristic forms of tributary valleys in two cliff-making formations. The Tonto platform below shows acute, gully-like notches between rounded spurs; the upper bench shows rounded cirque-like valley heads between acute cusps. In other words, the lower bench has the topographic form characteristic of running water. The forms in the upper bench are those of the retreating cliff. Both types of valley head are found at both high and low levels. (*U. S. Geol. Survey.*)

Gorge is in the Kanab division, 4¾ miles, where the depth is more than a mile. At Havasupai Point there is a drop of 4,500 ft. in 1½ miles.[1] This is the steepest slope if the entire depth be considered, although there are vertical cliffs more than 1,000 ft. high.

The Stream in the Canyon.—The discharge of the stream varies from 1,300 to 200,000 sec.-ft. with an average of about 23,000 sec.-ft.[2] A depth of 40 ft. and width of 300 to 400 ft. are common. In flood it may rise 50 to 60 ft. higher. A stream of these dimensions with a fall of 7½ ft. to the mile may well be expected to erode effectively. The work of the Colorado is favored by the large amount of mud and sand which it carries. It is thirty times as muddy as the Ohio. Dutton has estimated that a boulder of hard rock six feet in diameter would be reduced to sand or mud in four years.[3]

Kaibab Division.—The portion of the canyon most seen by travelers is that which lies opposite Kaibab Plateau. It is not only the deepest (maximum 6,000 ft.) but, on the whole, the widest; a width of 10 to 15 miles is common. But this does not mean that there is any lack of steep, even vertical, faces, for the dissection of the slopes is very profound and highly intricate. If both sides sloped equally and uniformly toward the river, the descent would be but one foot in five or six. Such moderate slopes are indeed rare because of the profound chasms and deep alcoves which fringe the main trench or give detail to its sides. Some of the upper beds are red and the wash from these has stained the very massive Mississippian limestone known as the Redwall, the most conspicuous cliff maker in the canyon. Most of the formations retreat in terraces with cliffs from a few feet to a hundred feet high, but the Redwall formation rarely fails to stand out in a huge cliff several hundred to a thousand feet high. From end to end of the canyon, zigzagging around lateral chasms, surrounding majestic alcoves, encircling residual moun-

---

[1] For noteworthy figures see NOBLE, L. F., U. S. Geol. Survey, *Bull.* 549, pp. 23–25, 1914.

[2] SMITH, G. E. P., Univ. of Ariz. Agr. Exper. Sta. *Bull.* 95, p. 532, 1922. For amount available for power and irrigation, see LA RUE, E. C., and HOLBROOK, GEORGE, F., U. S. Geol. Survey, *Wat. Sup. Pap.* 556, Appendix A, 1925.

[3] DUTTON, C. E., U. S. Geol. Survey, *Mon.* 2, p. 243. For data on suspended matter in the Colorado River see HOWARD, C. S., U. S. Geol. Survey, *Wat. Sup. Pap.* 636, pp. 15–44, 1929.

tains, the same richly colored wall may be traced to the limit of vision.[1]

The northern brink of the canyon is here much farther from the river than the southern. The excellent topographic sheets of the U. S. Geological Survey show a dissected strip on the north side of the river fully three times as wide as that on the south side. Two principles of wide application are here concerned: (1) The slope and drainage of the plateau on the north side are toward the river; those on the south side, from the river. (2) The much greater height of the Kaibab Plateau induces greater rainfall. Both these factors give to the ravines on the north more water and more rapid growth. All such tributary valleys are

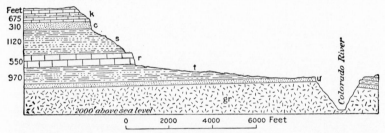

Fig. 107.—Section in south wall of the Grand Canyon at Grand Canyon station, Arizona. *k*, Kaibab limestone; *c*, Coconino sandstone; *s*, Supai formation; *r*, Redwall limestone; *t*, Tonto group (Cambrian); *u*, Unkar group (Algonkian); *gr*, granite. (*Darton, U. S. Geol. Survey.*)

short and steep and generally dry. Shinumo Creek at the west side, one of two or three living streams, is 12 miles long and has a fall of 5,400 ft. or 450 ft. to the mile.[2]

A highly significant feature in the Kaibab division is the Tonto Platform, a terrace about 3,000 ft below the brink (Figs. 107 and 108). It has a gently sloping surface with a maximum width of more than a mile. The canyon thus appears in cross-section to have a flat bottom of considerable width trenched by a steep-sided gorge. The substratum of the Tonto Platform is the resistant Tapeats sandstone, the lowest Cambrian formation in this section. As seen in the table on page 293 this strong formation is overlain by the Bright Angel shale, a weak formation easily stripped by erosion where the overlying Muav limestone

[1] The reader should if possible look up the descriptions of Captain Dutton. —U. S. Geol. Survey, *Mon.* 2, p. 145.

[2] NOBLE, L. F., *loc. cit.*, p. 23.

FIG. 108.—Tonto Platform: View eastward up the Kaibab division of the Grand Canyon from the level of the Esplanade under Havasupai Point. *PS*, end of Point Sublime; *V*, Vishnu schist; *T*, Tapeats sandstone (the strong formation underlying the Tonto platform); *BA*, Bright Augel shale; *M*, Muav limestone; *R*, Redwall limestone; *Ss*, Sandstone of Supai icrmation; *Ssh*, shale of Supai formation; *C*, Coconino sandstone.   (*Photo by N. W. Carkhuff, U. S. Geol. Survey.*)

has been removed. With insufficient attention to these stratigraphic facts, the Tonto Platform has sometimes been regarded
as evidence of two erosion cycles in the making of the present
canyon (see page 292).

Fig. 109.—Grand Canyon at mouth of Toroweap Valley. The level of the
plateau surface is maintained by the Kaibab limestone *k*, whose edge is caused
to retreat by the wasting of the underlying Coconino sandstone *c* and Hermit
shale, thus stripping the strong sandstone beds of the Supai formation which
underlies the broad rock terrace or Esplanade. Below that level the rocks are
almost all strong. This is one of the steepest parts of the Grand Canyon, the
width at the level of the Esplanade being about equal to the depth below that
level. (*Photo by J. K. Hillers, U. S. Geol. Survey.*)

Kanab Division.—About at the place where the Kaibab
Plateau gives way to the Kanab, the canyon changes its form.
The Tonto Platform is at first interrupted and then disappears.

At the same time another shelf comes into prominence some 2,000 ft. higher. This is the Esplanade (Fig. 109). The valley above the Esplanade is about 2,000 ft. deep and five or more miles wide, limited by continuous walls, kept steep by a capping of Kaibab limestone. The rocky floor of this upper valley is not far from level. The inner gorge is steeper and simpler, more like the ordinary conception of a canyon than is any other part of the Grand Canyon, unless it be the Marble Gorge. Opposite Toroweap Valley the inner gorge is 3,000 ft. deep and only 3,500 to 4,000 ft. wide at the top. Both inner and outer canyons in the Kanab division are therefore more steeply walled than any portion of the Kaibab division. They are also less dissected by lateral ravines because of the smaller rainfall on the lower plateau.

The substratum of the Esplanade is the strong Supai sandstone. This and all the lower formations are exposed in a series of vertical cliffs some of which are 600 ft. high. These are separated by talus-covered platforms so narrow that the entire descent of 3,000 ft. appears to be by an almost simple cliff with a slope of at least 60 deg.

The cross-section of the canyon in the Kanab, as in the Kaibab division, is strikingly similar to that of a graded valley deeply trenched by reason of regional uplift and renewed erosion. This deceptive resemblance is all the more striking because the Toroweap Valley and several other dry canyons enter at the level of the Esplanade. It is not to be wondered at, therefore, that at one time the canyon was interpreted as the product of two erosion cycles. The Esplanade was seen as the downstream continuation of the Tonto Platform before exact surveys showed the two actually present in the same section, separated by a vertical interval of 2,000 ft.

West of the Kanab the character of the canyon changes but little. It ends abruptly at the Grand Wash fault, where the level of the plateau drops from 6,000 ft. down to 2,000 ft. West of that the stream has unimpressive bluffs, at most a few hundred feet high.

Relations of Form to Structure.—The interest which should attach to these varied forms is in large part lost, unless they are considered in the light of the structures which determined them. For this purpose a section of the formations traversed is here given.

STRATA EXPOSED IN THE GRAND CANYON[1]

Formation	Age
Kaibab limestone	
Coconino sandstone	Permian.
Hermit shale	
Supai formation	Permian and Pennsylvanian.
Redwall limestone	Mississippian.
Temple Butte limestone (local)	Devonian.
Muav limestone	
Bright Angel shale	Upper Cambrian.
Tapeats sandstone	
Sandstone, limestone, shale, and igneous	Algonkian.
Vishnu schist	Archean.

[1] NOBLE, L. F., U. S. Geol. Survey, *Prof. Pap.* 131, p. 60, also pl. XIX; MOORE, RAYMOND C., U. S. Geol. Survey, *Wat. Sup. Pap.* 556, p. 127.

Some of the relations between rock structure and valley form are here stated beginning with the Kanab division. The Kaibab limestone and the Coconino sandstone, which make the upper part of the wall of the outer canyon, are strong formations underlain by 550 ft. of weak Hermit shales. This relation results in sapping. The Supai is mainly a strong sandstone, flooring The Esplanade and making the brink of the inner canyon. All the beds exposed beneath it are strong as might be inferred from the almost simple wall. The Tapeats sandstone in this section is below the river level, hence there can be no Tonto platform.

Passing upstream (east) to the Kaibab division, the weak Hermit shale becomes thinner and the overlying Coconino sandstone thicker and stronger. The exceptional sapping of the upper wall therefore disappears. This alone would probably cause the absence of the Esplanade. At the same time the Redwall is sapped by the wasting of the Bright Angel shale which, in this section, is well above the river. The strong Tapeats sandstone is thus stripped, forming the Tonto Platform. It thus becomes clear why the Esplanade and the Tonto Platform are not well developed in the same section, though in less typical form they do overlap, a fact not observed by those who have interpreted both as parts of a valley floor developed in a cycle which has since been interrupted.[1]

[1] NOBLE, L. F., The Shinumo Quadrangle, Grand Canyon District, Arizona, U. S. Geol. Survey, *Bull.* 549, pp. 21–22, 1914.

In the western part of the Kaibab division, because of the structural uplift, the river cuts entirely through the Cambrian into the very strong Archean. Here the gorge below the Tonto platform is very narrow and steep. In the eastern part of this division weaker Algonkian rocks intervene beneath the Cambrian. The latter is sapped and the narrow inner gorge is absent.

The East Kaibab monocline carries these softer rocks down beneath the level of the river. The Marble Gorge is therefore cut in the strong Redwall and associated hard strata. The features of the inner Kanab Gorge are therefore reproduced. Still farther upstream where the Echo Cliffs monocline carries the Carboniferous below stream level, the valley is necessarily crossed by the outcrop of the soft Triassic (see geologic map, Fig. 110, page 300). Here, for a short distance near the mouth of the Paria (Lees Ferry) there is no canyon, but open monoclinal tributary valleys instead. Above this monocline, the valley is cut in the same Triassic and Jurassic sandstones which make the Vermilion and White Cliffs; the canyon walls are correspondingly steep and brilliant.[1]

Some of the forms shown in the canyon have been much relied on in the interpretation of its history. It is therefore highly important to note the close correspondence, here described, between geologic structure and topographic form.

HIGH PLATEAUS OF UTAH

Delimitation.—On many of the older maps the Wasatch Mountains are made to extend south by west almost to the southern border of Utah. Properly speaking, the range ends with Mount Nebo in lat. 39°45′. The village of Nephi and the San Pete Valley Railroad mark their southern limit. South of that line are the High Plateaus. The western scarp of the plateaus is in line with the western slope of the mountains. The plateau strip is, however, somewhat broader than the Wasatch Range and it continues northward on the east side of the mountains. The High Plateaus section is arbitrarily limited on the north by a transverse valley 1,000 to 2,000 ft. deep, followed by the Denver and Rio Grande Railroad. The width of this section ranges from about 30 miles at the north to nearly 150 miles in lat. 38°.

[1] Davis, W. M., An Excursion to the Plateau Province of Utah and Arizona, Mus. Comp. Zool. Bull., vol. 42, p. 32, 1905; Gregory, H. E., and Moore, R. C., U. S. Geol. Survey, Prof. Pap. (in press).

Its total length is about 175 miles. Its altitude increases somewhat from north to south, culminating in Aquarius Plateau, 11,600 ft. high, in lat. 38°. On the west these plateaus overlook the Great Basin from a superior altitude of 3,000 to 5,000 ft., the descent being for the most part an escarpment. On the east the canyon lands of Utah are overlooked in the same way. From the brink of the precipices at the south end, the view extends beyond the Grand Canyon, 100 miles away.

General Character.—These highlands are in the truest sense plateaus. The rocks which compose them are horizontal and they have broad undulating surfaces. To an observer at the same altitude they appear flat. The rims, however, are notched by erosion; therefore, to an observer looking up from the base they appear serrated; hence the older conception of a mountain range.

The entire belt of the High Plateaus is again subdivided by two trenches of great depth into three longitudinal strips. Each of these strips in turn consists of from two to four plateaus generally separated one from another by escarpments or valleys.[1]

The plateaus of the western strip named in order from north to south are Pavant, Tushar, and Markagunt; those of the central strip are Sevier and Paunsagunt; those of the eastern strip, Wasatch, Fish Lake, Awapa, and Aquarius.

Sevier-San Pitch Valley.—The western one of the two longitudinal depressions is occupied for 125 miles in its southern part by the Sevier River flowing north by east. The northern part of the valley for 50 miles is occupied by the San Pitch River flowing south to join the Sevier. The combined stream then breaks through the western line of plateaus into the desert of the Great Basin.

The chief cause of this continuous and nearly straight depression is the great Sevier fault on its east side. This fault forms the western scarps of the Paunsagunt and Sevier Plateaus, with throw ranging from 800 to 3,000 ft. Farther north it crosses the valley and the throw is toward the east. Here it forms the west wall of the San Pitch Valley as far north as the Wasatch Mountains. The east wall of the valley at this place is formed by a gigantic monocline 7,000 ft. high, leading up to the flat top of the Wasatch Plateau.

[1] Consult Atlas accompanying U. S. Geol. Survey *Mon.* 2, Tertiary History of the Grand Canyon District.

Near the junction of the two streams, the Sevier and the San Pitch, the Sevier Valley is 8 miles wide at the base and 30 miles from summit to summit of the opposing slopes. In its native state it was a sage-brush desert. With increasing altitude, toward the south, there is good pasture. With irrigation this valley has become one of the most important in Utah. As early as 1880 Dutton spoke of it as the "granary of Utah." It has many villages and is traversed by a railroad for more than 100 miles.

Grass Valley.—East of the Sevier Valley and almost parallel to it at a distance of 15 to 25 miles is Grass Valley. It is occupied in its southern part by the north-flowing East Fork and in its northern part by the south-flowing Otter Creek. This northern portion, and sometimes for convenience the entire depression, is known as Grass Valley.

This valley is on one of the greatest known lines of displacement. In its central portion it is a great fault with downthrow to the west, its scarp forming the east wall of Grass Valley. Farther north it becomes the great 7,000-ft. monocline dividing the Wasatch Plateau from the San Pitch Valley to the west. In line with it to the south is the East Paunsagunt fault. Here the Paunsagunt Plateau (the downthrown block on the west) rises high above the Paria Valley on the east, showing that the present east-facing scarp is due to erosion in a later cycle after the first topographic effects of faulting had been obliterated[1] (page 324).

Structural Features.—The western boundary of the province is itself in part determined by a great fault, parallel to those which have caused the longitudinal valleys. This is the northward extension of the Hurricane fault, best known in the Grand Canyon district (page 280). Its scarp bounds the Markagunt on the west where its maximum throw is 5,000 ft. Farther north it diminishes. On the west boundary of the Tushar, it dies out or is obscured by lava flows.

The general plan of the High Plateaus is therefore clear. They are broken into three strips or series by great faults (locally monoclines) trending nearly north and south. The throw of these faults (with few exceptions) is to the west. Each plateau, therefore, overlooks other plateaus to the west and

---

[1] Moore, Raymond, C., personal communication; see Gregory, H. E., and Moore, R. C., U. S. Geol. Survey, *Prof. Pap.* (in press).

slopes to the east. The slope of the surface agrees in direction with the dip of the beds which rarely exceeds 3 deg.

Some of the plateaus are capped by lava flows which have at the same time increased their height and protected them from erosion. This cannot be regarded as an essential factor, however. While the highest of all, Aquarius, is lava covered, much of the southern margin is not thus protected and the Wasatch Plateau, 11,000 ft. high, has no lava at all. Where not protected by lava, the plateaus are maturely dissected into rounded hills often 500 ft. or more in height, generally covered with open forest above the level of 9,000 or 10,000 ft. The lava-capped members are found in various stages of dissection. Their valleys are, in general, younger and more angular as befits the lesser age and greater strength of these rocks as compared with the Eocene sediments.

Description of the Several Plateaus.[1]—The *Pavant* and *Tushar* on the west are least typical of the group. The former is "a curious mixture of plateau and sierra," its eastern side being tabular. The Tushar bears high mountains at its northern end where its rocks are also deformed, but farther south the whole is tabular. Here it averages 10,000 ft. high with "ridges of erosion, covered with spruce and aspen and grassy parks."

The *Markagunt Plateau*, the southernmost and farthest west of all, 11,000 ft. at highest, is covered in the northern and greater part with lava. This portion is "rough with hills and rocky valleys." At the south end the surface is on the Eocene, exposed at the edge in the great Pink Cliffs of which the "Cedar Breaks" are a detail. In this southern part the surface is one of "rolling hills rarely exceeding 600 ft., . . . grassy slopes and scattered groves of pine."

The *Sevier Plateau*, the most centrally located of all, is 70 miles long and 10 to 20 miles wide, more than 10,000 ft. high, lava-covered, its "summit carved into rolling ridges and valleys, deepening eastward into canyons." This plateau overlooks Sevier Valley to the west from the top of a great escarpment of dark volcanic rock, at places more than a mile high. The East fork crosses it in a profound canyon from Grass Valley to join the Sevier. Presumably the stream is antecedent but the extent to which these great faults are of the second generation is not accurately known.

[1] Most of this description and all of the quotations are taken from Dutton, "Geology of the High Plateaus of Utah."

South of the Sevier Plateau and overlooking the deeply denuded and rugged border country to the south and east and the Sevier Valley to the west is the *Paunsagunt Plateau*. The view from the brink of the limiting precipice is made memorable by the classical description of Captain Dutton.[1] Eocene strata form the surface and are exposed in the great Pink Cliffs of which the justly famous Bryce Canyon, now a national monument, is a detail.

The eastern strip begins at the north with the *Wasatch Plateau*, more than 11,000 ft. high, almost as high as the peaks of the Wasatch Mountains. It is 75 miles long, and generally less than 6 miles wide at the summit. It is capped by Eocene beds which break off at the east in the same Pink Cliffs already mentioned, whose westward retreat has all but consumed the Wasatch Plateau. On the west it descends 5,500 to 6,000 ft. to the San Pitch Valley in the great monocline mentioned on page 296. It has a rugged surface as might be expected from its exposure to rapid erosion.

South of Wasatch Plateau and separated only by the narrow valley eroded by Salina Creek, is *Fish Lake Plateau*, a narrow strip 12 miles by 2 with an altitude of 11,000 to 11,400 ft., forest-clad and included in a National forest. From its summit, the peaks of the Wasatch Mountains, 150 miles away, are plainly visible.

Next to the south comes *Awapa Plateau*, 2,000 ft. lower than Fish Lake Plateau but still rising 1,800 to 3,000 ft. above Grass Valley on the west. Despite its more than 9,000 ft. of altitude (at the western edge) this plateau of volcanic rock bears almost no trees but only sage brush and some grasses. It has no springs or running water; "an endless succession of hills and valleys with stony soil; here and there a sharp canyon 400 to 500 ft. deep."

The eastern line of plateaus ends at the south in the *Aquarius Plateau*, 35 miles long by 10 to 18 miles wide and 10,500 to 11,600 ft. high, the highest and most beautiful and interesting of all; a great lava-covered remnant bounded by lofty retreating cliffs throughout more than three-fourths of its circumference. The descent from its eastern rim is 5,500 to 6,000 ft. Looking up to this plateau from all sides, its nearly straight rim is seen

[1] DUTTON, C. E., *loc. cit.*, p. 253.

"like the threshold of another world." Its name[1] suggests at once its character and the classical tastes of the man who first made this region known to science. Among all the plateaus, this alone was high enough to support glaciers in the Pleistocene period. The effect of these is seen in the numerous lakes which are still fed from melting snows. The abundant precipitation supports dense spruce forests which open here and there in grassy parks. The view from its summit is vividly described by Captain Dutton.[2]

ROCK TERRACES OF SOUTHERN UTAH

General Description.—The descent from the southern end of the High Plateaus to the plateaus of the Grand Canyon district is by a series of great rock terraces with an aggregate height of 6,000 ft. (Fig. 102 page 279). The width of the terrace belt is generally 30 to 40 miles. For 100 miles east and west it is typically developed. Toward the east, as Colorado River is approached, the terrace belt widens greatly and loses its simple character. Throughout the entire length three cliffs are continuous and, for a part of the distance, two others. The platforms leading out from the foot of one cliff to the brink of the next are generally not more than 10 miles wide. The heights of the several cliffs range from a few hundred to two thousand feet. Far from being straight, their edges are indented by branching canyons, large and small, notched by reentrant angles, serrated by great promontories, and attended by island-like outliers. This carving of the margin is important in determining the rate of cliff recession.

The drainage of the great terraces is southward toward the Colorado. Only the Virgin River at the west is perennial throughout its course; the Paria in the east, and the Kanab in the center are "interrupted"; all others carry water only in floods, some of them at long intervals. Numerous dry canyons dissect all the terraces. The major streams flow in a series of canyons, cutting deep into the southern edge of each terrace and emerging upon the surface again at the foot of each great escarpment.

---

[1] Aquarius was the water bearer of Roman mythology. His name is given to the eleventh sign of the Zodiac. Among other classical names note *Tantalus Creek* flowing east from this plateau.

[2] Geology of the High Plateaus of Utah, p. 286.

These great rock terraces give evidence at the same time of retreat to the north and of a former southward extension. Of the 10,000 ft. of strata now exposed in them at least 6,000 ft. covered the wide plateaus on both sides of the Grand Canyon. Mean-

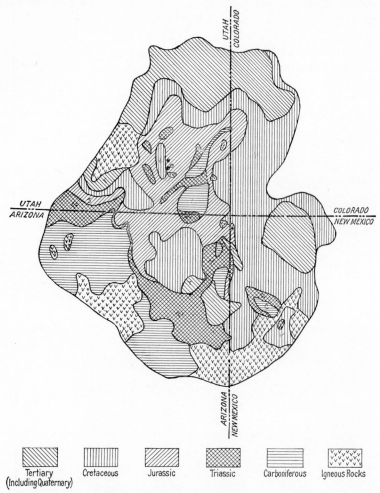

| Tertiary (Including Quaternary) | Cretaceous | Jurassic | Triassic | Carboniferous | Igneous Rocks |

Fig. 110.—Generalized geologic map of the Colorado Plateau province.

time the cliffs continue their northward retreat and the High Plateaus are wasting away.

It is not to be understood that the wasting and retreat of these cliffs goes on everywhere at the same rate; or that the retreat already accomplished has been mainly since the last great uplift. Parts of these cliffs have been greatly freshened since that uplift rejuvenated the streams and inaugurated the "canyon cycle." It is within the basins of such rejuvenated streams that wasting is rapid, giving rise to such-spectacular features as Bryce and Zion Canyons and the Vermilion Cliffs near the Marble Gorge. However, this difference among localities in the rate of wasting should not obscure the major fact that the present position of such escarpments represents only one transient stage in the great process of denudation (consult geological map, Fig. 110).

The Pink Cliffs.—The highest in order of the great cliff series are the Pink Cliffs of the lower Eocene. These begin at the brink of the High Plateaus. They present precipices 800 ft. high around the Paunsagunt and are especially high and imposing on the southern promontories of the Aquarius Plateau. Weathering along vertical joints has at places carved the wall into the likeness of a colonnade. Bryce Canyon in the edge of the Paunsagunt Plateau and the Cedar Breaks in the edge of the Markagunt are the most celebrated localities of intricate dissection.

Cretaceous Slope and Kaiparowits Plateau.—Beneath the Eocene, the Cretaceous consists of 4,000 to 5,000 ft. of pale yellow and brownish sandstones with shales of various grays. West of the 112th meridian this system does not generally make cliffs. The descent across its great thickness is by a rough sloping belt, 4 to 10 miles wide; "rolling ridges of yellow sandstone, long sloping hillsides and rocky promontories clad with large pines and spruces."[1]

At the 112th meridian, Paria River flows south to join the Colorado. The headwaters of this stream have pushed back the great cliffs to the north in a gigantic amphitheater 20 miles in diameter. Within this amphitheater and farther east, the Cretaceous beds make a stairlike succession of cliffs aggregating 4,000 ft. in height. At their summit a platform reaches back to the foot of the Pink Cliffs. This Cretaceous platform extends southeastward in a great peninsula to the Colorado River. This extension is the Kaiparowits Plateau, 60 miles long by 30 to 40 miles wide, between two southeast-flowing tributaries of the Colorado, the Paria River on the west and the Escalante

[1] DUTTON, C. E., *loc. cit.*, p. 31.

on the east.[1]   Its arid surface more than 7,000 ft. high is dissected
by complicated systems of dry canyons which almost prohibit
crossing.   It is surrounded on three sides by the Cretaceous
cliffs which appear in the Paria amphitheater.   The unbroken cliff
on the northeast side overlooking Escalante Valley is practically
unscalable for a distance of more than 50 miles.

The White Cliffs.—At the foot of the Cretaceous slope and
west of the Kaiparowits Plateau, is a drop of 1,000 ft. over the
White Cliffs in which are exposed the edges of the Jurassic sandstone.   This sandstone, 1,000 ft. thick and white at the west,
is reinforced at the east by 300 to 500 ft. of red sandstone above.
The white sandstone is a single stratum, marvelously cross-
bedded.[2]   On this structure differential weathering and wasting
has carved "filigree tracery as beautiful as frost work."

The Vermilion Cliffs.—At the foot of the White Cliffs begins
the rolling and canyon-cut platform which slopes south 5 to 10
miles to the brink of the Vermilion Cliffs.   In these cliffs,
appropriately named by Major Powell, from 1,400 to 2,000
ft. of Triassic or Jurassic beds are exposed in a series of ledges
separated by steep slopes.   The rocks are mainly sandstones
of a rich red color.   Near the base are shales of the same color
which aid in sapping the cliffs.   Most of the sandstones are
closely and distinctly bedded, but at the top is a massive bed
200 ft. thick at the east, gradually increasing to 1,200 ft. at the
west end in the valley of the Virgin River.   The whole thickness
is affected by vertical joints which weathering has followed in
such a manner as to carve great columns and buttresses.   The
distinct and close bedding of the central mass gives the abundant
detail of alternating ledge and slope; the weakness of the shales
near the base and the strength of the sandstone above combine
their effects to maintain the steepness of the cliff.   Dutton
found this line of cliffs second only to the Grand Canyon in beauty
and grandeur.   "Throughout more than 100 miles the Vermilion
Cliffs present to the southward a majestic front richly sculptured
and blazing with gorgeous colors."[3]   As in most mountain views,

---

[1] The Kaiparowits Plateau is shown on the geologic map as an extension
of the Cretaceous system, surrounded by Jura-Trias.

[2] Excellent views of this and other features of the Grand Canyon district
are published by W. M. Davis with his paper, An Excursion to the Plateau
Province of Utah and Arizona, Mus. Comp. Zool. *Bull.*, vol. 42, 1903.

[3] Dutton, C. E., *loc. cit.*, p. 40.

especially in the desert or where color is an important element, the cliffs vary greatly in impressiveness according to the hour of day and the state of the weather.

East of long. 112° the Vermilion Cliffs make a southward detour into Arizona. The platform at their summit is thus broadened into the Paria Plateau[1] between 6,000 and 7,000 ft. high. This is distinctly lower than the Kaibab Plateau to the west from which it is separated by Houserock Valley, following the great East Kaibab monocline. It is this monocline that makes possible the preservation of Triassic and Jurassic rocks on the east by dropping them to a level at which they escaped erosion. The desert surface of the Paria Plateau is "scored with a labyrinth of dry canyons," tributary to the Paria and the Colorado.

Chocolate Cliffs.—Locally there is yet another terrace and cliff south of the Vermilion line before the broad plateau is reached in which the Grand Canyon is cut. These local cliffs, 400 to 1,000 ft. high, have sometimes been called the Chocolate Cliffs, though the word scarcely expresses the richness of their coloring. The rocks exposed in these cliffs are of Triassic age mainly the Moenkopi formation of weak sandstone and shale. The steepness of the cliff is due to a capping of strong Shinarump conglomerate 40 to 100 ft. thick. The position of these cliffs is indicated on the geologic map by the edge of the Triassic. At places the Vermilion Cliffs lie a few miles to the north; elsewhere the two lines of cliffs may merge.

Relation of the Great Cliffs to Geologic Structure.—The aggregate thickness of all formations cut across in these great rock terraces is about 10,000 ft.,[2] yet the summit of the Markagunt Plateau is only about 6,000 ft. above the desert at the foot of the Chocolate Cliffs. The maximum cliff heights named above, if added, would exceed 6,000 ft. The discrepancy results from the northerly dip of the strata, generally more than one foot in 100. If all the platforms intervening between cliff and cliff were free from talus, each would slope north to the foot of the next cliff. This is true of some of the terraces and especially of the great arid plateau south of the Chocolate Cliffs.

[1] This plateau is shown on the Willis geological map of North America as an area of Jura-Trias just south of the Utah-Arizona boundary between the Colorado River and the 112th meridian.

[2] Dutton, C. E., *loc. cit.*, p. 47.

UINTA BASIN SECTION

Structural Relations.—It has been pointed out (page 277) that the most uplifted portions of the Colorado Plateau are also the most deeply denuded and that those parts which, like the High Plateaus of Utah, now rise highest are in the synclines or structural depressions. The northern margin of the province is characterized by such a structural depression just south of the Uinta Mountains. Corresponding to this depression there

Fig. 111.—Little Book Cliffs near Palisade, Colorado, on the Colorado River east of Grand Junction looking north. The plateau above the escarpment is the edge of the Uinta Basin section. The valley of the Colorado at the foot of this escarpment is several miles wide at this place. This is one of the wide fertile valleys mentioned on page 308 as exceptional features of the Canyon Land section. (*U. S. Geol. Survey.*)

is a broad east-west strip of higher plateau which rises sharply above the denuded country to the south. It appears on the geologic map as a strip of Eocene sediments continuous with that of the High Plateaus and bordered on the south by older rocks. The Pink Cliffs of the Eocene in the High Plateaus turn east just below the 40th parallel and become the Roan Cliffs facing southward. There is no name in common use to designate the entire plateau north of these cliffs, but the term Uinta Basin is applied by geologists to more than its western half and the entire Eocene plateau may be called the Uinta Basin section.

The descent of 3,000 ft. from the Eocene plateau on the north to the general level of eastern Utah on the south, is made in two steps, the upper one of which is the Roan Cliffs. A few miles farther south the Book Cliffs[1] cross the edges of the coal-bearing beds of the Cretaceous. Eastward in Colorado the two lines of cliffs are poorly distinguished and the names Roan and Book are used interchangeably.

The plateau of which these cliffs are the southernmost edge slopes north in agreement with the dip of the rocks. Its high cuesta-like southern margin is known as the Tavaputs Plateau, divided into an east and a west member by the Green River which crosses it in a 3,000-ft. gorge known as Desolation Canyon. Throughout its length this plateau exceeds 8,000 ft. in height and much of it is over 9,000 ft. The northward dip and slope continue almost to the foothills of the Uintas where the beds again turn up. The wide open trough thus formed is drained by two tributaries of the Green River, the White on the east and the Du chesne (with its branch the Uinta) on the west. Large areas near these streams are below 6,000 ft. in altitude and some below 5,000 ft.

Topography.—Most of the section here described is a deeply dissected plateau, difficult to cross and but little known. Badlands occupy considerable areas especially in the basins of the White and Ashley Rivers. The crest of the Tavaputs alone remains fairly entire, not yet being notched to great depths by the headwaters of streams flowing down its slopes. East of the Green River this crest is followed by a long-established Indian trail, to the south of which sharp ravines descend the escarpment, while to the north many parallel streams separated by even-topped ridges descend in deep valleys to the White River.[2]

The Colorado River crosses this section near its eastern end cutting off an area some 40 miles in diameter in which are preserved fragments of a lofty lava cap forming Grand Mesa and Battlement Mesa. North and west of the Colorado, there is also an area of similar size called the Book Plateau, which is almost detached from the main body. Both these areas are

[1] So named by Captain J. W. Gunnison who traversed this country to determine possible routes for the Union Pacific Railroad.

[2] See description by ENDLICH, F. N., "Hayden Survey," 10th Ann. Rept., pp. 67–68, 1876.

dissected by radial streams leaving relatively narrow patches of uncut plateau between headwaters.[1]

Resources.—On the lower lands near the larger streams are some hundreds of square miles of good agricultural land, with a favorable climate and abundant water for irrigation.[2] Higher up, many of the slopes are too steep and the climate too severe for agriculture, but grass increases with altitude and grazing will no doubt flourish. Forests of pine are also important. Coal is found in the Book Cliffs throughout their length. The largest volume of oil shale known in the United States is in the Uinta Basin.

CANYON LANDS OF UTAH

General Character and Limits.—Next in geographical order comes a great area known as the "Canyon Lands" in southeastern Utah and southwestern Colorado, bordered on the west by the High Plateaus, and on the north by the Book Cliffs, reaching to the Rocky Mountains on the east and merging on the south with the deserts surrounding the Hopi and Navajo Indian Reservations. Canyons characterize the whole Colorado Plateau and the greatest of them is not in this area. Nevertheless the name Canyon Lands belongs to this section by preeminence. The Colorado flows through its middle portion in a deep, ragged canyon with many beautiful entrenched meanders, receiving tributaries in similar canyons, hundreds, sometimes thousands of feet in depth, each of which has its tributaries. In its most dissected parts, occurring mainly near the Colorado River or between it and the High Plateaus, the original plateau surface is left standing only in wandering ridges and irregular remnants. The climate, especially in its western and southern parts, is very arid, springs are rare, the streams are few, muddy and warm, the vegetation mainly sage and cactus with juniper and pinyon trees where the altitude is sufficient. The country is extremely difficult to cross without a knowledge of its few highways.

No other equally large plateau area in the United States has the ruggedness of these Canyon Lands. It is not to be expected, however, that a region so characterized should be

---

[1] These areas are best identified on the topographic and geologic maps of Colorado.

[2] POWELL, J. W., "Lands of the Arid Region," 1879.

everywhere uniformly rugged or that it should be sharply delimited from less dissected parts of the province. Northeastern Arizona has similar rocks, structure, and climate and it may at first seem strange that it is not so deeply eroded. The reason for the greater dissection of southeastern Utah is found largely in the eminences which border it on three sides. These provoke a larger rainfall and feed the main streams which thus become perennial. Such are the San Juan, Dolores, and Colorado from the Rocky Mountains, the Green from the Tavaputs and Uintas, and the Price, San Rafael, Fremont, and Escalante from the High Plateaus. A few deep canyons like these, well distributed through the area, lower the local base level of all minor streams and make profound and intricate dissection possible.

Margin in Western Colorado.—On the eastern margin of the Canyon Lands, the Colorado, Gunnison, and Uncompahgre Rivers have eroded relatively broad valleys in the less resistant Cretaceous rocks. This margin is not typical of the section but cannot well be separated in the discussion. Deriving their perennial flow from high mountains, these streams not only have larger valleys than do the streams of the same length wholly within the plateau, but afford the necessary water for irrigation.

The master valley of western Colorado is a great trough marked by the course of the Uncompahgre and its continuation in the Gunnison and Lower Colorado Rivers.[1] Generally the width of this valley ranges from 10 to 20 miles. In its northwesterly course to Delta, Colorado (lat. 38°40'), it follows a syncline between two parallel swells of the plateau structure. These swells determine the Mesa Inclinado on the east and the Uncompahgre Plateau on the west. Northwest of Delta it becomes a monoclinal valley, following the strike of strata which dip northeast from the Uncompahgre uplift toward the Grand Mesa, a part of the Uinta Basin section. This character is strikingly shown between Delta and Grand Junction (the mouth of the Gunnison) where, for some distance, the lowest axis of the wide valley lies on the outcrop of soft shales a few miles east of the river, while the river itself is entrenched in a fine 800-ft. canyon on the flank of the Uncompahgre uplift and

[1] This may be seen on the 3-sheet contour map of the United States, or, better still, on the contour map of Colorado issued by the Geological Survey of that state.

separated from the wide open valley by a cuesta of strong sandstone.[1]

Along the eastern margin of the section, the Uncompahgre, Gunnison, and Colorado Rivers generally have flood plains. At places these are fertile and may reach a mile in width, or several miles where rivers unite as at Grand Junction. Above this are sloping terraces, some with deep fertile soil already farmed, some with equally good soil still bearing sage brush, others covered with gravel or barren adobe, and still others white with alkali.

The relatively small areas lying above 7,000 or 8,000 ft. are more favored than the lower Canyon Lands.   The Uncompahgre Plateau in western Colorado is a long structural uplift with a summit level approaching 10,000 ft.[2] Gannett thus describes its higher levels:

Nowhere is the influence of elevation on the character of the vegetation more plainly marked.   In the interior, near the crest, the land is, to the Utes, one flowing with milk and honey.   Here are fine streams of clear cold water, beautiful aspen groves, the best of grass in the greatest abundance, and a profusion of wild fruit and berries, while the country is a perfect flower garden.   This extends as low as 7,000 ft., below which the scene changes to one in all respects the reverse.

Mesa Verde.—In the partial stripping of an arid plateau whose rocks are of unequal strength and not far from horizontal the retreating escarpment is as common as the canyon wall. Mesas result, either isolated or abutting terrace-like against still higher ground.   Where beds dip slightly, cuestas take the place of mesas.   Mesa Verde, in southwestern Colorado, really a cuesta, is of more than usual interest, partly physiographic and partly archeological.   It is the northwestern edge of a great coal-bearing sandstone formation which dips beneath the San Juan Basin of New Mexico (see page 314).   It rises to 8,000 ft. and is covered with cedar and pinyon.   The escarpment on the north is 2,000 ft. high, overlooking the lower plateau, arid and desolate except for several irrigated valleys.   The ramifying

---

[1] See GANNET, HENRY, "Hayden Survey," 8th Ann. Rept. p. 424, 1874.

[2] The Uncompahgre Plateau is easily identified on the U. S. contour map as the ridge whose northwest end is within the bend of Colorado River near the Colorado-Utah line, and which trends southeast between Gunnison and Dolores Rivers.

canyon of Mancos River, nearly 2,000 ft. deep, skirts it on the south.

A massive sandstone preserves the remnants of a south-sloping plain, but the many parallel canyons leading south to the Mancos have left the original plateau only a "hollow shell," like a "worm-eaten log."[1] The still almost unbroken crest at the northern edge of this plateau, reached but not yet seriously indented by ravine heads on the south, is similar to that of the Tavaputs Plateaus.

This small upland (some two or three hundred square miles) is of great interest because of the remains of cliff dwellings in the canyon walls, especially in the alcoves at their heads. This is one of the many localities on the Colorado Plateau whose archeological remains show ⁺ʰat inaccessibility was the prime requisite of a home among many Indian tribes of the southwest. It is not improbable that the rainfall was formerly greater. Water is now so scarce on this mesa that it would have to be carried long distances to these habitations. It does not seem probable that Indians who adopted such homes for fear of enemies, would take the risks involved in such remoteness from water. Nevertheless, the common assumption of a once greater rainfall is disputed. It is pointed out by H. E. Gregory that (1) water was collected in tanks or cisterns; (2) the Hopi Indians even at the present time are skillful in finding water beneath the dry sand washes; (3) such water was carried long distances and conserved, as shown by the fact that water jars and large containers were among the principal objects of Indian art; and (4) the use of water was reduced to a minimum.

The "Great Sage Plain."—A few large districts of the Canyon Lands show sufficient unity of character to justify separate description. One of these in southeastern Utah and southwestern Colorado is known as the "Great Sage Plain." The name is highly fitting if allowance be made for occasional canyons, hundreds of feet deep. In such distant views as may be had from Abajo, Ute, or other mountains, one sees a remarkably level and monotonous expanse of sage-covered plain. Even the canyons escape notice unless it be in the immediate foreground. The substructure of this wide flat is the strong Dakota sandstone

[1] NEWELL, F. H., *Nat. Geogr. Mag.*, vol. IX, 1898; see also ATWOOD, W.W., A Geographic Study of the Mesa Verde, Assoc. Amer. Geogr. *Ann.*, vol. I, 1911.

from which most of the higher and weaker Cretaceous beds have been stripped.   This description applies to an area limited on the south by the San Juan River and the Mesa Verde, on the east by the San Juan Mountains and on the west by Butler Wash, a monoclinal valley in long. 109°40′.   On the north the plain approaches the La Sal Mountains and the Dolores River.

The Dakota sandstone is a poor soil maker and the Great Sage Plain is mostly barren, but locally, as near the Abajo Mountains, the overlying Mancos shale has not been wholly carried away.   There remains a faintly rolling topography and a fertile soil, irrigated around Blanding by water from the Abajo Mountains.

Monument Uplift.—Another important unit, just west of the Great Sage Plain, is 100 miles long from north to south and 40 to 50 miles wide.   Structurally this large area of horizontal rocks is raised several thousand feet, being almost surrounded by outward-dipping monoclines.   In large part the upraised block has been stripped of its Mesozoic strata.   No one formation now forms the surface everywhere but for dozens of miles near the middle of the area the surface on the Coconino (Permian) sandstone bears the appearance of a stripped plain scored by canyons not closely spaced.   This is the "Grand Flat."   South of the San Juan, stripping is less complete.   The landscape is characterized by great steep-sided mesas and buttes of red Triassic rocks.   These are the "monuments" that give name to the district.   Again, north of the middle, Triassic rocks span the uplift in a great east-west causeway 15 to 20 miles wide and more than 1,000 ft. above the general level, or 8,000 ft. above the sea.   The higher part of this is Elk Ridge.   The entire uplift may be identified on the geologic map, Fig. 110, page 300.

This Monument uplift is almost surrounded by inward facing cliffs.   Comb Ridge monocline on the east is one of the most remarkable monoclines of the province.   It is marked for 100 miles by the serrated Comb Ridge formed by the Navajo-Wingate (Jurassic) sandstone.   Only locally does this crest rise above the plateaus on either side but it lies between deep and continuous monoclinal valleys.

Economically, the lower parts of the Monument uplift are, at best, but moderate pasture land.   Elk Ridge has forests of pine and excellent pasture.   Intermediate levels including the Grand Flat have thickets of pinyon and juniper.

Local Uplifts.—Within the great area of the Canyon Lands are a number of volcanic and orographic features in which the country deviates from a typical plateau character. The Henry Mountains west of the Colorado River and south of the Fremont are a group of laccoliths,[1] rising 4,000 ft. above the plateau surface. Of similar character are the La Sal and Abajo Mountains east of the Colorado River, Ute Peak near Mesa Verde, and the Carrizo Mountains in the northeast corner of Arizona. Navajo Mountain near the Colorado River on the Utah-Arizona boundary is a laccolith of special interest because it is so young that the sedimentary covering of the igneous rocks is still entire. Viewed from a distance it is described by Dutton[2] as a segment of a sphere cut off at 70 deg., but this description is not applicable from all sides.

These laccoliths may occur singly, as in the example just given, or a single mountain group may contain many laccoliths. They may be almost uneroded like Navajo Mountain, or, as in the Henry Mountains, the intruded igneous rock may now be exposed in the crest while the former sedimentary cover appears only in hogbacks or in far-off cuestas.

Mild flexures and warpings are common in the Canyon Lands as in other sections of the Colorado Plateau. The largest feature of this kind is San Rafael Swell between the San Rafael and Fremont Rivers. It is a mild doming of the strata the upper ones of which have been truncated, producing inward-facing escarpments similar to the great rock terraces of southern Utah. Of equal interest, although smaller, is the elliptical uplift farther south, bounded on the east by the Water Pocket flexure and descending westward beneath the Kaiparowits Plateau. In its central portion the older and now denuded strata rise in a much eroded dome, rimmed in by the "Circle Cliffs" about 1,000 ft. high, the outcropping and retreating edges of the younger beds which once covered all. The erosion of still higher strata has gone further; they now form concentric cliffs and cuestas farther back. The whole is a rather desolate waste of varicolored rocks

[1] GILBERT, G. K., Geology of the Henry Mountains, U. S. Geogr. and Geol. Survey of the Rocky Mountain Region, 1880. In this memorable volume the word *laccolite* (since changed to *laccolith*) was first used. The report also discusses various physiographic processes which had been little discussed at the time but which are now treated in textbooks.

[2] "Geology of the High Plateaus of Utah," p. 290, U. S. Geol. and Geogr. Survey of the Rocky Mountain Region, 1880.

exposed in scalloped cliffs and deeply scored platforms.   All these structural features are wholly ignored by the major lines of drainage while their tributaries follow courses in obvious conformity with the structure (see page 320).

(see page 320)

NAVAJO SECTION

General Description.—A vast region in northeastern Arizona and northwestern New Mexico is here designated the Navajo section from the name of an Indian reservation which has thus far been its chief economic use.   It is mainly a country of sandstone with lesser amounts of shale.   As the beds are generally not quite horizontal and have been subject to great erosion in an arid climate, the mesa, cuesta, rock terrace, retreating escarpment, canyon, and dry wash are the distinctive features of the landscape.   In some parts volcanic necks and buttes are abundant.   Altitudes are for the most part between 5,000 and 7,000 ft., with considerable areas outside of both limits.   No stream except the San Juan receives water from outside the area.   Rainfall is only moderate even in the higher parts and probably as low as three inches in parts of the Painted Desert on the west.   Hence the volume of flowing water is too small to cut great canyons as in the section to the north.   None the less, the canyon is the dominant type of valley and no large area is without them, most of them carrying water only after rains.   Gregory[1] calls attention to the enormous accumulations of coarse alluvium always waiting to be forwarded by the occasional floods.   At the same time, despite the prevalence of cliffs, talus slopes are rare, as in the Sonoran Desert to the south.

As in other parts of the Southwest, pinyon and juniper are almost the only trees on the mesas and slopes below 7,000 ft. Near the upper limit they are at places abundant, elsewhere scattered, and the greater part of the area bears only sage brush and bunch grass and their associates.   Even these give way at places to blown sand or bare rocks.   The mountains and mesas, of limited extent above 7,000 ft., are in part covered with yellow pine.

Structurally, this large area consists of two synclinal basins separated by the east-dipping Defiance monocline which trends north-south near the state boundary (Fig. 113).   On this trun-

---

[1] U. S. Geol. Survey, *Prof. Pap.* 93, p. 12.

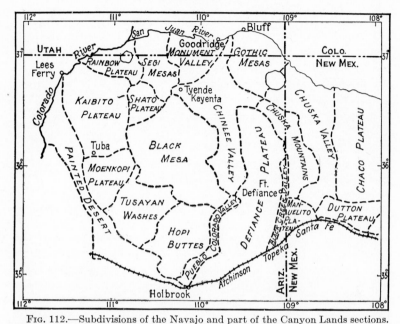

Fig. 112.—Subdivisions of the Navajo and part of the Canyon Lands sections. The general map (in pocket) should be so drawn as to include Numbers 7, 18, 19, and 20 in the Canyon Land section. (*After Gregory, U. S. Geol. Survey.*)

The following subdivisions are distinguished and described by Gregory: (1) Dutton Plateau; plateaus and mesas rising to 7,500 ft. A. T.   (2) Chaco Plateau: broad scarped plains bearing mesas, with wide swales trenched by shallow canyons.   (3) Chuska Valley; similar to Chaco Plateau but lower surface truncating the dipping beds of a shallow syncline, making some cuestas and hogbacks.   (4) Manuelito Plateau; steep-sided flat mesas above 7,000 ft., separated by flat valleys or washes.   (5) Chuska Mountains; steep-sided, flat-topped remnants of horizontal sandstone reaching to 9,000 ft. A. T. and in part forested. (6) Carrizo Mountains; laccolith truncated by roughly flat surface 8,000 to 9,000 ft. high.   (7) Gothic Mesas; sandstone plateau much dissected by shallow canyons.   (8) Black Creek Valley; chiefly the flat open valley of Black Creek. (9) Defiance Plateau; a domed plateau 6,000 to 7,000 ft. high with wide flat valleys trenched by canyons of streams from the Chuska Mountains.   (10) Chinle and (Pueblo, Colorado) Valley; arid plains at several stratigraphic levels, the higher ones on more resistant rock much dissected.   (11) Hopi Buttes; an arid platform of red sandstone and shale affording all types of badlands and bearing about 100 lava-capped mesas and buttes; (12) Tusayan washes; characterized by sand washes from the Black Mesa between which are mesas from 200 or 300 ft. high at the south to 1,000 ft. at the north.   (13) Moenkopi Plateau; a plateau of rock terraces rising to 5,800 ft.   (14) Black Mesa; a faintly synclinal plateau with outfacing cliffs; eastern edge 8,000 ft. high and forested.   (15) Kaibito Plateau; a little-dissected plateau on strong sandstone surmounted by mesas.   (16) Painted Desert; a narrow belt roughly eroded by wind and water on the dipping edges of (mainly) bright-colored Triassic rocks.   (17) Shato Plateau; a high south-sloping plateau, little dissected in the center but sharply cut by canyons on all sides.   (18) Rainbow Plateau; deeply and intricately dissected bare red rocks.   Navajo Mountain is a young laccolith 10,416 ft. high.   (19) Segi Mesas; "a series of mesas piled on mesas"; canyons to a maximum depth of 1,200 ft.   (20) Monument Valley; an anticlinal uplift stripped (except for residual mesas) to a level 1,000 ft. below the mesas on the west.

cated monocline rests a remnant of horizontal Eocene sediments making the so-called "Chuska Mountains," a narrow strip of forested upland trending east of south, having considerable areas above 8,000 ft. and exceptional mesas 1,000 ft. higher.

East of the Defiance monocline is the deeper of the two structural depressions, the Upper San Juan Basin. All around its edges the late Cretaceous coal-bearing rocks (Mesa Verde series) come to the surface from beneath the deep cover of younger rocks in the center. This coal is an important resource and is being mined, especially at Gallup, New Mexico, on the south; and Durango, Colorado, on the north.

Black Mesa.—The western one of the two basins is much less depressed and barely preserves in its highest central part the beds

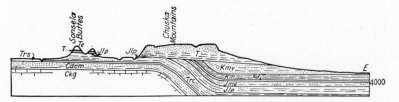

Fig. 113.—East-west section across the Defiance monocline and Chuska Mountains. Post-Cretaceous warping made the upper San Juan Basin on the east and the Defiance Plateau on the west. The area was approximately peneplaned before the Tertiary beds were deposited. The sandstone and shale beds (Eocene?) which constitute the Chuska Mountains are apparently a remnant of a once continuous sheet extending north to the Uinta Basin and west to the High Plateaus of Utah. (*After Gregory.*)

that appear at the rim of the eastern basin and are deeply buried at the center. The central portion of this western or Navajo Basin is topographically the highest. This is the Black Mesa, a dissected or dissecting plate of sandstone 60 miles in diameter with outfacing cliffs on all sides. On the north and east these are almost continuous and 1,200 to 2,000 ft. high. The plateau edge is here 8,000 ft. above the sea and forms an important divide. The slope and direction of streams is toward the southwest. On that side the escarpment is not only lower but scalloped by erosion.

As in some other high parts of the Navajo section there are on the Black Mesa wide shallow valleys, generally being trenched by small canyons. The higher parts are forested. The nomadic Navajo Indians raise sheep and do some farming but this mesa is noteworthy on account of the agricultural and conservative

Hopi tribe.   This tribe has skillfully adjusted its agriculture to
the severe conditions of the desert but compromises slowly with
civilization.   Its 2,300 members live mainly in a few villages
on the more or less isolated mesas of the ragged southern edge.

Borders of the Navajo Basin.—On all sides of the Black
Mesa the surface is lower, the drainage being to the San Juan on
the north, the Little Colorado on the west, and the Puerco on
the south.   A characteristic feature on the south is the "wash,"

Fig. 114.—Bed of the Puerco River at Navajo Siding, eastern Arizona.   This
stream marks the southern boundary of the Navajo section.   It is a typical
youthful stream on a desert plateau.   The only valley it has is the channel
between its banks.   The desert a few feet away is unaffected.   Generally there
is no water, but the brief torrential rains of the arid region may fill the channel
to the brink.   (*U. S. Geol. Survey.*)

a flat sand-floored valley one to five miles wide, sometimes
trenched by a vertical-walled channel and generally dry.   The
exceptional development of these washes on this side is due in
part to the fact that the Black Mesa drains to the southwest and
in part to the large amount of sediment furnished by its sandstone beds, washed by the greatest rainfall in the Navajo section.

In this surrounding country the canyons are generally of
moderate depth, and the dissection is not intricate.[1]   However,

[1] This entire area is divided into smaller units separately described by
H. E. Gregory in U. S. Geol. Survey, *Wat. Sup. Pap.* 380, 1916.   His divi-
sions are shown in Fig. 112, above.   See also U. S. Geol. Survey, *Prof.
Pap.* 93, by the same author.

the San Juan River on the north (west of Goodridge) and the Colorado on the northwest run in canyons 1,500 to 2,500 ft. deep. These canyons offer a relatively low local base level and dissection is correspondingly favored. A strip south of the San Juan is therefore included in the Canyon Lands section. This includes the Rainbow Plateau which spans the Utah-Arizona line below the mouth of the San Juan River. It is in this extremely rugged district that Navajo Mountain is situated.

Painted Desert.—On the west, before the Colorado and Little Colorado Rivers are reached, the structural basin is limited by an

Fig. 115.—Effects of wind erosion in the Navajo section. The locality here pictured is on the Kaibito Plateau and therefore east of Echo Cliffs, but similar scenes are found in the Painted Desert west of Echo Cliffs. Interspersed with such wind-swept areas are sand dunes. (*Gregory, U. S. Geol. Survey.*)

upturned rim, the Echo Cliffs monocline. East of this line the rocks at the surface are Triassic and Jurassic, by no means lacking in bright colors but relatively unfamed in this respect because of the startling display of red, yellow, chocolate, and white in the Triassic rocks to the west. This is the "Painted Desert," extending from the 35th parallel to Lees Ferry where the Echo Cliffs monocline crosses the Colorado. Because of its lower altitude the valley of the Little Colorado is the driest place in northern Arizona, the average annual rainfall being locally as small as three inches. The country is not all bare rocks and drifting sand but these are characteristic features (Fig. 115).

Habitation.—The Navajo section as a whole (about 35,000 square miles), has about one inhabitant per square mile, mainly Indians who lead a nomad life, farming some but depending more on sheep than on any other animal or crop. Mormons settled in a few of the favored spots, notably at Tuba.[1] The farms here have been bought by the United States Government and worked as an experiment station for the benefit of the Indians.

DATIL SECTION

The southeastern part of the Colorado Plateau is a region of diverse features among which those of volcanic origin are foremost. It would be difficult to make any other general statements concerning this region except those already made for the entire province. Some of its details, however, are abundantly worth consideration as among the best illustrations of their kind and illustrating principles of wide application in western United States.

Zuni Uplift.—The most prominent feature of this region is the so-called "Zuni Plateau," an elongated dome like the Black Hills but smaller and less accentuated. Similar features elsewhere are called "swells," particularly the San Rafael Swell in the Canyon Lands of Utah. The Zuni uplift is an elliptical uplift 70 miles long and less than half as wide, its southeastern end being in lat. 35° and long. 108°. The surrounding plateau is about 7,000 ft. high and the dome culminates in Mt. Sedgwick 9,200 ft. above the sea. The general slopes are therefore not steep.

The strata are inclined outward more steeply than the surface slopes, but all dips are gentle except at the western end. The eroded edges of these strata face the central uplift in great retreating cliffs of red, white, and yellow, inferior only to the rock terraces north of the Grand Canyon. Except for lack of the Eocene in this locality the formations exposed in the two regions are the same and their respective characters not very different. From the crest of the dome all sedimentary rocks have been eroded, exposing the crystalline rocks. Outward from this center there follow in turn, each limited by one or more cliffs, the Carboniferous, Triassic, Jurassic, and Cretaceous systems.

---

[1] The peculiar features of this desert as they affect human habitation are well described by H. E. Gregory; see the Oasis of Tuba, Arizona, Assoc. Amer. Geogr. *Ann.*, vol. V, pp. 107–119, 1915.

A special interest attaches to the Zuni uplift because it exemplifies in typical form a principle which has been much stressed by some in explaining the mountains of western United States.   Its form and the total absence of plication in the rocks suggest a force pushing upward from beneath rather than lateral compression.[1]   It thus belongs to the class of "domed mountains" of which Davis has taken the Black Hills as the type.[2]

Surrounding Topography.—Views from the top of this dome as far as possible to the north and west show a succession of low mesas and erosion valleys, here bounded by desert cliffs and there by long barren slopes, the entire landscape being typical of the Colorado Plateau for hundreds of miles, resulting from the erosion of nearly horizontal rocks of diverse strength in an arid climate.

Twenty miles to the southwest, on a mesa 1,200 ft. high, surrounded by steep cliffs, the ancient tribe of Zuni Indians, after the manner of the tribes in this section, built their pueblo, the remains of which, still inhabited by the remnant of the tribe, afford one of the most interesting historic structures in America.

To the south and east the topography is the same where volcanic rocks do not cover the sediments.   But most of the area, especially toward the south, is covered with lava at least in spots.   "It is scattered about in an irregular way as if the molten stuff had been dashed over the country from a titanic bucket, and lies like great inky slops over the brightly colored soils and clays."[3]   The spots here mentioned are generally mesas, from a few hundred to several thousand feet above the denuded surface of the Cretaceous, remnants of once larger and more continuous lava flows.   Forty miles to the south, the lava cover becomes essentially continuous.[4]   The district has been little studied but it is known that the plateau character, after continuing some distance, gives way to a disordered structure and mountainous surface assigned on the accompanying map to the Mexican Plateau section.

Mount Taylor and Volcanic Necks.—Northeast from the Zuni uplift are many mesas, the greatest of which is 46 miles long

---

[1] DUTTON, C. E., Mt. Taylor and the Zuni Plateau, U. S. Geol. Survey, 6*th Ann. Rept.*, pp. 118 and 195, 1884.

[2] DAVIS, W. M., "Physical Geography," p. 169, 1898.

[3] DUTTON, C. E., *loc. cit.*, p. 126.

[4] DARTON, N. H., Geological map of New Mexico, 1927.

and half as wide, 1,900 ft. above the surrounding plain and capped
by 300 ft. of lava. Among other volcanic cones, half hidden
in the forest, this mesa bears Mt. Taylor, 11,389 ft. high and
young enough to retain its conical form.

The principal interest of this district is in its hundreds of
volcanic necks.[1] Some of them in various stages of destruction
stud the denuded Cretaceous plain. Others are just beginning to
be exposed in the retreating cliff which bounds the mesa. Some

Fig. 116.—Landscape among the volcanic necks and mesas in western New
Mexico. To the left is Prieta Mesa, the remnant of a basalt flow capping
Cretaceous beds. To the right is Cerro Cochino, a volcanic neck. The broad
semi-desert plain dotted with juniper is a local peneplain on Cretaceous shales.
(*Photo by Douglas Johnson.*)

of these still rise to half destroyed volcanic cones for which
the now choked conduits furnished the material. It should be
observed that the volcanoes which once surmounted these
scattered necks rose, not from the denuded plain from which the
necks now rise, but from the level of the mesa nearly 2,000 ft.
higher. Hence it is not correct to think of these necks as
representing the former throat of the volcanic cone itself, but
rather the long conduit leading up to the volcano through the
sedimentary rocks.

[1] JOHNSON, D. W., Volcanic Necks of the Mt. Taylor Region, New
Mexico, Geol. Soc. Amer. *Bull.*, vol. XVIII, pp. 303–324, 1907.

Physiographic History

Early Uplift and Folding.—The physiographic history of the province may be said to begin with the uplift and folding that followed the Cretaceous, *i.e.*, at the time of the widespread Laramide revolution. Almost all of the beds that are not now horizontal received their tilt at that time. The great east-dipping monoclines were made then as were also the domed uplifts, San Rafael, Zuni, and others. The great importance of these deformations lies in the fact that, in changing the position or the relative elevation of great masses consisting of hard and soft rocks, conditions were created which have governed erosion ever since.

Earlier Degradation.—Following these crustal movements there was extensive erosion before the late Eocene sediments were deposited over almost the entire province, thus leveling the area once more for a new start. The total thickness of beds stripped from the Canyon Lands and Grand Canyon section in this and later cycles of erosion is perhaps 6,000 ft. An undetermined, but certainly large, portion of this stripping was done before the deposition of the Eocene.[1] It is not improbable that a general peneplain resulted. All this work was done by streams whose location is unknown.

Eocene Deposition.—It is believed that Eocene sediments then covered almost the entire province, connecting those remaining in the High Plateaus with other remnants to the south and east, as in the Chuska Mountains of New Mexico. The great importance of this lies in the fact that the drainage became superposed.[2] The major streams of today are believed to have been consequent on the Eocene cover which has since disappeared. With its disappearance the streams were let down on older rocks. Most of them are now quite out of harmony with the structure. On the contrary, the smaller streams, developing later, generally after the main streams had cut through the Eocene mantle, obey the conditions imposed by structures in the older rocks. Aside from the courses of the main streams

---

[1] Dutton, C. E., "The High Plateaus of Utah," U. S. Geol. and Geogr. Survey of the Rocky Mountain Region, p. 294; Gregory, H. E., U. S. Geol. Survey, *Prof. Pap.* 93, pl. XXII, 1917; Fig. 113, p. 314, is a small part of this plate showing an unconformity below the Eocene.

[2] Moore, R. C., Significance of Enclosed Meanders in the Physiographic History of the Colorado Plateau Country, *Jour. Geol.*, vol. XXXIV, p. 99, 1926; Dutton, C. E., *loc. cit.*, p. 292, 1880.

the topographic features of the province reflect the structure to a remarkable degree.

As to the course of the Colorado River across the Kaibab Plateau and through the great canyon, it is not so certain that superposition can be invoked, as the burial of the Kaibab under Eocene sediments may not have been complete. So far as this uplift stands in the way of a river which in Utah was borne on the surface of the Eocene, it is suggested by Davis that the local uplift came after the river was following its present course but before the general rise that inaugurated the canyon cycle.[1]

Later Degradation.—With the uplift of the surface after Eocene deposition begins a long period of erosion of which the final results are known better than the progress of events. This is the period assigned by Dutton to the "Great Denudation," now believed to be in large part earlier (see above). It is also the period of Davis' "plateau cycle," assumed to have ended with a widespread peneplain in which, after uplift, the Grand Canyon was cut. Such a peneplain was, without doubt, produced in that region, though perhaps not just before the canyon cycle and not at the level of the canyon rim. There are also remnants of peneplains here and there beveling the strata of the Canyon Lands and Navajo section (Fig. 117). More recent crustal movements make it difficult to decide to what extent these may be correlated or whether they were merely local.

Extensive stripped plains like the Great Sage Plain (page 309) and the Grand Flat on the Monument uplift (page 310) were probably developed not far from base level. No formation is sufficiently resistant to stand very widespread stripping without dissection when far above its local base level. Moreover, there are evidences of approximate base-leveling not far removed from these stripped plains and at similar altitudes. The outstanding example is that of Comb Ridge (page 310) whose jagged crest is essentially at the level of the Great Sage Plain to the east.

Even if the Great Denudation be assumed to have resulted in a general peneplain, this feature was not dominant when the canyon cycle began. The aspect of the province at that time was much the same as it would be now with the canyons filled up. In the Canyon Lands were mesas and structural terraces and

---

[1] DAVIS, W. M., An Excursion to the Grand Canyon of the Colorado. Mus. Comp. Zool. *Bull.*, vol. 38, pp. 185–186, 1901.

retreating escarpments then as now, perhaps several thousand feet high.[1]   The High Plateaus and Uinta Basin stood above the level of what is now the Canyon Lands section.   It is not improbable that the pre-canyon landscape contained peneplain remnants of several cycles.   Some of the remnants represent the work of the last cycle immediately preceding entrenchment.[2]   It was upon a newly begun peneplain of this kind that the streams developed those remarkable meanders which are now entrenched 1,000 to 2,000 ft.[3]

Fig. 117.—Local peneplain developed on relatively soft Jurassic (?) rock at the west foot of the Black Mesa in the basin of the Moenkopi Wash.   The highest level represents a peneplain of considerable extent.   The two lower levels, likewise truncating the dipping beds, are apparently planation surfaces. (*Photo by W. C. Mendenhall, U. S. Geol. Survey.*)

Likewise in the Grand Canyon section the present topography is probably not that which resulted from the Great Denudation. Throughout the Grand Canyon section the present plateau surface is generally on the Kaibab limestone.   Here and there are patches of lava forming higher plateaus.   Generally these lava sheets do not rest directly on the Kaibab but on pedestals

[1] Moore, Raymond C., *Jour. Geol.*, vol. XXXIV, pp. 118–120, 1926.

[2] Moore, R. C., *loc. cit.*, p. 110; Gregory, H. E., U. S. Geol. Survey, *Prof. Pap.* 93, p. 120, 1917.

[3] Moore, R. C., *loc. cit.*, pp. 29–57 and 97–130.   These papers contain not only good descriptions of these valleys but historical interpretations of the various topographic features.

of soft shale, hundreds of feet thick (see description of Uinkaret Plateau, page 280). It is plain that the lava flowed out on a peneplain developed on the weak rocks, and that later the weak rocks were stripped away except where covered and protected.

In the original concept of a plateau cycle Dutton assumed that base level during the Great Denudation agreed essentially with the upper surface of the Kaibab formation. This theory is no longer tenable in view of the known facts pertaining to the faults (page 324). It is now agreed that the remnants of nearly flat surface on which the lavas rest represent a widespread peneplain,[1] developed only locally on the Kaibab formation and elsewhere on softer rocks hundreds, even several thousands, of feet above it.

It has commonly been assumed that the canyon cycle was inaugurated by the uplift of this peneplain to something like its present level. It is further assumed that while the canyons were being cut, the weak rocks overlying the Kaibab were stripped away throughout the Grand Canyon section. Moreover, the streams that did the stripping are assumed to have cut into the underlying limestone leaving its surface marked almost everywhere by a mature system of valleys rarely deeper than several hundred feet[2] (page 281).

Some geologists have trouble in conceiving of such deep and extensive denudation by small, probably intermittent, streams and interstream wash, within the time occupied by a powerful throughflowing stream in cutting a narrow canyon, no matter how deep. The difficulty is made greater by the sudden transition at the brink of the canyon, from the mature features of the broad upland to the youthful aspect of the rapidly growing canyon. The ravines and gorges which are tributary to the latter have little or nothing to do with the wide-open mature valleys which furrow the plateau. They seem to belong, if not to a different world, at least to a different age. On account of these relations it has been suggested[3] that another cycle intervened between

---

[1] DAVIS, W. M., Mus. Comp. Zool. *Bull.*, vol. 38, p. 139, 1901; HUNTINGTON, E., and GOLDTHWAITE, J. W., The Hurricane Fault in the Toquerville District, Utah, Mus. Comp. Zool. *Bull.*, vol. 42, pp. 199–258, 1903, have called this the Mohave peneplain.

[2] DAVIS, W. M., *loc. cit.*, p. 137.

[3] ROBINSON, H. H., A New Erosion Cycle in the Grand Canyon District, *Jour. Geol.*, vol. XVIII, pp. 742–763, 1910. On p. 751 Robinson gives the assumed height of the old peneplain above the present stripped surface at different places.

the Great Denudation and the canyon cycle. It is believed by Robinson that this intermediate cycle was inaugurated by moderate uplift and that it was carried far toward completion, thus stripping away the softer rocks above the present surface of Kaibab limestone and carving in that formation a mature system of valleys before the final uplift brought in the canyon cycle.

The Great Faults.—At some time since the Eocene the great west-throwing faults were made which outline the several plateaus north of the Grand Canyon. Their striking scarps were formerly regarded as due directly to displacement. It is now known that they are not, in that sense, fault scarps but "fault-line" scarps due to differential erosion after the original faulted surface was base-leveled. The important fact concerning their age is that they antedate the general peneplain which obliterated their initial scarps. In the pre-canyon cycle described above the tilted Kaibab limestone was stripped and its broken edges exposed in the present scarps.[1]

Canyon Cycle.—The final uplift resulted in deep canyon cutting. At places the great escarpments have been freshened and their retreat greatly accelerated.

Résumé.—Ignoring exact geologic dates the events leading up to the present physiographic forms may be summarized as follows:[2]

1. Crustal movements at the close of the Cretaceous resulted not only in general uplift but in local swells and in the great east-dipping monoclines.

2. The general wasting of the surface set in and made great progress before the Eocene beds were deposited.

3. After Eocene deposition and uplift, the present major lines of drainage were established and erosion continued throughout the plateau cycles.

---

[1] The evidences for this history cannot be discussed here. They relate chiefly to (1) the unequal recession of the Vermilion Cliffs on opposite sides of a fault line; (2) the drainage pattern as now found, contrasted with what it should be if the faults were recent; (3) occasional patches of lava resting on level surfaces which cross the fault lines, thus protecting both sides from stripping.

For discussion see: DAVIS, W. M., Mus. Comp. Zool. *Bull.*, vol. 38, pp. 142–150; also vol. 42, pp. 2–18; and HUNTINGTON, E., and GOLDTHWAITE, J. W., Mus. Comp. Zool. *Bull.*, vol. 42, pp. 223–238.

[2] This summary agrees with that given by Gregory, U. S. Geol. Survey, *Prof. Pap.* 93, p. 122, so far as they cover the same ground.

4. Meanwhile, at a time that need not be accurately dated for physiographic purposes, there was further warping, including the making of the Uinta Basin. Most of the great faulting also took place early enough so that fault scarps disappeared in the base-leveling process.

5. Uplift made possible the final stripping of the Kaibab limestone in the Grand Canyon section and gave rise to new scarps along the old fault lines.

6. At or after the beginning of the Quaternary, the canyon cycle was inaugurated by great general uplift.

A detail of physiographic history appears in the accumulation of alluvium in valley bottoms within the time of human occupation and in the still more recent trenching of this by vertical-walled channels, some of them 80 to 100 ft. deep. These channels or "canyons" are matters of great concern to present settlement, although practically all of them are less than 50 years old and most of them not over 30. Various explanations are offered, some based on climatic changes, some on overgrazing or other incidents of civilization which may have disturbed the delicate balance to which gradients had been adjusted. The phenomenon is interestingly discussed by Gregory,[1] Bryan,[2] and others.

[1] GREGORY, H. E., *loc. cit.*, p. 131.

[2] BRYAN, KIRK, Date of Channel Trenching in the Arid Southwest, *Science*, vol. XLII, pp. 339–343, 1925. This discussion is not limited to the Colorado Plateau. Abundant references are given.

CHAPTER VIII

BASIN AND RANGE PROVINCE

THE PROVINCE AS A WHOLE

GENERAL DESCRIPTION

Distinctive Features.—A great region west and south of the Colorado Plateaus, embracing one-tenth of the United States and extending into Mexico, is aptly styled the Basin and Range province (Fig. 118; also Fig. 4, page 10 and Fig. 132, page 368). Topographically it is distinguished by isolated, roughly parallel mountain ranges separated by desert basins, generally almost level. Climatically it is characterized by want of sufficient run-off to reach the sea or to forward its load of detritus. In the northern half, *i.e.*, in the Great Basin, drainage generally leads to enclosed basins. In Arizona and New Mexico such basins are by no means universal. Much of the area there has slopes on which water might run directly to the sea but it is too arid to supply continuous flow and considerable areas have no run-off at all.

Boundaries.—While interior drainage is highly characteristic, this affords a poor criterion for drawing boundaries. For example, the basin of internal drainage includes the eastern slope of the Sierra Nevada which belongs quite as much to the Mountain province as does the western slope. Moreover, the Pitt River, a tributary of the Sacramento, drains the northeast corner of California, a characteristic portion of the Great Basin province. In like manner a considerable portion of southern Nevada is traversed by canyons leading to the Virgin River and thus to the sea. The fact that the drainage from these marginal portions is outward does not differentiate them physiographically from neighboring portions whose drainage leads to salt lakes.[1]

The area characterized by the "basin ranges" has a different limit. Except for their greater size, the Wasatch on the east

---

[1] It is true that the term "Great Basin" is often used in a hydrographic sense but its more general use is physiographic. Care must be exercised to avoid confusion.

and the Sierras on the west are of the same type as many of the ranges in the Great Basin. In the northern end of the province the basin ranges become widely spaced and it is impossible to draw a line which shall surround them all without passing in an arbitrary course through broad areas of plains. In southern California this criterion fails for the opposite reason that some similar mountains are excluded from this province.

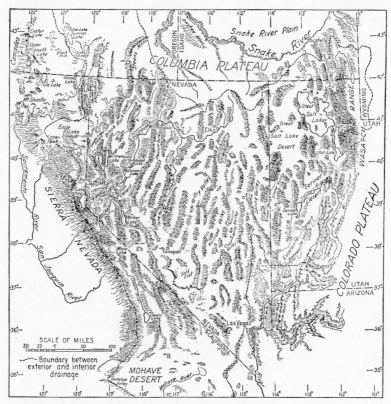

FIG. 118.—Index map of the Great Basin. (Drawn by Guy-Harold Smith.)

A significant feature is the presence of the subaerial waste which coats the intermont deserts, though even this is not universally present. On the one hand it expresses climatic factors, being determined by a degree of aridity which makes it impossible for streams to transport their loads. On the other hand these deposits are for the most part associated with the peculiar structure of the province, for they belong character-

istically at the foot of steep wasting slopes, covering the intervening troughs or basins where streams lose their velocity or
disappear. It must, however, be remembered that the province
as a whole is not the exact area covered by such deposits. The
typical "bolson" or concave basin, coated, and in some cases
deeply filled, with detritus is a very characteristic but not universal
feature. The line delimiting the area thus characterized must,
in parts, be arbitrary. The boundaries chosen are in part
determined by the more easily defined limits of neighboring
provinces, such as the edge of the Colorado Plateau and the foot
of the Sierra Nevada.

Subdivisions.—The province here outlined is divided into
five sections of unequal size. The *Great Basin* lies north of
lat. 35°30'. In this the space taken by the mountains is about
half of the total. Only minor marginal tracts may drain to
the sea. South of this, in California and southwestern Arizona,
is the *Sonoran Desert* section, much lower in altitude, in which
mountain ranges are smaller and perhaps older, occupying
perhaps one-fifth of the space. Moreover, large areas are without concave basins of internal drainage. The *Salton Trough*,
whose center is several hundred feet below sea-level, deserves
separate treatment. Its southward extension in Mexico embraces
the Gulf of California. Between the Sonoran Desert and the
Colorado Plateau, stretching east beyond the Rio Grande, is a
northward continuation of the *Mexican Highland* not unlike the
Great Basin in its major features. However, as the Plateau
province is approached some of the mountains are transitional
in type from that of the basin range to that of the plateau out-
lier. In central Arizona the drainage from this section is to the
sea. Finally, on the eastern margin of the province, mainly
in New Mexico, there is a north-south strip which combines some
features of this province with others of the Colorado Plateau.
At the north end where its plateaus are of horizontal rocks,
it has the drainage features of the Great Basin. Elsewhere,
and for the greater part, its plateaus are tilted like the mountains
in the northern part of the Great Basin. This is the *Sacramento
section.*

Climate

The province as a whole is the driest in the United States,
being dependent for its moisture on winds from the Pacific and

lying in the rain shadow of the intervening mountains. The southern half contains the points of least rainfall and highest temperature. At Yuma, Arizona, the average annual rainfall is 2.84 in.; at Needles, California, it is 2.47 in. These are places where the plain is low and mountains are few and small. Here there is no marked seasonal distribution except a deficiency in the spring. Farther north and east where mountains are larger and more numerous, precipitation is greater. To the north, in the Great Basin, the maximum precipitation is in the late winter (west coast type of climate). To the south, in the Mexican Highland, precipitation is of the subtropical type with the maximum in the hot season although parts of this area may also be affected by a winter maximum. July and August have afternoon showers which, in the mountains, come almost daily.

Whether the maximum rainfall comes in the winter months, as in the Great Basin, or in the summer, as in New Mexico, or whether there be two maxima, as in parts of Arizona,[1] neither season can be trusted to bring relief every year, for it is notorious that the smaller the annual rainfall the greater are the departures from the yearly average and the greater are the unaccountable differences between nearby places: hence one year may bring many times the rain of the next and in the drier parts large areas may be practically skipped for one or more seasons.

In Papagueria (southwestern Arizona and part of Sonora) where the mean annual precipitation is probably no more than 3 or 5 in., and many tracts of 1,000 square miles or over are missed by the midwinter or midsummer storms of one or more years, the freshet-making storms may be three or five years in coming, and the great mantle-moving torrents are apparently separated by decades or centuries.[2]

Along with this fitful character of the seasonal rainfall, goes a tendency toward concentration into brief and violent showers or "cloudbursts." Observations at Tucson, Arizona,[3] show that rains frequently have a "density" of 1 cm. in 10 or 15 min., or in other words, that rain frequently falls at the rate of $1\frac{1}{2}$ to $2\frac{1}{2}$ in. per hour. The geological work is therefore not done by perennial streams.

[1] U. S. Dept. Agr., Weather Bur. *Bull.* N, chart, 1905; also *Bull.* Q, 1906.

[2] McGEE, W. J., Sheetflood Erosion, Geol. Soc. Amer. *Bull.*, vol. 8, p. 108, 1897.

[3] Observation at the Desert Botanical Laboratory, Tucson.

As this region also has a high temperature, its relative humidity is very low, especially during the day. Evaporation in the southern half of the Basin and Range province is, therefore, at a higher rate than anywhere else in the United States. Much of this region, especially its lower western half, is almost without flowing water. For an area of 60,000 square miles east and west of the Lower Colorado the United States Government issues guides to springs, wells, and other watering places[1] which may be 10 miles or 50 miles apart. In an area of 10,000 square miles in California and Nevada only 323 such places are listed and some of these afford only warm and unpalatable water.

BASIN RANGES

Topography.—Among the mountains of this province certain characteristics are prevalent, so much so that the term "typical basin range" conveys to geologists a fairly definite impression. Usually the range is one of many more or less parallel ranges. Lengths of 50 to 75 miles are common; there are more smaller than larger ones. Within its length, whatever it be, there is no great and sudden variation in height and breadth though the crest may be very jagged; the range is not deeply notched and segmented; the bulk is fairly continuous; a general straightness is more noteworthy than the opposite. In many cases the straightness of the foot is more marked than that of the range itself and is quite independent of a complex structure of strong and weak rocks. The generalized slope from base to summit is not excessive but the appearance of steepness is enhanced by the fact that the slope does not flatten out near the base. The abrupt meeting of valley floor and mountain side, and the uniform slopes of the latter, are among the striking features of the province.

A characteristic that is somewhat surprising in this arid region is the frequent occurrence of ravined slopes, especially in the northern part. Some entire mountain sides are wholly occupied by sharp ravines whose slopes meet in equally sharp divides (Fig. 119). Speaking of ranges in the basin of Lake Bonneville, Gilbert says, "Every water parting is a sharp ridge and every

[1] MENDENHALL, W. C., Some Desert Watering Places in Southeastern California and Southwestern Nevada, U. S. Geol. Survey, *Wat. Sup. Pap.* 224, 1909; U. S. Geol. Survey, *Wat. Sup. Pap.* 490, 1920 to 1922, by various writers embodies these surveys to date; BRYAN, KIRK, The Papago Country, U. S. Geol. Survey, *Wat. Sup. Pap.* 499, 1925. Pl. I shows the area covered by such guides issued up to 1925.

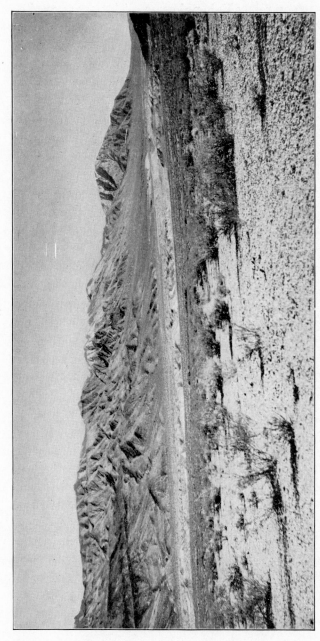

FIG. 119.—West front of the Argus Range, southwest California.   This range has most or all of the features listed as characteristic of the basin ranges.   Its continuity of crest and mature dissection are striking.   The graded slope at its foot is also typical.   Such slopes are commonly spoken of as alluvial fans.   In this case recent gullying, due to piracy from the left, shows that the stream deposits make only a thin veneer over older tuffs and marl (Tertiary?) which could not have been derived from the adjacent mountains.   (*Photo by Blackwelder.*)

waterway an accurately V-shaped gorge. These are carved only by running water."[1] Such mature dissection by angular valleys is more prevalent in the Great Basin than farther south but even there it is not universal. Such ravines are apt to be cut in bare rock with little or no detritus in their beds. Other slopes are almost ungullied, some of them being composed of talus blocks too large to be moved by the wash, others of solid rock either washed bare by cloudbursts or standing in cliffs too steep to retain their waste.

In the more arid parts, single uniform slopes or cliffs range in steepness from 15 to 90 deg. The angle of slope seems to depend more on the character of the rock than on any other factor.[2] For any given rock type the slope does not vary greatly. It is about as steep near the base as near the summit instead of flattening out below like the stream profile. Moreover, the degree of slope remains constant as the mountain wastes away, *i.e.*, the slope retreats but does not become flatter as in humid climates. From descriptions of these mountains as tilted fault blocks, it is frequently inferred that they are plainly unsymmetrical in slope, a steep scarp slope on one side being clearly contrasted with a gentler dip slope on the other. In most cases there is no striking contrast of slopes. The structure is complex and unless covered by a sheet of lava, neither side could be called a dip slope.

Rocks and Structure.—The rocks which compose these mountains are in large part sedimentaries older than Cretaceous. Generally they have been somewhat metamorphosed but contrasts in strength and in resistance to erosion are still common. They were much deformed by folding and faulting and then so wasted by erosion that the present positions of the beds bear no simple relation to the forms of the mountains.[3] In any case the present trend of the ranges is rarely parallel to the strike. Many of the ranges consist partly or wholly of igneous rocks.

[1] GILBERT, G. K., U. S. Geol. Survey, *Mon.* 1, p. 91, 1890.

[2] LAWSON, ANDREW C., The Epigene Profiles of the Desert, Univ. Calif. *Bull.*, Dept. Geol. Sci., vol. 9, no. 3, pp. 23–48, 1915; BRYAN, KIRK, Erosion and Sedimentation in the Papago Country, Arizona, U. S. Geol. Survey, *Bull.* 730, 1922. Pages 42 to 46 of this paper deal with mountain slopes suitably classified.

[3] LOUDERBACK, G. D., gives certain cross-sections of fairly typical ranges; see Basin Range Structure of the Humboldt Region, Geol. Soc. Amer. *Bull.*, vol. 15, pp. 289–346, 1904; SPURR, J. E., Origin and Structure of the Basin Ranges, Geol. Soc. Amer. *Bull.*, vol. 12, p. 259, 1901. Many structural sections are given.

Many of these mountains are desert. Much of the surface is bare rock, frequently brilliant in color

. . . astonishing one reared beneath more humid skies. The color is due to purple trachytes, volcanic tuffs of all shades and tints from pure white to luminous red; also deeply colored rhyolite; beside this are dark basalts partially buried by dunes of soft creamy sand.[1]

Certain names are significant, for example, Chameleon Mountains, and Harlequin Hills.

ORIGIN OF THE BASIN RANGES

Hypothesis of Faulting.—In southern Oregon, the northernmost part of the Great Basin, the mountains are obviously fault blocks in the youth of their first erosion cycle. It has long been believed that the mountains of Nevada are also fault blocks with a longer and more complex history.[2] The assumption commonly

[1] RUSSELL, I. C., Lake Lahontan, U. S. Geol. Survey, *Mon.* 11, p. 39, 1885.

[2] First announced by G. K. Gilbert in 1873 and adopted by Powell, Dutton, King, Russell, and others who did much work in this province. The history of the question is reviewed in a posthumous paper by Gilbert, U. S. Geol. Survey, *Prof. Pap.* 153, 1928.

The subject is discussed by W. M. Davis in the following papers: The Ranges of the Great Basin, *Science*, vol. XIV, 457–459, 1901; The Mountain Ranges of the Great Basin, Mus. Comp. Zool. *Bull.*, vol. 42, 1903; The Wasatch, Canyon, and House Ranges, Utah, Mus. Comp. Zool. *Bull.*, vol. 49, 1905.

More recently Geo. D. Louderback has published the following papers based on extensive field studies: Basin Range Structure in the Great Basin, Univ. Cal. *Bull.*, Dept. Geol. Sci., vol. 14, pp. 329–376, 1923; Period of Scarp Production in the Great Basin, Univ. Cal. *Bull.*, Dept. Geol. Sci., vol. 15, pp. 1–44, 1924; Morphological Features of the Basin and Range Displacements, Univ. Cal. *Bull.*, Dept. Geol. Sci., vol. 16, pp. 1–42, 1926.

J. E. Spurr, Origin and Structure of the Basin Ranges, Geol. Soc. Amer. *Bull.*, vol. 12, 1901, asserts that should the Appalachian region now be overtaken by a climate like that of the Great Basin, there would result a combination of degrading mountain ridges and aggrading desert valleys similar in all essential respects to those of the Great Basin.

C. R. Keyes, Erosional Origin of the Great Basin Ranges, *Jour. Geol.*, vol. XVII, 1909, believes that a general peneplain existed somewhere near the present mountain tops and that the basins have since been excavated on the weaker rocks, primarily by wind.

Eliot Blackwelder, while not discussing the Great Basin as such, discusses the principles involved and uses illustrations from this province in his paper, The Recognition of Fault Scarps, *Jour. Geol.*, vol. XXXVI, pp. 289–311, 1928. His suggestion that the mountains are fault blocks in their second cycle of erosion is mentioned below (p. 334, 338).

made is that the mountains made by faulting are still in their first erosion cycle. Recently published observations by Black-welder tend to show that most of the features which have been interpreted as indicating block mountains in their first erosion cycle belong equally to fault blocks in later cycles. As the fault theory is challenged[1] from time to time, the chief points on which it rests are here set forth.

Fig. 120.—East front of the Inyo Range facing Saline Valley (north of Owens Lake, California). Note that the whole mountain front is an inclined plane somewhat eroded. Note also the fresh fault cutting the alluvial fan. (*U. S. Geol. Survey.*)

Fresh Faulting.—At the foot of many ranges (the Wasatch among them) are found small fresh fault scarps from a few inches to forty feet in height; so recent that the soil or recent wash in which they occur still supports an open fissure or a vertical face (Fig. 120). The upthrow is generally though not always on the side toward the mountain. Large numbers of these recent faults

[1] Rival hypotheses are based mainly on the assumption that these ranges are residual forms resulting from long-continued erosion of a much folded and faulted region. Along with this assumption there commonly goes another, namely, that the climate was more humid and that aridity is relatively recent.

have been described and mapped by Russell.[1] A fault of this
kind in Owens Valley at the foot of the Sierra Nevada Mountains
originated during the great earthquake of 1872.[2] Like others of
its kind, it has been generally interpreted as indicating continued
displacement along the great fault marked by the course of the
mountain front. Similar faulting has been observed during other
earthquakes, notably in the Pleasant Valley earthquake of 1915.[3]

Fig. 121.—Fault scarp southeast of Deep Springs Valley, eastern California.
The short, steep spurs end in triangular facets, the bases of which form a gentle
curve in ground plan. Narrow V-shaped canyons have abnormally small
alluvial fans at their mouths. The lowest part of the valley, now occupied by
a salt pan, is situated at the base of the scarp instead of in the middle of the
basin. From these features it is inferred that the major topographic features
result directly from faulting. (*Photo by Blackwelder.*)

Faceted Spurs.—In many cases the mountain spurs between
these characteristic stream gorges do not taper down to the plain
but are cut off abruptly by facets whose steepness reaches in
some cases 40 deg. but rarely exceeds 30 deg. (Fig. 121). The
suggestion that such facets are sea cliffs is disproved in some

[1] U. S. Geol. Survey, *Mon.* 11, p. 275; also pl. XLIV, 1885. Such features
were first noted and explained by Gilbert in 1876.

[2] WHITNEY, *Overland Monthly*, vol. IX, pp. 30–40 and 266–278, 1872;
reference by C. D. Walcott in *Jour. Geol.*, vol. V, p. 347.

[3] JONES, J. C., The Pleasant Valley, Nevada, Earthquake of Oct. 2,
1915, Seismol. Soc. Amer., *Bull.* 5, pp. 190–205, 1915.

cases by their relations to the old shore lines. They have been interpreted, therefore, as representing the fault plane itself, perhaps reduced somewhat in steepness by erosion. Facets of this kind are present on many ranges from the Wasatch to southern California.[1]

Discordance of Outline and Structure.[2]—The most essential feature of residual mountains resulting from long erosion of a deformed region is agreement of topographic form with geologic structure. This goes with adjustment of drainage. After such a history most of the features are subsequent. Where contrasts in strength of rocks exist, the ridges must therefore be of the

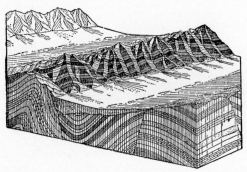

Fig. 122.—Diagram of a mountain carved on a faulted block of previously deformed and denuded strata. The base of the range is fairly straight and its direction is independent of the strike. (*After Davis, Science,* 1901.)

stronger rocks and the valleys on the weaker, and the trend of the subsequent ridges and valleys must agree with the strike of the strata. Mountains remaining after such profound erosion should show no continuity of range crest (except it be in a second cycle as in case of the Appalachian ridges, and then only in strict agreement of form with structure). Such residual mountains should, on the other hand, be irregular and patchy, with long spurs and outliers interlocking with broad valleys reaching far into the mountains.

If mountains are fault blocks not yet worn down, the base on the fault side should be straight (or as nearly so as a fault should be). If such a straight base is found cutting across the strike

---

[1] WALCOTT, C. D., *Jour. Geol.*, vol. V, 1897; BLACKWELDER, E., *loc. cit.*, p. 297, Fig. 3.

[2] For discussion see Davis; three papers cited above.

of strong and weak rocks alike, the presumption is very strong that it represents a fault in its first erosion cycle.

This latter description applies to some ranges in Utah and Nevada. The continuity of the range masses (despite jaggedness of crest) has been noted by all observers. It is less remarkable than in the Appalachians but remains without explanation except on the basis of some kind of relatively recent uplift of the mountain or lowering of the valley.

Valley Forms.—Small streams descending the western side of the Wasatch[1] occupy valleys which are characteristically V-like and steep, down to the very point of issuance from the mountains. This seems to indicate continued rising of the mountains

Fig. 123.—Ravines, spurs, and terminal facets of the Spanish Wasatch, looking east; drawn from sketch and photograph. (*After Davis.*)

or a rapid lowering of the valleys, otherwise the lower end of the valley would soon become broad. The case is made stronger by noting that some of these little streams have convex profiles, *i.e.*, abnormally steep gradients and even falls and rapids within a few hundred feet from the ends of their gorges.

Springs.—Still another evidence of faulting is found in the springs, both hot and cold, which occur in significant numbers along the lines which are believed on other evidence to be fault lines. Such hot springs, not in regions of recent vulcanism, are accepted as evidence of deep circulation of ground waters, thereby bringing up the heat of the earth from great depths. In the Great Basin they have all temperatures below the boiling point. Many of the springs, but not all, are known to be connected with

[1] The western base of the Wasatch Mountains is taken as the boundary of this province. However, with respect to the effects of faulting the Wasatch is typical of the basin ranges.

recent faulting[1] but such a relation is not universal.   Hot springs may occur also on lines of ancient faulting as in Arkansas.

Tilted Peneplain.—In a few of the ranges a sheet of lava is found tilted, exactly as in the young block mountains of southern Oregon, but resting on a peneplain which truncates a complicated structure.[2]   In the Oregon mountains the thickness of the lava is greater than the throw of the fault so that no structures appear except that of the simple block of lava.   In the older mountains of Nevada both the throw and subsequent erosion are so great that the main structures exposed are those of the folded beds below.

"Second Cycle" Interpretation.—There can be no doubt that some of the ranges exemplifying the features described above are fault blocks not yet worn down.   The number of such is not known since most of the ranges have not been closely studied. The tendency has been to assume that this is by far the leading type of basin range.   Recent studies have established certain facts which tend to reduce (perhaps to a minority, perhaps a small minority) the number of ranges to be explained in this way. Among these facts are the following:

Most of the features listed are consistent with the hypothesis that the ranges are in their second cycle, *i.e.*, that the original topographic effects of faulting have been erased by erosion; that some of the fault blocks have since been exhumed by the cutting out of basins on the weaker rocks; in other words, that the present "fault scarps" are really "fault-line scarps."   Among the features that may develop in the second cycle[3] are sharp V-shaped valleys maintaining their youthful form to the very foot of the mountain and even having profiles that are convex upward; likewise triangular facets terminating the ridges between such valleys.   Of the features named above, a straight mountain foot, cutting obliquely across the strike of deformed strata of diverse hardness, is not consistent with a second-cycle inter-

[1] RUSSELL, *loc. cit.*, p. 276.

[2] LOUDERBACK, G. D., Basin Range Structure of the Humboldt Region, Geol. Soc. Amer. *Bull.*, vol. 15, pp. 289–346, 1904; also Basin Range Structure in the Great Basin, Univ. Cal. *Bull.*, Dept. Geol. Sci., vol. 14, pp. 329–376, 1923.

[3] The points here noted under this head are a few of those mentioned by Blackwelder in his paper on The Recognition of Fault Scarps, *Jour. Geol.*, vol. XXXVI, pp. 289–311, 1928.   Only the most prominent points are mentioned here.

pretation but this feature is not found in a majority of the ranges. Another feature not often seen in unmistakable form and likewise requiring that the mountains be in their first cycle, is an old topographic surface of the mountain, identifiable with a similar old surface on the valley floor.

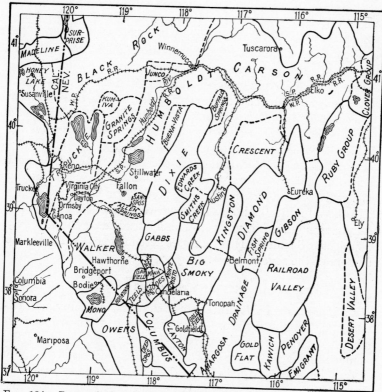

Fig. 124.—Parts of Nevada and California showing independent basins of internal drainage. (*E. E. Free, U. S. Dept. Agr.*)

In a considerable number of cases (according to Blackwelder a majority of those carefully studied) it has been found that basins believed to be filled to great depths with wash from the mountains are really only coated with such material, the substratum being of soft Pliocene or Miocene sediments, generally deformed by folding and truncated by erosion. Presumably these soft beds, mistaken for recent detritus, were involved in the faulting that made the mountains, and their surfaces have since been much degraded. In any case it is a significant fact

that, where the substratum of the central basin can be deter
mined, it consists in a large proportion of cases of soft rocks.
In some cases the soft rock even forms the mountain spurs being
separated from the main mountain mass by the fault which elsewhere follows the mountain foot.   Many of the striking "alluvial
fans" have also been found to be mere veneering on rock surfaces
(Fig. 119).

Such facts as these give support to the hypothesis that the
relief which resulted directly from faulting is not that which we
have now.   It may have been eroded by water and wind to
maturity or old age in one or more cycles and the present mountains and basins may be due to selective erosion on rocks of diverse
strength which have been complexly faulted and folded.   On
this hypothesis it is necessary to assume that the partial filling
of the valleys is due to a recent climatic change.

It cannot be doubted that there are mountains in the Great
Basin of both types, namely block mountains in their first erosion
cycle and block mountains in their second (or later) cycle.   In
still others faulting is not yet known to be an essential factor.
Many ranges have not yet been closely studied and others may
be subject to dispute.   No attempt is here made to fix the relative
numbers of the several kinds.

INTERMONT BASINS

In a large part of this province the mountains occupy approximately half of the surface.   Elsewhere, as in the southwestern
part, five-sixths of the area is plain.   By contrast with the
mountain sides these intermont plains appear almost or quite
level.   This may be true in the middle of a basin but toward the
mountains the surface rises with increasing steepness until the
slope may reach 6 or even 9 deg., but this is extreme.   The average
is about 3 deg. or five feet in a hundred.   A fall of 300 to 700 ft.
from the edge of the basin to its center is not uncommon.[1]   In
Owens Valley at the foot of the Sierra Nevada such slopes are
2,000 ft. high.[2]

Alluvial Fans.—Generally these piedmont slopes have the
form of alluvial fans or slopes built from the waste of the mountains, though in some cases the alluvium is a mere veneer on

[1] LOUDERBACK, G. D., gives these figures for the western part of the
Great Basin, Geol. Soc. Amer. *Bull.*, vol. 15, 1904.

[2] RUSSELL, I. C., U. S. Geol. Survey, *Mon.* 11, p. 9, 1885.

solid rock.   Such slopes occupy a belt some miles in width (it may be 20 or more) surrounding the mountain range.   Where streams emerge from the mountains the fans are distinct, but soon they merge, producing one broad slope toward the center of the basin. Near the apex of the fan where the stream retains its power the material may be very coarse.   Fragments as large as a house have been noted at a distance of several miles from canyon mouths,[1] but such remarkable cases are due to mud flows, the work of which has not until recently been appreciated.[2]   Farther out,

Fig. 125.—Lobate edge of a thin mud flow on the east side of Stillwater Range, Nevada.   The process here exemplified is believed to be accountable for a considerable part of the deposits in the great fans of the Basin and Range province.   Thicker mud flows may carry huge boulders many miles.   In some cases the mud is so intermixed with coarse material as to resemble glacial till. (*Photo by Blackwelder.*)

with diminishing slope, the material is finer; in some basins only the finest mud reaches the center.

Playas.—The alluvial slope from one range may extend outward until it meets the slope from another range and the line of meeting may be marked by a "wash" which once in a long time carries water.   All surface water not absorbed by the air or the ground sooner or later reaches a basin without outlet to the sea.

[1] DAVIS, W. M., Mus. Comp. Zool. *Bull.*, vol. 49, p. 39.

[2] BLACKWELDER, ELIOT, Mud Flow as a Geologic Agent in Semiarid Mountains, Geol. Soc. Amer. *Bull.*, vol. 39, pp. 465–484, 1928.

In a few cases permanent lakes result.   Generally there is a flat
where water may stand at intervals and where mud alone accumulates.   This flat is a playa[1] or, when covered by water, a
playa lake.   The bottom is flat and a sheet of water one foot
deep may extend for miles.   Playa lakes in the Black Rock
Desert (northwestern Nevada) may extend for 50 or 60 miles
in length and 20 miles in width in winter and disappear entirely
in the summer.   Playas may fill by a single shower, perhaps
several times in the same day and then perhaps not again in the
same year, or the interlake interval may be many years.

In order that any given closed basin shall contain a playa
it is necessary that the run-off from the drainage basin shall
occasionally reach the center.   Such run-off in the desert is
charged with salts and thick with mud.   When standing in the
playa lake it generally has a buff-brown color.   The water evapo-
rates and percolates and the mud settles.   If a local hollow exists,
the water is deeper there and the mud layer is correspondingly
thicker, so that inequalities of level are soon eliminated.   When
dry, the mud makes a smooth floor, often creamy or light buff
in color and usually hard, sometimes so hard that horses hoofs
clatter as on a pavement.[2]   The general aspect of a playa is
shown in Fig. 137, page 379.[3]

In some playas the amount of mineral substances (common
salt and others) left by the evaporating water is so great as to
encrust the entire area, sometimes to a depth of several inches.
Such an area is then called a *salina*.   The salt covering is
sometimes pure white like fresh snow.   Playas and salinas are
absolute deserts.   Around their edge may be found a fringe of
salt-tolerant plants.

The depth of filling is in most cases unknown.   In some
basins alluvial filling is underlaid by soft sediments not easily
distinguished.   A well 2,000 ft. deep in the Salt Lake Desert
failed to reach hard rock, but it is not known how much of the
material passed through was alluvium and how much was soft
sediment of other origins.   Another well near Sevier Lake found

---

[1] The word "sink" as used in this province means essentially the same
thing.   Such sinks must not be confused with the "sinkholes" or "limestone
sinks" of humid regions.

[2] RUSSELL, I. C., Geological History of Lake Lahontan, U. S. Geol.
Survey, *Mon.* 11, p. 9, 1885.

[3] For further mention of playas, see Lakes, p. 349.

1,944 ft. of unconsolidated material resting on a granite base.[1]
In Railroad Valley similar material was penetrated to a depth of
1,204 ft.[2]

Rock Pediments.—In some cases the sloping margin of an
intermont basin is what it appears to be, namely, an assemblage
of deep alluvial fans. In other cases the fans are superficial,
forming a relatively thin covering on a sloping surface or "pediment" of solid rock (see page 346 for origin). Opinions among
scientific workers in this field differ greatly as to the relative
frequency of each case.[3] Pediments, either bare or fan-covered,
are a prominent and characteristic feature of the country south
of the 38th parallel. Farther north the semblance of thick
alluvial fans is more striking but not much is known of the actual
depth to rock except where revived erosion has revealed the rock
at unexpectedly small depths.

Ground Water.—From the forms of the filled basins it follows
that the ground water received from the mountain streams
which disappear on reaching the alluvium, moves down the slopes
toward the center. It might be reached by wells within the
central sink but by the time it has reached that place it is generally too alkaline for use. If intercepted by wells at the edge
of the sink it may be potable. The wells dug in the desert are
generally at places where the water table is not more than 40
ft. from the surface. A depth of 100 ft. to the water table is
more common; it may be several hundred feet, or the underlying
solid rock may be reached without finding water.

In some of the basins the alluvium affords beds of clay alternating with sand or gravel, and in a few cases water is found under
artesian pressure. It is not to be understood that all the wells in
these basins derive their water from the Pleistocene wash. Those
along the Santa Fé Railroad, for example, find their water in
porous volcanic ejecta of Miocene age.[4]

[1] BOUTWELL, J. M., cited by Lee, U. S. Geol. Survey, *Bull.* 352, p. 68.

[2] U. S. Geol. Survey, *Wat. Sup. Pap.* 365, p. 76, 1915.

[3] Estimates of the ratio between these two are to some extent linked
with estimates of the ratio between first-cycle and second-cycle block
mountains. Blackwelder doubts whether alluvial fans can be built under
static conditions and believes that thick alluvial fan formations can be
deposited only in a region of active diastrophic movements.—Origin of the
Piedmont Plains of the Great Basin, Geol. Soc. Amer. *Bull.*, Cordilleran
sec., abst., 1927.

[4] BLACKWELDER, ELIOT, personal communication.

The relation which streams bear to ground water is characteristic of the desert.   In humid regions the channel is cut below the water table which therefore slopes toward the stream.   The latter receives water from the ground and grows larger as it proceeds.   In the desert, the channel is filled by storm waters alone.   The general surface of ground water is lower and slopes away from the channel.   Hence, the water enters the ground from the stream and the latter diminishes as it proceeds.   The disappearance of the streams described above is due chiefly to such percolation but in part also to evaporation.

Since the general level of ground water is far below the surface of the intermont valleys, springs are necessarily rare.   The condition most apt to cause a spring is some inequality in the surface of the impervious rock floor beneath the loose sediment.   Where the surface of the ground is low and that of the underlying rock is high the lateral movement of ground water may bring it to the surface and an oasis may result.

Dunes.—With a rainfall and run-off insufficient to make playa lakes, the center of the basin will be covered by the graded slopes from the margins or will be subject to drifting sands and dust. Some basins have considerable areas of sand dunes but, while very impressive, these must not be thought of as occupying any considerable fraction of the province, certainly not 1 per cent. North of Winnemucca, Nevada, is a dune area 40 miles long by 8 or 10 miles wide.   The sand here averages fully 75 ft. thick and the dunes are rapidly migrating eastward.   In some places telegraph poles have been spliced to prevent total burial by sand. In a dune area south of Carson Desert a belt of migrating sands four to five miles wide reaches a maximum depth of 200 or 300 ft.[1] The dunes of the Salton Basin are unexcelled in the beauty and symmetry of their forms (Fig. 136, page 377).

Where the vegetation, or the lack of it, is such as to allow the wind to comb the surface freely a curious pavement of stones results, known as the "desert pavement."   The sand and dust are blown away, but the contained pebbles accumulate until the surface is covered and thus partially protected from further wear. A striking example of this is noted on the old flood plain of the Colorado River.   Tolman writes:

There the surface is covered with a perfect mosaic of fitted stones, polished and flattened to the last degree of perfection by the wind.

[1] RUSSELL, I. C., *loc. cit.*, p. 154.

The light of the early or late sun is thrown back from uncounted faceted mirrors in a dancing blaze. Step on this pavement and you are surprised to find the apparently solid rock yielding underfoot. Scratch it with your boot and you find that there is only a single thickness of pebbles in size up to a quarter of an inch thick, covering a deposit of hot dry dust.[1]

Except for playas, washes, and bare rock surfaces, the desert pavement is the characteristic surface south of lat. 38° where the creosote bush and cactus predominate as do the sage brush and greasewood farther north.

ORIGIN OF THE BASINS

The history of the basins is of course involved in that of the ranges. The main point at issue is whether they are diastrophic troughs in process of filling and obliteration or primarily erosional depressions modified in detail by accumulation of detritus in a recent episode of exceptional climate. That both types are represented has already been implied in discussing the mountains. In the consideration of individual basins certain considerations, based partly on observations, partly on deduction,[2] are of value.

Early Stages of Diastrophic Basins.—In a mountain region of more or less fortuitous slopes and insufficient rainfall for external drainage there may be many hydrographic basins, the center of each being the ultimate goal of drainage. All are receiving sediment and each has its own base level. Sea-level is out of the question. At this stage a single basin may be divided into two or more by great alluvial fans crossing the basin or meeting similar fans advancing from the other side. In accounting for the origin of individual basins in this province the possibility of such subdivision must often be taken into account.

It may and does happen, however, that one basin becomes full to the level of the divide separating it from a lower neighbor. It may fill with water as Utah Lake fills its basin. The case is not very different if a basin fills with sand, gravel, and silt instead

[1] TOLMAN, C. F., Erosion and Deposition in the Southern Arizona Bolson Region, *Jour. Geol.*, vol. XVII, p. 149, 1909.

[2] A valuable piece of deductive reasoning by W. M. Davis, The Geographic Cycle in an Arid Climate, *Jour. Geol.*, vol. XIII, pp. 381–407, 1905, begins with a constructional surface such as our Great Basin may have had on the assumption that its mountains are in their first erosion cycle, or (let us say) such a constructional surface as it may have had *in those parts which are* in the first cycle of erosion.

of water. In that case the graded slope leads entirely across a former basin to a lower basin not yet filled. However rare the flow of water from one to the other may be, the slope becomes continuous and the drainage is unified. The same end may be accomplished by the headward growth of drainage lines from the lower basins, thus effecting capture of the higher (Fig. 119). In either case a step is taken toward the integration of the originally

Fig. 126.—Red Mountain, east of Randsburg, California. These mountains have been reduced in size by wearing back their slopes but the steepness continues. Long graded slopes like those that surround this mountain are commonly taken for alluvial fans, but this is a mining district and numerous prospect shafts show that solid rock, chiefly granite, underlies this sloping surface for a distance of at least two miles from the base of the mountain and only two to five feet below the surface. It is evident that this rock plain or pediment has been developed by the retreat cf the mountain front. (*Photo by Blackwelder.*)

non-integrated drainage. The effect of these processes is cumulative, more and more basins being thus united, the ultimate tendency being to form continuous drainage lines. The final slopes may or may not end at the sea. It is not yet known to what extent the fairly well integrated drainage in the very desert Sonoran section has had such a history.

Development of the Rock Pediment.—Mountain streams in an arid climate may or may not bring to the base of the mountain more waste than they can forward on the plain. If they bring more, the alluvial fan results. If the load is considerable but not excessive, the stream on reaching the plain may still shift, and wander widely, corrading laterally, cutting away spurs and, in general, planing off the rock surface to a pediment. Floods of mountain streams often become sheet floods (page 371) on the plain and these help to reduce minor irregularities. The total result of these processes, together with a recession of the mountain front, is a rock platform, broadening at the expense of the mountain. It may be bare or covered with a very few feet of detritus capable of being moved at intervals. Its slope is generally less than that of the fan and its profile parallel to the mountain foot is horizontal instead of convex like that of the alluvial fan. Such pediments comprise a large portion of the area in the southern part of the Basin and Range province, although often covered by relatively thin alluvial fans. Detritus of any considerable thickness resting on such platforms appears to indicate some recent climatic change.[1]

The Work of Wind.—Unlike water, which always tends to fill and destroy basins, wind may produce them. Such work on a small scale is universally recognized, but geologists are far apart in their estimates of the efficiency of wind in producing the larger features of the landscape. Actual wind erosion (the natural sand blast) produces curious forms, toadstools, etc., in solid rock but they are rare and insignificant in comparison with ravines. The carving of rock, even in the desert, is all but universally the work of water.[2]

This known work of water in arid regions makes it unnecessary to appeal to wind as a major agent of erosion. There remains, however, the work of carrying away the products of erosion, and in a region of interior drainage this must be done by wind if done at all. The actual *capacity* of winds to deflate dust is known to be vastly in excess of all theoretical needs, so much so that if the average wind carries a very small fraction of what it is capable of doing the continent might be degraded faster than

[1] For further discussion of the rock pediment see the following: PAIGE, SIDNEY, Rock-cut Surfaces in the Desert Ranges, *Jour. Geol.*, vol. XX, pp. 442–450, 1912; LAWSON, A. C., The Epigene Profiles of the Desert, Univ. Calif. *Bull.*, Dept. Geol. Sci., vol. 9, pp. 23–48, 1915; BRYAN, KIRK, Erosion and Sedimentation in the Papago County, Arizona, U. S. Geol. Survey, *Bull.* 730, pp. 53–65, 1922; BLACKWELDER, ELIOT, Origin of the Piedmont Plains of the Great Basin, Geol. Soc. Amer. *Bull.*, vol. 40, 1929.

[2] C. R. Keyes (see footnote, p. 333) greatly magnifies the work of wind, believing that it was the main agent in excavating the basins of this province and even in eroding the hard rocks.

running water is doing it.[1] No figures are available on what the wind actually *does* carry over a long period of time. Casual observation in a region of playas supports the belief that deflation is a *very real* process that must be reckoned with.[2]

Some concave basins in this province are hard to explain except by deflation. Generally these "bolsons" are either elongated troughs between mountain ranges or segments of such troughs separated from the rest by low transverse swells, perhaps a few hundred feet high. Such swells may be transverse anticlines or fault ridges; or they may be alluvial fans; but there are cases where neither of these explanations seems applicable. The basin itself seems to have been lowered by some process. Solution is out of the question. As great clouds of dust are frequently seen rising from the central playa and disappearing in the higher air currents, there is a strong supposition that wind is an excavating agent where the material is loose and fine. The argument as here presented relates only to the local depressions. It may be applied to these with or without raising the question of the origin of the great inter-range troughs.

THE GREAT BASIN

The Term "Basin."—The name Great Basin was first applied by John C. Frémont who crossed this area in his expeditions of 1843 and 1845. The term misleads many into thinking of this province as an area surrounded by a rim. There is no such rim surrounding the entire area, although there are within it about one hundred separate basins. Filling these with water would result in overflow from one to another and the water would escape to the sea long before the entire area was covered. Nevada is like Minnesota in having many basins. If the latter had the

---

[1] FREE, E. E., A Possible Error in the Estimates of the Rate of Geologic Denudation, *Science*, vol. XXIX, pp. 423–424, 1909; UDDEN, J. A., Erosion, Transportation, and Sedimentation Performed by the Atmosphere, *Jour. Geol.*, vol. II, pp. 318–331, 1894.

[2] It must be acknowledged that the subjective element in such casual observations is large. According to convictions already formed the imagination may see great quantities of dust exported or see it all caught on the mountains and returned by the next rain. Davis, *loc. cit.*, minimizes the work of deflation until the mountains are much worn down (presumably much lower than the present basin ranges). By implication he would not favor the deepening of present basins by wind. His treatment of the subject is based on the assumption that the function of surface agencies is to destroy the basins, not to make them.

arid climate of Nevada, she would have desert basins and lakes without outlet. If Nevada had the rainfall of Minnesota, all the basins would overflow to the sea.

Mountains of Nevada and Western Utah.—Throughout most of the Great Basin the mountain ranges have the character described above (pages 330–333) as typical. The ranges vary in size but lengths of 50 to 75 miles are common; likewise widths of 6 to 15 miles. Perhaps the most frequent altitudes are 3,000 to 5,000 ft. above their bases and 7,000 to 10,000 ft. above the sea. While the prevailing trend is not far from north-south, a deviation to the east of north is more common than the opposite. Locally, as in southern Nevada, the trends are various. The total area of the section is about evenly divided between mountains and basins.

Mountains of Southern Oregon.—A belt of 50 to 100 miles wide across the northern part of this province, chiefly in southern Oregon but lapping over somewhat into Nevada, differs in important respects from the country farther south. The mountains of this district are exceptional in being more simply and obviously monoclinal than those farther south. This is mainly because of the thickness of the relatively young volcanic rocks, fragmental below and covered by lava. Since no other rocks are exposed and the volcanic beds are undeformed except by simple faulting, each upraised block has a gentle dip slope and a steeper scarp slope. Moreover, most of the faulting in this district is relatively recent. Several of the larger ranges, Steens Mountain, for example, are much eroded but others have suffered relatively little.[1] In general the mountains in this northern district are in the youth of their erosion cycle whereas maturity prevails in the better known parts of the Great Basin. Most of these also are smaller, escarpments of several hundred to 2,000 ft. being common.

The alluvial filling of the valleys is not known to be deep or extensive. Some of the basins receive sufficient drainage to maintain permanent lakes.

Lakes

Relation to Climate.—Most of the basins of the Great Basin never contain standing water, and most of the rest contain

[1] RUSSELL, I. C., A Geological Reconnaissance in Southern Oregon, U. S. Geol. Survey, *4th Ann. Rept.*, 1882–3; WARING, GERALD A., U. S. Geol. Survey, *Wat. Sup. Pap.* 220, 1908.

mere playas. Certain lakes, Pyramid, Winnemucca, Great Salt Lake, and others, are classed as permanent but all change greatly in area from month to month or year to year and no sharp line can be drawn between permanent and playa lakes. Honey Lake, California, North Carson Lake, Nevada, and Sevier Lake, Utah, all become dry occasionally.

In the northern part of the Great Basin some of the lakes overflow and are fresh, as Klamath Lake at the foot of the Cascades. The rest vary greatly in area from time to time. None are over 25 ft. deep and some are mere playas. These also vary in salinity, according to their several histories, from nearly fresh to more salty than the sea. Goose Lake, in California and Oregon, overflowed into the Pitt River in 1869, four years before Great Salt Lake reached a maximum height. Silver Lake, Oregon, disappeared and a crop was raised in its bed in 1887 to 1888,[1] when Great Salt Lake was near a minimum, and was again under cultivation in 1929.

Every lake without outlet rises and expands until its increasing area causes the rate of evaporation to equal the rate of inflow. Hence the area of the lake is, in some measure, an index to the humidity of the climate. This, however, is true only so long as sedimentation has not constructed a flat within the basin. After that, the evaporating surface may be much larger than necessary but the lake comes and goes. It might be said that evaporation, on account of too great facilities, is working part time only. A strict use of the term playa lake would restrict it to cases in which this part-time arrangement has been reached because sedimentation has produced a flat surface too large to support a permanent evaporating surface. It should be understood, however, that slow evaporation from the ground water continues in the interval between inundations.[2] In eastern United States where the annual rainfall approaches or exceeds 40 in., the evaporation from a constantly exposed water surface is generally less than that amount, hence it would be impossible to have lakes without outlets even if their basins were vertical-walled tanks. They would overflow by reason of rainfall alone without inflow from the sides.

---

[1] These and other facts of interest concerning the lakes of this district are found in U. S. Geol. Survey, *Wat. Sup. Pap.* 220 by G. A. Waring, Geology and Water Resources of a Portion of Southwest Oregon, 1908.

[2] MEINZER, OSCAR E., Map of Pleistocene Lakes of the Basin and Range Province, Geol. Soc. Amer. *Bull.*, vol. 33, p. 546, 1922.

Great Salt Lake, on the other hand, has less than one twenty-fifth the area of its hydrographic basin and yet loses by evaporation all the water that drains into it. With sufficient intake to cause overflow, lake levels become essentially stable, and Utah Lake which discharges by the Jordan River into Great Salt Lake is thus permanent, and Humboldt Lake in western Nevada, though recently dry, has been fairly stable.

Great Salt Lake.—The oscillations of the level of Great Salt Lake since the settlement of Utah, amount to more than 10 ft. The maximum area has been fully 25 per cent more than the minimum and the maximum volume 75 per cent more than the minimum.[1] The maxima and minima have not been equally high or low, nor have they recurred at uniform intervals. There is a very faint suggestion of a period approximating 35 years as in case of the Caspian Sea.[2]

As might be expected, the salinity of the water varies inversely with the volume of the lake.[3] In the high water of 1873 the weight of the dissolved salts was only 13.42 per cent of the weight of the water. In the low stage of 1903 the salinity rose to 27.72 per cent. The average percentage in the Dead Sea is about 25.[4] With even the lowest percentage here given, Great Salt Lake is about four times as salty as the ocean. The specific gravity of the lake water exceeds that of fresh water by 10 to 22 per cent according to the changing salinity. The human body therefore does not sink.

Distribution of Lakes.—It should be observed that the distribution of lakes in the Great Basin is far from uniform. Precipitation on the Sierra Nevada Mountains is sufficient to maintain at their foot a line of permanent lakes, Owens Lake in lat. 36°30′ being the most southerly. In like manner the Wasatch Mountains and the High Plateaus support a line on the east, of which the semipermanent Lake Sevier (lat. 39°) is the most southerly. The interior basin ranges do not occasion sufficient rain and snowfall

---

[1] GILBERT, U. S. Geol. Survey, *Mon.* 1, pp. 243 and 316.

[2] BRÜCKNER, E., "Klimaschwankungen seit 1700," Vienna, 1890. Assuming Brückner's 35-year cycle to be operative here, it is probable that the climate is influenced also by other cycles both shorter and longer. Hence maxima and minima of different cycles may reinforce or neutralize one another. The result to date is a curve of somewhat uncertain meaning.

[3] EBAUGH, W. C., and McFARLANE, WALLACE, *Science*, vol. XXXII. p. 568, 1910.

[4] "Universal Cyclopedia."

to support permanent lakes south of the 40th parallel, but north of that, especially in Oregon, are a number of permanent lakes, though in desert valleys.[1]

The more southerly lakes of the Great Basin, like Mono and Owens, are more salty than the ocean and Sevier Lake (lat. 39°) is an unsteady body saved from intense salinity only by occasionally evaporating to dryness and then getting a new start.

Streams

In considering the streams of this province it is essential to remember, in addition to the topographic features already described (1) that the precipitation is largely on the mountains, (2) that it comes chiefly in the winter, (3) that there are no glaciers and no great accumulation of snow, hence the flow of streams is concentrated into a small part of the year closely following the larger rainfall and snowfall. Some streams on the mountains are perennial; others flow in the late winter and spring; sometimes in the dry season a small stream may flow by night but not by day.[2] Very few survive long in any season after reaching the plain. As summer advances, even the stronger streams are progressively shortened in their lower courses. The Quinn River, long. 118° and near the Nevada-Oregon boundary, has a swift muddy current which carries it far into the desert while the snows are melting, but as summer advances it gradually shrinks back until it has lost 100 miles of its lower course.

All the streams of any importance, except one, are fed from the high mountains on the east and west. The Humboldt alone derives its waters from the interior basin ranges, largely from the Ruby and East Humboldt Mountains, more than 10,000 ft. high and therefore exceptional. Leaving this source the river pursues a dwindling course for 200 miles and is lost. In the winter it reaches North Carson Lake, but shrinks back during the summer and stops at Humboldt Lake. This is the most important stream of the Great Basin and is followed by two transcontinental railroads.

A characteristic of the desert climate, somewhat paradoxical it may seem, is the torrential character of the rains. It may

[1] *Cf.* Meinzer, Oscar E., Map of Pleistocene Lakes of the Basin and Range Province, Geol. Soc. Amer. *Bull.*, vol. 33, pp. 541–552, 1922.

[2] This occurrence is described by Davis, W. M., Mus. Comp. Zool. *Bull.*, vol. 49, p. 39, 1905.

almost be taken as a general principle that the drier the climate the more is the rainfall concentrated into heavy showers or "cloudbursts." During these, great channels may be torn out capable of carrying considerable streams but left dry after a few hours and not used again for years. The number of such dry channels or gorges is impressive. They are frequently mistaken for regularly used drainage lines of a former more humid time. Most of such inferences are unwarranted. There have been more humid epochs and there are some valleys which point back to such times; but the "arroyos" here described are quite as apt to be made now as then.

The Landscape

Seasonal Changes.—Excellent descriptions of seasonal changes in the Great Basin are given by Russell.[1] Speaking of summer in central Nevada he says:

On the desert valleys the scenery is monotonous in the extreme, yet has a desolate grandeur of its own, and at times, especially at sunrise and at sunset, great richness of color. At midday in summer the heat becomes intense and the mirage gives strange delusive shapes to the landscape and offers false promises of water and shade where the experienced traveler knows there is nothing but the glaring plain . . .

As autumn advances, but little change appears in the color of the landscape, excepting, perhaps, a spot here and there of gold or carmine high up on the mountains, where a clump of aspens or of dwarfed oaks marks the site of a spring that trickles down and loses itself among the rocks. The valleys with their scanty growth of sage remain unchanged, as do the dusky bands of pines and cedars on the higher mountains . . .

As winter approaches, the storms amid the uplands become more frequent, until every range is white as snow can make it, and the tent-like mountains gleam like the encampment of some mighty host. Long after they are covered, the valleys between are bare as in midsummer, and the snow seldom lies upon them for more than a few days at a time. The highlands retain their snow far into summer, but on none of the ranges can it be said to be perpetual. In the valleys there are flowers beneath the sage brush by the middle of April, but from that time until November scarcely a drop of rain falls. For many days and sometimes for weeks the skies are without a cloud.

[1] Geological History of Lake Lahontan, U. S. Geol. Survey, *Mon.* 11, pp. 13–14.

Vegetation.—Most of the mountains of Nevada and western Utah are almost as desert as the valleys but a few have scattered pinyon or dwarf cedars on their middle slopes or mountain mahogany in their sharper valleys. There is even a little yellow pine on some of the higher ranges. The distribution is not clearly according to altitude but rather determined by water, sun, and wind. There is no clear "timber line" here, but in general it may be said that only the straggling bush-like cedar and pinyon pass below 6,000 ft. at the south.

Fig. 127.—A group of Pleistocene cinder cones and basalt flows east of Beatty, Nevada. In the background are cuestas of Pleistocene tuff and other stratified deposits with thin basalt flows. The foreground shows one of the more desert aspects of the Great Basin. (*Photo and interpretation by Blackwelder.*)

Farther north in Oregon, the aridity is less severe and pine forests descend to 5,000 ft. and even lower. Thus many of the ranges in this part are well timbered and are included in the national forests. Where living streams can exist in the basins their banks are generally lined with cottonwood trees.

The almost universal habitant of this region is the sage brush. It is excluded only from the relatively small forest areas on the one hand and from the absolute deserts on the other. It may form thickets as tall as a man in favored localities or dwarf to a few inches on the desert mountains too dry for trees below and too cold above.

The companion of the sage brush, but less widely distributed in this province, is bunch grass, the most valuable plant in the province. Generally speaking, wherever water can be found for cattle, this grass is at hand for pasture. In many localities it is exterminated by overgrazing and then its place is quickly taken by plants of no value to man.

Considerable areas must be classed as absolute desert. The best known is Great Salt Lake Desert west and south of Great Salt Lake. In northwestern Nevada, Black Rock and Smoke Creek Deserts cover hundreds of square miles. Carson Sink is another absolute desert; so also are all true playas (Fig. 137, page 379). Around such deserts there is generally a fringe of greasewood and other salt-tolerant plants. The "desert pavements" in the southern part are without vegetation in proportion to their perfection.

SHORES OF FORMER LAKES

Distribution and Appearance.—Among the striking features of the landscape in northern Utah and western Nevada are certain horizontal lines against the mountain sides easily seen to be the shore lines of former extensive lakes. These lines are marked chiefly by sea cliffs and cut terraces on the headlands and by long bars and beaches in the more protected valleys which were the bays of the ancient lake. The alternation of cut and fill often strikingly resembles the grading for a railroad but on a much grander scale.

Features of this kind surround Great Salt Lake and overlook the best known parts of both Utah and Nevada. The Southern Pacific Railroad through Nevada runs for 165 miles over the bed of one of these ancient lakes and generally in sight of its shore lines. The Western Pacific leaving the same course at Winnemucca follows another arm of the same lake through Black Rock and Smoke Creek Deserts. So also the Tonopah Railroad in its southeastward course, parallel to the California-Nevada boundary, affords excellent views of these old shores near Walker Lake and elsewhere.

Lake Bonneville Shores.—Of these former lakes, the one in western Utah is called Lake Bonneville. Great Salt Lake, Provo Lake, and Sevier Lake are its remnants. Lake Bonneville occupied an irregular branching area of 19,750 square miles, 10 times the area of Great Salt Lake. Many of the basin ranges of western Utah were islands or peninsulas in this lake. The total extent of shore line at its highest stage was 2,550 miles. The highest shore line, known as the Bonneville shore, is 1,000 ft. above Great Salt Lake or nearly a mile above sea-level. This is not the level at which the water stood longest or did the most work, but it is prominent because it is the highest of all horizontal lines, the topography above being characterized by the steeply inclined lines of stream-carved forms (Fig. 128).

Fig. 128.—Lake Bonneville shore at Brigham, Utah, north of Ogden and about five miles from Great Salt Lake. The top of the cut terrace shows as a light line. The steep front of this terrace is a cliff, cut back when the lake stood at a lower level. The lowland is an old delta built in the lake. Note the ravines above but not below the old shore line. (*U. S. Geol. Survey.*)

Ninety feet lower is another shore line, less bold but very significant in the history of the lake (page 362). The clearest of all lines is the Provo shore, about 375 ft. below the Bonneville shore or 625 ft. above Great Salt Lake. At this level are the boldest and most continuous cliffs and the broadest cut terraces. Here also are great deltas, almost wanting at the other levels.

At various intervening and lower levels fainter shore lines may be discerned in favored localities, sometimes 20 or more in a single view.[1] Each marks a level which the old lake surface maintained long enough to do a little work on its shores. Near Great Salt Lake the prominent shore lines are well up the slopes

[1] Davis, W. M., The Wasatch, Canyon, and House Ranges, Utah, Mus. Comp. Zool. *Bull.*, vol. 49, p. 36, 1905.

of the mountains, but farther away where the lake was shallower, the same lines are often found in the incoherent material of alluvial fans like those now forming. At the lower levels of the lake much of the shore line was against such alluvial fans. On such shores very short halts in the falling lake level were registered.

All these shore features, cliffs, terraces, beaches, bars, deltas, etc., are beautifully preserved, largely because of the aridity of the climate, but partly because the time has been short since the withdrawal of the lake. In their present condition, not covered by water, and here and there cut through by a new ravine exposing their inner structure, these fossil shore lines offer opportunity for investigation, better in some ways than any to be found on the shores of present lakes and seas.[1]

Of the nearly 20,000 square miles of the former Lake Bonneville about 2,000 remain in Great Salt Lake. The lowlands adjacent to this lake, especially the basins of the Bear River on the north and the Jordan River on the south, are the center of population and industry in Utah. A large part of the old Bonneville Basin west and southwest of Great Salt Lake is an absolute and irreclaimable desert.

Lake Lahontan Shores.—In western Nevada an area of 8,422 square miles, embracing the best known parts of the state, has features similar to those just described. This is the basin of former Lake Lahontan.[2] It is of exceedingly irregular shape, ramifying among the closely spaced basin ranges or surrounding them as islands. Near Humboldt Lake in the lowest part of the Humboldt Valley, traversed by the Southern Pacific Railroad, the old shores rise nearly 500 ft. above the valley floor. The same shore line is 530 ft. above Pyramid Lake 25 miles northeast of Reno in the deepest part of the Lahontan Basin. Pyramid Lake itself is 356 ft. deep, hence the total depth of Lahontan was 886 ft. Three distinct terraces are seen, respectively 110, 320, and 530 ft. above Pyramid Lake.

---

[1] U. S. Geol. Survey, *Mon.* 1, Lake Bonneville, by G. K. Gilbert, is a classical treatise, not only on the area here described but on shore features in general. A large part of the data here given concerning this lake basin as well as many points relating to the Great Basin as a whole are taken directly or indirectly from Gilbert's work.

[2] I. C. Russell has described this area in a work similar to that of Gilbert on Lake Bonneville.—Geologic History of Lake Lahontan, U. S. Geol. Survey, *Mon.* 11, 1885.

Résumé of History

Crustal Deformations.—All crustal deformations are factors in physiographic history, the later ones because they affect relief directly, the earlier ones because they imparted the structure which has ever since conditioned erosion. The geologic dates of these are not important but are mentioned here because, in some cases, they afford a basis of inference as to the probable history of this province by comparison with that of others.[1]

The crustal deformation by which the rocks of the Great Basin were folded, faulted, and overthrust occurred mainly in four different epochs. Of these the oldest was post-Jurassic, most intense in the west and dying out in eastern Nevada. Farther east the deformation was largely post-Cretaceous. Strong compression in the mid-Tertiary (post-Miocene) with folding and overthrusting was specially felt in the southern part of the province. A final deformation at the close of the Tertiary was widespread but left its greatest effects in the west.

It would be desirable, if possible, to classify these movements categorically into two classes, those whose direct topographic effects have disappeared, and those which still affect the relief directly; but such an attempt would involve the main question at issue in the Great Basin, *i.e.*, to what extent the mountain ranges are in their first cycle of erosion. That the direct effects of post-Jurassic mountain making have long been erased will not be questioned. Almost the same is true of the post-Cretaceous deformation. When it comes to relief made by post-Miocene deformation, questions are raised concerning its complete destruction. Without doubt the Pliocene was a time of extensive peneplaning but students of some other western provinces believe that important relics of pre-Pliocene relief still remain. It may be doubted whether, in this most arid of the provinces, the work of base-leveling in that period was more complete than elsewhere. At all events it is mainly to post-Tertiary deformation that we must look for the making of mountains that are now in their first erosion cycle.

---

[1] It would be sufficient for the purpose here in hand to assume, as J. E. Spurr does, in Origin and Structure of the Basin Ranges, Geol. Soc. Amer. *Bull.*, vol. 12, p. 248, 1901, that deformation has gone on "steadily though spasmodically from the close of the Mesozoic until the present day," provided, only, that those deformations whose direct topographic effect still survives be distinguished from the rest.

Summary of Events.—In so far as the mountains are in their first erosion cycle the facts of physiographic importance are the following: After much folding and faulting of sedimentary rocks and associated volcanics, much or most of the surface was greatly subdued by erosion. To call the whole a peneplain would be unwarranted, but in places it was such; elsewhere it may have been rock pediment. The surface here referred to was locally buried by volcanic rocks, after which came the last great deformation, including faulting which has not wholly ceased.

Fig. 129.—Upland surface of the Virginia Range, six miles north of Virginia City, Nevada. The view shows an old subdued erosion surface which is assumed to have been widespread and at a relatively low level before the present range was faulted up. The landscape here shown is cut off abruptly by a very steep mountain side due to faulting. (*Photo by Gionella.*)

The subdued surface was raised, tilted, and eroded but patches of it are preserved beneath volcanic covers (Fig. 130). Some of the faults are so recent that their scarps, although generally eroded to maturity, form the slopes of existing mountains. On the tops of some such mountains are old surfaces very much subdued, scarcely affected as yet by revived erosion (Fig. 129). These old surfaces are probably of later date than the widespread subdued surface mentioned above as preserved only under volcanic cover. No area has been found which is known to be part of that surface.

Volcanic eruptions have occurred at irregular intervals especially since the early Tertiary. There are some fairly fresh lava flows and several hundred young volcanoes, some of them absolutely fresh cinder cones (Fig. 127).   Most of these are in the southwestern part of the section.

Many of the ranges have reached maturity in their cycle of erosion.   Correlative with the valleys carved in these mountains is the filling of the valleys.   In an area of mountains and undrained basins due directly to faulting, carving and filling are the two

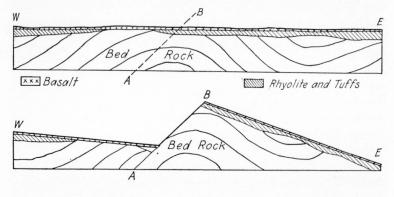

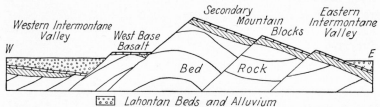

Fig. 130.—Diagrammatic sections showing the late history of the Humboldt region, Nevada, as interpreted by George D. Louderback.   The structure is typical, not representing any particular section.

The first diagram shows the structural features at the time of the outpouring of the basalt.   The deformed sedimentary rocks had been approximately peneplaned and then covered by volcanic rocks.

The second diagram shows the structure as affected by simple faulting.

The third diagram shows the inferred mode of formation of some minor features of the Humboldt Range.   The valleys are represented as filled with alluvium and Quaternary deposits.   Erosional features omitted.   (*After Louderback.*)

indexes of progress.   As already stated, some of the ranges are believed to be due to differential erosion since the making of the great faults which now determine their fronts.   In such cases the filling of valleys must be regarded as a minor incident, temporarily interrupting the dominant process which is erosion.

All escarpments should, of course, be retreating.   When a triangular facet is spoken of as representing the original fault plane a moderate retreat may be assumed as a detail.   Weathering in an arid climate would in time reduce its slope to the angle of repose (36° or less) but after that its form might remain constant despite retreat.[1]

Causes of Pleistocene Lakes.—An increase in the size of lakes without outlet may result from either an increase of precipitation or a decrease of evaporation, due perhaps to lower temperature. In the glacial period no ice cap covered western United States, but the mountain glaciers expanded greatly.   Both the Wasatch and the Sierras show abundant evidences of this expansion. Among the basin ranges, significant glaciers were limited to a very few ranges,[2] among which are the Snake, Ruby, and East Humboldt.   It may well be assumed that the same climate which permitted an ice cap north of the Missouri and Ohio Rivers was marked by lower temperatures beyond the limits of the ice cap if not also by greater precipitation.   Direct evidence that the epoch of the former great lakes coincided with that of glaciers is found in the relation of the shore lines of Lake Bonneville to the moraines of the Wasatch.[3]

The climate of that epoch was only relatively humid.   For the greater part of its duration all the drainage of the Bonneville Basin evaporated from a water surface covering less than a third of its area, and the drainage of the Lahontan Basin for little more than a fifth of its area.   It has been estimated[4] that an annual rainfall of 20 in. would restore Lake Lahontan.   When it is remembered that the Bonneville Basin had essentially its present topography, even down to individual gorges and alluvial fans, before the advent of the younger Pleistocene lakes, it will be understood that, so far back as we can see in the current erosion cycle, the climate was about the same as now.   The epoch of the great lakes was exceptional, perhaps mainly in being cooler, but not of a different order.

Stages of Lake Bonneville.—With the advent of the Pleistocene climate, Lake Bonneville first began to fill its basin, rising over the débris fans and then against the mountain sides to a height

[1] This subject is discussed more fully on p. 346.
[2] RUSSELL, U. S. Geol. Survey, *Mon.* 11, p. 266, 1885.
[3] GILBERT, U. S. Geol. Survey, *Mon.* 1, p. 318, 1890.
[4] JONES, J. C., *Science*, December, 1914.   On the climate of the Great Basin in Pleistocene time, see Oscar E. Meinzer, Map of the Pleistocene Lakes of the Basin and Range Province and Its Significance, Geol. Soc. Amer. *Bull.*, vol. 33, pp. 541–552, 1922.

of about 910 ft. above Great Salt Lake. In its rise, 10 or 12 separate basins became confluent, as they again became independent when it vanished. The lake remained long enough at approximately its maximum height to make distinct shore features, but having no outlet, its level changed from time to time, hence its efforts were more or less dissipated at different levels. Aridity then returned and the lake dwindled or disappeared. It was during the highest rise in this epoch that the lake etched its shore line 90 ft. below the maximum rise.[1]

With the return of a favorable climate the lake again expanded, rising this time 90 ft. above its former maximum and finding an outlet at Red Rock Pass on the north, thus reaching the Snake River by the route since followed by the Oregon Short Line.[2] While standing at that level, the lake cut its highest or Bonneville shore line. The outlet thus found was over unconsolidated material into which the strong stream quickly cut its channel 375 ft. deep. At that depth rock was encountered and the level of stream and lake became relatively stationary. At this level (the Provo shore line) the lake stood longer than at any other, cutting its highest cliffs and broadest platforms and building its greatest beaches, bars, and especially deltas. The deltas are accounted for as follows: In its previous high stage, streams dropped their burdens either in the margin of the lake or in their valleys above. In either case they were above the Provo shore and were carried down into the lake to make deltas during the long halt at that level.

From the topographic features of each epoch it is clear that the post-Bonneville time has been short in proportion to the Bonneville epoch and that the latter was very short in proportion to the pre-Bonneville erosion cycle. It likewise appears that the duration of the first rise of the lake was five times that of the second rise, and that the inter-Bonneville epoch of desiccation was much longer than the post-Bonneville.[3]

Stages of Lake Lahontan.—The history of Lake Lahontan is in the main analogous to that of Lake Bonneville. Its first rise

[1] GILBERT, G. K., *loc. cit.*, pp. 199 and 316.

[2] Guidebook, the Overland Route, U. S. Geol. Survey, *Bull.* 612, p. 116, 1915.

[3] GILBERT, G. K., *loc. cit.*, p. 316. Interesting quantitative estimates of time involved in the making of Great Basin topography are given by W. M. DAVIS, The Basin Range Problem, *Proc. Nat. Acad. Sci.*, vol. 11, pp. 387–392, 1925.

was over alluvial fans and desert-carved mountains, having much the same appearance as at the present day. Like Lake Bonneville, the lake rose not quite to its later maximum, stood long enough at that level to cut bold cliffs with rock shelves locally 200 to 300 ft. wide, and then disappeared, perhaps entirely; then rose again, in a shorter epoch, a little above its former height. But Lahontan never overflowed. During the rise to this second maximum there were two stops of sufficient duration to cut strong shore lines. Other halts, both rising and falling, are marked by faint and local lines.

The fossil shores of Lake Lahontan are marked by the usual topographic features and also by great deposits of calcareous tufa. At each of the long halts a distinctive kind of tufa was formed.[1] The coating of tufa is locally so abundant as to distract attention from the primary feature, which is the shore line itself. The vicinity of Pyramid Lake, with its steep and picturesque slopes and islands, is especially rich in shore forms and tufa deposits. Some islands are of bedrock, heavily and fantastically covered with tufa. Other islands and crags, one hundred feet or more in height, consist entirely of tufa.

Freshening of Recent Lakes.—The waters of present lakes in the Lahontan Basin, while not fresh, are by no means the strong brines which would be expected if these lakes be considered as shrinking remnants of a former great water body. To explain the relatively fresh waters of the present time it has been suggested[2] that the former waters in such basins were evaporated to dryness, thus precipitating all the mineral matter, and that the present lakes have appeared since such desiccation.

In the case of Pyramid Lake it has been pointed out that a rise of 70 ft. would cause it to overflow to Smoke Creek Basin. Evaporation and concentration would then take place in the latter basin while the waters of the upper basin would freshen. Strangely enough a still higher water level, causing the two lakes to merge without an intervening current, would again make Pyramid Lake salt. With partial desiccation again, the divide

[1] JONES, J. C., Origin of the Tufas of Lake Lahontan; abstr., Geol. Soc. Amer. *Bull.*, vol. 26, p. 392, 1915. It appears that all the tufa deposits are due directly to work of blue-green algæ and not to saturation of the water, although at one stage, and only one (that of the Thinolite terrace), the water was actually saturated with calcium carbonate.

[2] RUSSELL, *loc. cit.*, p. 224, refers to Gilbert's explanation for parts of the Bonneville Basin.

would be once more uncovered, the level in Smoke Creek Basin would fall first, the interlake current would again appear and Pyramid Lake would again freshen. Somewhat paradoxically both Provo and Humboldt Lakes, now kept fresh by overflow, were salt during the more humid Pleistocene when the Bonneville and Lahontan levels rose above their rims. In the case of Provo Lake, exception must be made of the time during which Lake Bonneville overflowed.

It is probable that Pyramid Lake was freshened in the manner here described[1] but the level of the Lake in Smoke Creek Valley never rose to the divide. It is certain that Pyramid Lake overflowed at no very remote time. The channel to Smoke Creek Desert is well preserved. Owens Lake once discharged into the basin south of it and may then have become fresh; but the subsequent desiccation of Owens Lake has been much greater than that of Pyramid Lake. The former has fallen 220 ft. since overflow and occupies but a small fraction of its former bed. Accordingly, its waters are very alkaline.

Resources of the Great Basin

Mineral Resources.—One of the chief matters of economic interest in the Great Basin, namely the search for potash salts,[2] is connected with the factors that control the salinity and desiccation of lakes. The basins where such accumulations are likely to be found are those which have been centers of evaporation for the largest drainage areas and for the longest time. These can only be determined by a complete unraveling of the physiographic history, taking into account the basins determined by geologic structure, the subdivision of basins by alluvial fans, overflow of water or detritus from one to another, the coalescence of lakes when divides were submerged, and their separation again in consequence of greater aridity. The search for potash deposits in this manner is a problem of economic physiography, but the method of the prospector may succeed first.

A less physiographic phase of the problem arises from the fact that in order to be commercially valuable, the salts sought, for example potash, must have been to some extent segre-

---

[1] GALE, HOYT S., *Science*, vol. XLI, p. 209, Feb. 5, 1915.

[2] FREE, E. E., The Topographic Features of the Desert Basins of the United States with Reference to the Possibilities of Occurrence of Potash, U. S. Dep. Agr., *Bull.* 54, 1914.

gated, *i.e.*, laid down by themselves, and not indiscriminately mixed with others. Potash deposits of considerable value are known at Searles Lake, California. Others are being sought by applying the principles mentioned above. Owens Lake is said to be so concentrated that bicarbonate of soda precipitates naturally during the winter. Soda is now being extracted from its waters.[1] Among the commercially valuable deposits of the playas are the great borax deposits of Death Valley, California. These have not been buried by sediments. These long-famous deposits are not now mined because richer deposits were found in Miocene sediments covered by gravel in the Mohave Desert.

Gold and silver are mined in a number of the basin ranges. The Comstock Lode (chiefly silver ores) at Virginia City, Nevada, which first became known to the world in 1859, was one of the richest deposits of the precious metals ever discovered. It was worked on a large scale in the two decades which followed. It was largely on this account that the population of Nevada Territory rose to nearly 70,000 and that Nevada was admitted to the Union as a state. With the depletion of this group of mines the population of the state gradually decreased. In the census of 1900 it had but 42,335 inhabitants. Other mining districts have since proved profitable, and the population to be credited to that industry has again increased.[2]

Agriculture and Grazing.—With the exhaustion of the humid farming lands of the public domain and settlement of the western part of the Great Basin by miners, the valleys of the Humboldt and of the three main streams from the Sierra Nevada, the Truckee, the Carson, and the Walker Rivers, were rapidly occupied by irrigated farms (Fig. 131). Agriculture was made possible on a much larger scale by the work of the United States Reclamation Service in the Truckee and Carson Basins in the first decade of the century. These farm lands in Nevada are supplied with water by rain and snow which falls mainly in another state and in another physiographic province.

The line of valleys at the east foot of the Sierra Nevada, extending southward and including Mono and Owens Lakes, affords much irrigable land. It is estimated that the Owens River receives from the mountains 400,000 acre-feet of water per year. It was chiefly the use of water from this stream for

---

[1] Lee, Willis T., U. S. Geol. Survey, *Wat. Sup. Pap.* 181, p. 21, 1906.
[2] The population of Nevada in 1930 was 90,559.

irrigation that caused the level of Owens Lake to fall 16 ft. in the decade preceding the year 1905.[1]

In like manner the eastern edge of the province is irrigated from the rain and snow which falls on the Wasatch and Uinta Mountains. These waters reach the lands on which they are used, largely by the Bear, Weber, and Jordan Rivers. This is the chief agricultural district of the Great Basin and one of the principal irrigated districts of North America

Fig. 131.—East front of the Carson Range, overlooking Carson Valley, Nevada. The base of this range is marked for many miles by fresh faulting. The flat Carson Valley several miles wide is the most important agricultural area in Nevada. A part of its western margin is swampy as though thrown down by recent faulting. (*Louderback.*)

In the lake district of southern Oregon are some important irrigated areas deriving their waters from the basin ranges. The irrigation of several hundred thousand acres near Klamath Lake is one of the most important projects of the United States Reclamation Service. South of Oregon the only irrigation of importance from streams originating in the Great Basin is from the headwaters of the Humboldt and its tributaries in north central Nevada, but most of the ranches thus watered are widely spaced and can scarcely be said to constitute a community.

Grazing is the most widespread industry and probably destined to continue the most important when the resources of the province

[1] Lee, Willis T., *loc. cit.*, p. 19.

shall have been fully realized. Where water is available grass is the limiting factor, but some grass is not available because of the distance to water. In parts of Oregon there is good reason to hope for success with artesian wells,[1] not necessarily flowing, but affording water under pressure from deeply buried sandy beds as in Washington (see page 256). It may thus be possible to extend the range for cattle by establishing drinking places at suitable intervals.

Owens Valley is believed to be an artesian basin but the extent of the yield of water cannot be fairly estimated. Doubtless there are other similar basins but at best the supply is small in proportion to the need.

SONORAN DESERT

Extent and Distinguishing Characteristics.—The term "Sonoran," long in use with a biological significance, is taken from the state of Sonora in northwestern Mexico, whose western half belongs to this section. The Sonoran section as here defined includes also the Gila Desert of southwestern Arizona and the Mohave Desert of southeastern California (Fig. 132).

In common with the Great Basin, this extensive area is characterized by basin ranges and intervening desert plains. In contrast, however, the altitude is lower, the ranges are smaller and occupy not more than a fifth of the area. Rock pediments are much more prevalent and undrained basins are less general.

An insignificant portion of the plain surface lies above 3,000 ft. and more than half of it is below 2,000. A large fraction lies between sea-level and the 1,000-ft. contour. In a very general way the level declines from all directions toward the Gulf of California.

Mountains.—The mountain ranges are of all sizes from mere hills or buttes up to ranges rising 4,000 ft. above the sea. A minority of these in the Arizona portion have been interpreted as fault blocks.[2] These are mainly near the margin of the Mexican Highland. Most of the ranges, especially the smaller ones nearer the Gulf of California,[3] are without the straight base

---

[1] WARING, U. S. Geol. Survey, *Wat. Sup. Pap.* 220.

[2] BRYAN, KIRK, U. S. Geol. Survey, *Bull.* 730, pp. 36, 65, and 83, 1922.

[3] McGEE, W. J., Sheetflood Erosion, Geol. Soc. Amer. *Bull.*, vol. 8, pp. 93–95, 1897. McGee describes these mountains as having the features of residuals after long erosion without reference to the particular mode of origin.

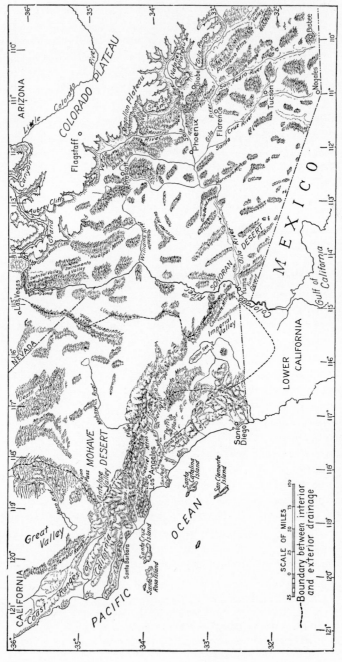

FIG. 132.—Index map of the Sonoran Desert and adjacent sections.   (Drawn by Guy-Harold Smith.)

lines and other features (page 333) relied on as evidence of fault origin. These consist largely of granite and volcanics and have not the pronounced parallelism of those basin ranges whose history is clearer. For aught that is known most of them might be residuals of a long erosion cycle[1] (*cf.* Fig. 126, page 346).

Despite the negative character of the evidence, the association of these ranges with those of the Great Basin, their similar distribution, and the fact that old block mountains should have the features of these, create a tendency to extend the interpretation of the Great Basin to this area. The physiographic development of mountains in their later stages would be much the same whatever their origin.[2]

Basins.—Undrained basins are here known as "bolsons."[3] Some of these, like some in Nevada, are deeply filled in their central parts, apparently with wash from the mountains. The evidence for this is the same as in the Great Basin and subject to the same possible error in interpretation, namely, the confusion of older sediments with recent wash. Well borings near Phoenix have gone 348 ft. in loose sediment,[4] and others, near Tucson, 500 to 1,800 ft. deep, failed to reach the rock floor.[5]

While the area occupied by mountains is smaller in this section than in the Great Basin, the extent of rock platforms, bare of detritus or only thinly covered, is correspondingly large. It is estimated that, of the entire area of southwestern Arizona and northwestern Mexico, one-fifth is occupied by mountains, two-fifths by rock platforms, or mountain pediments, and the remaining two-fifths by deposits of detritus.[6] If all detritus were removed the mountains would have the appearance of being two-thirds consumed by some agency eating away at their flanks, shaving them off to nearly horizontal platforms.

Stage of Physiographic Development.—Several characteristic features of the Sonoran section suggest that the normal develop-

---

[1] *Cf.* Spurr, J. E., Origin and Structure of the Basin Ranges, Geol. Soc. Amer. *Bull.*, vol. 12, 1901.

[2] Davis, W. M., The Basin Range Problem, *Proc. Nat. Acad. Sci.*, vol. 11, pp. 387–392, 1925.

[3] Mexican word for purse.

[4] Lee, W. T., U. S. Geol. Survey, *Wat. Sup. Pap.* 136, p. 104, 1905.

[5] Tolman, C. F., Erosion and Deposition in the Southern Arizona Bolson Region, *Jour. Geol.*, vol. XVII, p. 140, 1909.

[6] McGee, W. J., *loc. cit.*, pp. 91 and 109.

ment of the arid cycle has proceeded further here than in the Great Basin. The greatly eroded mountain forms, the striking development of rock plains and the union of basins in a common drainage system, are all features toward which the Great Basin is tending (see page 345). However, even if age be disregarded, it cannot be affirmed that the histories of these sections are alike. Some facts are already known to the contrary, but the assertion may be made that *if* their histories are otherwise alike and their ages different, their topographies should differ in the manner observed. Whether or not the Sonoran section ever was like the Great Basin, the Great Basin will some day be like the Sonoran section in these essential respects, always providing that the present cycle be not interrupted.

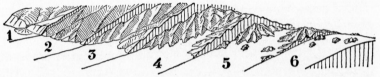

Fig. 133.—Stages in the erosion of a typical block mountain in its first cycle. In (1) the base of the fault scarp is in general *fan-free* but locally *fan-based*. In (2) the gorges are sufficiently developed to divide the face into spurs on whose ends triangular facets are preserved. On account of the accumulated detritus in the valley mouths the front is called *fan-dented*. In (3) the triangular facets are lost and the spur ends rounded off but their position still marks the nearly straight line of the former base; the detritus-filled indentations are getting large and the front is now *fan-bayed*. In (4) the spurs are irregularly worn back and cut by tributary gorges; the front is *fan-frayed* and no longer straight. In (5) some of the former spurs appear as detached fragments which are *fan-wrapped*, as the remnants of the range itself become at a later stage. In (6) the mountains have practically disappeared and the surface is in its *pan-fan* stage. (*Davis, Proc. Nat. Acad. Sci., vol.* XI.)

Drainage.—In describing the Great Basin, stress was laid on the independence of the drainage basins, the goal of drainage in each being a central playa or sink, toward which all slopes tend. In parts of the Sonoran section the same law holds. There are many such basins in the California portion and in southeastern Arizona. Much of the region here considered has no such centripetal drainage. The mountains divide the plains into more or less distinct parts commonly called "basins" but many of them are without central depressions. Instead of that, the slopes of one such basin lead into other basins and thus by devious courses to the sea.[1] That most of the area fails to send

[1] BRYAN, KIRK: U. S. Geol. Survey, *Bull.* 730, p. 66, 1922.

drainage to the sea is, therefore, not due to the direction of its slopes but to aridity. The area in which the drainage is most integrated is, in general, the area in which rock pediments occupy the largest fraction of the total surface.

The behavior of running water in a region of this character presents some peculiarities. In the mountains it is much the same as in other climates except for the suddenness of the floods rushing down rock-walled ravines which are usually dry. In many cases these ravines are almost as free from rock waste as from water.

Such a rocky ravine may be continued for some distance out on the Piedmont slope in an *arroyo* (Mexican term for a sharply incised channel that is usually dry). Commonly the arroyo shallows and disappears before reaching the axis of the basin.

Where the basin is incompletely rimmed it follows that no playa can be formed. If the slope leading to the next basin has a gradient of more than 15 or 20 ft. per mile, the axis of the basin may be occupied by a "wash." Such a wash is the channel of an occasional stream, perfectly flat in cross-section but bounded at places by almost vertical banks of alluvium. The channel may be as wide as a great river and yet be used but once in many years and never carry a stream 50 miles long. Instead of being less desert than the adjacent plain it is more so for the occasional torrent leaves only the coarser materials in its bed. "During most of the year nine-tenths of the few streamways are broad wastes of barren sand, the most forbidding lines of the desert often littered with the skeletons of famished stock."[1] Nevertheless even these forbidding lines are not wholly without significance when water is being sought. At least they follow the lowest line in the valley, hence ground water may sometimes be reached by digging in those sands when it is inaccessible elsewhere. Even the skeletons indicate that cattle staked their last efforts on finding water here.

Sheet Floods.—This region also affords the phenomenon of the "sheet flood," not known in humid lands and nowhere else in the United States so important as here. In this phenomenon the water from a cloudburst, occurring either on the plain or in the hills, runs over the gently sloping plain in a sheet; it may be a few inches thick or even two or three feet. As may be imagined it churns up the loose material of the surface so that it is at every

[1] McGee, *loc. cit.*, p. 98.

step loaded or overloaded with detritus. It therefore fills incipient channels as fast as they are formed. The real reason for flowing in a sheet is not the excess of water but the inability to form channels. As the water is constantly being absorbed, a great sheet flood may disappear within a mile of its origin.

To produce such a moving sheet of water it is evident that the rainfall must be very rapid and equally evident that the necessary topographic condition is a sloping plain; but given both these conditions, a sheet of water would quickly resolve itself into streams if not supplied at all times with all the load it could carry. Overloaded water cannot scour enduring channels, for any chance beginning of scour is at once undone by deposition. The basic condition is climate. Given long continued aridity in a mountain country, a cycle of changes will, no doubt, follow in which cycle the present combination of circumstances favorable to sheet floods marks one of the natural stages.

Much stress was laid by McGee[1] on the work of sheet floods. It is obvious that the mantle of detritus would be urged down the slope and that if the entire mantle were moved the rock floor would be abraded. In this way McGee explained the reduction of rock knobs to the common level. He also ascribed to such floods an important share in cutting against the mountain base and steepening its slope by a kind of retrogressive or headward erosion, thus causing the sharpness of angle between mountain and plain to increase with time. Others lay less stress on sheet floods in modifying topography, believing that sheet floods are related to the topographic features as a result rather than a cause.[2]

A process tending more directly to cut away the mountain base is the lateral swing of streams resulting in planation.[3] This tends to shave off all interstream areas to the level of the stream channels thus extending the rock pediment. The torrents which occupy the ravines of such desert mountains may well be imagined as very efficient in this work of planation as soon as they have

---

[1] *Loc. cit.*, p. 109–110. This well-known paper on sheet floods should be considered in connection with Blackwelder's more recent study of mud flows, Geol. Soc. Amer. *Bull.*, vol. 39, pp. 465–484; and *vice versa*. The ratio of solid matter to water may be almost anything.

[2] Paige, Sidney, Rock-cut Surfaces in the Desert Ranges, *Jour. Geol.*, vol. XX, p. 450, 1912.

[3] Gilbert, G. K., Geology of the Henry Mountains, U. S. Geogr. and Geol. Survey of the Rocky Mountain Region, p. 120, 1880.

reached the level at which they are no longer able to cut down. Such torrents may become sheet floods on reaching the pediment.

Mohave Desert.—In most respects the description of the section as a whole suffices for the California portion. It is a land of broad pediments surmounted by much wasted mountains. Here, however, the drainage is mainly to enclosed basins except near the Colorado River. Small ranges of bare mountains separate the basins whose centers are marked by "soda lakes," "borax lakes," "dry lakes," and "alkali marshes."

FIG. 134.—Coyote Well; one of the sources of water in the Mohave Desert. Through an area of 60,000 square miles the United States Geological Survey has listed and mapped all the places at which it is possible to obtain water. The water in this well stands 15 ft. below the surface and is slightly brackish but fairly abundant. The nearest water in one direction is 14 miles away and in another direction 17 miles. In some parts of this section watering places may be 30 to 50 miles apart. (*U. S. Geol. Survey.*)

The principal stream, and almost the only one, is the Mohave River, descending from the San Bernardino Mountains and pursuing its stealthy course 100 miles north and east, hiding most of the time beneath its gravel bed and coming to light only where forced to the surface by impervious rock. Like the Humboldt of Nevada, it guides transcontinental railroads. It is lost at last in the soda lakes.

The western end of the Mohave Desert (called Antelope Valley) contains spots in which ground water rises under artesian pressure. Here there is a substantial supply of pumped water for irrigation.[1]

Gila District.—East of the Colorado River enclosed basins are less general. Most slopes, however arid, may be followed to the sea. The Williams River (lat. 34°15′) carries water derived mainly from the Colorado Plateau or the bordering strip of Mexican Highland. So also does the Gila. South of that for 500 miles no living stream reaches the sea despite the favoring

FIG. 135.—Fresh lava flow and cinder cone in the Mohave Desert. The cinder cone is Mount Pisgah near Barstow, California. The ropy surface of the lava in the foreground shows broken blisters and caverns. (*U. S. Geol. Survey.*)

slopes and despite the lines representing rivers on the maps.[2] Between the rather small and scattered mountain ranges, the several plains are known as basins, but many of these are now connected by continuous slopes.

Portions of the Gila Valley near where it emerges from the Highland, and therefore where the stream carries most water, had been irrigated and cultivated by Indians from time immemorial. A great area in this valley and a still greater area in Salt River Valley surrounding Phoenix are now reclaimed for agriculture by

[1] JOHNSON, HARRY R., Water Resources of Antelope Valley, California, U. S. Geol. Survey, *Wat. Sup. Pap.* 278. 1911.

[2] McGEE, W. J., *loc. cit.*, p. 91.

the construction of dams and the storage of flood waters in the Highland to the east. The Roosevelt Dam and Reservoir, on the Salt River 75 miles above Phoenix, are among the largest in the world. The area thus made fertile produces cotton and also fruits similar to those of southern California.

The Valley of the Colorado.—The immediate valley of the Colorado below the Grand Canyon seems to bear no relation to the slopes of mountains and basins which lie in its way. That stream passes in succession through a half dozen or more bolsons, separated by mountains through which the stream has cut deep apparently very young canyons.[1] The river might avoid most or all of these mountains by following ready-made valleys which are known to be filled with unconsolidated sediments to great depths. From a study of the valley filling and the river's course, Lee concludes[2] that the river once followed such a course through the detrital Sacramento Valley which it first enlarged and later filled with its own gravels. However, as only a thin surface sheet of gravel is known to be horizontal, and the beds below it have dips as high as 30 deg., it is plain that the filling of these valleys occurred before the last folding. This throws back the making of these valleys into an older cycle in which the lines of drainage are little known. The alternation of degradation with aggradation occurred several times, and aggradation at some time seems to have been so extensive as to bury many of the present mountain ranges and superpose the river in its present course. As similar superposition is noted in the case of the Salt River,[3] it is apparent that this region has had a complex history of crustal movements or climatic change, or both.

As far as to the end of the fourth (Black) canyon, 80 miles from the mouth of the Grand Canyon, the Colorado is a swift-flowing stream falling five feet per mile. Between that point and Yuma, Arizona, 150 miles to the south, the stream flows more leisurely though not without occasional canyons. In this distance its flood plain affords 375,000[4] acres, nearly 600 square

[1] The third of these is the now famous Boulder Canyon; Black Canyon is the fourth.

[2] LEE, WILLIS T., Geologic Reconnaissance of a Part of Western Arizona, U. S. Geol. Survey, *Bull.* 352, 1908; also Geology of the Lower Colorado River, Geol. Soc. Amer. *Bull.*, vol. 17, pp. 275–284, 1906.

[3] LEE, WILLIS T., U. S. Geol. Survey, *Wat. Sup. Pap.* 136, p. 125.

[4] LEE, WILLIS T., U. S. Geol. Survey, *Bull.* 352, p. 75.

miles, of irrigable land. This is mainly below the mouth of the Williams River where the Colorado seems to have found its old broad valley.

Comparison with the Nile.—The Colorado is sometimes called the Nile of America. Its chief points of resemblance are: (1) an annual flood at a time when the water is useful for irrigation; (2) the vast quantities of mud carried and left on its flood plain; (3) both are perennial streams flowing through arid regions by reason of ample supplies at their headwaters. The floods of the Colorado come in the early summer, May, June, or July, and are fed by the rains and snows on the mountains during the late winter.

In the muddy character of its waters, the Colorado agrees with other desert streams. Absence of vegetation, torrential rains, and strong dust-laden winds, all help to give the high mud content, and evaporation tends to make its proportion still higher. The proportion of suspended matter to water is sometimes 1 in 50.[1] Seven-tenths of 1 per cent is believed to be the average.[2] The stream is therefore thirty times as muddy as

[1] FREEMAN, W. B., and BOLSTER, R. H., Surface Water Supply of the United States, U. S. Geol. Survey, *Wat. Sup. Pap.* 249, p. 34, 1910.

The following comparisons of the Nile, Colorado, and Susquehanna, taken from Freeman and Bolster, are instructive:

	Nile	Colorado (taken as 1)	Susquehanna
Drainage area..........	5.7	1	0.12
Rainfall in basin........	3.8	1	4.50
Run-off per square mile..	1.9	1	37.00
Ratio of run-off to total rain.................	0.5	1	8.20
Discharge.............	10.8	1	4.50
Maximum flow in second-feet.................	353,000 about Sept. 1	70,000 to 100,000, May, June, July	200,000 to 400,000, March, April, May.
Minimum flow in second-feet.................	14,500 about May 30	2,500 to 3,000 January to February	2,500 to 5,000 September to October
Mean flow in second-feet.	115,000	10,700	43,000

[2] LaRue. E. C., U. S. Geol. Survey, *Wat. Sup. Pap.* 395, p. 222, 1916.

the Ohio. The sediment carried annually is equivalent to a square mile of dry earth 125 ft. deep. Most of this silt is left in thick films on the flood plain by the annual floods, but a minor fraction is carried out to sea.

Unfortunately, much otherwise good farm land in the lower basin of the Colorado lies too high to be watered from the river except by means of pumps. These are used to a limited extent. In addition to cotton and alfalfa, the fruits which characterize southern California may be grown.

Fig. 136.—Sand dunes in the Colorado Desert (Salton Trough) of southern California. (*W. C. Mendenhall, U. S. Geol. Survey.*)

SALTON BASIN

Near the southern boundary of California and 80 to 90 miles north of the mouth of the Colorado River, at the head of the Gulf of California, is the Salton Sink, a depression 273.5 ft. below sea-level. It is the topographic center of a great concave basin, having an area of more than 2,000 square miles between the Coast Ranges on the southwest and the Chocolate Range on the northeast. Between these ranges the basin runs northwest almost to the 34th parallel, followed for more than 150 miles by the Southern Pacific Railroad.

At a former geological time this down-warped or down-faulted area was a part of the Gulf of California into which the Colorado

River discharged at Yuma, 60 miles above its present mouth and 150 miles below the head of the gulf at that time.   It has been thought that the rapidly growing delta of the muddy river spread westward across the gulf and rose in a great alluvial fan with its apex at Yuma and its lower edge against the Cocopa Mountains on the western shore.   The dam thus formed rose 40 ft. above the level of the sea.   It is quite as probable that the entire area was above sea-level when the alluvial fan was built.[1] As is the habit of streams on alluvial fans, the Colorado flowed now in one direction, now in another, from the apex, discharging at times into the basin to the north.   At one such time the basin filled to the level of the dam and, while at that level, cut cliffs and built beaches which remain almost intact.   When the Colorado drained again to the Gulf of California, the lake quickly dwindled and disappeared by evaporation.   The run-off of the basin itself is not sufficient to maintain a lake, however small. Within historic times there have been many natural discharges of the Colorado into Salton Sink,[2] the last being in 1891.

Part of the water of the Colorado has been diverted by a ditch below Yuma and used to irrigate the Imperial Valley on the north side of the great alluvial fan.   In 1904 to 1905 occurred a winter flood (not usual in the Colorado) and this was followed by more than ordinary summer floods in 1905.   The Imperial Ditch, having an excessive gradient and having no proper head-gate to protect it against erosion, began to be scoured and enlarged.   In July, 87 per cent of the Colorado's flow was pouring through the ditch and by way of several generally dry "washes" to the reappearing "Salton Sea."   Thus a fresh-water lake was formed in the bottom of the basin.   The break was not finally repaired until February, 1907.   By that time the depth of the lake was 67.5 ft. and its area 443 square miles.   Had this lake risen to the point of overflow (40 ft. above sea-level) its area would have been about 2,100 square miles.   It is probable that before reaching this area, evaporation would have equaled the entire inflow of the Colorado River.

[1] BUWALDA, JOHN P., and SANTON, W. L., Geological Events in the History of the Indio Hills and the Salton Basin, *Science*, vol. LXXI, pp. 104–106, 1930.

[2] FREEMAN and BOLSTER, U. S. Geol. Survey, *Wat. Sup. Pap.* 249, p. 49; MACDOUGAL, D. T., The Salton Sea, Carnegie Inst. *Pub.* 193, p. 19, 1914. In 1891 the lake rose so high as to endanger the tracks of the Southern Pacific Railroad.

When inflow was stopped in February, 1907, evaporation began at once to reduce the lake. In the five years following, the level fell 25 ft.[1] This fall of five feet per year is somewhat less than the annual evaporation, for it received some water from the overflow and seepage of irrigation ditches. Within two and one-half years after the Salton Lake began to reappear, its water was four times as saline as that of the river from which it was derived. In the dry condition of the sink previous to the break, great areas

Fig. 137.—Margin of the Salton Sea, Imperial Junction Beach, as it appeared in 1912. In the shrinking of the sea, the water had withdrawn from this area about a year before the photograph was taken. The general appearance is that of a playa but the mud deposit of the typical playa is smoother and less cracked. (*Photo by D. T. MacDougal, reproduced by courtesy of the Carnegie Inst. Wash.*)

were covered with crystalline salt which was being commercially exploited. As the lake again evaporated, this was found covered by a few feet of silt.

MEXICAN HIGHLAND

Boundaries and Description

East of the Sonoran Desert section and south of the Colorado Plateau is a vast area extending southward far into Mexico, known as the Mexican Highland. Like the Great Basin, it is approximately half mountain and half plain, many of the moun-

[1] MacDougal, D. T., *loc. cit.*, p. 6.

tains being typical basin ranges. Mention of other types is deferred to the pages of local description. Of the total intermont area, perhaps half is bolson. The remainder drains, or at least slopes, to the branches of the Williams and Gila Rivers in Arizona and the Rio Grande in New Mexico.

Throughout the Arizona portion, the boundary on the side of the Colorado Plateau is fairly definite. Separation from the Sonoran section is more arbitrary, being determined by the size and spacing of the mountains. Nevertheless, even without the aid of science, custom has long recognized the Highlands north and east of a line which passes near Nogales, Tucson, Florence, Phoenix, and the mouth of the Williams River.

In New Mexico the mutual boundary of the Colorado Plateau and the Mexican Highland is less known and probably not clear (page 381). The section as here defined and described extends east of the Rio Grande as far as pronounced basin ranges continue to alternate with basins. Along a line not far from the 106th meridian, this type of topography ceases and gives way to the faulted and sloping plateaus of the Sacramento section (page 393).

In general the intermont basins of the Mexican Highland are 4,000 to 5,000 ft. above the sea but in the western part the altitude declines greatly, especially between the Gila and the Colorado where it is about 2,000 ft.

While less desert than the Sonoran section, the Mexican Plateau has the distinguishing limitations associated with aridity. The rocks decompose but slowly while wind and sheet floods carry away the finer particles, hence there is a scarcity of soil. The cactus, yucca, and creosote bush, so closely associated in most minds with Arizona, are most abundant below 3,500 ft. From 3,500 to nearly 5,000 ft., the dominating vegetation is sage brush and greasewood. Above this zone cedars are characteristic, but not abundant, up to about 7,000 ft. Above that are pine and fir.

Mountains

Western Part.—Near the Mexican border the trend of all mountains is nearly north and south. The same tendency is seen throughout New Mexico except near the Arizona boundary. West of that, including most of the Arizona portion, the trend is northwestward, parallel to the province boundary. A number of ranges in this western portion are tilted fault blocks resembling those of the Great Basin in their dimensions, in the rocks that compose them, in structure, and in history.[1] In other ranges, the Bradshaw for example, though folding is important, no significant faulting has been discovered.[2]

Near the edge of the Colorado Plateau, many mountains are fault blocks without alignment, mere fragments of the plateau that have suffered displacement and erosion. There is here a kind of transitional zone between the two physiographic provinces. In the Clifton mining district near the New Mexico border, the entire area when seen from a high point is one of irregular ridges and uplands without apparent plan or order. It does not in the least conform to the simple conception of basin ranges, but with its complicated history of intrusion, faulting, lava flows, and various erosion cycles[3] it resembles still less the horizontal plateau on the north. At some places, particularly in the mining districts, the results of faulting reach the last degree of complexity. Areas of many square miles may be broken by faults of various trend, into blocks so small that the whole district is but a huge mosaic of angular blocks.[4] To a remarkable degree the drainage of such areas has been guided by fault lines or by differences in hardness among the several blocks.

Features of the Plateau Border.—In western Arizona there is not much question as to the proper location of the province boundary. North of the Colorado River the lower and upper Carboniferous rocks and the Kaibab limestone (Permian) are almost coextensive and their combined escarpments form the Grand Wash Cliffs, the western limit of the Colorado Plateau. South of the river, the upper Carboniferous and Permian fall back many miles to the east, leaving the Lower Carboniferous (Redwall) to form the plateau surface. The height of the cliffs which limit this plateau is increased by the thickness of the underlying Cambrian (Tonto) as in the Grand Canyon (page 294). This condition persists as far east as long. 112°30′, and throughout that distance the Plateau province is coextensive

[1] RANSOME, F. L., Geology of the Globe Copper District, U. S. Geol. Survey, *Prof. Pap.* 12, p. 16, 1903. Ransome here cites Gilbert.

[2] JAGGAR, T. A., and PALACHE, CHARLES, Bradshaw Mountains folio 126, U. S. Geol. Survey, 1905.

[3] LINDGREN, W., Clifton folio 129, U. S. Geol. Survey, 1905.

[4] See geological maps in Globe folio 111; also Bisbee special folio 112, U. S. Geol. Survey.

with the Carboniferous.[1] The cliff is known in succession as
Grand Wash, Yampai, Juniper, and Black Mesa. The height
varies from a few hundred to 4,000 ft.

North of lat. 35° and at the foot of Yampai Cliffs, is a volcanic
plateau called Truxton, itself fronted by good cliffs facing southwest. However plateau-like this appears, it is strictly a part
of the Basin and Range province. Lava flows have here inundated and filled up the inequalities of the widespread granite
and schist which make the neighboring mountains.[2]

East of long. 112°30', the lower Carboniferous shelf is deeply
eroded and its topography is complicated by the deformation
which made the neighboring ranges.[3] General usage here assigns
this belt of lower Carboniferous to the Basin and Range province,
and makes the Aubrey Cliffs the province boundary.[4] The upper
Carboniferous, capped for many miles by lavas, here forms a
gigantic escarpment called the "Verde Breaks" and, farther
east, Mogollon escarpment, 1,000 to 2,000 ft. high, overlooking
the rough upper basins of the Verde River and Tonto Creek.
At places in these basins the upturned edge of the Redwall
limestone makes a ridge or even a mountain range. Such are
the Black Hills northeast of Prescott (lava capped),[5] the Sierra
Ancha, and the Apache Mountains, the last named being also
affected by faulting. Still farther east near Camp Apache
(long. 110°) is a considerable area in which the lower Carboniferous is more or less horizontal but deeply eroded and scored by
canyons guided among lava flows. From the Grand Wash
Cliffs on the west to this locality, the Aubrey Cliffs are bold
even if locally notched. For a considerable distance the divide
between the Salt River on the south and the Little Colorado is
at the top of these cliffs.

Mountains in New Mexico and Texas.—In the eastern half
of the section, as in the western half, the dominant type of
mountain is that of the Great Basin. Such, for example, are the

---

[1] See geologic map of Arizona; also DARTON, N. H., Reconnaissance in
New Mexico and Arizona, U. S. Geol. Survey, *Bull.* 435, 1910, map, pl. I.
The Kaibab limestone, called Pennsylvanian on this map, is now classified
as Permian. See also LEE, WILLIS T., Reconnaissance of Part of Western
Arizona, U. S. Geol. Survey, *Bull.* 352, map, pl. I, 1908.

[2] LEE, WILLIS T., U. S. Geol. Survey, *Bull.* 352, p. 13, 1908.

[3] GILBERT, G. K., Wheeler Survey, vol. III, p. 47.

[4] RANSOME, F. L., U. S. Geol. Survey, *Prof. Pap.* 12, p. 14, 1903.

[5] GILBERT, *loc. cit.*, pp. 23, 36, and 60.

Sandia and Manzano Ranges east of Albuquerque, the San Andreas and Caballos on either side of the Santa Fé Railroad between Socorro and Las Cruces, the Franklin Mountains north of El Paso, and probably the little known Sierra de Santiago (Ord Mountains) in Texas south of the 30th parallel and within the bend of the Rio Grande.[1] Some of the mountains owe their height, or at least their mass, to being centers of eruption. Some are almost isolated volcanoes; others are broad masses of lava and fragmental material. Of this character are the Socorro,

Fig. 138.—Tres Hermanas; mountains of volcanic rock in southwestern New Mexico. (*U. S. Geol. Survey.*)

Magdalena, and San Mateo Ranges west of Socorro (lat. 34°) and the Mogollon near the Arizona border.[2] Some of these ranges may be due primarily to deformation and only increased in size by volcanic materials. Laccoliths are represented by the Ortiz, Carillos, and San Pedro groups midway between Santa Fé and Albuquerque.[3]

An exceptional group of folded mountains is represented on the geologic map by the patch of old Paleozoic rocks north of the 30th parallel and west of the 103d meridian. These are typically

[1] U. S. Geol. Survey, *Prof. Pap.* 68, p. 26.

[2] *Idem*, p. 26; and U. S. Geol. Survey, *Wat. Sup. Pap.* 188, p. 9.

[3] U. S. Geol. Survey, *Prof. Pap.* 68, p. 26.

Appalachian[1] in the age of the rocks, the northeast-southwest trend, the close character of the folding, and the results of erosion which have left parallel ridges on the harder strata. Even the height of the ridges above the valleys (1,200 to 1,500 ft.) is similar. The age of the folding is not definitely known, but it is possible that these mountains represent a southwestward extension of the Appalachian folding, separated by hundreds of miles from the Ouachita Mountains, just as the latter are separated from the Appalachians of the Eastern states.

Near the edge of the Colorado Plateau, here as in Arizona, the trend becomes inconstant and the mountains are irregularly tilted fault blocks. It is as though the plateau margin had been deformed by intrusion and block faulting, and the resulting mountains largely covered with lavas which have since been partly eroded away. The result is a gradation between mountains of deformation and lava-capped mesas reaching heights of 8,000 to 9,000 ft. Thus the flood of lava overlapping the edges of two provinces has made it impossible to draw a clear line between them.

INTERMONT BASINS OF ARIZONA

Drainage and Filling.—In the western half of this region the basins are better drained than those of Nevada. The long headwaters of the Gila, Salt, Verde, Williams, and a few other rivers carry water to the sea from a great distance and from a considerable area. A glance at the ordinary map would, however, lead to an overestimate of the amount of water thus carried and of the area draining to the sea. The streams named do indeed carry water from the Mexican Highland in central Arizona, but in the western part of the state, and more especially in the southeastern part and in New Mexico, typical bolsons prevail. Concerning the depth of unconsolidated sediment in these, see pages 343 and 344.

Badlands on Gila Conglomerate.—In eastern Arizona and western New Mexico the mountains are frequently bordered by a fringe or irregular belt of badlands carved from a conglomerate of poorly assorted sand and gravel. This is the Gila conglomerate. It may once have constituted débris fans but has since been folded and faulted and graded down by erosion, probably

[1] HILL, R. T., Physical Geography of the Texas Region, U. S. Geol. Survey, Topographic folio 3, p. 4.

to ordinary pediments. To what extent its present dissection is due to diastrophism and to what extent to climatic or hydrographic changes is undetermined. The dry washes which cross these badlands to the younger débris slopes farther from the mountains afford natural highways, subject always to the risk of sudden and dangerous floods.[1] They also afford the best sites for temporary wells. It is not uncommon to find ground water by digging 40 ft. into these dry channels.

INTERMONT BASINS OF NEW MEXICO

The several mountain ranges in New Mexico may be grouped into three or more north-south lines 10 to 50 miles apart. Between these are fairly continuous flat-floored troughs subdivided by transverse divides into bolsons or minor drainage basins.

Tularosa Basin.—Extending due north from El Paso for 250 miles is a line of mountains, mainly independent fault blocks, most of them 3 to 10 miles wide and reaching altitudes of 8,000 to 10,000 ft. Named in order from El Paso northward the chain embraces the Franklin, Organ, San Andreas, and Oscura Ranges, followed by the Chupadera Mesa and then by the Montoso, Manzano, and Sandia Ranges, the last named being across the Rio Grande from Albuquerque.[2] Southward the line continues into Mexico.

East of this line of mountains and 30 to 40 miles away is the almost continuous west-facing escarpment of the Sacramento and other ranges which constitute the Sacramento section. Between these mountains is a desert plain, 125 miles long in New Mexico and extending across Trans-Pecos Texas into Mexico. This trough ends at the north against the Mesa Jumanes, 7,000 ft. high. It has a nearly flat floor, but sloping southward 7 feet to the mile, from 4,500 ft. at the northern end to 3,500 at its southern end in Mexico, but this regional slope is interrupted near the Texas border by a low divide which separates the Tularosa Basin on the north from the Hueco on

---

[1] RANSOME, F. L., *loc. cit.*, p. 19.

[2] For useful maps of this part of New Mexico see: HILL, R. T., Physical Geography of the Texas Region, U. S. Geol. Survey, Topographic folio 3; U. S. Geol. Survey, *Prof. Pap.* 68; U. S. Geol. Survey, *Wat. Sup. Pap.* 123, 188, 275, 343, 345-C; also geol. map of New Mexico by R. W. Ellis, 1925.

the south.[1] The New Mexico portion is a bolson. The main portion of this valley is on a down-faulted block between the fault scarps of the San Andreas on the west and the Sacramento and Blanca on the east.

The lowest level in the Tularosa Basin is less than 4,000 ft., near the southern end. From this the surface rises toward the valley ends, beginning at the rate of a little more than three feet per mile, but the gradient increases greatly as the rim is approached. South of lat. 33°30′, the basin is floored with Quaternary sediments. The marginal débris slopes surround and partly bury occasional rocky buttes. As in other desert basins of centripetal drainage, the slopes are scored by occasional arroyos and broad washes which rarely carry water and never reach the central depression.

At various levels below 4,250 ft. are local escarpments and terraces which seem, in some cases at least, to be old shore lines and suggest a history like that of the Bonneville Basin (page 362).

An interesting feature here is the "alkali marsh" or "salt marsh" covering 165 square miles and occupying a place similar to that of the playa in the Great Basin. The alkali marsh is, as nearly as possible, a perfect plane, but not necessarily level as is the playa. The flat in this basin (extending south from lat. 33°) is 30 miles long and is 100 ft. lower at the south end than at the north. Its edge is definitely marked at places by an almost vertical rise of 10 to 20 ft. Dunes may surmount the banks and increase their height by 50 or more feet. Beneath this flat or "marsh," the surface of ground water is never more than a few feet deep, often but a few inches, so that the surface is habitually damp. Evaporation leaves incrustations of "alkali."

East of the flat is a belt of gypsum dunes, generally 6 to 12 miles wide, locally 100 ft. high and composed at places of almost pure crystalline gypsum; elsewhere of a gypsiferous clay. They migrate eastward, perhaps a mile in 20 years. In some basins similar dunes are known as "clay hills." The valley also contains sand dunes, about which there is nothing peculiar.

The determining factor in producing these features rather than the playa lies in the large amount of gypsum believed to be derived ultimately from the Carboniferous and Permian rocks

---

[1] A full description of this basin is given by O. E. Meinzer and R. F. Hare in U. S. Geol. Survey, *Wat. Sup. Pap.* 343, Geology and Water Resources of the Tularosa Basin, New Mexico, 1915.

of the bordering mountains. Ordinary clay rarely drifts into dunes. These gypsum-laden clays are readily picked up and blown away. But such deflation must stop at the water table, which is essentially a plane, lowered, of course, by evaporation due to stripping. Thus the alkali flat practically represents the water table laid bare by wind erosion. The prevailing winds are from the west, hence a dune belt on the east is the natural accompaniment of the alkali marsh.

Where dunes do not overwhelm the surface, dust may lodge on the moist or grass-covered soil around a spring which constitutes a "dust trap." There it is held and accumulates into mounds, some of which are 10 to 20 ft. high and 600 ft. in diameter.

Outside the alkali marsh, where the ground water lies farther below the surface, sink holes are locally abundant. Some of them are in the limestone pediment where the Quaternary sediment is thin or wanting. Others are in the gypsum which forms in places a solid stratum many feet—it may be several hundred feet—in thickness.

Concerning the depth to the rock floor beneath the unconsolidated material little is known. A 1,250-ft. well beside the railroad near the eastern edge did not reach hard rock.

The northern end of the Tularosa Basin beyond the flat floor (in a very rough way north of lat. 33°30′) is above the level of alluvial deposits or contains them only in local basins. It has a rocky surface rising northward in 50 to 60 miles to the level of Mesa Jumanes, 7,000 ft., and almost that high on the west to the crest of Chupadera Mesa. This rocky surface or pediment on faintly eastward-dipping strata is dissected to approximate maturity. The axis of this valley is occupied by a recent and unweathered flow of basalt 44 miles long and averaging 5½ miles wide, and having a southward gradient of 30 ft. to the mile. This northern end of the Tularosa Basin is an excellent type of the rocky plateau surfaces, semi-desert to desert, which occupy portions of the Mexican Plateau not covered by mountain or bolson.

Hueco Basin.—Southward from the low divide near the Texas-New Mexico border, the structural trough extends another 100 miles under the name of Hueco Basin. Its eastern rim is the Hueco and Finlay Mountains and others in line to the southeast. On the west and south it extends to unnamed mountains in Mexico. The Hueco is not a typical bolson with centripetal drainage; it has, in fact, very little drainage of any kind. The Rio Grande traverses it for 100 miles southeastward from El Paso, cutting a broad trench 200 to 500 ft. below the desert floor. Well drilling shows that clay, sand, and gravel, locally cemented to a firm conglomerate, fill the valley at least 600 ft. deep, perhaps much more.[1]

Jornada del Muerto.—West of the line of mountains on the meridian of El Paso is another great trough similar to the one containing the Tularosa Basin. For most of the distance from Albuquerque to El Paso it is followed by the Rio Grande. In latitude about 33°30′ the river departs from this trough, making a westward detour around the Fra Cristobal and Caballos Ranges, returning to this trough in lat. 32°30′. The portion of the trough cut out by this detour lies between the San Andreas Mountains on the east and the ranges named on the west. This is called the Jornada del Muerto (Journey of Death). The ancient Mexican trail to Santa Fé followed the river where convenient, but did not make the detour. Death by thirst and by the hands of robbers is said to have marked the route with bones.[2] The same route is now followed by the Santa Fé Railroad.

Ignorance of ground-water conditions maintained this deadly nature of the Jornada more than 300 years. At length (1871) a well was dug to the base of the mantle rock, 160 ft., thus reaching the water which enters from above or creeps outward from the base of the mountains. Since the Caballos Mountains on the west are tilted east and the San Andreas Range on the east is tilted west, the Jornada lies in a synclinal trough. Many other wells have since been put down, some flowing, some pumped. Most of them do not reach the bottom of the unconsolidated material which is known to be more than 300 ft. deep. An extensive strip along the west side is but thinly veneered with detritus. There is here a rock plain, or pediment, formed on steeply inclined strata.

The Jornada is not a single enclosed basin but contains a number of basins which receive the occasional drainage. Some of them retain shallow, ephemeral lakes. The general slope of the trough is southward from an altitude of 4,700 ft. at San Marcial to 4,200 ft. at Las Cruces, a fall of 450 ft. in 100 miles,

[1] El Paso folio, p. 11, U. S. Geol. Survey.

[2] KEYES, C. R., Geology and Water Conditions of the Jornada del Muerto, New Mexico. U. S. Geol. Survey, *Wat. Sup. Pap.* 123, 1905.

or about the same gradient as that of the Rio Grande. Into this plain the Rio Grande has incised itself several hundred feet both north and south of the Jornada. To the south, the same southward-sloping desert surface, under the name of La Mesa, extends far into Mexico. Wells in La Mesa show that the hard-rock surface is at least 945 ft. deep.

Plains of San Augustin.—West of the Rio Grande Valley the orderly arrangement of mountains and basins is wanting. Many have no generally recognized names, or the naming differs on different maps. The one prominent bolson known by name

Fig. 139.—Dry bed of the Mimbres River east of Spalding, New Mexico. The shallow depression in the middle ground is the river bed. (*U. S. Geol. Survey.*)

is the Plains of San Augustin. This elongated basin has its center in lat. 34°, long. 108°. Its central detrital plain is 60 miles long northeast to southwest, 12 to 20 miles wide and 6,900 ft. above the sea. Above this plain the marginal rock slopes rise to the surrounding mountains, many of them nearly or quite 10,000 ft. high. Of these the San Mateo and Magdalena masses border the basin on the southeast side, near the Rio Grande. Next to the latter, at the northeast end of the basin, is Bear Mountain (see U. S. Land Office map). West of that and bordering the basin on the north (lat. 34°) are the Gallina and Datil Ranges which may be regarded as standing at the edge of the

Colorado Plateau.   On the west are the Tularosa, San Francisco, and Mogollon Ranges (to be distinguished from like-named mountains in Arizona).   On the south the basin is less completely closed in by the Mimbres, Black, and several other ranges. Generally speaking, the mountains on the east and south, while in some cases increased in height by volcanic flows, are due primarily to deformation and hence have more in common with the Mexican Plateau than with the Colorado Plateau.

HISTORY OF THE RIO GRANDE

The structural features of the Mexican Plateau in New Mexico were outlined some time in the Tertiary, largely by faulting.   A significant part of the upheavals came late in that period or at its close.   Along with these earth movements came eruptions which built some of the mountains and greatly increased the mass of others.

If it be assumed, as is commonly done, that most of the mountains and basins are the direct result of diastrophism, the Rio Grande picked its way across this disordered surface from basin to basin, being ponded in some of them and cutting gorges through the dams; or there may have been no throughflowing stream until the several basins were filled to overflowing with detritus from the mountains.   If the unconsolidated material in the great troughs is, in the main, Quaternary wash from the present mountains, one of these pictures is correct.   If it be found (as suggested by Blackwelder for much of the Great Basin) that a large part of the loose material in the basins is of Tertiary age,[1] or at least older than the mountains, the work of aggrading becomes merely incidental and of secondary importance.   On this supposition the work of streams has been mainly to deepen these valleys on the softer rocks, shaving them off to form pediments as some of the harder rocks have evidently been planed off in the Tularosa and other basins.

A lava-covered alluvial terrace 800 ft. above the river, near Albuquerque, is interpreted on the first assumption (*i.e.*, that the mountains and basins are wholly diastrophic), as showing that the whole valley of the Rio Grande was once filled from the level of the hard-rock surface, far below the river, up to the terrace

---

[1] A part of it is known to be Tertiary, as stated by LEE, U. S. Geol. Survey, *Wat. Sup. Pap.* 188, p. 19.

level 800 ft. above it.[1]   On the second assumption (*i.e.*, that the great troughs are in considerable part erosional) such terraces are incidental to down-cutting.   On either assumption the river once flowed at the level of this high terrace, then cut down 500 ft., at which level it remained a long time developing a very wide valley floor, of which the Jornada del Muerto seems to have been a part.   In the upper course of the river this floor is a planation surface on hard rocks.   In the lower course (Jornada del Muerto)

FIG. 140.—Bed of the Rio Grande near the Mexican boundary. Note the two channels (one at the extreme left) and the broad expanse of sand, also the narrows in the distance. It is proposed to build a dam at this place to create the International Reservoir for the benefit of irrigation. (*Keyes, U. S. Geol. Survey.*)

the valley floor was either aggraded or was cut on older soft material which has not yet been distinguished from the recent detritus. Renewed erosion later caused the stream to entrench itself 300 ft., at which level it has made new bottom lands with a maximum width of four or five miles.   Below El Paso[2] the actual entrenchment probably exceeded 300 ft., as that is the height of the present bluffs and the river seems to be again aggrading.   It was

[1] No calculation has been made to compare the volume of such filling with that which has been lost by erosion from the mountains.

[2] For observations on the Rio Grande below El Paso see U. S. Geol. Survey, folio 166.

before this last entrenchment that a lava flow dammed the stream at the north end of the Fra Cristobal Mountains and turned it to the west, leaving the Jornada waterless.

At present the Rio Grande in New Mexico traverses a series of eight basins alternating with canyons or narrows.[1] Some of these alternations are produced by crossing the main structural lines, as at El Paso. Other constrictions are produced by volcanoes which have crowded the stream aside as at Isleta (lat. 35°), or by lava flows which the stream has been obliged to cross and trench as at San Felipe (lat. 35°30′).

Resources of the Mexican Highland

Agriculture.—Agriculture in the Mexican Highland is necessarily by irrigation and limited by the amount of water and the extent of low-lying alluvial plains. The irrigable lands along the Rio Grande are the alluvial plains 300 ft. (more or less) below the floor of the desert. The eight basins mentioned above from the Espanola Valley north of Santa Fé to the El Paso Valley in Texas have bottom lands ranging in width from two to five miles.

The Rio Grande, 2,000 miles long, is a stream of uncertain and highly variable flow. In so far as its flow in New Mexico is constant, it comes largely from rain and snow on the mountains of southern Colorado. Most of the additions farther south are from immediate run-off or storm water, and therefore highly inconstant. In its course from Colorado to the Mexican border the summer flow generally decreases. In this part of its course the floods come in the early summer when the snow melts on the mountains. On the Mexican border, floods come mainly in the tropical rainy season of the late summer. Hence it is no uncommon occurrence that the Rio Grande should be dry at El Paso and flooded in its lower course.

In central Arizona the Roosevelt Dam arrests the drainage of the upper Salt River Basin in a great artificial lake impounding one million acre-feet of water. The water is used to irrigate land around Phoenix, located in the Sonoran section rather than in the Mexican Highland.

When the Spaniards entered the Rio Grande Valley early in the 16th century, they found the Pueblo Indians irrigating by

---

[1] These basins with intervening narrows are named and described by Lee, U. S. Geol. Survey, *Wat. Sup. Pap.* 188, pp. 12–16.

methods still in use, as are some of their old ditches. Their crops were largely grains. Alfalfa is now the chief crop. Fruits and melons are becoming highly profitable.[1]

Back from the narrow strips of farmed land, the great industry is, as it always has been, grazing. The herding of sheep is a characteristic employment of the Mexican population of the Rio Grande Valley and adjacent provinces.

Minerals.—The Mexican Highland in Arizona is one of the chief copper-producing regions of the world. The region contains the three great centers, Globe, Clifton, and Bisbee. The occurrence of ores, chiefly of copper, is closely connected with the history of deformation, volcanic action, and erosion. The study of this history and even of the physiography have been closely connected with the investigation of mining districts and the search for underground water.

SACRAMENTO SECTION

Boundaries and Description.—Intervening between the Mexican Highland on the west and the Pecos Valley (Great Plains) is a north-south strip 300 miles long and nowhere 70 miles wide which needs separate description. It is more or less plateau-like throughout, undissected north of lat. 34°, faulted, strongly sloping, and dissected elsewhere. It lacks the steep tilting of the fault blocks in the Mexican Highland but is allied to that section by the prominence and importance of its bolsons.

The northern end of this section illustrates the difficulty of dividing up a natural area into homogeneous parts, each one clearly distinguished from all its neighbors. This small district is one of horizontal rocks like the Great Plains on the east and the Colorado Plateau on the west. On the other hand its central feature is the Estancia Valley or Sandoval Bolson, a prominent representative of the great bolsons which characterize the Basin and Range province.[2] Its western rim is the Sandia and Manzano block mountains. On its eastern rim is, first, the

[1] SULLIVAN, VERNON L., Irrigation in New Mexico, Dept. Agr., Exper. Sta., *Bull.* 215, pp. 17–19, 1909.

[2] MEINZER, O. E., Geology and Water Resources of the Estancia Valley, New Mexico, U. S. Geol. Survey, *Wat. Sup. Pap.* 275, 1911. It is not implied that such basins of centripetal drainage are confined to one province, but they are insignificant elsewhere. Two small bolsons, Encina and Pinos Wells. lie east of the line which is used as the province boundary.

Glorietta Mesa, a fantastically carved divide of horizontal rocks whose eastward escarpment is the province boundary. Farther south, on the boundary, are the hills of Pedernal, a north-south ridge of granite. South of the basin is the elevated and extensive Mesa Jumanes suggesting at once the Colorado Plateau and the Las Vegas Plateau.

Estancia Valley.—The topographic center of the Estancia Basin is occupied by "salt basins," the same as the alkali flats described on page 386. In this case numerous small basins are interspersed among the "clay hills," which are dunes, some of them 100 ft. high, consisting of material blown out to make the salt basins. This basin has clear records of a former extensive lake whose existence is recorded by shore features of the same nature as those of Lake Bonneville, though less impressive. The salt basins and dunes are in the center of its ancient bed. As in the Tularosa Basin, ground water is found near the surface in the central depression, but the water table is flatter than the land surface so that its depth increases to more than 100 ft. beneath the marginal débris slopes. From well borings it is known that the basin is filled to a depth greater than 312 ft., but how much greater is not known.

Mountains.—South of the Mesa Jumanes the plateau is divided by faults into many blocks, all dipping eastward. In lat. 34° the Chupadera Mesa slopes east to the Tularosa Basin. South of the east end of Mesa Jumanes are first the Jicarilla Mountains, followed in succession southward by the Sierra Blanca, Sacramento, Guadalupe, and Delaware Mountains, all monoclinal ranges bounded on the west by fault scarps and consisting largely of eastward-dipping Carboniferous limestone. Sierra Blanca (partly volcanic) reaches a height of 12,003 ft. It retains snow much of the year, hence its name (White Range). The Capitan Mountains are an eastern volcanic spur.

The Sacramento Ranges are noteworthy for their long eastward slope, plateau-like though maturely dissected.[1] South of the Sacramento Range and offset a little to the east is the Guadaloupe. Its southern extension, the Delaware, is similar in every way to the Sacramento, though less high and fading out southward. The Guadalupe proper is more complex but of the same structure. Just south of the Texas-New Mexico boundary

---

[1] U. S. Geol. Survey, *Wat. Sup. Pap.* 343, p. 26; see topographic map of Alamo National Forest, pl. III, in pocket.

is Guadalupe Peak, 9,500 ft., the highest point in Texas. The altitudes of all these ranges except the Sierra Blanca are between 8,000 and 10,000 ft. The plateau character of the upraised fault blocks ends at the east-west trough followed by the Texas-Pacific Railway.

In New Mexico, except in the extreme southern part, the Sacramento section is limited to the plateaus and mountains named. Near the Texas boundary there rises another, the Diablo Plateau, farther west, bounded by faults and sloping eastward like the rest. The dissected fault scarps on both sides appear as mountains when viewed from the basins. That on the west, 2,000 ft. high, is known as the Hueco Mountains and farther south as the Finlay Mountains. The somewhat lower scarp on the east is the Diablo Range.[1]

Bolsons in Texas.—Between the Diablo Plateau and the Guadalupe Mountains is the Salt Basin,[2] similar in all essentials to the Tularosa Basin. Its bottom is 800 ft. below the lowest point of the rim and covered with detritus over an area 150 miles long and 8 to 20 miles wide. Toward both ends the bottom rises and merges into rocky plateaus. For centuries this basin was a source of salt to Indians and Mexicans.

A similar description might be given of the Gypsum Plain east of the Guadalupe Mountains and separated from the Pecos Valley by the inconspicuous Rustler Hills. The floor of this basin is a layer of gypsum several hundred feet thick resting unconformably on the tilted Carboniferous.

---

[1] RICHARDSON, GEO. B., Reconnaissance in Trans-Pecos Texas, Univ. Texas Mineral Survey, *Bull.* 9, p. 18, 1904. This paper is accompanied by a good geologic map and sections of Trans-Pecos Texas north of the Texas Pacific Railway.

[2] RICHARDSON, GEO. B., *loc. cit.*, gives a full description.

CHAPTER IX

SIERRA-CASCADE PROVINCE

GENERAL RELATIONS

The Sierra Nevada and Cascade Mountains together constitute a single province but they are unlike in character, and the several sections of the Cascades also differ among themselves. It would be difficult to make many valuable statements which would be true of the whole province. Its unity consists chiefly in the fact that it constitutes a single mountain barrier between the plateaus on the east and the Pacific valleys on the west.

The length of this great barrier is more than 1,000 miles and its average width 50 to 60 miles with a maximum of 90 miles at the Canadian boundary and a little less at the 40th parallel. The general crest height varies greatly but not within short distances. It is 12,000 to 14,000 ft. in the southern Sierra Nevada where Mt. Whitney rises to 14,497 ft., the highest peak in the United States excepting Alaska. The lowest average height is in the southern Cascade Mountains in northern California and southern Oregon. Here, though isolated mountains are high (Mt. Shasta, 14,380 ft.), there is no continuous crest. Several broad and irregular transverse passages are little higher than the floor of the Great Basin, and the Pitt River crosses the range. The province is also narrowest at this place so that the "barrier" is by no means perfect. There is a gradual but not uniform decline in altitude from the latitude of Mt. Whitney to northern California. Farther north a general crest level of 6,000 to 8,000 ft. is common. The altitude above the Columbia Plateau and the Great Basin in Washington and Oregon ranges from 2,000 to 5,000 ft. A little north of the International Boundary the Cascade Range ends abruptly, giving way to the Plateau of British Columbia several thousand feet lower.

A characteristic which is more nearly universal than any other, except trend, is an accordance of altitude among neighboring summits, giving the ranges in a large way the appearance of dissected plateaus, but this feature fails in the southern Cascade

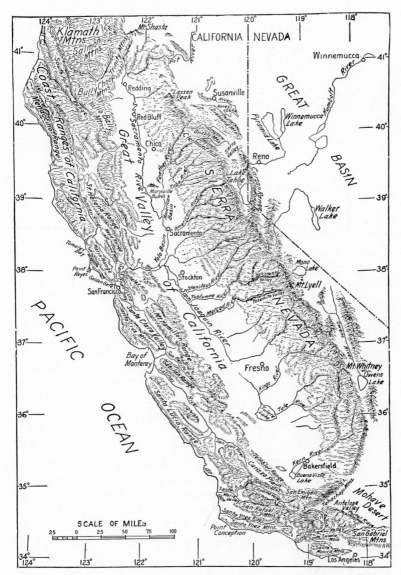

FIG. 141.—Index map of the Sierra Nevada and adjacent sections.   (Drawn by Guy-Harold Smith.)

section, where mountain heights and valley depths seem almost haphazard. The several sections of this province have, each within its own limits, a considerable degree of uniformity.

SIERRA NEVADA SECTION

General Description

The Sierra Nevada is a massive and continuous range extending in a north-northwesterly direction from lat. 34°50′ to lat. 40°20′, a little more than 400 miles. The greatest width, a little more than 80 miles, is near the north end where the Sierra Nevada section includes Lake Tahoe and the Carson Range east of it and thus occupies a small area in Nevada.

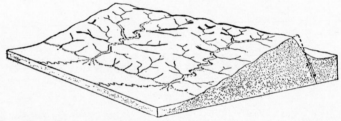

Fig. 142.—Generalized diagram of the tilted Sierra block. The surface sloping toward the left (west) is assumed to have been hilly rather than mountainous, lying at a low altitude with little slope east or west. Faulting and tilting then occurred. The steep east-facing fault scarp has been somewhat worn back. The major west-flowing streams, being accelerated by the tilt, have cut deep canyons but many of their tributaries, being at right angles to the direction of tilting, have not entrenched themselves; hence they drop into the canyons from hanging valleys. The Valley of California on the west and Owens Valley on the east are seen to be floored with sediment derived from the mountains. This diagram represents conditions previous to glaciation. (*U. S. Geol. Survey.*)

Summary Statement.—In a general way the Sierra Nevada may be described as a block of resistant rocks; locally of unequal strength and complex structure, eroded to moderate or low relief; uplifted by faulting, with a decided westward tilt; submaturely dissected by deep valleys, and, in its higher parts, strongly glaciated. This formula does not embrace quite all the features nor does it distinguish one part of the Sierra from another, but every fact therein mentioned is essential to the consideration of any part of the range (*cf.* Fig. 142).

Rocks.—Three-fourths of the rocks of the Sierra Nevada are granitic. Belts of alternating hard and soft rocks are therefore absent from most of the range. Faulting has doubtless produced certain weak zones, as for example the one which is followed by the straight north-south valley of the upper Kern River.[1] It is also a well-established fact that many prominent domes and knobs like Half Dome and others in Yosemite National Park are essentially *monoliths*, *i.e.*, single blocks of granite unaffected by joints. On this account they have withstood erosion both by water and ice.[2]

North of lat. 37°20′, about one-third of the rocks are sediments, now metamorphosed and in part schistose. They are collectively called the "auriferous slates," though they are not all gold-bearing nor all slates.[3] These beds are all closely folded. Contrasts among these strata give rise to belts of greater and less resistance but such contrasts are poorly marked here as compared with those of the non-metamorphosed rocks of the Appalachians.

These strata are what is left of that broad expanse which was lifted up by the intrusion of the granites. They are part of the so-called "roof" of the ancient batholith. Because of less uplift at this place, or because in some way the roof of the batholith was folded down into its mass, the strata have here escaped erosion. This surviving belt of sedimentaries, well shown on the geologic map of North America, is of great economic interest because it comprises the greatest gold fields of California.

A still smaller proportion of the rocks of the Sierra Nevada consists of the late Tertiary volcanics related to those of the Great Basin. They increase in abundance toward the north and merge with those of the southern Cascades. These rocks are lavas and tuffs which were extruded near the crest of the range and for the most part flowed west in shallow valleys, thus displacing the streams. Following a later uplift these displaced streams cut deep valleys between the tongues of lava, leaving the latter as high divides. Thus the lava now caps long ridges of upland, transverse to the trend of the range, and forms the divides. At places it conceals ancient river channels several thousand feet above the beds of present streams. Some of these ancient channels are rich in gold-bearing gravels. Still more recent lavas have

[1] LAWSON, A. C., Univ. Calif. *Bull.*, Dept. Geol. Sci., vol. III, p. 340, 1904; see also Fault Map of California issued by the Seismological Society of America, 1922.

[2] MATTHES, F. E., Sketch of Yosemite National Park, etc., U. S. Dept. Int., p. 36, 1912.

[3] For description see TURNER and RANSOME, Sonora folio 41, U. S. Geol. Survey, 1897. A general description of the "Gold Belt" is given in this folio.

flowed out into the canyons of the present erosion cycle, some so recently that but little erosion has been effected since.

FEATURES DUE TO FAULTS

Eastern Slope.—The crest of the Sierra Nevada is near its eastern margin. Because of this fact and the height of the range, the eastern slope is one of the steepest mountain slopes on the continent. For more than 200 miles south from Lake Tahoe (at the angle of the Nevada-California boundary) the main divide is within 10 miles of the foot of the range. Where the range is highest, the average eastward slope from crest to foot is more than 1,000 ft. per mile. At the southern end where the range curves strongly to the west under the name "Tehachapi," the slope which overlooks the Mohave Desert, though less than 3,000 ft. high, is almost as steep. The straightness of the base is as remarkable as the steepness of the slope. There is a notable lack of far-reaching spurs.

All the features of this front point to the conclusion that it is a fault scarp. Among these are abundant springs,[1] some of them hot. Fresh fault scarps are found in incoherent detritus. One of these is 40 ft. in height.[2] After the great earthquake in 1872 in Owens Valley, new fault scarps were observed, some large blocks of the crust being dropped 20 to 30 ft. There was also horizontal displacement amounting at one place to 18 ft.[3]

The evidence that the eastern slope of the Sierra is a fault scarp consists chiefly in the topographic features here mentioned and not in the actual exposure of the contact between the adjacent earth blocks. It is not to be understood that one crack necessarily continues throughout the whole distance. Doubtless there are many, some of them *en echelon*, others side by side, making compound faults. Some minor spurs and offsets may be produced in this way rather than by erosion. The fault zone as a whole is, however, remarkably continuous.

[1] JOHNSON, HARRY R., Water Resources of Antelope Valley, California, U. S. Geol. Survey, *Wat. Sup. Pap.* 278, p. 20, 1911; also, LEE, WILLIS T., Geology and Water Resources of Owens Valley, California, U. S. Geol. Survey, *Wat. Sup. Pap.* 181, pp. 7–8, 1906.

[2] LINDGREN, A., and KNOWLTON, F. H., Age of the Auriferous Gravels of the Sierra Nevada, *Jour. Geol.*, vol. IV, p. 902, 1896.

[3] WHITNEY, J. D., The Owens Valley Earthquake, *Overland Monthly*, June, 1872, cited by Lee, U. S. Geol. Survey, *Wat. Sup. Pap.* 181, p. 12.

Fig. 143.—East front of the Sierra Nevada seen from Owens Valley. The foreground shows a typical landscape in the Great Basin. There is a distinct alluvial slope from the base of the range. The nearly level skyline in the middle of the picture represents the subsummit upland mentioned on page 406. (*Charles H. Lee, U. S. Geol. Survey.*)

Subordinate Ranges at North End.—Near Lake Tahoe, the effect of nearly parallel faults is evident. The main crest of the range lies west of the lake and is continuous with the crest to the south. East of the lake is the subordinate Carson Range (Fig. 144), an uplifted block between parallel faults, a separate range from the Sierra Nevada but included in the same physiographic section. Lake Tahoe occupies the "moat" between the fault scarps of the main Sierra and Carson Ranges.[1]   The lake

Fig. 144.—Genoa Plateau, summit of the Carson Range (Sierra Nevada) east of Lake Tahoe. The striking feature shown in this view is the straight sky line. The summit of the range at this place is a remnant of an old surface of small relief. *(John A. Reid, Univ. Calif. Bull., Dept. Geol.)*

itself is at least 1,645 ft. deep, its surface being 6,247 ft. above sea-level and its area 195 square miles.[2]   For beauty of setting, this lake has few rivals.

North of the Tahoe Basin the Sierra Nevada consists of three ranges rather than one, each having the essential features of the single great range farther south, *i.e.*, each is a fault block tilted toward the southwest, presenting a scarp to the northeast and a long, gentle but dissected slope to the southwest.[3]   Named in

[1] REID, JOHN A., Geomorphogeny of the Sierra Nevada northeast of Lake Tahoe, Univ. Calif. *Bull.*, Dept. Geol. Sci., vol. VI, p. 106, 1911.

[2] RUSSELL, I. C., U. S. Geol. Survey, *Mon.* 11, pp. 11 and 71, 1885.

[3] DILLER, J. S., Geology of the Taylorsville Region of California, U. S. Geol. Survey, *Bull.* 353, p. 7, 1908.

order from east to west these minor ranges are Diamond Mountain, Grizzly Mountain, and Clermont Hill. The crest of Diamond Mountain is almost in line with that of the Carson Range east of Lake Tahoe. It has a fine fault scarp 2,000 ft. high on the northeast, overlooking the desert valley which contains Honey Lake. This scarp curves round to the west and marks the northern limit of the Sierra Nevada Mountains. At its foot flows the Susan River, southeastward into Honey Lake, marking the boundary between this section and the Great Basin. Farther west the North fork of the Feather River, which flows southwest to the Sacramento, is not far from the boundary between the Sierra Nevada and the southern Cascade section.

THE OLD SUBDUED SURFACE

Northern Part.—The dominant feature of the western slope of the Sierra is an approximate uniformity of summit altitudes giving the appearance of a widely extended and deeply trenched plateau. The words "western slope" are somewhat misleading since the slopes in view are in all directions. The general slope of the summit level is so gentle as not to be apparent. In a width of 70 miles in the latitude of Lake Tahoe the decline is about 7,000 ft. or 100 ft. to the mile. This is less than that of some railroads built for heavy traffic. The Southern Pacific Railroad running northeast from Sacramento ascends the grade without difficulty, running a part of the distance on the upland level instead of in stream valleys. In this part of the range the flatness of the horizon when seen from any slight elevation is very marked.

This old surface of moderate relief, now deeply trenched, is frequently spoken of as an upraised peneplain. It was indeed much subdued by erosion and there are localities farther south where the term peneplain is almost justified. However, the flatness of the surface in the northern part, where it is most marked, is increased by the lava flows which did much to fill the old valleys (some of them more than 1,000 ft. deep) and thus obliterate such relief as remained on the old erosion surface which, though greatly subdued, could not fairly be called a peneplain. The observer who now sights over the ridges from one of their number has his flat horizon determined by lava flows more than by peneplain[1] (see Fig. 146 page 406). The

[1] LINDGREN, W., *loc. cit.*, p. 897.

thickness of this lava near the main crest is at places more than 1,000 ft., though it diminishes rapidly to the west and is generally but a few hundred feet.[1] Nevertheless, after making all necessary allowance for the leveling effect of lavas, it is seen that the highly complex structures of this portion of the ancient Sierra are truncated to a remarkable degree by an erosion surface of moderate relief. Where it is spoken of in the literature as the "Sierra peneplain" its imperfections should be borne in mind. This old subdued surface is well preserved on the resistant, massive, granitic rocks of the Yosemite region and constitutes the Yosemite upland. Its rolling surface has a relief of about 1,000 ft.

Monadnocks.—Above the subdued surface here described rise more or less isolated monadnocks. Many of these likewise rise to accordant levels suggesting that they are remnants of an older nearly plane surface, presumably a peneplain.[2] In the central and western part they are not numerous, but they increase in frequency toward the main crest. West of Lake Tahoe the summits over a considerable area rise to this upper and older plain now profoundly dissected. Here it seems that the lower and younger surface, the Sierra peneplain, was developed only locally if at all. Similar residual forms prevail with increasing altitude toward the south throughout the High Sierra (Fig. 145).

The distribution of these higher masses is not merely haphazard, as they might seem to be if the drainage were purely dendritic. The headwaters of most of the main rivers, the Stanislaus, Tuolumne, Merced, San Joaquin, Kings, and Kern, are roughly parallel with the trend of the main range. Parallel to these headwaters is a system of subordinate ranges rising 2,000 to 3,000 ft. above the general upland level. Wherever bedded rocks remain they are seen to have been folded along axes having the general direction of the present residual ranges. It is inferred, therefore,[3] that these subordinate ranges are an inheritance from the mountain system of Appalachian type that was formed on the site of the present Sierra at the close of Jurassic time. Most of the strata involved in that ancient folding have been eroded away but the drainage lines and divides

---

[1] LINDGREN, W., Geol. Soc. Amer. *Bull.*, vol. 4, pp. 266–267.

[2] LINDGREN, W., *Jour. Geol.*, vol. IV, p. 897, 1896.

[3] MATTHES, F. E., Personal communication. See forthcoming *Professional Paper* 160 of the U. S. Geol. Survey.

near the crest of the main range retain something of their original longitudinal pattern, while the lower courses of the same streams have become transverse by reason of general tilting (page 408).

On the Carson Range east of Lake Tahoe and on other fault blocks of that much broken region, the margin of the Great Basin, are flattish summits similar in every way to the Sierra peneplain and surmounted by similar monadnocks[1] (Fig. 144). Similar

Fig. 145.—Mount Langley and the subsummit plateau of the Sierra Nevada, west of the north end of Owens Lake. The summit of Mt. Langley (14,042 ft.) with that of Mt. Whitney and others represents the summit upland. To the right (west) is the subsummit upland. Mt. Langley is almost the southernmost of the high mountains that rise above the subsummit upland. Farther south the subsummit upland forms the crest of the great east-facing escarpment overlooking the Great Basin. (*Knopf, U. S. Geol. Survey.*)

surfaces characterize the long southwesterly slopes of the branch ranges at the northern end of the section with the exception of the middle one of the three, Grizzly Mountain, which is very uneven.

Topography of the Gold Belt.—The sedimentary rocks of the Gold Belt are, on the whole, less resistant than the granites, and in this region the Sierra peneplain is less preserved, especially near the southern end.[2] There are here few broad remnants

---

[1] REID, JOHN A., Geomorphogeny of the Sierra Nevada, Northeast of Lake Tahoe, Univ. Calif. *Bull.*, Dept. Geol. Sci., vol. VI, pp. 89–161, 1911.

[2] Inferred from TURNER and RANSOME, Sonora folio 41, p. 1, U. S. Geol. Survey, 1897.

except such as have been protected by volcanic rocks. Nevertheless the summits are of subequal height and represent the Sierra peneplain as shown by profiles plotted at right angles to the trend of the range.[1] The horizon determined by these summits is, in a broad outlook, approximately flat (Fig. 146). Between these residual forms erosion has made very wide valleys, amounting at places to the beginning of a newer peneplain, regarded by Matthes as Pliocene. West of the Yosemite National Park the contrast in elevation between the sedimentaries on the west and the granite on the east is striking, the difference being about 2,500 ft. and apparently due, in large measure, to erosion since the surface of low relief was elevated.

Fig. 146.—Outlook over the Sierra Nevada from near Gold Run, about 30 miles from the western foot of the mountains. The plateau-like aspect is striking. The rocks within the scope of this view are predominately slates and other sedimentaries but with large areas of volcanic tuffs and lavas. (*Photo by J. S. Hawver, U. S. Geol. Survey.*)

Southern Part.—In the highest part of the High Sierra, west of Owens Valley, in the upper basin of the Kern River, at least three levels are recognized above the present streams.[2] The one of greatest interest has been called by Lawson the "subsummit plateau." It is represented by remnants of a nearly flat surface of erosion at altitudes of from 11,200 to 11,500 ft. This is tentatively believed to correspond to Matthes' "Yosemite upland," both being parts of the Sierra peneplain. Above it rise the lofty peaks, Whitney, Lyell, Ritter, and others, to heights approaching 15,000 ft. Some of these have remarkably flat tops. The summit of Mt. Whitney itself is a rock-strewn plateau one-

<hr />

[1] Matthes, F., Personal communication.

[2] Lawson, A. C., Geomorphogeny of the Upper Kern River Basin, Univ. Calif. *Bull.*, Dept. Geol. Sci., vol. III, pp. 291–376, 1902 to 1904.

half mile square. The flat summits of these monadnocks, as of those farther north, suggest by their form that they may be remnants of a still older peneplain.

Some 2,500 ft. lower than the subsummit plateau are valleys of such remarkable flatness and width as to indicate a considerable erosion cycle after uplift of the subsummit plateau. Beneath these valley floors, known as the Chagoopa Plateau, the Kern

Fig. 147.—Crest of the High Sierra at Mammoth Mountain (latitude about 37°30'). The view shows the precipitous eastern face at the left and the gentler westward slope of the subsummit upland. The general upland level here is somewhat below 11,000 ft. Occasional peaks rise 1,000 to 2,000 ft. higher. (*Photo by J. B. Lippincott, U. S. Geol. Survey.*)

River and its tributaries have cut narrow canyons, already 2,000 to 3,000 ft. deep and rapidly deepening.

South from the latitude of Owens Lake the subsummit plateau disappears by complete dissection, but still farther south, notably in the Tehachapi[1] and the El Paso[2] Ranges and adjacent parts of the Sierra Nevada, very distinct indications of peneplains are

[1] LAWSON, A. C., Geomorphogeny of the Tehachapi Valley System, Univ. Calif. *Bull.*, Dept. Geol. Sci., vol. IV, pp. 431–462, 1904; see also Geomorphic Features of the Middle Kern Valley, Univ. Calif. *Bull.*, Dept. Geol. Sci., vol. IV, pp. 397–409.

[2] BAKER, C. L., Physiography and Structure of the Western El Paso Range and the Southern Sierra Nevada, Univ. Calif. *Bull.*, Dept. Geol. Sci., vol. VII, pp. 117–142, 1912.

noted, both on the mountain tops where they are dissected, and in broad down-faulted valleys including the western end of the Mohave Desert.   These are tentatively correlated with the high valley floors or Chagoopa Plateau of the upper Kern River Basin. It thus appears that in whatever part the Sierra Nevada has been carefully observed, there have been found plateau remnants ("Sierra peneplain"), mountains rising above them, valleys cut beneath them, and the floors of these valleys expanding and coalescing locally into a younger peneplain, and that these broad valleys (or younger peneplain) are trenched by canyons carved since the last great uplift.

Streams

Stream Courses.—Most of the streams of the Sierra Nevada flow southwest, *i.e.*, transverse to the trend of the range and down the slope of the peneplain, their courses doubtless being consequent upon the tilted surface.   Only their headwaters and some tributaries flow parallel to the general trend.   As stated above this is the direction of the axes of former anticlines and synclines which, no doubt, controlled the original drainage. After the destruction of the first mountains and after tilting toward the southwest the drainage pattern was altered by the shifting of divides involving a series of captures, the final result being that the transverse streams became the master streams. Headwaters are last to be affected by such rearrangement. Where strong longitudinal streams were able to incise themselves deeply, as the branches of the Kern did, the old drainage plan survives.[1]   Of the branch ranges at the north end, the western one, the Clermont Hills ridge, is crossed by the main streams which are apparently antecedent.

Canyons.—The southwest-flowing streams run in canyons, in some cases 4,000 to 5,000 ft. deep.   As these incise the peneplain it is evident that the cutting of them was made possible by uplift and tilting.   The greatest canyon depths are in the middle courses of the streams.   They are therefore in large part confined to a zone along the middle of the range.   Decreasing elevation toward the west does not admit of such deep cutting.   Moreover, the rocks of the western margin are in some cases weaker and

[1] The fact that the valley of the Kern River follows an old fault is not inconsistent with the assumption made here.—See Fault Map of California, Seismol. Soc. Amer., 1922.

the topographic development has passed the canyon stage. In any case the lower course of a revived stream is the first to pass through its youthful stages. A belt between the canyon zone and the crest of the range has not yet been reached by rejuvenation. In some cases streams are still flowing in wide shallow valleys. The largest of such shallow valleys are near the north end where parallel faulting has made the range triple and the rise of the western range has reduced the gradient of the upper stream courses. But even where no such structural reason exists, the headwaters are much less incised. This is well illustrated on the Diamond Range which shows a distinct canyon zone and a comparatively plain surface near the crest.[1] This feature of the topography is a normal accompaniment of rejuvenation by moderate tilting.

GLACIAL FEATURES

The topography of the higher parts of the Sierra Nevada is controlled in detail by glacial sculpture. Most of the hills are rounded knobs or domes of granite, many of them without soil. Among these the streams pick their way, interrupted by lakes and falls. Some of the valleys are typical glacial troughs heading in cirques. With lower altitude this ice-made topography of a recent epoch gives way to the more orderly branching valleys carved by the streams that now occupy them.

South of the latitude of Owens Lake (36°20′) there is little glacial sculpture and the mountains retain the mature erosion topography[2] which those farther north no doubt had before the glacial epoch. Farther north small glaciers even now survive. Glaciers descended the western slope to a minimum altitude of about 3,500 ft. in the valleys of the American and Yuba Rivers.

YOSEMITE VALLEY

The Merced is one of half a dozen major streams flowing southwest from the crest of the range to the Great Valley of California. Only its upper third is on the granite rocks. Within this third, almost straight east from San Francisco, is the Yosemite Valley, seven miles long and one mile wide. Its level floor lies 3,000

[1] DILLER, J. S., Geology of the Taylorsville Region of California, U. S. Geol. Survey, *Bull.* 353, p. 10, 1908.

[2] LAWSON, A. C., Geomorphogeny of the Upper Kern Basin, Univ. Calif. *Bull.*, Dept. Geol. Sci., vol. III, p. 366, 1904.

ft. or more below the surrounding surface of granite hills, a typical portion of the Sierra peneplain, here known as the "Yosemite upland." With a general relief of less than 1,000 ft. its rounded and forested hills of accordant height have a plateau-like aspect. Rising conspicuously above this surface are the isolated monadnocks, Half Dome being one of many.

In form the Yosemite Valley, though more picturesque than the others, is typical of the group to which it belongs. The

Fig. 148.—Massive granite, not jointed and therefore not susceptible to glacial plucking, abraded and polished by the ice. This is the effect of the last (Wisconsin) ice invasion. The recency of the work is shown by the preservation of the glaciated surface. Post-glacial weathering, on such a surface as this, is at most a fraction of an inch. (*Matthes, Dept. of the Interior.*)

difference between it and others is merely one of degree. The steep-sided gorge is only its lower part. If the gorge were filled from brink to brink there would still remain a valley but it would be wide and of gentle slope and its depth would be similar to that of other valleys in the upland. For convenience let this be called the outer valley (Fig. 150, page 415). This statement applies only to the immediate vicinity of the Yosemite where the glacial trough has been greatly broadened. Farther up stream and down stream where the gorge is narrower there is (even ignoring the gorge) a distinct valley within a valley (Fig. 151, page 415), the younger one, which we may call for convenience the inner valley, being about 1,000 ft. deep below the older surface and being itself trenched by the steep-sided glacial trough[1] (Fig. 151, page 415). Where the valley was never occupied by glaciers a

Fig. 149.—Bird's-eye view of the Yosemite Valley. *RF* Ribbon Fall, *EC* EL Capitan, *EP* Eagle Peak, *YF* Yosemite Falls, *R* Royal Arches, *W* Washington Column, *ML* Mirror Lake, *TC* Tenaya Canyon, *ND* North Dome, *BD* Basket Dome, *MW* Mount Watkins, *C* Clouds Rest, *HD* Half Dome, *L* Mount Lyell, *LY* Little Yosemite, *LC* Liberty Cap, *B* Mount Broderick, *G* Glacier Point, *SD* Sentinel Dome, *SR* Sentinel Rock, *CR* Cathedral Rocks, *BV* Bridal Veil Fall, *YV* Yosemite Village, *MR* Merced River. (*U. S. Geol. Survey.*)

stream-carved V-shaped gorge occupies the axis of the valley. Such also was the predecessor of the flat-bottomed, steep-sided glacial trough in the Yosemite, but it has entirely disappeared

[1] Matthes, F., The Story of the Yosemite Valley, printed on back of topographic map of Yosemite National Park, U. S. Geol. Survey, 1929. Figs. 150 and 151 are taken from this description.

in the making of the latter. In the Yosemite Valley proper the surface of the inner valley also has been largely destroyed by the great broadening of the glacial trough (Fig. 152). This inner valley is the correlative of other wide valleys in the Gold Belt and elsewhere which expand or coalesce at places into a lower peneplain.

All lateral tributaries to the Merced at this place have hanging valleys, *i.e.*, they descend to the main stream by falls. Obviously the tilting of the range favored erosion by the main stream to such a degree that the lateral tributaries fell behind in the work of downcutting. The different heights of such falls are interestingly associated with the history of the gorge. A few, like the upper falls of the Yosemite, enter the canyon almost at its brink. These streams flow over resistant massive granite and have incised their channels but little since the present Yosemite upland was a lowland. Others (Indian and Illilouette Creeks) enter the gorge 600 to 1,200 ft. lower. These flow over granite that is more jointed and more able to cut down to the grade of the main stream as it was when the upper river valley was made. Still a third set of hanging valleys like that of the Bridal Veil end at the canyon wall only 600 to 1,500 ft. above its base. These valleys were graded down before the advent of the glaciers to the level of the stream-made gorge which was carved in the inner valley as the result of later westward tilting of the range.

The distinctive features of Yosemite Valley on the Merced River and Hetch Hetchy Valley on the Tuolumne are due to excessive glacial erosion where the granite was closely jointed and to the extraordinary resistance of the granite where jointing cracks are absent. Thus Half Dome, El Capitan, and other gigantic monoliths withstood the action of ice as they had long withstood that of the atmosphere and water. Probably a low buried ridge or swell of similar unjointed granite lies across the stream's course between Cathedral Rocks and El Capitan. Up stream from this resistant mass the glacier seems to have gouged out a basin 100 to 300 ft. below the present surface in which a lake was retained after the glacier disappeared. Later this lake was filled by sediment, thus producing the flat floor which abuts against the almost vertical walls of the U-shaped valley. All this is inferred from the fact that the valley above is filled to a depth of 100 to 300 ft. with sediment, and it is not believed that the moraine at the lower end of the meadows has more than a fraction of the thickness necessary to make so deep a basin. Glaciation in the last or Wisconsin stage, though very important in the cirques and valleys in the higher parts of the Sierra, had little effect on the Yosemite Valley except to build terminal moraines within it, thus causing lakes which have since given place to meadows.

Résumé of Physiographic History

Early History.—Like other great mountain ranges the Sierra Nevada has had a complex history involving repeated uplift and partial base-leveling. The thick sediments and some volcanic rocks which accumulated in a former geosyncline were folded and raised into mountains at the close of the Paleozoic, approximately at the time of the Appalachian revolution.[1] When these mountains had been worn down and part of the area had again been long submerged, *i.e.*, at the close of the Jurassic period, there came another uplift. Folding was repeated and there were also some lava flows, but the main feature of this complex event was the rise of the great granitic batholith. This is one of the greatest batholiths of the country. It is almost coextensive with the range and its top was higher than any surviving peak. The range was then again worn down. It has been suggested[2] that the remains of the first peneplain may perhaps be seen at the tops of the monadnocks which rise above the general westward slope, and perhaps in the horizon itself of the High Sierra. There followed other uplifts, accompanied by faulting along the eastern margin and a tilting toward the west. No doubt the first master streams followed the old folds which were parallel to the range. As the gradients of west-flowing streams were favored by the tilt the longitudinal drainage ultimately gave way, probably by a series of captures, to the present transverse drainage.

The Making of the "Peneplain."—Uplifts during and after the Cretaceous inaugurated the erosion cycle which ended in the production of the surface of moderate relief which is frequently called the Sierra peneplain.[3] This was a rolling surface on which the prevalent relief was from a few hundred to more

---

[1] Turner and Ransome, Sonora folio 41, p. 1, U. S. Geol. Survey.

[2] Lindgren, W., *Jour. Geol.*, vol. IV, p. 897.

[3] First recognized as such by G. K. Gilbert, *Science*, vol. I, pp. 194–195.

than 1,000 ft., and above which monadnocks rose 1,000 to 2,000 ft. in the northern part and 3,000 ft. in the southern part. Its general altitude above sea-level was, of course, small. The geologic date of this peneplain, *i.e.*, of its best development, is assigned to various epochs of the Tertiary but it may be assumed that the land lay comparatively low, at least until the close of the Miocene.[1]

Auriferous Gravels.—In the valleys of the Sierra peneplain, gravels accumulated which were rich in gold, being derived in part from the rocks of the Gold Belt (page 399). The sorting process in streams tends to eliminate the gravel by carrying it down stream and to allow the gold to accumulate because it is heavier. In the normal process of stream work, gravel would probably not have accumulated to any great depth. Its accumulation in this case was aided by a moderate tilting of the surface. While on the one hand this would increase the gradient and thereby the transporting power of the streams, it might on the other hand greatly increase the amount of gravel brought to the streams. Under suitable circumstances the latter effect would predominate, at least for a time, and the valleys would aggrade. It is assumed that this was the case with the Sierra streams.[2] The first effect of this tilting was increase of power, with the resultant cutting of narrow valleys several hundred feet deep within the old wide valleys.[3] These were first filled with the deepening gravel, which then spread over the older and broader valley floors, sometimes to a depth of 200 to 300 ft.

After the accumulation of these auriferous gravels came the extrusion of lavas and tuffs which filled the old valleys, preserved the gravels, and displaced the streams, at the same time leveling up the inequalities of the imperfect peneplain so that, despite later erosion, the horizon over large areas is nearly flat.

[1] Matthes in all his papers assigns the peneplain to the Miocene. So also DILLER, J. S., Tertiary Revolution in the Topography of the Pacific Coast, U. S. Geol. Survey, 14*th Ann. Rept.*, pt. II, 1892, and various other papers. Whitney also assigned the auriferous gravels which lie on this erosion surface to the Pliocene. Lawson in various physiographic papers assigns the making of this surface to the Pliocene.

[2] DILLER, J. S., Tertiary Revolution in the Topography of the Pacific Coast, U. S. Geol. Survey, 14*th Ann. Rept.*, pt. II, p. 425, 1892.

[3] LINDGREN, W., *Jour. Geol.*, vol. IV, p. 893, distinguishes the "deep gravels" in the central canyons from the "bench gravels" (miners' terms) overspreading the wider valleys.

Successive Uplifts.—After the Sierra peneplain was made, the range was tilted and the surface raised in two distinct acts. The first great rise made possible the development of the broad valleys

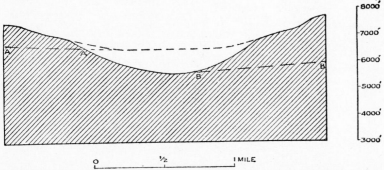

Fig. 150.—Section of the "two-story valley" which the Merced River had cut by the end of the Tertiary period. The broken line merging with the upper slopes indicates the floor of the older valley called Miocene by Matthes. The solid line shows his Pliocene valley. *AA* is the profile of a side stream which was unable to trench as rapidly as the Merced, and whose valley therefore remained hanging. *BB* is the profile of a side stream which cut down its channel concurrently with that of the main stream. (*Matthes, U. S. Geol. Survey.*)

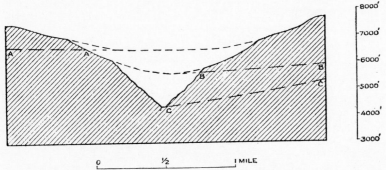

Fig. 151.—Section of the "three-story canyon" which the Merced occupied early in the Quaternary period just before glaciation. The features shown are the same as in Fig. 150 with the addition of an inner gorge which represents rapid down-cutting as the result of uplift. The gorge was cut so rapidly that the valley of the stream *BB* was left hanging. But a third stream *CC*, favored by less resistant rocks, has succeeded in cutting down to the level of the river. (*Matthes, U. S. Geol. Survey.*)

and local peneplains described on page 406. Matthes assigns this rise to the close of the Miocene and estimates that it amounted to 3,000 ft. at the eastern edge of the range. The second rise, assigned to the beginning of Quaternary time,[1] is believed to have elevated the central part of the range another 6,000 ft. above its former height. This introduced the "canyon cycle" in which the former valleys, generally broad, were trenched by narrow gorges, the higher parts of which were later occupied and altered in shape by alpine glaciers.

Glacial Epochs.—Glaciation is almost the last chapter in the history of the topography. Indeed it can scarcely be said to be closed in the High Sierra where a number of small glaciers still survive, chiefly in the gigantic cirques. The southernmost of

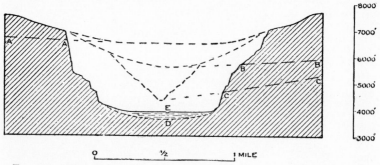

Fig. 152.—Section of the broad, steep-sided Yosemite trough as it is today. The transformation from the original "three-story canyon" was accomplished mainly by the quarrying action of glaciers. The floor of the glacial trough is at *D*. The present valley floor is at *E*. *DE* is the depth of the basin of ancient Lake Yosemite, now filled with river-borne sediment. As a result of further deepening of the chasm and of its widening by the ice the valley of the stream *C-C* now also hangs, so there are three sets of hanging valleys, one above another, with waterfalls from all. (*Matthes, U. S. Geol. Survey.*)

these is a few miles north of Mt. Whitney. In these high mountains the work of the post-glacial cycle is almost *nil*. A little talus is beginning to accumulate at the foot of the cirque walls, but rocks, even though bare, as most of them are, may retain the striations and polish imparted by the glaciers (Fig. 148). Farther down the western slope the time which has elapsed since the disappearance of the ice is longer and the effects of post-glacial weathering and erosion increase with decreasing altitude.

[1] This is the judgment of Matthes. Lawson has expressed the view that the first and smaller uplift occurred at the beginning of the Pleistocene and the second or chief uplift occurred when that period was far spent; Geomorphogeny of the Upper Kern River Basin, Univ. Calif. Bull., Dept. Geol. Sci., vol. III, pp. 364–365; also Geomorphogeny of the Tehachapi Valley System, Univ. Calif. Bull., Dept. Geol. Sci., vol. IV, p. 453, 1904.

Two epochs of glaciation are plainly distinguishable, each with its distinctive effects on topography. In addition there is evidence of a much older glaciation whose topographic effect is now indistinguishable. Moreover, the last glacial epoch (the Wisconsin) embraces two distinct advances of the ice just as it did in eastern United States.[1] In the older of the two well-recorded epochs (presumably Illinoian) the ice advanced some miles farther than in the later epoch, *i.e.*, to the western limit of Yosemite Park (El Portal). Its well-weathered lateral moraines border the Merced Valley but no terminal moraine crosses it because the stream-carved gorge was, in large part, cut later, *i.e.*, in the long interglacial epoch.

Even in this long epoch of deglaciation in the Yosemite region it is not known that the ice ever vanished from the High Sierra, although this may have occurred. It may also have disappeared after the last glacial epoch, *i.e.*, at the close of the Pleistocene. At all events there has been within a very few centuries just passed a new advance. Since that very recent maximum, half the ice has again melted away.

Within the limits of the area covered by the glaciers of both epochs it is generally impossible to distinguish their effects. There it is customary to speak of the glacial epoch as a unit and as being more recent than the canyon-cutting cycle, though as indicated above this is not literally true.

SOUTHERN CASCADE MOUNTAINS

GENERAL DESCRIPTION

A distinct change in the character of the Sierra-Cascade province is seen near the 40th parallel. South of a line connecting Susanville and Chico are the steeply tilted auriferous slates and intrusive granitic rocks, all truncated by the Sierra peneplain, itself broken by faults, tilted and partly covered by volcanic rocks. North of that line is the Southern Cascade section, stretching north at least 150 miles. It is essentially a group or belt of volcanoes in which and between which are beds of lava and

[1] This whole subject of glacial epochs in the Sierra Nevada is summarized by Matthes in *Science*, vol. 70, pp. 75–76, 1929. For earlier mention by the same writer see Geol. Soc. Amer. *Bull.*, vol. 35, pp. 69–70, 1924; *Pan-Amer. Geol.*, vol. 41, pp. 138–139, 1924; Wash. Acad. Sci. *Jour.*, vol. XVIII, p. 260, 1928.

tuff. Patches of these latter have already been described in the Sierra Nevada but the volcanoes or fissures from which they came are generally not identified. In the southern Cascades these volcanic rocks are so abundant as to bury all others except for a somewhat arbitrarily included margin on the west. Many of the volcanoes from which they were erupted remain distinct though in various stages of erosion. One hundred and twenty of these volcanoes have been counted in the first 50 miles, that is in the portion known as the Lassen Peak Range between the Feather River on the south and the Pit River on the north. As the breadth of this belt is less than 25 miles, it may be seen that the average distance between volcanoes is but little more than three miles. The greatest of these is Lassen Peak which erupted in the years 1914 and 1915. North of the Pit River the range is less known but it includes Mt. Shasta, the most prominent volcanic cone in the United States.

In contrast with the Sierra Nevada the southern Cascade Mountains do not owe their height to uplift either by faulting or by folding. They are essentially an accumulation of eruptive materials from hundreds of centers irregularly distributed and marked by cones, domes, and plateaus of very unequal height. There is no dominant level as in the Sierra Nevada, above which the peaks rise and beneath which the valleys are cut. The southern Cascades are far from being a distinct range with definite limits. The high points are very irregularly distributed, and between them the country is much like the adjacent part of the Great Basin, though on the whole higher and having a stronger relief. The mountain belt is crossed by the Klamath and Pit Rivers to which most of the minor streams are tributary. There are other broad and relatively smooth passes at altitudes but little higher than the level of the adjacent Great Basin.

Borders

Such being the character of the range, it is not to be expected that the line which separates it from the Great Basin can be accurately located. The latter itself contains some mountains of similar character though more widely separated. Nevertheless, an observer approaching the range from the east and viewing it from a distance would at most points of approach see before him a relatively continuous line of mountains.

The mountains as above described merge gradually at the north into a marked linear range with a definite crest. Moreover, as this range is followed northward from southern Oregon, evidences of crustal uplift begin to appear (see page 432), indicating that the range owes a part of its height to diastrophism instead of being due purely to volcanic accumulation. The point at which the continuous linear range begins is in southern Oregon not far from the California boundary and this is adopted as the limit of the Southern Cascade section.

It is noteworthy that throughout Washington and Oregon as far south as Crater Lake (lat. 43°) the crest of the Cascades is followed by county boundaries. The same is true of the Sierra Nevada throughout its length. The location of such lines is significant of a well-recognized crest. In the intervening space, occupied by the southern Cascades, the county boundaries are independent straight lines.

The western boundary of the Southern Cascade section is against the Klamath Mountains except at the south end where this section borders on the Great Valley of California. The line between Cascade and Klamath Mountains is not everywhere apparent topographically. Locally it is marked by valleys. From near the 42d parallel southward to a point west of Mt. Shasta it is approximately followed by the Southern Pacific Railway. This allots to the Cascades, in southern Oregon and nothern California, a foothill belt of sedimentary rocks, which is exceptional according to the criteria here used for delimiting the province. With this exception the line described separates the volcanic rocks on the east from the metamorphosed sedimentaries and granites which constitute the Klamath Mountains. South of Mt. Shasta the province boundary turns sharply to the east, departing widely from the valley followed by the Southern Pacific Railway. Where the Southern Cascade section borders the Great Valley of California, the former includes a sloping and much dissected plateau of Tertiary sediments which the volcanic rocks have failed to bury. This belt is 4,000 ft. high on the eastern side, declining westward to an altitude of 800 ft. from which altitude it falls off in a bold bluff to the level of the Great Valley. This sloping plateau is rough, dry, and stony, and is very properly classed as a foothill belt belonging to the mountain province.

Rocks

The great volcanic accumulation within the belt here described was no doubt favored by crustal disturbances which caused fractures and vents. It was favored also by the nature of the rocks erupted. The lavas which cover or constitute much of the plateaus to the east are mainly basalts. When erupted they were almost as fluid as water. Hence they spread out in wide horizontal sheets instead of coming to rest on steep slopes. Most of the lavas of the Cascades are more siliceous (andesites). These when melted were more viscous and more quickly congealed, sometimes while descending steep mountain slopes (page 433). Local accumulation was aided in both provinces, but especially in the Cascade belt, by the eruption of fragmental products—bombs, lapilli, dust, and "cinders." Such deposits, while generally minor in quantity, are sufficiently abundant to be important topographically. In the great cones like Lassen Peak and Mt. Shasta they alternate with lava flows and help to determine the topographic form.

Local Descriptions

Mount Shasta.—Two localities of the southern Cascades possess special interest, Mt. Shasta because of its great prominence and typical character as a volcanic cone, and Lassen Peak because of recent volcanic activity.

Mount Shasta is a clean-cut cone which, seen from the north, rises almost two miles above its base or 14,350 ft. above the sea. It is typical of volcanic cones composed of alternating lavas and tuffs and in the youth of its erosion cycle. The base of the cone at about 5,000 ft. above sea-level is 17 miles in diameter. With a height of a little less than two miles this calls for an average slope of about 15 deg. The actual slope in the upper third is about 35 deg., but this flattens progressively to the base where it is less than 5 deg.[1] The volume of the cone has been estimated at 84 cubic miles. Above 10,000 ft. the cone is double. The western summit, called Shastina, $1\frac{1}{2}$ miles distant

---

[1] DILLER, J. S., Mount Shasta a Typical Volcano, *Nat. Geogr. Monograph* 8, 1897. Most of the facts here mentioned concerning Shasta are given in this paper to which the reader is referred for a full description of Mt. Shasta and vicinity.

from the main summit and 2,000 ft. lower, preserves an almost perfect crater, thus attesting the youth of the structure.

The accretion was of course accomplished by repeated eruptions, some of the lava flows being so recent that for several miles vegetation has not yet started. The mountain as a whole is older. Erosion has made a good beginning, having already scored the slopes with radiating canyons, one of which is nearly 1,000 ft. deep. Above 10,000 ft. these canyons broaden into glacial cirques. The mountain now supports five glaciers which almost encircle its top. The longest, Whitney Glacier, is 2⅕ miles in length and descends to a level of 9,500 ft. On the lower slopes are secondary lava and cinder cones. Some of these are highly perfect and evidently very recent.

Lassen Peak.—Lassen Peak (10,437 ft.) is noteworthy as the only volcano in the United States which has had a generally observed eruption. (For other eruptions see page 425.) It had been classed as extinct (which means only that it had not been active in historic times) but began to be active in 1914, the eruption becoming violent in May, 1915, but no lava was extruded.[1]

The immediate vicinity of this mountain embraces many interesting features due to recent vulcanism.[2] Among these are cinder cones and lava flows, also lakes and meadows produced by the obstruction of older valleys. There are also solfataras, hot springs, boiling mud pools, and a single small and waning geyser which in 1894 continued to throw its little column of water one foot high.

PHYSIOGRAPHIC HISTORY

When the approximate peneplain was produced over what is now the Sierra Nevada Range it is probable that the same low relief was developed far to the north and east; to the west also, in so far as there was land in that direction. The development of this low surface was followed in the Sierra Nevada by uplift and further volcanic eruptions. It was mainly in this same stage of volcanic activity that the vast accumulation occurred in the southern Cascades. Uplift is also recorded here in the foothill

[1] HOLWAY, R. S., and DILLER, J. S., Geol. Soc. Amer. *Bull.*, vol. 26, p. 397, 1915.

[2] Well described in attractive style by J. S. Diller, Lassen Peak folio 15, U. S. Geol. Survey. This paper contains a good general discussion and good illustrations of volcanic features.

belt now 4,000 ft. high, east of the Sacramento River, but throughout the main part of the range the lavas are so deep that, for aught that is known, the base on which they rest might even be below sea-level.

The time since the uplift and lava flows in the Sierra Nevada, which has there been occupied largely in valley cutting, has not passed without similar effects in the southern Cascades. In this section, however, the cutting of valleys has been more or less hindered by intermittent renewals of eruption. Valleys have thus been partly filled and streams displaced. These accidents have caused erosion features in the southern Cascades to be highly varied, ranging in stage from infancy to maturity.

NORTHERN CASCADE MOUNTAINS

GENERAL

The topographic characters of the middle and northern Cascade Mountains will be best understood by taking up the northern section first. Of the three sections this is most like the Sierra Nevada, so much so that if the two stood adjacent they would be included in a single section. Like the northern part of the Sierra Nevada, the northern Cascades consist of ancient sediments vastly older than the present topography, strongly folded, generally metamorphosed, and intruded by granitic batholiths. They are contrasted in this respect with the middle and southern Cascades which consist almost wholly of volcanic rocks. Defined in this way, this section extends south from the Canadian boundary to lat. 47°30' on the west side and a little farther south on the east side. Its southern boundary is marked approximately by the Northern Pacific Railway running from Ellensburg to Seattle.

CASCADE PLATEAU

Description and Illustration.—The most striking feature of these mountains is the approximately uniform altitude of their peaks and ridges (Fig. 153). These summits collectively, or rather the nearly plane surface from which they seem to have been carved, was called by Russell the Cascade Plateau.[1] Uniformity of summit level is not more marked here than in many other ranges, but in this case it is more remarkable because of

[1] U. S. Geol. Survey, 20*th Ann. Rept.*, pt. II, p. 144, 1899.

the extreme ruggedness of the crests and the steepness of the slopes. In some places so many sharp peaks and crests rise to so nearly the same height that the horizon when viewed from one of the summits is nearly level. The altitude of this horizon varies from 6,000 to 8,500 ft. in the higher parts but declines toward the sides of the range. The higher parts of the Northern Cascade section are so little visited that it is not possible to cite familiar illustrations of such views. The horizon at an altitude of 7,500 ft. on the east side of Mt.

FIG. 153.—High Cascades from the head of Gold Creek, Washington. The view shows the uniformity of altitude suggesting a peneplain at the summit level. (*Willis, U. S. Geol. Survey.*)

Rainier is better known. This is in the Middle Cascade section, but the locality serves well to illustrate the feature referred to.[1] One such view in the northern Cascades is six to eight miles west of Mt. Stuart, midway between the Northern Pacific and Great Northern Railroads, *i.e.,* in the northeast corner of the Snoqualmie quadrangle. Here the horizon is at 6,000 ft. Another is from Boston Mountain (8,300 ft.), just north of Cascade Pass over the main divide (lat. 48°30′, long. 121°). Another is from Stormy Mountain (7,219 ft.), a few miles southeast of Cascade Pass.[2]

[1] SMITH and CALKINS, Reconnaissance across the Cascade Range near the 49th Parallel, U. S. Geol. Survey, *Bull.* 235, p. 86, 1904.

[2] For mention of these localities and others see WILLIS, BAILEY, U. S. Geol. Survey, *Prof. Pap.* 19, p. 48, 1903.

Equally good views are obtained in the little-visited region east of Mt. Baker near the Canadian boundary. Here the altitude of the accordant crests declines westward from 6,000 ft. It is not to be assumed that the outlook from every peak is over such a level horizon. The view must necessarily be a distant one. There are moreover, considerable areas in which erosion has reduced the sharpened crests to lower levels, others in which the plane was deformed during uplift and still others in which it was never well developed.

The range is thus seen to be a dissected upland rather than a ridge. The main divide is a very sinuous line easily traced on the map by the county boundaries which follow it, but not a conspicuous ridge. In a general way it is located in the higher parts of the range but it has passes as low as 3,500 ft. Most of the high peaks stand at a distance from the main divide.

Glacial Features.—Most of the peaks and ridges owe much of the detail of their forms to glaciation. Cirques are numbered by the hundred. Such features are especially dominant near the northern end where many mountains are almost surrounded by cirques and partly consumed by glacial erosion, being thus sharpened to the Matterhorn form.[1] Mt. Hozomeen near the 49th parallel is a typical example. The importance of glacial erosion decreases southward and becomes small (may be said to end) near the southern limit of the section.[2] Farther south it is limited to certain volcanoes of exceptional height like Rainier.

Several hundred small glaciers remain in the northern Cascade Mountains. Nearly all of them occupy cirques carved in the glacial period. None are known to be longer than two miles. Most of them, or all, are shrinking in size.[3] Their lower limits are generally not far from 6,000 ft. above sea-level. The larger number of these surviving glaciers is west of the main divide. The largest cluster of them is around Glacier Peak, an extinct volcano near the main divide just north of the 48th parallel. From the summit of this mountain more than 50 glaciers have

[1] SMITH, G. O., and CALKINS, F. C., Reconnaissance across the Cascade Range near the 49th Parallel, U. S. Geol. Survey, *Bull.* 235, p. 16, 1904.

[2] SMITH, G. O., Mount Stuart folio 106, p. 3, U. S. Geol. Survey, 1904; SMITH, G. O., and CALKINS, F. C., Snoqualmie folio 139, p. 12, U. S. Geol. Survey, 1906.

[3] RUSSELL, I. C., A Preliminary Paper on the Geology of the Cascade Mountains in Northern Washington, U. S. Geol. Survey, *20th Ann. Rept.*, pt. II, p. 192, 1889.

been counted within a radius of 30 miles. From a vast nevé of more than 10 square miles covering this mountain and filling its ancient crater, numerous glaciers radiate.[1] On account of its height, Mt. Baker near the western border of the mountains and near the 49th parallel is also a center of radiating glaciers. Others persist in the high mountains overlooking the headwaters of the Skagit River near long. 121° and close to the International Boundary.

HIGHER PEAKS

Volcanoes.—The relatively even skyline of the Cascades as described above, is broken here and there by isolated mountains which rise thousands of feet above the horizon. These are of two kinds, volcanoes and granite mountains.[2] Most of the well-known examples of the former (Rainier and others) are in the middle Cascades, but two of them, Mt. Baker and Glacier Peak, are in this section. The former (10,827 ft.) is an isolated cone near the western border and northern end of the range. It is generally snow clad and rises more than 5,000 ft. abruptly above the dissected plateau. Glacier Peak (10,436 ft.) is the only mountain of exceptional height in Washington which stands very near the main divide. It rises about 3,000 ft. above the level of the surrounding crests. Like other typical volcanic cones the two here mentioned are built wholly of lavas and tuffs ejected from their craters. They are therefore independent structures not related to the dissected plateau which surrounds them except that they stand upon it as a base. John C. Frémont reported both Mt. Baker (page 424) and Mt. St. Helens (page 430) in violent eruption in 1843 and brought home samples of ash ejected. It is also stated that Mt. Baker was in eruption in the years 1854, 1858, and 1870, but none of these eruptions included lava flows.[3] Ash alone was ejected.

Granitic Peaks.—The granitic peaks of exceptional height are less regular in form than the volcanoes. They may have any height up to a maximum of several thousand feet above the general level. The highest and perhaps the best known is Mt. Stuart (9,470 ft.) in the Wenatchee Mountains, a great spur

---

[1] See Glacier Peak topographic sheet, U. S. Geol. Survey.

[2] RUSSELL, I. C., *loc. cit.*, p. 140.

[3] DILLER, J. S., The Relief of Our Pacific Coast, *Science*, vol. XLI, pp. 48–57, 1915. Mount Rainier continues to emit steam from its crater which is not yet destroyed by erosion.

trending southeast between the Yakima and Wenatchee Rivers. Among the neighboring lower crests and peaks no common level is clearly detected but there is a suggestion of such a level at about 8,400 ft.   Mt. Stuart and other granitic peaks have been variously explained, sometimes as monadnocks, sometimes as the result of recent uplift.   Some of them may be purely monadnocks and probably Mt. Stuart is such in part[1] but it is fairly well

Fig. 154.—Mt. Hood from Portland, Oregon.   The sides of this volcanic cone have been made angular by water and ice erosion.   Like other volcanoes, Rainier, Baker, St. Helens, etc., this one rises sharply above the otherwise plateau-like summit of the Cascade Range.   This is more striking in a broader view.   (*Photo furnished by Portland Chamber of Commerce; copyright by Prentiss.*)

agreed that the entire Wenatchee spur represents greater uplift than that of the range as a whole.[2]   In other words, the range was not elevated as a unit but was more or less subdivided into blocks trending southeast.   The Wenatchee Range represents one of these blocks but Mt. Stuart on its crest was a mountain at least 1,000 ft. high before the last uplift.   On these subordinate

---

[1] Smith, G. O., and Calkins, F. C., Snoqualmie folio 139, p. 12, U. S. Geol. Survey, 1906; see also Willis, Bailey, U. S. Geol. Survey, *Prof. Pap.* 19, p. 75.

[2] Russell, I. C., U. S. Geol. Survey, *20th Ann. Rept.*, pt. II, p. 99.

axes of uplift in the northern Cascades it is not generally possible to say of any one granite peak how much of its altitude is due directly to uplift and how much is inherited from a former cycle.

VALLEYS

Depth and Grade.—The valleys which separate the ridges of the northern Cascades are deep and steep-sided. Depths of 2,500 to 3,500 ft. are common, and the trough that contains Lake Chelan is more than 5,000 ft. deep. The surprising feature of the main valleys leading east and west from the main divide is the low gradient of their axes. Their upper portions near the main divide are cut almost as deep as their lower portions. Where the Northern Pacific and the Chicago, Milwaukee and Puget Sound Railroads cross the main divide at Stampede Pass, the floor of Yakima Valley on the east is less than 2,400 ft. above the sea at a distance of two miles from the crest. Its flood plain averages almost a mile in width. Three miles west of the pass the floor of Green River Valley is only 2,000 ft. above the sea. The railroads follow these valleys without difficulty except for an air-line distance of three miles within which a tunnel is cut beneath the pass. These two valleys are typical of the main valleys throughout the section. Some of them have gradients of not over 10 ft. per mile to within four or five miles of the main divide. Rapids are wanting or, if present, are due to the super-posing of streams on rock ledges by deposits of glacial gravel. Most of these main valleys are floored with gravel which the streams are not very actively eroding. On the strength of this it has been affirmed that the northern Cascades are as deeply dissected as is possible with their present elevation and that their relief within the current erosion cycle is therefore at its maximum.

On the other hand the tributaries of these main east- and west-flowing streams are generally steep, often torrential. Some of them occupy hanging valleys, plunging into the main streams through canyons while their headwaters have relatively gentle slopes. These features suggest that the main valleys owe much of their depth and their low gradients to glacial erosion. The extent to which this is true remains undetermined.[1]

[1] SMITH, G. O., and CALKINS, F. C., U. S. Geol. Survey, folio 139, p. 1, definitely affirm a large amount of glacial erosion, although the area referred to in their report is near the southern limit of active glacial erosion. Russell,

Stehekin-Chelan Valley.—The effects of glacial erosion in the valley of the Stehekin River and Lake Chelan is unquestionable. This valley is 88 miles long from Cascade Pass to the Columbia River. Of this entire distance the lake occupies the lower 65 miles. Its width varies from one to two miles and its maximum depth is 1,419 ft. As the surface of the lake is but 1,079 ft. above the sea the lowest point in its basin is 340 ft. below sea-level. There is no evidence of an old channel at a corresponding depth farther down the valley. The mountains on either side rise to altitudes of more than 7,000 ft. in a distance of six or more miles, and long spurs reach within two miles of the lake at altitudes of more than 6,000 ft. The upper portion of the valley, occupied by the Stehekin River, is of the same character. All these features, the steep slopes, broadened bottom, hanging side valleys, and depth below sea-level, indicate glacial erosion on a grand scale. If the depth is due to stream erosion it is necessary to assume subsequent sinking of at least 500 or 600 ft. Of this there is no evidence. The ice in this valley must have had a depth of more than 4,500 (probably 5,000) ft. Like other streams heading at the main divide, the Stehekin has a low gradient near its head.[1]

Generally speaking the streams in the Cascade Mountains are not adjusted. In a few cases they are influenced by the distribution of strong and weak rocks, but on the whole the courses seem to be otherwise determined. They may have been consequent on the Cascade peneplain.[2]

Longitudinal Valleys at North End.—At the north end of the range the main streams are longitudinal, some flowing north, others south. Two such valleys are especially deep and significant, the Skagit which flows south near the 121st meridian and the Pasaytan which flows north in long. 120°30'. These valleys

---

U. S. Geol. Survey, 20th Ann. Rept., pt. II, p. 151, expresses the opinion that the Cascades were almost as deeply dissected before glaciation as at present. The discrepancy between these views is not necessarily great, since hanging valleys are caused by the broadening of main valleys as well as by their deepening.

[1] For an adequate description and discussion of this remarkable lake, see WILLIS, BAILEY, Contributions to the Geology of Washington, U. S. Geol. Survey, Prof. Pap. 19, pp. 58–63 and 81–83, 1903.

[2] RUSSELL, I. C., loc. cit., p. 146; also DALY, R. A., Geology of the North American Cordillera at the 49th Parallel, Can. Geol. Survey Mem. 38, p. 624, 1912.

subdivide the northern Cascades into three parallel subranges. The central or Hozomeen Range lies between the rivers named and is the direct continuation of the main Cascade divide. West of the Skagit River is the Skagit Range which includes Mt. Baker near its western margin. East of the Pasaytan River, and extending almost to the Okanogan River is the Okanogan Range. It includes the spacious upper valley of the Methow which flows south to the Columbia.

Climate and Its Effects

Climate is a very important factor in the Cascades, not only on account of its influence on vegetation but because of its influence on topography. Because of the prevailing westerly winds from the Pacific the precipitation is very great, especially on the western slope. Much of the precipitation occurs as snow. Snow squalls may occur any month in the year. Large banks of snow survive the short summer even on the eastern side. The most magnificent forests of the United States (except the small areas of Redwood in California) cover the slopes up to an altitude of about 7,000 ft. The more abundant rains of the western slope cause a rank growth of underbrush and moss, thus excluding grass. On the eastern slope are park-like openings with grass.[1] As might be expected, the western slope has most of the glaciers and its topography is more affected by glacial erosion in the past.

The three parallel subranges at the north end show a striking progression both with respect to present climate and vegetation and with respect to glaciation and its effects. In the altitude of their highest crests and peaks these ranges differ little. In the Okanogan Range on the east, the ridges are poorly forested and support much grass, dense forests being confined to the valleys of the larger streams. The few small glaciers which survive are on the highest peaks at the head of the Pasaytan River and are confined to slopes protected from the sun. Past glaciation has left the higher peaks surrounded by cirques and has affected most of the ridges[2] but broad areas of moderate slope remain at high altitudes.[3]

---

[1] RUSSELL, I. C., U. S. Geol. Survey, 20*th Ann. Rept.*, pt. II, pp. 91–93, 1899.

[2] SMITH, G. O., and CALKINS, F. C., U. S. Geol. Survey, *Bull.* 235, pp. 15–19, 1904.

[3] DALY, R. A., *loc. cit.*, p. 619, 1912.

The Hozomeen or central range is similar on its eastern side
to the Okanogan Range but its denser forests with more undergrowth and less grass begin to show the effects of greater precipitation as its sharper alpine features indicate greater effects
of glaciation.   These features are very marked in its western
part where all the higher peaks support glaciers even now.
Hozomeen Mountain, Castle Peak, and many others are typical
Matterhorns.   The Skagit or western range, though no higher
than the others, is still more rugged because of the greater effects
of alpine glaciation.   With its dense forests and rank undergrowth it is practically impassable and unknown even to pros-
pectors.   Glaciers are more abundant in these mountains than
in any other locality except around Glacier Peak.   The western
portion of the range is lower and characterized by accordant
ridges giving the appearance of a dissected plateau.   The
vicinity of Mt. Baker is described on page 424.

MIDDLE CASCADE MOUNTAINS

DESCRIPTION

Northern End.—The southern end of the Middle section
strongly resembles the Southern Cascade section as the northern
end resembles the Northern section.   Between the two types
there is a transition, probably gradual, in the imperfectly known
central portion of the section.   In the northern part of this
section the accordance of crests is similar to that in the northern
Cascades.   Here also the peaks are separated by similar deep
valleys and the horizon is surmounted by towering volcanoes
built since the development of the nearly level surface in which
the valleys are cut.   Mt. St. Helens (10,000 ft.) and Mt. Adams[1]
(12,470 ft.) much farther south (lat. 46°) stand in the same
relation to the surrounding topography, and also Mt. Hood
(11,225 ft.) south of the Columbia River (Fig. 154).   Similar
descriptions have even been applied to the vicinity of Mts.
Jefferson and Washington between the 44th and 45th parallels,
but this part of the range is imperfectly known.   It is known,
however, that peaks of exceptional height rise above the average

---

[1] A beautiful view showing Mt. Adams and the platform on which it
stands is given by M. R. Campbell in the Guidebook of the Western United
States, Part A, Northern Pacific Route, U. S. Geol. Survey, *Bull.* 611, pl
XXIII, p. 167.

level. Among these, named in order from north to south, are Mt. Jefferson and Mt. Washington, Three Sisters, Mt. Theilson and Mt. Pitt, the last named being in lat. 42°30′ at the southern end of the Middle section. Except for the deep transverse valley of the Columbia the general crest level is similar to that of the northern Cascades though on the whole it declines southward. Near Mt. Rainier it is 7,500 ft., but levels of 6,000 and even 5,000 ft. are known farther south.

FIG. 155.—Summit of the Cascade Range south of Crater Lake. Union Peak at the right and Mt. McLoughlin in the distance are volcanic cones. The moderately level horizon above which these peaks rise is largely determined by the surface of lava flows. Unlike the isolated volcanoes of the Northern Cascades, which stand on an older surface, these cones are of the same age as the surrounding plateau. The forms, both of the cones and of the plateaus, are constructional rather than destructional. (*Copyright by Fred H. Kiser.*)

Southern End.—In southern Oregon the range is clearly but a phase of that which has been described as the southern Cascades. It differs from the latter only in being a more continuous range and in affording greater evidence that its height is in part due to crustal movement instead of wholly to volcanic accumulation. Near the southern limit it lacks the accordant summits and hence the plateau-like appearance of the Cascades farther north. Moreover the volcanoes which crown it represent sources of the material which constitutes the range instead of being later super-added or secondary features. Where a plateau level is found at intermediate heights its history has not been essentially different from that of the cones.

This difference in the relation between volcanic cones and the general surface affords the great genetic contrast between the northern and southern Cascade types.   It is possible to conceive of gradation between these types by assuming the widely spaced cones of the north to become more and more abundant toward the south until their lava flows and slopes meet.   On this supposition the peneplain of the north may not be found at the south, simply because it is covered up.[1]   It is, however, not known to have been developed in the southern half of the range.

STRUCTURE

Crustal Uplift.—The evidences of uplift as contrasted with mere accumulation are clearest at the north end.   The widely extended summit level or uplifted peneplain is here continuous from the crest of the range to the eastern foothill belt where, in the vicinity of Ellensburg and North Yakima, it is well preserved at altitudes ranging from 3,000 to 4,000 ft.   This latter district has been well studied[2] and affords conclusive evidence of crustal uplift which increases westward.   However thick the lava may be on the summits to the west, the range owes its present altitude to uplift, not to accumulation.

The Columbia River in its great transverse gorge has cut down through thousands of feet of lava.   The several lava flows are here arched upward in a complex anticline.   On the assumption that they were originally horizontal, the range has been lifted some thousands of feet along its axis.[3]   Farther south the evidence is less clear.   The steepness of the escarpment west of the Deschutes River has been thought to suggest faulting but this is not demonstrated.   In southern Oregon, however, the eastern front of the range has locally all the features which in the basin ranges are ascribed to faulting.   In the Calapooya Mountains, a western spur at the south end of the Willamette Valley,

---

[1] DILLER, J. S., Tertiary Revolution in the Topography of the Pacific Coast, U. S. Geol. Survey, *14th Ann. Rept.*, pt. II, p. 410, 1892.   Diller here suggests a single extensive peneplain over middle and northern California and southern Oregon, passing beneath the lavas of the southern Cascades and the Great Basin.

[2] U. S. Geol. Survey, folios 86, 106, and 139.

[3] RUSSELL, U. S. Geol. Survey, *20th Ann. Rept.*, pt. II, p. 145, gives a nearly uniform eastward dip of 4 deg. along a line somewhat south of the Northern Pacific Railroad.   In the gorge of the Columbia there are easterly dips as high as 14 deg.

the lava flows, which cover the spur at its eastern end, dip both ways from the crest. This would indicate that the spur is an anti-cline[1] similar to those on the east side of the range in Washington.

Volcanic Accumulation.—Throughout the southern part of this section the lavas are like those of the southern Cascades, andesitic and hence less fluid when melted than are the basalts of the plateaus to the east. Generally the line between the two kinds of rock at the foot of the mountains is marked by abrupt change of slope.[2] While allowing for an undetermined amount of uplift, Diller calls the range south of the Columbia River and including the southern Cascades "a great pile, chiefly of viscous andesitic lavas from many confluent cone-capped vents in strong contrast to the coneless basalt plains in the formation of which the high degree of fluidity was the most important factor."

Local Descriptions

Crater Lake.—Probably the best known landmark in the middle Cascades is Crater Lake[3] situated at an altitude of 6,117 ft. in the crest of the range in lat. 43°. The lake is nearly circular, having a diameter of five to six miles (Fig. 156). Its greatest depth is 2,000 ft. The walls of the basin rise precipitously to heights ranging from 500 to 2,200 ft. above the water. From this jagged rim the surrounding country slopes away in all directions as from a volcanic cone (Fig. 157). It is plain that this truncated cone is the basal portion of a volcano whose top has disappeared. Geological evidence shows that it must have been engulfed. The resulting basin is the best example of a *caldera* in America. Renewal of volcanic activity has started a new cone within the caldera. This almost perfect cone rises 763 ft. above the surface of the water and is called Wizard Island. It consists of scoria, so fresh and piled with so steep a slope that they slide down beneath the feet of the climber, thus making ascent very tiresome. The exceptional scenic grandeur and scientific interest of this feature have caused the United States

[1] Suggested by DILLER, J. S., The Bohemian Mining District, U. S. Geol. Survey, *20th Ann. Rep.*, pt. II, p. 10, 1899.

[2] DILLER, J. S., The Relief of Our Pacific Coast, *Science*, vol. XLI, p. 56, 1915.

[3] See Crater Lake topographic sheet of the U. S. Geol. Survey. A description and explanation of the lake and vicinity are printed on the back of the map.

FIG. 156.—Model of Crater Lake and vicinity.   Note that the drainage on all sides is away from the lake.   Wizard Island, less than a mile in diameter, is a perfect cone built by eruption since the lake basin was made by the engulfment of the great cone which formerly stood above the present rim.   (*U. S. Geol. Survey.*)

FIG. 157.—Rim of Crater Lake as seen from the south.   The rim is a truncated cone rising above a plateau.   Its outer slopes may be extended upward to show the form of the old volcano before its upper part fell in.   (*Photo by Diller.*)

Government to set aside the Crater Lake National Park. The peaks on the jagged rim of Crater Lake are collectively known as Mt. Mazama, this name being applied also to the now vanished cone.

Border Features.—On the west the Middle Cascade section borders on the Puget trough (which includes the Willamette Basin) as far south as lat. 44°. South of that a transverse spur (the Calapooya Mountains mentioned above) connects the Cascade Mountains with the Oregon Coast Range. This spur is generally regarded as a part of the Cascade Range. Except in its eastern part it is not composed of the late eruptives which cover the Cascades nor was it built up in the same manner. Its rocks and structure are more like those of the Oregon Coast Range.[1] This transverse ridge constitutes the divide between the longitudinal Willamette on the north and the transverse Umpqua on the south. South of this divide the main streams are transverse and flow from the crest of the Cascades directly to the Pacific. This continues to be true until the end of the Middle Cascade section is reached; beyond that, in the southern Cascades, the Klamath River crosses the entire Mountain province.

For 20 miles south from the Calapooya Mountains the boundary between the Cascade Range on the east and the Coast Range and Klamath Mountains on the west is clear, but for the next 90 miles to the south it is topographically obscure. It is fixed by definition at the contact of the volcanic rocks which make the Cascades with the sedimentaries which make the Coast Range and the Klamath. This criterion is too significant to be ignored despite the weakness of the topographic contrast. A rather prominent and continuous valley followed by the Southern Pacific Railway lies 10 to 35 miles farther west within the Coast Range and Klamath sections.

The boundary on the east is not defined by any other criterion than that of slope. Throughout most of the distance "the foot of the range" is fairly clear. Probably for most of the distance south of the Columbia the base of the range is not far from the line where the less fluid andesites of the mountains give way to the more highly fluid basalts of the Great Basin and Columbia Plateau.

[1] DILLER, J. S., Guidebook of the Western United States, Part D, The Shasta Route and Coast Line, U. S. Geol. Survey, *Bull.* 614, p. 39, 1915.

From the latitude of Crater Lake to Upper Klamath Lake at the south end of the section, the Williams River flows south at the foot of the range. Russell states that between the headwaters of the Williams and the Deschutes (lat. 43° to 44°) the young volcanoes of the Great Basin simply increase in number and height toward the west until by their close crowding they form the Cascade Range.[1] Even here the line is fairly clear. West of the Deschutes Valley the mountain front is continuous and clear (page 432). The boundary north of the Columbia is described on page 264.

Physiographic History of the Middle and Northern Cascades

Pre-peneplain History.—The first chapter in the history of the Cascade Mountains is recorded only in their structure, not in the topography. This indicates that a previous range probably contemporary with the older Rockies[2] occupied the site of the present one, but probably only in the northern part. These earlier mountains were made by folding, not very different from that of the Appalachians,[3] but there were also batholiths of granite similar to but smaller than those of the Sierra Nevada. These mountains have been worn away and the truncated strata which composed them are now found steeply inclined. Rocks of somewhat different hardness are thus exposed and it is a significant fact that the present drainage has not become adjusted in any marked degree to these differences.[4]

---

[1] RUSSELL, I. C., U. S. Geol. Survey, *Bull.* 252, p. 15, 1905. This is not necessarily inconsistent with the previously cited statement by Diller that the rocks of the Cascade Range differ from those of the Great Basin.

[2] SMITH, G. O., Ellensburg folio 86, U. S. Geol. Survey; also SMITH G. O., and CALKINS, F. C., Snoqualmie folio 139, U. S. Geol. Survey.

[3] RUSSELL, I. C., U. S. Geol. Survey, *20th Ann. Rept.*, pt. II, p. 138, 1899.

[4] DALY, R. A., Can. Geol. Survey, *Mem.* 38, pp. 620 and 627, 1912. The account of Cascade history here given is the one commonly accepted, at least in the United States. It assumes the development of a peneplain in Pliocene time and its subsequent uplift and dissection, to make the present mountains. This has been controverted at length by Daly in the *memoir* referred to. The most weighty objections raised are based on (1) the short time allowed for one complete erosion cycle and another brought to maturity whereas in eastern United States it has been customary (at least up to the time of Daly's writing) to allot a vastly longer time to such tasks; (2) the lack of stream adjustment, it being generally agreed that in the base-leveling

The making of the first mountains was followed by other crustal disturbances so that effective base-leveling was deferred until the latter part of Tertiary time. The vast inundations of basalt which covered the Columbia Plateau and much of the Cascade Range came relatively late (Miocene) but even at that time the surface was still rough, at places mountainous. On the eastern flank of the range in Washington the outflow of basalt was followed or accompanied in its later stages by sinking which made broad lake basins and by the filling of these with lake and stream sediments. This must have taken considerable time. Still later came an uplift by which the range was raised, not as a unit but as a series of blocks or folds trending east by south. This event followed the Miocene period.

Cascade Peneplain.—If the history of the range as a whole may be inferred from that of its eastern flank, it was not until after all these events that erosion was permitted a relatively free hand in base-leveling the range. The time was thus limited to the Pliocene.[1] The minimum relief which remained to be erased in the middle Cascades was that which was imparted by the last (post-Miocene) uplift. In the Yakima Basin this was at least several thousand feet. To this must be added the altitude (whatever it may have been) of the lava surface previous to the uplift. It cannot be positively asserted that this altitude

---

of mountains the streams should adjust themselves within the first cycle. He substitutes for the two-cycle hypothesis one which provides for post-Cretaceous mountain making (with minor uplift later) and the employment of all Tertiary time in the reduction of these mountains to their present form. The accordance of crest levels is explained by the more rapid wasting of high peaks and crests than of lower ones, partly because of the protection afforded by forests and partly because of the great effectiveness of cirque erosion at a level not far from the timber line. (Only major points here stated.) He finds, however, that the general level and the relief at the close of the Miocene were much lower than now, perhaps "late maturity or even old age locally," and that an uplift at that time occasioned the present canyons. It should be noted that the tendency to reduce the geologic age of peneplains in eastern United States has grown rapidly since the time of Daly's writing. This would remove one of the motives for propounding a different theory. The prevailing lack of adjustment still remains something of a problem. Examples of local adjustment in the Mt. Stuart quadrangle are given both by G. O. Smith, folio 106, and by I. C. Russell, U. S. Geol. Survey, 20*th Ann. Rept.*

[1] Willis, B., U. S. Geol. Survey, *Prof. Pap.* 19, p. 69, 1903, would allot "most of the Pliocene" to this peneplaning. Russell, *loc. cit.*, p. 144, thinks it may have lasted into Pleistocene time.

was anything at all, for volcanic accumulations may subside, as in the Ellensburg Basin (page 232), and the surface was also being lowered by erosion during the deposition of the sediments farther east. As to the height imparted by the post-Miocene uplift, the cross-folds on which all the evidence depends seem to die out toward the west. It thus appears that the amount of relief to be reduced in the Pliocene base-leveling process may have been comparatively small. There is nothing to show that it was anywhere greater than in the Yakima Basin.

In the Northern section where the lava cover is absent, the total relief to be erased in the final epoch of peneplanation is that which was imparted by the post-Miocene uplift plus that which existed before that event. The former is an unknown factor over most of the range. As for the relief which existed before the uplift, it is inferred from the vicinity of Mt. Stuart that it was as much as 1,500 ft.[1] This is a district of strong rocks which has at present, and may well have had at that time, approximately the maximum relief for the range.

It is thus seen that the amount of relief remaining to be erased by Pliocene base-leveling was not demonstrably large and may have been small over most of the range. It is likewise uncertain how much relief remained at the close of the epoch when the so-called "peneplain" was uplifted and a new erosion cycle was begun.[2]

Uplift of the Peneplain.—The final uplift of the Cascade peneplain gave to the range its present height, made possible the cutting of deep valleys, and conditioned the glaciers. As in the preceding uplift, the range was not lifted as a unit, but, on the east side at least, was more or less subdivided into blocks or folds trending east by south, but this condition is not known to affect the west side nor does it extend south of the Columbia River. These transverse uplifts followed old axes more or less closely and revived the long spurs on the east side like the Wenatchee

---

[1] Smith, G. O., Mt. Stuart folio 106, p. 7, U. S. Geol. Survey.

[2] The reason for this discussion, showing that the task of Pliocene peneplanation was not necessarily large, is found in Daly's argument (footnote, p. 436) based on the insufficiency of time allowed for the task to be performed. His argument was based largely on the assumption that a Cretaceous peneplain is in part preserved in eastern United States. As this so called "Cretaceous peneplain" is now believed to be of later origin, the difficulty with respect to Pliocene peneplains in the West is not what it was at the time of Daly's writing.

Range and the lower swells described on page 426. At the same time the range was divided at the north end by longitudinal depressions into the three subranges. This last uplift raised the peneplain in Washington to altitudes ranging from 6,000 to 8,000 ft. Disregarding the minor transverse folds, the last deformation was in the form of a broad arch 50 to 100 times as wide as it is high. The top of the arch is, however, notably flat, as compared with the steeper flanks.[1]

Fig. 158.—Lava flow partly burying an old surface on the Cascade Mountains of Oregon. This suggests the manner in which the Middle Cascades were covered and built up. (*Photo by H. W. Fairbanks.*)

Drainage History.—To some extent the present streams are consequent on the slopes of the deformed peneplain. It was believed by Russell that the main divide was thus fixed and the major east- and west-flowing streams thus determined.[2] This remains unverified and is not essential to the peneplain hypothesis. It involves the assumption that the peneplain was reduced to extremely low relief, since otherwise the very gentle lateral slopes of the arch would have been insufficient to divert the former streams from their established courses. On the other hand the north and south slopes of some of the transverse folds are much

---

[1] WILLIS, B., U. S. Geol. Survey, *Prof. Pap.* 19. Plate VII is a contour map of the Wenatchee-Chelan district showing by contours also the altitude of the restored peneplain.

[2] RUSSELL, I. C., *loc. cit.*, p. 146.

steeper and seem without doubt to have controlled the present drainage lines.[1]

Examples of well verified consequent drainage can, however, be more than matched by others of antecedent drainage. Of these, the striking example of the Yakima River has already been mentioned (page 265, Columbia Plateau). At the north end the Skagit River after following its well open valley south across the International Boundary turns west in a deep wild canyon, cut across the rising Skagit Mountains.

The course of the Columbia is plainly antecedent to the last uplift. The mountains rose across its course in a complex fold or series of folds; the channel was lifted and rapids resulted but the stream held its course. Even now the channel is far from graded. At the Cascades (from which the range takes its name) 40 miles east of Portland, the Columbia descends to sea-level by a series of rapids 50 ft. in height. This may indicate that the grading of the streams has never yet caught up with the opposing process of uplift; or the uplift may have been renewed by folding or by faulting. It is possible, however, that a rock slide or slump may be the cause of the Cascades.[2]

Dissection of the Peneplain.—Since its uplift the peneplain has been maturely dissected. Its former existence in the mountains is inferred, not from flat remnants but from the accordant heights of neighboring ridges. Where these are broad-topped and smooth it may be inferred that they rise approximately to the level of the old peneplain. Where they are sharp, jagged crests, their altitude is already decreasing. The amount of such decrease already accomplished can only be conjectured but has been placed at not less than 200 to 600 ft.[3]

In general the localities of greatest uplift have been those of most complete dissection and greatest subsequent loss of altitude. This is well illustrated by comparing the vicinity of Mt. Baker with the district just east of it. The former, having an altitude of less than 6,000 ft. (exclusive of Mt. Baker), has preserved its broad smoothly rounded crests which collectively are strikingly like a dissected plateau. To the east and in the same view are crests several thousand feet higher, steep, narrow, craggy, and

[1] SMITH, G. O., and CALKINS, F. C., Snoqualmie folio 139, U. S. Geol. Survey.

[2] DILLER, J. S., U. S. Geol. Survey, *Bull.* 614, p. 27, 1915.

[3] WILLIS, B., U. S. Geol Survey, *Prof. Pap.* 19, p. 75, 1903.

often impassable. Both topographies were apparently carved from the same peneplain, the difference being due to unequal uplift. There is a similar but still greater contrast at the northern limit of the province a few miles north of the International Boundary. Here the Cascade Mountains with peaks of 7,000 to 8,500 ft overlook the Plateau of British Columbia several thousand feet lower and consisting of broad rolling uplands and rounded divides, separated by valleys of no great width. Greater uplift on the south has caused more rapid advance in the erosion cycle.[1]

To whatever extent the Columbia Plateau remains uncovered by later lavas, its surface is part of the same peneplain. Students of its western margin have so regarded it.[2] As compared with the mountains, the lower elevation and drier climate of this margin have favored the preservation of the upland surface. On the broad ridges of the Yakima district the peneplain has been little affected by erosion (page 264).

In the vicinity of Lake Chelan there is evidence that the uplift was not all at one time.[3] Here it appears that an uplift of several thousand feet was followed by mature dissection and that the remainder of the rise came in relatively recent time, causing the already mature valleys to be deeply trenched by canyons.

Volcanic Cones.—The eruptions which made the great cones from Mt. Baker on the north to Mt. Hood and probably even farther south occurred at some time after the making of the peneplain. Some of them at least, as in the case of Mt. Baker, came after the present deep valleys had been cut.

[1] SMITH, G. O., and CALKINS, F. C., U. S. Geol. Survey, *Bull.* 235, p. 90, 1904.

[2] WILLIS, B., *loc. cit.*, p. 71, 1903.

[3] WILLIS, B., *loc. cit.*, p. 68, 1903.

CHAPTER X

PACIFIC BORDER PROVINCE

GENERAL

Chain of Coast Ranges.—Throughout most of its length from north to south the Pacific Border province is divided into a chain of mountains on the west and a chain of valleys on the east. Most of the mountains are familiarly called the "Coast Ranges" but the application of this term is not uniform. Their northernmost representative in the United States is the Olympic group in Washington. The chain is continued northward in Vancouver Island, British Columbia, and the Queen Charlotte Islands. Named in order from north to south, the chain in the United States includes the Olympic group, Oregon Coast Range, Klamath and California Ranges, and the ranges of the Angeles section, sometimes called the "Southern California Coast Ranges." (For index maps see Fig. 83, page 226; Fig. 132, page 368; and Fig. 141, page 397.)

Line of Great Valleys.—East of the Coast Ranges is a line of valleys, though the line is not uninterrupted. North of the 44th parallel is a continuous trough embracing the Willamette Valley of Oregon and the Cowlitz, upper Chehalis, and Puget Sound Valleys in Washington. It is continued northward in the sounds separating Vancouver and the Queen Charlotte Islands from the mainland of British Columbia. This great trough represents a continuous axis of crustal deformation.[1]

---

[1] Unfortunately the term "Coast Range of British Columbia" has been applied to the mountains lying east of this trough. If the name were merely a descriptive term this would be suitable enough since they occupy the coast of the mainland, but the term "Coast Range" has come to be understood as a proper name rather than a common noun. As such it should have been applied to the mountains of Vancouver Island in order to be consistent with custom which applies it to the much better known Coast Ranges of the United States. The mountains of British Columbia, while not a continuation of the Cascade Range, are closely related to it and not to the Coast Ranges of the United States.

The series of great valleys is interrupted in northern California and southern Oregon (lat. 40°30' to 43°45'), where the Klamath Mountains are in contact with the Cascades. The interruption would probably be less were it not for the vast accumulations of lava which have, in places at least, filled a depression before piling up as mountains. South of that barrier is the Great Valley of California.

The Gulf of California, though separated by important mountain ranges from the Great Valley, is sometimes spoken of as continuing the same great series of depressions toward the south.[1] This gives a line of Pacific Border depressions 2,500 miles long, the ends of which are submerged beneath the sea and the intermediate portions in part filled with surficial deposits to great depths. The Gulf of California may be regarded as a member of this series or it may represent a more easterly depression to be correlated with Death Valley and others east of the Sierra Nevada. The former view would be correct if the great mountain mass of Lower California is looked upon as a continuation of the Coast Ranges of California. In the scheme of divisions here used, this question is left open by making it a separate province. Its relations to the Sierra Nevada may be quite as close as to the Coast Range.

PUGET TROUGH

GENERAL

The Puget Trough is a long valley enclosed on the east by the Cascades and on the west by the Olympic Mountains and the Oregon Coast Range. Its northern end (within the United States) is occupied by Puget Sound. Its southern end is the Willamette Valley in Oregon. Between the latter and Puget Sound are the valley of the south-flowing Cowlitz and the upper basin of the Chehalis River which flows directly west to the Pacific. That part of the trough which lies in the United States is 350 miles long and about 50 miles wide at the north, narrowing irregularly toward the south and coming to an end where the Cascades meet the Coast Range of Oregon. Aside from a few exceptionally hilly areas, the altitude of its floor rarely exceeds 500 ft. and is generally less.

[1] SMITH, G. O., and WILLIS, B., Tacoma folio 54, p. 1, U. S. Geol. Survey.

BASIN OF PUGET SOUND

Distinguishing Features.—With respect to surface features the Puget Trough must be subdivided into three or more districts of very different character. The northernmost and most important of these is the immediate basin of Puget Sound. In distinction from the rest of the section this is the glaciated portion and also the depressed and partly submerged portion.

The topography of this portion is almost wholly due to glacial ice and glacial waters. The ice came mainly from the north and was a lobe or tongue of the Cordilleran ice cap[1] (Fig. 81, page 212). North of the Straits of Juan de Fuca the ice was predominantly an eroding agent but farther south deposition was the rule.[2] So thick are these glacial and glaciofluvial deposits that were they removed the entire basin would probably be an inland sea instead of being merely traversed by marine channels.[3]

Morainic Border.—The southern limit of this deposition of drift was 10 to 15 miles south of the sound. From Le Grande on, the Nisqually River (lat. 46°50′) at the west foot of Mt. Rainier, the boundary line runs west by north across the valley. On the west side it conforms in a rough way with the foot of the Coast Range. It agrees rather closely with the divide which separates the drainage to Puget Sound from the basin of the Chehalis River. A belt along the margin is ground moraine and terminal moraine, locally very rocky and hummocky. This ice-laid drift is deposited on the slope which rises southward and limits the Puget Sound depression.[4] The altitude of this moraine varies from 150 ft. to more than 1,400 ft. above the sea according to the nature of the surface on which or against which the ice terminated. South and west of this morainic belt, in the valley of the Chehalis River, are great areas of barren gravel and sand, due to outwash from the glacier, which followed the Chehalis River to the Pacific.

[1] BRETZ J HARLEN, Glaciation of the Puget Sound Region, Washington Geol. Survey, *Bull.* 8, p. 17, 1913.

[2] BRETZ, J HARLEN, Glacial Lakes of Puget Sound, *Jour. Geol.*, vol. XVIII, p. 448, 1910.

[3] BRETZ, J HARLEN, The Terminal Moraine of the Puget Sound Glacier, *Jour. Geol.*, vol. XIX, p. 162, 1911.

[4] This specially depressed district of which Puget Sound is the center is more extensive than the sound itself but, on the other hand, it must not be confused with the Puget Trough as defined above.

Gravelly Plains.—Inside the morainic belt the general level descends toward Puget Sound. Here and there the ice-laid moraine rises in hills, or forms larger patches of rolling country, as around Seattle, but between and around such areas is a lake-dotted and, in part, swampy plain whose substratum consists largely of gravel which was deposited as outwash from the glacier during its final shrinkage. The work of ice and the work of water are so commingled that it is difficult to classify the deposits and their characteristic surface forms accurately, but nine-tenths of the material is said to be water-laid.[1] The gravel which occupies much of the area, especially south of Tacoma, is almost free from clay, hence barren and almost worthless.

Such tracts are in large part natural prairie, locally too porous to permit the formation of streams. Some of these prairies bear small mounds of roughly uniform size which, when well developed, suggest haycocks scattered over a field. (See page 271; also Fig. 100, page 270.) Their origin has been much debated.[2] Where the sorting effect of water is less marked and some clay remains mixed with the sand and gravel the forests are very dense and the details of topography are very imperfectly known. A large area east of Tacoma is known as "the Wilderness."

Erosion has modified these forms very little. The larger streams heading in the mountains reach the sound by broad flat-bottomed valleys, the lower ends of which represent filled portions of the sound itself instead of recent erosion.

Some of the streams descending from the mountains have lost their old courses by being superposed on the drift (probably of an early stage). Thus the Nisqually lost its way near Le Grande where it has since cut a canyon two miles long and, at one point, 400 ft. deep.[3] Seattle derives power from the Cedar River whose rapids are caused by similar superposition.

The White River, which enters the flat Duwamish trough between Tacoma and Seattle is an interesting stream. It takes its name from the milky appearance of its water due to the "glacial flour" supplied by the glaciers of Mt. Rainier. On

[1] BRETZ, J HARLEN, Wash. Geol. Survey, *Bull.* 8, p. 15, 1913. For more detailed descriptions see Tacoma folio 54, U. S. Geol. Survey.

[2] In *Bull.* 8, Wash. Geol. Survey, 1913, Bretz devotes a chapter to these mounds, recounting the work and stating the interpretations of earlier writers. For one class of these mounds he offers a plausible explanation.

[3] SAUNDERS, EDWIN J., U. S. Geol. Survey, *Wat. Sup. Pap.* 313, pp. 15 and 55, 1913.

reaching the level floor of Duwamish Valley it deposits much of its load, building a low alluvial fan. On this fan the stream divides, most of it flowing north, the remainder flowing south to join the Puyallup.

Rock Hills.—Exceptions to the topography above described are found in certain areas where the pre-glacial rock hills rise above the level of deposition. Some of these areas stand out like monadnocks on a peneplain, as indeed they may have been. Of this nature is Squak Mountain, southeast of Seattle, 2,000 ft. high. The Blue Hills between the two main "inlets" or "canals" of the sound are of the same kind. But the main area thus characterized lies north of Seattle, stretching in a broad north-west-southeast belt from Vancouver Island to the Cascade Mountains. It includes the San Juan Islands and the spurs of the Cascade Range east of Mt. Vernon.

Puget Sound.—Puget Sound is a partially drowned drainage system, so modified by temporary glacial channels that its valleys branch and reunite. Its lower northern portion is the broad Strait of Juan de Fuca, more than 20 miles wide opposite Victoria, British Columbia. Toward the south it branches out into various "inlets" or "canals" having a total shore line of 1,750 miles. Generally these troughs have steep banks several hundred feet high with steep slopes below water level leading down to maximum depths of 600 to 900 ft. The gradual displacement of the water surface by mud bars, marsh, and finally solid ground is well depicted on the U. S. Geological Survey topographic map of the Tacoma quadrangle (see Fig. 159).

The system of valleys which embraces the "inlets" or "canals" of the sound is much more extensive than the submerged area. The upstream portions of these partly submerged valleys are floored with silts and almost as flat as the former water surface. An excellent illustration is the Puyallup Valley southeast of Tacoma; also the Duwamish Valley connecting this with the sound at Seattle and followed by the Northern Pacific Railroad. The only difference between these valleys and the "canals" is that the former are already filled and the latter not yet filled. Most of these bottom lands are liable to floods but they are nevertheless the chief farming districts of the region. The streams which traverse these flats are extending them by means of deltas in the inlets, slowly, of course, because of the great depths to be filled. Still other troughs are occupied by lakes, such as Washington and Sammamish Lakes east of Seattle, but all these troughs, whether filled with salt water, fresh water, or silt, are parts of the same system and have a common history except for the last chapters. The gently rolling lands between the troughs are known as plateaus or "islands" whether the adjacent troughs are occupied by water or by alluvium.

Fig. 159.—Drowned Valley of Chambers Creek at low tide. This small valley opening into Puget Sound is of the same kind as the "canals" or "inlets" which constitute the sound except that it has been filled by alluvium up to the level of low tide. The Puyallup, Duwamish, and other valleys several miles wide are of the same kind but filled above high tide. (*Bretz, Wash. Geol. Survey.*)

The shores of Puget Sound are marked at many places by fragmentary terraces ranging in altitude from 20 to 100 ft. above sea-level. Marine shells indicate that some of these terraces mark the position of sea-level when the land stood lower.[1] The extreme of submergence indicated by shells is 250 to 280 ft.[2] but there are no terraces above 100 ft. Necessarily this low stand was since the glacial period.

[1] Tacoma folio 54, p. 5, U. S. Geol. Survey; also Bretz, *Jour. Geol.*, vol. XVIII, p. 457.

[2] Bretz, J Harlen, Wash. Geol. Survey, *Bull.* 8, p. 22; a good summary of the geology of Puget Sound is given by J. S. Diller in his Guidebook of the Western United States, U. S. Geol. Survey, *Bull.* 614, pp. 11–12, footnote, 1915.

UPPER CHEHALIS AND COWLITZ VALLEYS

South of the glaciated area above described, the general elevation is much the same but there are more rock hills. Several prominent lines of hills lie just south of the glacial margin, the drift being laid up against their slopes. This line embraces the Bald Hills, several hundred feet high, near the Cascade margin, and the Black Hills of equal height near the western margin.[1] Other groups connect these, making what is sometimes called a spur of the Cascades. Similar but generally smaller hills and groups of hills lie farther south. All these are of the same character as those of pre-glacial origin mentioned above. The lowland has in part an old-age topography developed on non-resistant rocks. Much of it is covered with subaerial and stream deposits derived chiefly from the neighboring mountains during the glacial epochs. Cowlitz River has a broad valley much of which is occupied by gravel terraces.[2] Except for small tracts, the entire area was once densely forested with Douglas fir, hemlock, and cedar. Much of it has since been logged or burned.

LOWER COLUMBIA VALLEY

After crossing the Cascade Mountains, the Columbia River flows north 40 miles before turning west through the Oregon Coast Range. Throughout this portion the Columbia is drowned, the tide extending up to the Cascades, *i.e.*, to the rapids from which the range takes its name. These rapids are 40 miles east of Portland, and 140 miles from the sea. On both sides of the north-flowing part of the river and for 20 miles south of Portland, the valley is more or less occupied by hills of basalt rising from 700 to more than 1,000 ft. above the sea. Near the river, especially on the north side, they are widely spaced or wanting. Elsewhere they are more closely set, so closely at places that they merge into a maturely dissected plateau. Council Crest on the west side of Portland is a part of this plateau; so is the hilly belt which crosses Willamette Valley at Oregon City, 10 miles south of Portland.[3] Within this belt are Willamette Falls (40 ft.) at Oregon City, and Clackamas Rapids a little lower down.

[1] BRETZ, J HARLEN, *Jour. Geol.*, vol. XIX, p. 163, map.

[2] SAUNDERS, EDWIN, J., U. S. Geol. Survey, *Wat. Sup. Pap.* 313, p. 26, 1913.

[3] See DILLER, J. S., Guidebook of the Western United States, U. S. Geol. Survey, *Bull.* 614, pp. 29 and 30, 1915.

WILLAMETTE VALLEY

The part of the Willamette drainage basin which belongs to the Puget Trough is for the most part the very flat alluvial plain of the Willamette and its tributaries.   This constitutes two-thirds

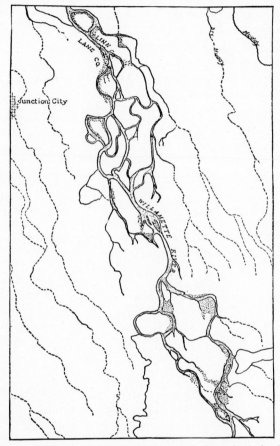

FIG. 160.—Detail of a portion of the braided channel of the Willamette River, Oregon.   The load carried by this stream is large in proportion to its power; hence the numerous bars and channels.   On account of the excessive load the river is unable to cut down; hence the adjacent land does not slope toward the river.   Extreme flatness of the surface is suggested by the parallelism of the intermittent streams.   (*Modified from the U. S. Geol. Survey by Warren Du Pre Smith.*)

of the district here concerned.   The remaining third belongs to the country of low basalt hills described above or has a moderate relief developed on young and non-resistant rocks.   This valley is about 125 miles long and generally not more than 20 to 30 miles wide.

Above (south of) Oregon City, the Willamette River is a sluggish stream with an intricate series of meanders. Apparently a fault crosses the stream at this place, the block on the south side being uplifted at the edge and tilted south, thus helping to stagnate the stream higher up. Near Eugene, at the head of the valley, it is a web of sloughs or bayous (Fig. 160). The fall of the river measured along a straight line from Eugene (altitude 450 ft.) to Portland, is less than four feet per mile and is very much less than that when the meanders are followed. By reason of insufficient fall and ample load of sediment from the adjacent mountains, it is an overloaded stream. The tributaries on account of their smaller volume are even less able to transport their loads. Because of the feeble currents, trees and other vegetation are able to invade the streams and help to crowd them aside thus still further impeding their flow and lengthening their courses. Floods are therefore common. The growing flood plains are confluent and together constitute a vast alluvial plain sloping north. The level of ground water is necessarily near the surface. This is the chief hindrance to agriculture.[1]

Despite these adverse conditions the Willamette Valley is by far the most important agricultural district of Oregon. It raises nearly one-half the hops of the United States. Much more than half of the population of Oregon live in this valley including, of course, the city of Portland.

PHYSIOGRAPHIC HISTORY

Pre-glacial History.—About the time when the first Cascade Mountains began to rise (post-Cretaceous), and possibly even earlier, the Puget Trough began to sink and it remained for much of Tertiary time a sinking geosyncline.[2] During this time it was receiving the sediments which constitute at present the underlying rock, not very resistant. These strata were then folded, closely at least in places. After that they were deeply eroded.

[1] WILLIAMS, IRA A., Drainage of Farm Lands in the Willamette and Tributary Valleys of Oregon, Mineral Resources of Oregon, vol. I, no. 4, 1914; for a geographic discussion of the Willamette Valley, see Warren Du Pre Smith, Commonwealth Review of Oregon, Univ. Ore. *pub.*, vol. 7, p. 145. Figure 3 of that paper is here reproduced as Fig. 160.

[2] WILLIS, B., Drift Phenomena of Puget Sound, Geol. Soc. Amer. *Bull.*, vol. 9, p. 113. 1898.

The Cascade peneplain must have covered this area so far as it lay above sea-level. It is probable that the accordant tops of the basalt hills near the Columbia River represent this peneplain.[1] If so, the same plain which in the Cascade Mountains was lifted 6,000 to 8,000 ft. was here lifted about 1,000 ft. plus the amount of later sinking. Since that uplift the Columbia has eroded a valley many miles in width and the peneplain, where not wholly destroyed, is post-maturely dissected. During the erosion of the basalt to the stage now seen, the old peneplain on the softer rocks in other parts of the trough was completely destroyed, giving way to the more recent lowlands of the Willamette and Sound Valleys. These newer lowlands have since been in large part buried; in the north by glacial drift and outwash; in the south by sediments deposited when the Willamette and lower Columbia Valleys stood for some time below sea-level. Locally this newer lowland may have been a well-developed peneplain; elsewhere high hills remained (page 446).

As suggested above, the Cascade peneplain was lifted above its present height, and the Columbia Valley was cut below its present depth. Later subsidence submerged the river valley up to the border of the Cascade Mountains and caused a deep deposit of gravel and sand.[2] The channel at present presents a remarkable assemblage of islands, sand bars, and shoals.[3]

Glacial History.—There were at least two advances of glacial ice with a long interglacial epoch. During each time of glacial occupation (Admiralty and Vashon epochs) the land around what is now Puget Sound stood approximately at its present level or a trifle lower. In the Puyallup interglacial epoch the level was 1,000 ft. above the present. The deposits and topography now seen, in so far as they are not pre-glacial, were made mainly by erosion in the interglacial epoch and deposition in the last glacial epoch.

The ice which came down as Piedmont glaciers from the mountains on both sides did not advance far into the basin. That which covered the larger central area came from the north following the great trough described on page 442. The front of

[1] DILLER, J. S., U. S. Geol. Survey, *Bull.* 614, p. 30, footnote, says that this peneplain is "related to a similar one in central Washington."

[2] Repeated oscillations of level, not important in so general an account as this, are mentioned by Diller, *loc. cit.*, p. 30.

[3] See Topographic Atlas, Portland sheet, U. S. Geol. Survey.

this lobe stopped on the hilly slopes south of the Puget Sound depression. The abundant waters from the ice, heavily loaded with detritus, escaped mainly to the west by Chehalis Valley which became widely gravel covered. As the ice melted back toward the north, its abundant gravelly outwash built broad plains, partly alluvial, partly lacustrine, which largely buried the till deposits. As the ice front continued to retreat down the northward slope, but still blocking the natural drainage course by way of the Strait of Juan de Fuca, local lakes necessarily formed in front of the ice, and finally a larger lake developed known as Lake Russell.[1]

The work of water on the drift deposits was necessarily large. There was melting ice on three sides with a large surface drainage from the mountains and probably from the north. Lakes and broad alluvial flats lay in front. Moreover, the ice in its last advance moved over, and to some extent forwarded, immense deposits of sand and gravel laid down by water during the retreat of the older ice or in the interglacial epoch. It is not surprising therefore that the work of ice and the work of water are here inextricably mixed. Even the last deposits made by the ice were in large part rehandled by water.

Origin of Puget Sound.—Puget Sound obviously had its origin in a system of erosion valleys converging toward the north. As the drift of the last glacial epoch has been very little eroded, even small lakes and hummocks preserving almost their original form, it is plain that these valleys were cut before the last ice invasion.[2] There was ample opportunity for this in the Puyallup epoch when the land stood 1,000 ft. above its present level. The ice advancing from the north moved up these valleys, altering them a little by erosion but not changing their main outlines. A thin sheet of ice-laid drift covered the eroded surface, evening up its irregularities to some extent. The resulting sur-

---

[1] BRETZ, J HARLEN, Glacial Lakes of Puget Sound, *Jour. Geol.*, vol. XVIII, p. 458, 1910.

[2] WILLIS, B., Drift Phenomena of Puget Sound, Geol. Soc. Amer. *Bull.*, vol. 9, 1898, interprets these valleys as antedating the older glacier. Bretz in a later report, made after an extensive study, Wash. Geol. Survey, *Bull.* 8, p. 199, states that these valleys were made by streams that originated on the outwash plain following the disappearance of the older ice. That the valleys antedated the later ice invasion is agreed to by all. This is the point of interest to present-day physiography.

face was still further leveled up by outwash from the retreating ice front.[1]

Willis conceives that during the melting of the main ice sheet, stagnant ice filled the present "canals" and prevented their filling by outwash. The tabular character and abrupt slopes of the intervening "plateaus" favor the supposition that during outwash and aggradation the troughs had some kind of temporary filling.[2]

The possibility remains that a part of the depth of the "canals" is due to glacial scour. Considering the crooked courses of these valleys and their nearness to the edge of the ice, such scour could scarcely have been a major factor. It is therefore necessary to assume that since the valleys were cut the district about Puget Sound has been depressed about 1,000 ft. In agreement with this is the fact that the rock floor beneath the glacial drift is below sea-level.

When, by the disappearance of the ice, the sea was first admitted to the sound the land was several hundred feet lower than at present. This is known by the presence of salt-water shells up to a level of 280 ft. above the present sea-level and by shore lines as much as 100 ft. above the present. (For recent rise along Pacific Coast see page 471.)

The history of the Puget Trough south of Chehalis Valley involves glaciation only indirectly. The great subaerial deposits which cover so much of the valley floors were no doubt made in part during the time that glaciers were much more extensive and active in the adjacent mountains.

During the melting of the last ice sheet the Willamette Valley lay below sea-level, although probably the water that covered it was kept fresh by an outward current.[3] The same was true of a considerable area east of the Cascade Mountains. The valley of the Columbia both east and west of the Puget Trough was a strait. This was at the time when Puget Sound was last depressed, following the disappearance of the ice sheet. Over most of the

[1] BRETZ, J H., Glaciation of the Puget Sound Region, Wash. Geol. Survey, *Bull.* 8, pp. 18 and 215, 1913.

[2] WILLIS, B., Drift Phenomena of Puget Sound, Geol. Soc. Amer. *Bull.*, vol. IX, p. 155, 1898; also Tacoma folio 54, U. S. Geol. Survey.

[3] BRETZ, J H., The Late Pleistocene Submergence in the Columbia Valley of Oregon and Washington, *Jour. Geol.*, vol. XXVII, 1919; DILLER, J. S., Reconnaissance in Northwestern Oregon, U. S. Geol. Survey, *17th Ann. Rept.*, pt. I. p. 487, 1896

Willamette Basin the soil is derived from sediments laid down in this sound.[1] Boulders from the mountains, scattered over the plain, are accounted for by icebergs floating in this sound. Alluvium of the river and its tributaries and subaerial wash from the mountains cover, as yet, but a minor part of the valley floor.

RESOURCES

On the borders of Puget Sound is the chief coal field of the Pacific Coast. Washington produces about 4,000,000 tons yearly, most of it from this section. Some of it is excellent coking coal. Ordinary bituminous and subbituminous varieties are also supplied. This coal comes from the folded and much eroded Eocene strata which underlie the glacial drift.

Next to the products of the farm, timber and timber products constitute the largest item in the annual production of wealth in Washington where they amounted to $235,000,000 in 1919.[2] Five-sevenths of all timber in Oregon is said to be the Douglas spruce, commonly called "Oregon pine."[3] With respect to forest products the Puget Trough is much like the Cascade Mountains but more accessible. The forests are somewhat interrupted by prairies on the outwash plains of gravel near Puget Sound and more so on the plains of the Willamette Valley.

Salmon, the most important fish of commerce except herring and oysters (commercially included in fisheries), are commercially more important in this part of the United States than at any other place in the world, and preeminently so in the lower or drowned portion of the Columbia River.

Agriculture has displaced the forests in most of the flat-floored valleys around Puget Sound. Fruit growing is increasing. Dairying is exceedingly important. Two towns in Duwamish Valley between Tacoma and Seattle produce daily 25 carloads of condensed milk, much of which goes to Alaska for which Seattle is generally the point of departure. Chehalis is a similar dairying center.

[1] WILLIAMS, IRA A., Drainage of Farm Lands in the Willamette Valley, "Mineral Resources of Oregon," vol. I, no. 4, 1914.

[2] Fourteenth Census of the United States; $22,000,000 for Oregon in 1912, according to Diller, U. S. Geol. Survey, Guidebook, *Bull.* 614, p. 28.

[3] DILLER, J. S., *loc. cit.*, p. 28.

OLYMPIC SECTION

General.—The peninsula bounded by Puget Sound, the Strait of Juan de Fuca, and the Pacific Ocean is occupied mainly by the Olympic Mountains. A low strip on the east side from 2 to 10 miles wide belongs in the Puget Trough both as to elevation and as to topography and history. There is also a very narrow low strip on the north, one on the west 10 to 20 miles wide, and one on the south about 30 miles wide. For convenience these latter are treated as parts of the Olympic section. The section is almost severed from its neighbor on the south by the low valley of the Chehalis River whose lower course is drowned for 30 miles.

Olympic Mountains.—Surrounded by these low borders, the Olympic Mountains occupy an area of about 4,000 square miles. In their characteristic features they are not unlike the Cascades. Many ridges rise to altitudes of 4,500 to 5,000 ft., giving a nearly level or gently undulating horizon. Some of the tops are broad and nearly level, apparently remnants of a former plain. Above this horizon rise exceedingly sharp ridges and crags, many of them between 7,000 and 8,000 ft. high (Mt. Olympus 8,200 ft.). Most of these higher mountains are within a circle of 40 miles diameter near the center. Away from the center of the group the plateau level declines and the dissection becomes more complete. After declining to levels of 2,000 ft., more or less, the mountains fall off rather abruptly to the lowlands. Most of the rocks are sedimentaries, deformed and to some extent metamorphosed in the act of mountain making.[1]

Below 4,000 ft. the mountains are everywhere clothed with a dense forest made more impenetrable by a luxuriant undergrowth. Above 4,000 ft. the forest opens locally and is less luxuriant. Timber line is at 5,000 to 5,500 ft. The level which limits the dense forests is therefore not very different from the prevailing crest level.

The mountains which rise above the prevailing crest level have much park land and grass, but the higher peaks are in part snow covered. They support a number of small glaciers.[2]

[1] WILLIS, B., and SMITH, G. O., U. S. Geol. Survey, folio 54, p. 1, state that some of the higher mountains are volcanoes.

[2] U. S. Geol. Survey, *Prof. Pap.* 7, see descriptions of the several townships; GILMAN, S. C., The Olympic Country, *Nat. Geog. Mag.*, vol. VII, p. 134, 1896.

These mountains have been severely glaciated, as seen in all the details of their forms. From the cirques of this upper zone U-shaped valleys descend to the mountain foot. The gradients of the larger ones of these streams except near their heads are generally moderate, not too steep for railroad building.[1]

Surrounding Lowlands.—The lowland 10 to 20 miles wide on the west side forms a continuous belt from Chehalis River on the south to the low mountain spur along the northern coast. The line which separates it from the mountains is very irregular though generally clear. Most of it is less than 400 ft. above the sea toward which it slopes, but within the strip are many higher hilly districts. About one-fourth of the area is embraced in broad valley bottoms along the larger streams.[2] The smaller streams have cut only narrow valleys or canyons. Some large interstream areas are almost uncut by streams except near the shore or near the valleys of the larger streams.[3] Between the larger valleys this terrace is covered with Pleistocene deposits. It is believed to be a coastal plain uplifted, eroded, and in large part stripped of its sediments since the glacial epoch.[4] Most of this terrace is at least as densely forested as the mountains.

The same terrace extends around the mountains on the north. Here it is very narrow and interrupted by large rock hills and mountain spurs. The most important of these spurs extends in a direction parallel to the coast and close to it, all the way to Cape Flattery, the extreme northwest corner of the peninsula, the most westerly point of the United States proper.

The lowland south of the mountains is a continuation of that on the west. It has been raised high enough to be sharply dissected. It differs little except in altitude from the Oregon Coast Range to the south.[5]

Shore Lines.—The western half of the north shore and all of the west shore except at the south end are being vigorously worn back by waves.[6] Steep sea cliffs, 50 to 300 ft. high, often

---

[1] U. S. Geol. Survey, *Prof. Pap.* 7, p. 21, map in pocket; note the same feature in the Cascades.

[2] Gilman, S. C., *loc. cit.*, p. 137.

[3] Lupton, C. T., Oil and Gas in the Western Part of the Olympic Peninsula, Washington, U. S. Geol. Survey, *Bull.* 581, p. 36, 1915.

[4] Lupton, C. T., *loc. cit.*, p. 35.

[5] See Hoquiam topographic sheet, north of Gray's Harbor.

[6] Arnold, Ralph, Geological Reconnaissance of the Coast of the Olympic Peninsula, Washington, Geol. Soc. Amer. *Bull.*, vol. 17, pp. 451–468, 1906.

vertical or overhanging, face the sea for most of this distance. At their foot is a rocky platform or cut terrace, in some places two miles wide, so near the level of the water that much of it is laid bare at low tide. This indicates that a strip of land of that width has already been consumed by the waves since the land has stood approximately at its present level. It may not have stood entirely still for it is a habit of waves to reduce such platforms below the level of low tide. It may well be that continued

Fig. 161.—Shore of the Strait of Juan de Fuca at Pillar Point, Olympic peninsula, Washington. The niche in which the man stands was necessarily cut by the waves when the land stood lower than at present. At that time the narrow rock platform was not above low tide. The attack of the waves is now received mainly by the front of this platform rather than by the rock above it. (*Photo by Henry Landes, furnished by Ralph Arnold.*)

rising has prevented this. Old shore lines above the present level indicate that there has been such rising from time to time.[1] Standing on this cut terrace are the remains of former hills or islands[2] in various stages of destruction, some of them submerged at high tide, thus making the coast dangerous to vessels.

Physiographic History.—It may be inferred from the structure and topography that the Olympic Mountains are carved from an upraised peneplain. The central group of higher mountains,

[1] *Cf.* the coast of California, pp. 453, 463, 471, 483 and 503.

[2] GILMAN, *loc. cit.*, p. 136, gives a good description of Destruction Island, formerly inhabited by the Hoh Indians, now occupied by a lighthouse.

aside from possible volcanoes, may represent either monadnocks on the peneplain or a district of greater uplift and severer erosion. The fact that they stand in a nearly circular group instead of in a range would favor the former assumption. For aught that is known the dissected upland may be an outlying portion of the Cascade peneplain. In that case the peneplain, the uplifts which followed, the carving of valleys, and the glaciation may be correlated with the same features and events in the Cascades (page 438). The surrounding lowland is due primarily to less uplift and secondarily to degradation by normal erosion. To a smaller extent, and especially near the outer edge, it must have been further planed by marine erosion during the time that it was submerged. This coastal plain is apparently young in point of time[1] but since its last uplift vigorous streams fed by the heaviest rainfall in the United States have carried the erosion cycle to advanced youth. The last crustal movement recorded is an uplift which may be still continuing.

Resources.—The chief natural resources of this peninsula consist of its forests which share with those of the western slope of the Cascades the reputation of being the densest and most valuable in the United States except the redwood forests of California. Lumbering is therefore the chief industry, but the available openings in the forest on the low belts have been taken up by farmers. The high grasslands above 4,000 ft. would afford excellent grazing for the summer months but are not habitable in winter. Their use for grazing must await the development of agriculture on the lowlands. This must be slow because the clearing of the land of its trees, underbrush, and accumulated water-soaked and half-decayed logs involves too much labor.[2]

OREGON COAST RANGE

Definition and Limits.—The section between the Olympic Mountains on the north and the Klamath Mountains on the south is called the "Oregon Coast Range" because its larger and more typical portion lies in Oregon. It extends north into Washington, however, with little change of character to the Chehalis River. At the south end it is coextensive with the sedimentary rocks of Tertiary age. The Oregon Coast Range

---

[1] LUPTON, *loc. cit.*, p. 35, speaks of it as Pleistocene.
[2] U. S. Geol. Survey, *Prof. Pap.* 7, p. 14.

is distinguished in this respect from the Klamath Mountains which are made of older and stronger rocks and are in general higher. The latter have also had a longer history which has given different detail to the topography, but these contrasts are not marked along the boundary between the two sections.

Where the Oregon Coast Range descends on the east to the Puget Trough its foot is generally well marked. South of lat. 44° it borders on the Cascade Range. Here, between Eugene and Roseburg, an air-line distance of about 50 miles, is a north-south

Fig. 162.—Even crest of the Oregon Coast Range as seen from Roseburg. The altitude of the highest ridge is about 2,500 ft. It and the next lower ridge are of gently folded and peneplaned early Tertiary sandstone. The nearer hills are of much eroded basalt in the valley of Umpqua River, whose level is below 500 ft. (*U. S. Geol. Survey.*)

belt 10 to 20 miles wide lying west of the Cascades and in line with the Willamette Valley, to which the proper name "Coast Range" is not applied by local custom. It is, however, a rough country with hills rising 500 to 1,000 ft. above the valleys, composed of the same rocks and with essentially the same physiographic history as the Coast Ranges. West of it rises Tyee Mountain with a bold slope to a height of 2,600 ft., or 1,000 ft. higher than the hills to the east. The prominence of this mountain accounts for local custom in choosing it as the mountain front but the country around Roseburg compares favorably in altitude and relief with a large portion of the Oregon Coast Ranges and is

therefore included in the same physiographic section.[1]   On the
west the section includes a narrow and much interrupted strip
of coastal plain.

Rocks and Structure.—All the rocks of this section are of
Tertiary age and generally weak though not uniformly so.   The
details of topography are therefore determined in part by relative
resistance.   Thus Tyee Mountain west of Roseburg owes its
height to the strength of the sandstone which constitutes it.
There are also some volcanic rocks contemporaneous with or
intruded into these sediments.   These form the highest peaks,
some of which rise conspicuously above the general upland, like
Mary's Peak (4,097 ft.), Saddle Mountain, Larch Mountain, and
a few others.[2]

Structurally the range is a low anticlinorium.   Cross-sections
at most places would show from two to five minor folds.   Dips
do not generally exceed 10 deg. but in exceptional cases rise to
25 and even 35 deg.[3]

Peneplain and Monadnocks.—The general aspect of this range
is that of a dissected plateau or upraised peneplain.   The hilltops,
ridge crests, and in some cases tabular features which determine
the nearly level horizon on the sedimentary rocks, rarely rise
above 1,700 ft. in northern Oregon.[4]   The general level rises
toward the south and is 3,000 to 3,500 ft. at the limit of the
section.   The southward rise of the surface in the Klamath
section is more rapid.   Well-preserved patches of peneplain are
more abundant in the northern than in the southern part.[5]   East

---

[1] The local custom here mentioned is followed by J. S. Diller in the
Roseburg folio 49, U. S. Geol. Survey, 1898.

In this as in many other cases the student who goes to original sources
will find the proper name of a mountain range used with different limits,
involving many inconsistencies unless the boundaries assumed in each
case are ascertained.   In the division of a continent into natural provinces
and sections it is frequently necessary to call an entire section by the name
of some feature (range or otherwise) within it.   Unless this fact is born in
mind there may be apparent inconsistencies between statements made in a
treatise of this kind and those of the papers from which data are taken.

[2] WASHBURNE, C. W., U. S. Geol. Survey, *Bull.* 590, p. 6, 1914; SMITH,
WARREN DU PRE, Physical and Economic Geography of Oregon, *Commonwealth Rev.*, Univ. Oregon, vol. 8, p. 257, 1926.

[3] SMITH, *loc. cit.*, Figs. 1 to 4, pp. 272–273; WASHBURNE, C. W., *loc. cit.*, p. 7.

[4] DILLER, J. S., A Geological Reconnaissance in Northwestern Oregon,
U. S. Geol. Survey, 17*th Ann. Rept* pt. I. p. 488, 1896.

[5] *Idem*, pp. 487, 488.

and west from the higher central zone the level of the crests declines. Twenty miles west of Portland it is only 525 ft. above the sea but well developed, cutting neatly across the most steeply tilted strata of the range. The peaks which rise above this general level are all monadnocks and all, so far as known, are of igneous rocks.

Valleys.—The main streams of the region are transverse. Of these the Chehalis, Columbia, and Umpqua near the south end cross the entire section from east to west. The heads of three other west-flowing streams, Nehalem, Yaquina and Siuslaw, are so near the eastern foot of the range that they are separated from the Willamette Basin by divides less than 400 ft. above the valley floor. These streams run in entrenched meanders, those of the Umpqua being particularly striking. The tributaries are, at least locally, adjusted to the structure, hence in longitudinal valleys.[1]

Almost everywhere the cross-sections of the larger valleys show a narrow valley within a broad one which itself indents a peneplain.[2] The broad floors and long gentle slopes of the old, broad, upper valleys are themselves dissected by young valleys which also invade the remnants of upland between the broad valleys so that not much level land remains either at the summits or at the level of the older valley floors. Where the rocks are soft, as in the district east of Tyee Mountain, erosion in the later cycles has been so great that the upland and the older valleys have both been destroyed. The young, narrow, lower valleys are mere gorges or canyons where the rock is strong but widen and contain considerable flats where the rock is weak.

Coastal Plain.—Throughout much of their length the mountains are bordered by a narrow coastal plain generally not more than one to two miles wide but increasing to 20 miles north of the Columbia River. This is evidence of recent rising of the land, but a still more recent subsidence has drowned the streams not only across this coastal plain but far inland. Thus the Chehalis is drowned for 30 miles, the Columbia 140 miles, the Umpqua 25 miles, the Coquille 30 miles.[3]

The features of a low coast composed of weak rocks and exposed to prevailing winds from the ocean are here well exemplified.

[1] DILLER, J. S., Roseburg folio 49, p. 4, U. S. Geol. Survey.

[2] DILLER, J. S., Mineral Resources of Southwestern Oregon, U. S. Geol. Survey, *Bull.* 546, p. 13, 1914; also U. S. Geol. Survey, *Bull.* 614, p. 40, 1915.

[3] All these distances are measured along the rivers, not in an air line.

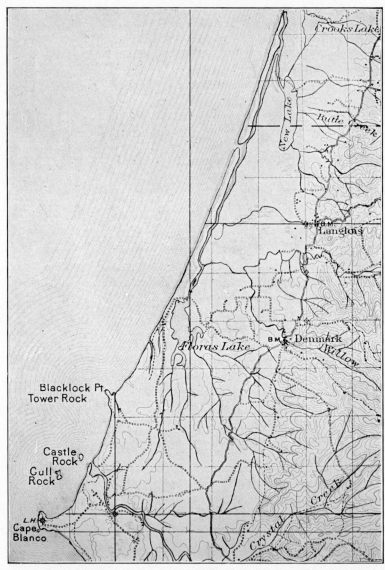

FIG. 163.—Narrow coastal plain of Oregon. The small squares indicate
miles. This locality is on the margin of the Klamath section. The plain
stops at Port Orford on the south (lat. 42°45′) but extends northward intermittently to the Olympic peninsula of Washington. In the part here shown
the last crustal movement has been a slight subsidence. The lakes are drowned
valleys shut off from the sea by beach ridges of later dates. Contour interval
20 ft. (U. S. Geol. Survey, Port Orford sheet.)

There are long stretches of sandy beach, several of them noted as resorts, and at intervals are belts of dunes. Bays or estuaries made by the partial drowning of streams are partly cut off from the sea by sand bars, or wholly cut off and thus converted into fresh-water lakes.[1] Here and there the low coast is interrupted by a bold headland composed of igneous rock.

Marine Terraces.—The coastal plain ranges in altitude from 200 or even 250 ft. down to sea-level. For a short distance south of lat. 44° where the rocks are less weak it is generally bounded on the seaward side by a cliff several hundred feet high. At places this descent of several hundred feet is marked by two or more terraces, showing that the emergence was gradual and interrupted. At some points these terraces are several hundred yards wide.

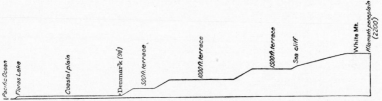

Fig. 164.—Profile of wave-cut terraces 12 miles north of Port Orford, Oregon. This locality is near the southern limit of the Oregon Coast Range. The total length of the section is seven miles. (*Diller, U. S. Geol. Survey.*)

Terraces of similar width mark the ascent from the coastal plain to the mountains up to an altitude of 1,500 ft.[2] The upper members have been much eroded during the making of the lower ones. These facts indicate that the coastal plain is not a peculiar feature but only one of a series of terraces although much the widest and most important. Probably all these terraces were covered with gravel or other sediments of the marginal sea. The gravel is preserved on the coastal plain but it has been in large part eroded from the older and higher terraces.

Physiographic History.—The low mountain range of this section is of relatively recent birth. To say the least it is entirely post-Eocene.[3] Presumably it has never been very high. The

[1] SMITH, WARREN DU PRE, *loc. cit.*, p. 276, cites these facts as evidence that the coast of Oregon is again rising. The reason for this interpretation is not clear.

[2] Coos Bay folio 73, p. 1, U. S. Geol. Survey; see also Port Orford folio 89.

[3] DILLER, J. S., The Relief of Our Pacific Coast, *Science*, vol. XLI, pp. 48–57, 1915.

gentle form of its folds does not require the assumption that a great thickness of rock has been eroded to produce the peneplain visible at its summit.   The geologic age of this peneplain is not older than Pliocene, for it truncates Miocene strata and was therefore not finished until after their formation and deformation.[1]   The peneplain, being developed on non-resistant rocks of very moderate elevation, was not necessarily long in the making and was brought to a fair degree of completion.   Only the igneous intrusives were left as monadnocks.

By the time the peneplain was completed, if not before the first uplift, the streams were flowing over it from east to west in their present courses.   The Columbia and the Umpqua are antecedent.   The uplift of the peneplain occasioned the cutting of the old, wide, now high-lying and deeply trenched valleys.   It was in these old, broad valleys that the streams developed their intricate meanders.   Renewed uplifts made possible the entrenchment of these meanders and the almost complete dissection of the peneplain.   With respect to entrenched meanders there are few more impressive streams than the Umpqua.

In the last great uplift the land was lifted much above its present height and included a strip on the west which is now beneath the sea.[2]   At this time it is believed that the Columbia, Coquille, Coos, and some other streams cut the trenches across the continental shelf which now extend from the mouths of these streams out to the deep ocean basin.   Then came the gradual but continued subsidence which drowned the land to the depth of the

---

[1] In approaching this section from the north there is a natural tendency toward correlating this peneplain with that of the Cascades, called Pliocene by its sponsors.   No decided break is found in the continuity of the Cascade peneplain unless it be in crossing the Puget Trough.   Its continuity across this valley on the summits of the basalt hills is provisionally accepted by Diller, U. S. Geol. Survey, *Bull.* 614, p. 30.   But the crests of the Oregon Coast Range are even more directly continuous with those of the Klamath at the south which Diller regards as Miocene, *Bull.* 196.   This assignment is not accepted by Lawson (Univ. Calif. *Bull.*, Dept. Geol. Sci., vol. 1, p. 271, 1894) and some others who would make the Klamath peneplain Pliocene. In such a study as this, geologic age is significant merely as an aid in correlating topographic features, usually peneplains.   Exact correlation is not yet possible in this case.

[2] Details of these several uplifts have been elaborated for the Klamath Mountains by J. S. Diller, U. S. Geol. Survey, *Bull.* 196, whose statements imply that the history of adjacent portions of the Oregon and California Coast Ranges was the same.

highest shore line, now seen in fragmentary form 1,500 ft. above the sea in southern Oregon and California. The series of fossil shore lines which now score or terrace the mountain slope, becoming increasingly clear and well preserved as the sea is approached, were made during the recovery of the land from the last great subsidence. By far the most important of these north of Cape Blanco is the Coastal Plain. It indicates the longest stillstand of the land during its intermittent rise and probably indicates also that the edge of the sea was at that time against a low slope so that the making of a broad subaqueous shelf was relatively rapid.

Northward from southern Oregon these old shore terraces gradually disappear. The order and approximate geologic dates of crustal movements of the Puget Sound region have been fairly well worked out (page 450). The same is true of the California Coast (page 488) but the correlation of some of these recent movements is uncertain.

This last rise, mentioned above, again carried the continent slightly above its present level from Cape Mendocino to the Chehalis River. Subsequent sinking has again drowned the main valleys. It is the effect of this last submergence which is now seen in the tidal portions of the rivers. For some distance south of the 40th parallel this last submergence is not observed. North of that latitude the extent of submergence increases with distance at least as far north as the Columbia River. The correlation of crustal movements in this latitude with those around Puget Sound is somewhat uncertain. There is reason to believe that the coast of the Olympic peninsula is again rising (page 457).

KLAMATH MOUNTAINS

Distinguishing Characteristics and Boundaries

The Klamath Mountains lie west of the Cascade Range between the Coast Range of Oregon and those of California. The differences between this section and its neighbors depend on its greater geologic age and more complex history. Most of its rocks are Paleozoic and more or less metamorphosed, hence resistant. With these are included many masses of ancient volcanic rock. There are also some Mesozoic rocks, most of which are fairly strong.

As compared with the Oregon Coast Range the Klamath Mountains are higher and include important residual subranges of an earlier physiographic cycle. There is, however, no sharp contrast along the boundary between the two. The contrast with the Cascade Mountains is partly in the degree of dissection (the Cascades being less dissected) and partly in the forms of the valleys. These are more complex in the Klamath. The boundary between these sections is, throughout most of its length, defined in terms of their rocks and is only locally marked by a valley.

The Klamath section is distinguished from the California Coast Ranges by the character of the drainage systems. The main streams of the former are transverse and their very devious courses give little suggestion of order and pay small heed to geologic structure. The main streams of the California Coast Ranges are longitudinal and the drainage pattern as a whole is crudely trellised. However, a boundary line based on drainage types would not quite agree with one based on the character of rocks and structure. On the southwest side the plan of longitudinal drainage begins with the South fork of the Trinity River. Judged by drainage patterns this stream should be the boundary but on its southwest side and parallel to it is the South Fork Range with the characteristic rocks, structure, and history of the Klamath Mountains. As these latter elements must be referred to oftener in descriptions and appealed to oftener in explanations than drainage, they are regarded as more fundamental and the South Fork Range is included in the Klamath section.[1] The altitude of the Klamath Mountains on their southern border is distinctly greater than that of the adjacent Coast Ranges of California.

Another exception to the general statement concerning drainage is found on the west side of the upper Sacramento Valley. At this place (north of the 40th parallel) is a relatively low plateau, sloping and draining eastward from the foot of the Yallo Bally subrange, which is the long southern extension of the Klamath. Judged both by rocks and by physiographic history, to be con-

---

[1] This is the practice of Diller, see *Science*, vol. XLI, p. 52, 1915, and other papers here cited. Lawson treats the South Fork Mountains as one of the Coast Ranges.—Report of California Earthquake Commission, vol. 1, 1908.

sidered later, this sloping plateau is a part of the Coast Range section.[1]

In its southern half the Klamath section is separated from the Pacific Ocean by the Coast Ranges. It reaches the coast between the parallels of 41° and 43°. Several short stretches of narrow coastal plain are thus included.

TOPOGRAPHY

Summit Peneplain.—Like so many other mountains which appear extremely rugged from the valleys, the Klamath Mountains when viewed from one of their summits appear to be a dissected plateau. In general the altitude of the nearly level horizon rises from north to south and from the coast inland, but the surface is warped. Generally the altitude near the coast is 2,000 to 2,500 ft. Near the Oregon-California boundary it is 1,700 ft. high near the coast but rises to 4,000 ft. at 25 miles inland. Another 25 miles northeastward brings the level to 4,400 ft. On South Fork Mountain, east of Cape Mendocino, the level crest is at 6,000 ft., and in the Yallo Bally Mountains there are traces of it at 7,000 ft. In the middle of the California portion (Salmon Mountains) the horizon is at least 6,000 ft above the sea.[2]

Most of these level horizons are due to the nearly equal height of narrow ridges but broad gently rolling areas, while not common, are not wholly wanting in southwestern Oregon. Occasional views there suggest the Appalachian Piedmont.[3] This upland

[1] DILLER, J. S., Tertiary Revolution in the Topography of the Pacific Coast, U. S. Geol. Survey, *14th Ann. Rept.*, pt. II, p. 404, pl. XL, 1892. Ten years later (Topographic Development of the Klamath Mountains, U. S. Geol. Survey, *Bull.* 196, p. 9, pl. I, 1902) Diller's boundaries of the Klamath Mountains were made more detailed. The boundaries here adopted are essentially those of Diller's later work.

[2] Most of these altitudes are taken from Diller, U. S. Geol. Survey, *Bull.* 196. O. H. Hershey Univ. Calif. *Bull.*, Dept. Geol. Sci., vol. III, pp. 423–475, 1904, gives altitudes in the central portion about 1,000 ft. higher. It is possible that the figures of both men are correct, measurements having been taken on the same old surface at different places. Due to later deformation the elevation might differ by 1,000 ft. in 10 to 20 miles. It is also true that men may differ as to what is the "general level" of an old peneplain surmounted by monadnocks and deeply dissected.

[3] See DILLER, J. S., Mineral Resources of Southwestern Oregon, U. S. Geol. Survey, *Bull.* 546, p. 14, pl. III B, 1914.

surface, preserved or hypothetically restored, is known as the Klamath peneplain[1] (see physiographic history, page 470).

Monadnock Ridges.—The parts of the Klamath mountains which have received individual names are residual ridges or groups located on the divides between the principal streams. A description of the main streams is necessary to the understanding of these subranges. The Rogue River crosses the section from east to west in latitude about 42°30'. North of it near the 43d parallel is the Coquille River. The so-called Rogue River Range is merely the east-west divide between these. Low monadnocks here surmount the upland. The Klamath River flows west a little south of the 42d parallel (Oregon-California boundary) before making a great southerly detour. The generally east-west divide between the Klamath and Rogue Basins is marked by the Siskiyou Mountains, a rugged monadnock ridge rising in Siskiyou Peak to 7,662 ft., or 3,500 ft. above the peneplain which abuts against its northern base. The Klamath has three large tributaries from the southeast, each one of which gives its name to a group or line of monadnocks crowning the divide at its head. These are the Scott Mountains (Mt. Eddy, 9,151 ft.), Salmon Mountains (Thompson Peak, 9,345 ft.), and Trinity Mountains. The Bullychoop group (7,073 ft.) marks the divide between the Trinity and Sacramento Rivers, as the Yallo Bally (8,604 ft.) crowns the long southern extension between the Sacramento and the streams of the California Coast Ranges.

In most of these cases it is clear that the peneplain abuts against the mountains which rise 1,000 to 5,000 ft. above it. In several of these localities and some others, the local relief is complicated by deformation, perhaps faulting of the peneplain, so that it remains undetermined whether a higher mass is a

[1] In describing former, now uplifted and dissected, peneplains there is constant danger that the reconstruction of the peneplain before the mind's eye may be too perfect. When the reader visits the field later he may be disappointed and skeptical. At present some geologists are not quite convinced of the reality of the Klamath peneplain. Perhaps the word "peneplain" should never have been used. The need of another word to designate an old or subdued surface of moderate relief is pointed out in the footnote on p. 187.

In the meantime it should be remembered that with mountains of sufficient age the peneplain is the normal and expectable thing. In the absence of known diastrophic events the burden of proof should be assumed by any hypothesis requiring that mountains should survive abnormally long.

monadnock or the result of deformation of the peneplain. Smaller monadnocks, from 100 to 600 ft. in height, are not uncommon on the upland elsewhere. In places the tops of these may represent an older peneplain (see physiographic history, page 470).

Valleys.—The valley forms described on page 461 for the Oregon Coast Range are typical of the Klamath Mountains. The streams run in narrow valleys which are mere canyons 1,000 to 2,000 ft. deep where the rocks are strongest but have narrow bottom lands where the rocks are weak.[1] From the brinks of these canyons the general level rises gradually to the full height of the upland, which is generally 1,000 ft. higher near the coast and several thousand feet higher in the interior. These gradual slopes are seen only by sighting over the hilltops and disregarding lateral valleys, for the whole surface is deeply carved by steep tributary valleys or canyons. The general relations of narrow, lower, young valleys and broad, upper, old valleys can be seen only from favorable points. From points of limited view, especially from the valley bottoms, the forms, while generally impressive, are not orderly. Neither the old nor the young valleys are simple in slope. Either may be interrupted by terraces, showing signs of discontinuous uplift and several partial erosion cycles (see physiographic history, page 470).

Marine Terraces.—In common with the Coast Ranges to the north and south the Klamath section has a clearly terraced coastal slope[2] (*cf.* Fig. 164). Eroded remains of sea cliffs and wave-cut terraces are found as high as 1,500 ft. above the sea. The narrow coastal plain found at places farther north is here represented by several small stretches. The Rogue River is drowned to about four miles inland.

Physiographic History

Mountains of the Older Generation.—The older history of the Klamath Mountains is essentially the same as that of the Sierra Nevada (page 413). This history concerns us merely because the present structural features are the results of it. There is here a great mass of ancient, closely folded and faulted rocks, generally metamorphosed and intruded by igneous rocks. The deforma-

---

[1] O. H. Hershey gives a good description of the Orleans Basin, a local broadening of the 3,500-ft. gorge of the Klamath River. Univ. Calif. *Bull.*, Dept. Geol. Sci., vol. III, p. 426, 1904.

[2] DILLER, J. S., Port Orford folio 89, U. S. Geol. Survey, and other papers.

tion is apparently due to repeated pushing from the east.   As if this push were mainly near the center, the folds are curved or crescent-like, striking northeast at the north and southeast at the south.   Continued in one direction they would join the Sierra Nevada, in the other the Blue Mountains of Oregon (page 229), which had a similar ancient history.   From both of these mountain ranges the Klamath Mountains are now separated by later deep depressions filled with lava.   It appears that long before the making of the Klamath peneplain the original Klamath Mountains occupied a peninsula projecting westward.   Continued pushing toward the west has made thrust faults along which the ancient metamorphic rocks of the Klamath section have been pushed out over the younger and softer rocks of the Coast Ranges both in Oregon and California.

Unlike the Oregon Coast Range, the older mountains of this section were not only composed of strong rocks but were high, as indicated by the structure.   The work of reducing them to base level must have occupied a long cycle.   Geologic history indicates that this was in progress long before the Oregon Coast Range rose above the sea.

Development of the Peneplain.—During the development of the Klamath peneplain (the oldest and highest represented) the main streams ran in transverse courses similar to those which they still follow.   This is indicated not only by their old wide valleys (partially preserved) but by the distribution of monadnock ridges.   These mark the main divides.   Elsewhere even the stronger rocks were cut down close to sea-level.

An interruption of the Klamath cycle may have been occasioned by an uplift near the coast which added new land.   But the land thus added was mainly of softer rock in the California Coast Ranges, and appears also to have been reduced to a peneplain by the time the Klamath peneplain was completed.   This peneplain, therefore, known as the Bellspring, generally occupies different territory from that of the Klamath.   Except in detailed and critical studies the two may be regarded as one, and represented by the general upland level (Fig. 164).

Valley Erosion.—Following the Klamath-Bellspring cycle came the several uplifts which occasioned the cutting of the older broad valleys.   At places these older valleys show by their terraced form that they were not cut out in a single cycle following a single uplift but in at least two partial cycles.   But this can be detected only here and there; hence, in a general way, the long time of peneplaning may be said to have been followed by a shorter time of broad-valley making. Locally the floors of these broad valleys are themselves widespread peneplains but this is mainly in the Coast Range section. Still later a great uplift caused the narrow inner valleys to be cut, added the narrow continental shelf to the land area, and made it possible for streams to cut valleys across it.

Glaciation.—At some time following the cutting of the narrow valleys, and probably late in the glacial period, the higher mountains supported alpine glaciers[1] in valleys which were relatively shady. Lakelets, meadows, and oversteepened rock walls are locally abundant but glacial erosion nowhere dominates the topography as it does in the High Sierra.

Events Affecting the Shore.[2]—The old shore lines cut during these several stands have long since been destroyed. The presence of surviving terraces calls for a more recent submergence and emergence. Such submergence, attested also by deposits in the valleys, occurred after the time of greatest uplift when the present continental shelf was land and scored by valleys. The depression was at least 1,500 ft. below the present level, for an old shore line is still preserved at places 1,500 ft. above the sea. With gradual emergence new shore lines were cut. One very prominent one, with a cut terrace locally a mile wide, is 1,000 ft. high. Another is 500 ft. above the sea. The fragments of the existing coastal plain represent another. There are many others less clear.

Like the great uplift which preceded it this last one raised the land above its present level, at least north of Cape Mendocino. North of that the stream valleys are again partly drowned, admitting tidewater up at least four miles from the sea throughout the Klamath Coast[3] and much farther in the Oregon Coast Range (page 461).

[1] HERSHEY, OSCAR H., Ancient Alpine Glaciers of the Sierra Costa Mountains in California, *Jour. Geol.*, vol. VIII, pp. 42–57, 1900.

[2] Note similar history of the shore line farther south (p. 483).

[3] This brief historical summary is practically that of Diller as given in U. S. Geol. Survey, *Bull.* 196. The order of events is generally accepted by geologists who have studied the Pacific Coast. Some of these do not however place the events so far back in point of time as Diller does. The latter assigns both the peneplains and the broad valleys (local peneplains) to Miocene time and begins the Pliocene with the great uplift which started the cutting of the narrow valleys. From studies in the Coast Ranges and

VALLEY OF CALIFORNIA

GENERAL RELATIONS

The Sierra-Cascade province on the east and the California Coast Ranges on the west enclose one of the most notable valleys of the world. It is more than 400 miles long, with an average width of about 50 miles and an area of 20,000 square miles. Throughout more than nine-tenths of its boundary, the mountains or their foothills rise abruptly, their boundaries being but little complicated by spurs and outlying hills.

The altitude of this widespread valley floor is for the most part less than 400 ft. and its general slope is toward San Francisco Bay from the north, south, and east. Only at the edges does it locally rise to higher altitudes. The extreme is reached at the south end where the steep alluvial slopes of the valley rest against the mountains at a height of 1,700 ft. Most of the eastern boundary is not more than 500 ft. above the sea and most of the western boundary ranges in height from 50 to 300 ft. Considerable areas near San Francisco Bay are below sea-level, being protected from overflow by dikes and natural levees.

TOPOGRAPHY

The larger part of the valley would be described by the casual observer as a dead flat. Its general slope is too slight to be observed. As seen on a contour map the general smoothness is emphasized rather than obscured by the faint beginnings of consequent drainage. The parallelism of these rudimentary channels is often so striking as to suggest the trickling of water down an inclined board or pane of glass.[1]

As the mountains are approached on any side, the alluvial slopes become progressively steeper. Gradients of 100 to 150 ft. per mile are occasionally reached. A much smaller part of the margin next to the mountains consists of slightly higher and older plains moderately to maturely dissected, the local relief being at some places as great as 150 or even 200 ft. Such a strip stretches for 100 miles south from Sacramento. Streams from the moun-

---

the Sierra Nevada (p. 413) Lawson would make the Pliocene the great base-leveling period and would place the great uplift which preceded canyon cutting at the beginning of the Quaternary.

[1] Well shown in many of the large scale (2 in. = 1 mile) topographic sheets of the U. S. Geol. Survey.

tains cross this strip in broad, terraced, flat-bottomed valleys. Such topography is in part due to erosion of the alluviated surface but in part to the erosion of older formations (Tertiary) not covered by the alluvial sheet except in the broad valleys.

An element of great significance in the topography is found in the natural levees of the larger streams. In the southern half of the Sacramento Valley these have so aggraded their beds that in some places the level declines 10 ft. in the first mile from the stream. Between the levee slopes of neighboring streams are "basins" some of which are inundated or swampy. Thus the American Basin and others mentioned below are bounded by the main streams instead of traversed by them. Smaller depressions of similar or other origin contain temporary lakes in the wet season.

An exceptional feature near the middle of the Sacramento Valley is the Marysville Buttes. These "buttes" are the remains of a nearly circular volcano about 10 miles in diameter. Their summits still rise 2,000 ft. above the flat valley floor. The lower formations of the elsewhere horizontal sediments of the valley are upturned against the volcanic core as though it had been pushed up through as a single stiff mass.[1]

DRAINAGE BASINS

The Great Valley comprises three hydrographic basins of almost equal extent. These are the drainage basins of the Sacramento and San Joaquin Rivers and the basin of internal drainage south of the San Joaquin. This is the Tulare Basin, so-called from the largest of its playa lakes.

Sacramento Basin.—Near Redding, 200 miles north of San Francisco Bay, the Sacramento River passes from the Klamath Mountains into the Great Valley at an altitude of 500 ft. Here the stream meanders in a broad valley (one to four miles wide) 100 ft. below the general level. Fifteen miles south of Redding the river encounters a broad belt (10 to 12 miles) of dissected upland due to a low anticline which crosses the valley, thus isolating the small lowland at the north from the vast lowland south of Red Bluff. South of this anticline in lat. 40°, while still more than 150 miles in a direct line from its mouth, the stream has ceased to have bluffs, and meanders broadly over a plain which is but 250 ft. above the sea. Not much farther down,

[1] LINDGREN, W and TURNER, H. W., Marysville folio 17, U. S. Geol. Survey, 1895.

the stream runs between natural levees bordered by "tule lands"[1] and attended by a plexus of sloughs (cf. Fig. 160, page 449). Opposite the Marysville Buttes, where but half its valley course has been run, the immediate banks, though 10 ft. higher than the adjacent country, are but 60 ft. above the sea. Similar features continue to San Francisco Bay.[2]

The western tributaries of the Sacramento coming from the low Coast Ranges are relatively weak. Most of those that do not give out on the arid plain lose themselves in the low belt of sloughs and tule lands which border the river. The chief eastern tributary is the Feather River which parallels the main stream for 60 miles before joining it 10 miles north of Sacramento. The Feather is a tributary of the "Yazoo type," finding its course where the eastward slope of the flood plain from the main stream meets the westward slope from the mountains.

In its intricate meanders, sloughs, and natural levees, the Feather River is like the Sacramento. The aggrading of these two streams has left between them the extensive and partly swampy Sutter Basin south of Marysville Buttes and Butte Basin farther north. The similar American Basin north of Sacramento is enclosed on the west by the levees of the Sacramento, on the south by those of the American River, and on the remaining sides by the regional slope of the valley floor. Below Sacramento and west of the river is the widespread Yolo Basin limited on the west by the alluvial slope from the Coast Ranges. As San Francisco Bay is approached the landscape assumes the character of a composite delta built by streams from the north, south, and east. The natural levees are dry land, the intervening basins being below sea-level and marshy except where protected by dikes.

The surface of the Sacramento Valley and adjacent to it has been classified as follows (Fig. 165):[3] (1) Foothills (not a part of

---

[1] The *tule* is a large bulrush that grows in overflowed lands.

[2] The gradient of the Sacramento would be no more than eight inches to the mile if the stream were straight, and is much less when meanders are taken into account. For a stream no larger than the Sacramento this is obviously too small to enable the water to transport all its burden without depositing.

[3] BRYAN, K., Geology and Ground-water Resources of the Sacramento Valley, California, U. S. Geol. Survey, *Wat. Sup. Pap.*, 495, 1923. This paper gives an excellent geographic and physiographic description of the Sacramento Valley. See also STEARNS, H. T., ROBINSON, T. W., and Taylor, G. H., Geology and Water Resources of the Mokelumne Area, California, U. S. Geol. Survey, *Wat. Sup. Pap.* 619, pp. 18–23, 1930.

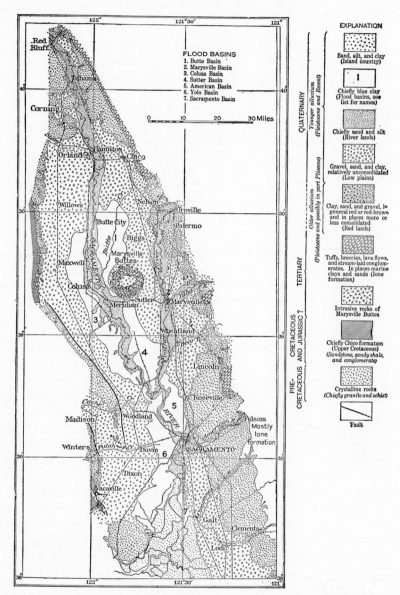

FIG. 165.—Map of Sacramento Valley, showing geology, physiography and location of flood basins. (*Bryan, U. S. Geol. Survey.*)

the valley), (2) red lands, (3) low plains, (4) river lands, (5) flood basins, and (6) the island country. The older Tertiary (including much of volcanic origin) and all rocks of greater age are in the foothills. The "red lands" are on the older alluvial slopes aggraded in a former cycle but now subject to erosion. The term "low plains" in its restricted sense designates the alluvial fans and slopes of the current cycle. The "river lands" are primarily the natural levees, which, by comparison with the lowland farther from the main streams, are relatively high and available for agriculture because better drained. The "flood basins" are the lowest parts of the flood plains, covered from time to time by standing water and accordingly underlain by very fine sediment, generally blue clay. The "island country" consists of the combined deltas of the streams that enter the Bay of San Francisco.

San Joaquin Basin.—The San Joaquin River is similar to the Sacramento except for the greater aridity of its basin. On this account the stream is much overloaded. It winds and braids excessively and is attended almost everywhere by a broad belt of swamp. Below the mouth of the Stanislaus River, 20 miles south of Stockton, the distributaries of the San Joaquin separate widely and the low plain may be classed as delta.

Each stream descending from the mountains on either side builds its own alluvial fan. For a few miles near the mountains these fans are distinct, but at no great distance all merge into a common alluvial slope. The position of the San Joaquin River is determined by the meeting of these slopes from opposite sides of the valley. Since the streams from the Sierra are much stronger and bring down more detritus their combined deposits have crowded the axial stream far toward the opposite side of the valley, locally to within five or six miles of the Coast Ranges. No perennial tributaries enter the San Joaquin from that side.

Tulare Basin.—Any alluvial fan of unusual size would not only crowd the main stream farther toward the opposite mountains but would in a measure dam the axial valley, causing swamps or even lakes on its upstream (south) side. In this way the great alluvial fan of the Kings River south of Fresno has occasioned the formation of Tulare Lake.

The south end of the Great Valley is relatively arid, but into this same part come the vigorous streams from the highest part of the Sierra, from the Kern River on the south to the Kings River on the north. The partial desiccation of these streams is

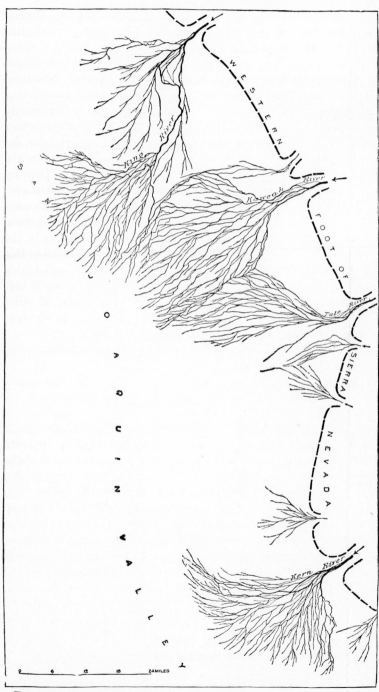

Fig. 166.—Map showing branching and braiding of streams from the Sierra Nevada on their alluvial fans in the San Joaquin Valley. Most of the water of these streams enters the porous deposits. The load it carries is added to the growing alluvial fans. (*U. S. Geol. Survey.*)

an important factor in making the alluvial fans which successfully obstruct the feeble flow in the axis of the main valley.   The first of these obstructing fans to be met in ascending the San Joaquin Valley is that of the Kings River which forms the northern rim of the basin of Tulare Lake.   All that part of the Great Valley which lies south of this obstruction is called Tulare Basin, the drainage from which rarely if ever overflows to the sea.   This basin is not a unit, for, farther south, the Kern River similarly obstructs the valley and forms the basins of Buena Vista and Kern Lakes.

All these lakes are of the playa type, *i.e.*, their waters (when present) cover the broad flat silt floors of basins of internal drainage (page 341).   A small area in Lake Tulare may be permanently covered with water but it is very shallow and the area of the lake varies greatly from season to season and from year to year. Extensive tule swamps border the lake on the north, east, and south.   It is not definitely known that the waters of Tulare Lake ever actually overflow.   On the margin of the alluvial fan to the north, the numerous distributaries of the Kings River pass into a plexus of sloughs which may yield water both to the lake on the south and to the stream on the north.   Thus there may be at times a water connection, but of actual overflow from lake to river, there is no proof.[1]

MATERIALS OF THE VALLEY FLOOR

The floor of the Great Valley is for the most part covered with alluvium which may be clay, sand, or gravel.   As the mountains are approached the material becomes progressively coarser. Boulders are strewn over some of the alluvial fans several miles from the mountains.   The depth of the unconsolidated sediment varies from zero at the mountain foot to more than 2,000 ft. Wells 1,000 ft. deep at Sacramento, 2,000 ft. deep at Stockton, and again more than 1,000 ft. near Tulare Lake, fail to reach the solid rock beneath.[2]   Just how much of this loose material is Quaternary alluvium is not known.   The underlying Tertiary comes to the surface locally at the edges and also around the Marysville Buttes.

[1] RANSOME, F. L., The Great Valley of California, Univ. Calif. *Bull.*, Dept. Geol. Sci., vol. I, pp. 373 and 381, 1896.

[2] RANSOME, F. L., *loc. cit.*, p. 381.

Physiographic History

The origin of the Great Valley is linked with that of the mountains that enclose it. For a long time the valley has been subject to sinking while the crustal movement on either side has been dominantly upward. Since the Coast Ranges were first made, no large division of geologic time has passed without deposition of sediments in a part or all of the Great Valley. Throughout this time the mountain belt on the east has been land subject to

Fig. 167.—Western front of the Sierra Nevada northeast of Bakersfield. The notch made by the canyon of the Kern River has the form commonly assumed to indicate recent or continued faulting. Despite this resemblance, there are here no decisive indications of a fresh fault scarp. As the mountains consist of hard rocks and the lowland is on soft rocks, Blackwelder interprets this as a fault-line scarp. The rapid lowering of the surface on the soft rocks by erosion is considered to have had the same topographic effect on valleys in the mountains as continued faulting should have. (*Photo by Blackwelder.*)

intermittent rise. Meantime the barrier on the west, while intermittently growing, has not always been complete. For much of the time it consisted of smaller masses separated by passages by which the sea reached the Great Valley. Many of the separate masses rose and sunk by turns but the dominant movement was upward and the barrier has been complete at least since the Quaternary period began.

The great structural trough beneath the valley has progressively deepened, though of course not uniformly and probably not even continuously. The contours of its rim did not remain unchanged. Sometimes a part of the margin was depressed and sediments accumulated where there had been none before; sometimes certain segments stood relatively high, and the sediments were eroded as some Tertiary rocks are now being eroded along the borders.[1]

Until recent years this valley has been thought of as due to downward bending rather than breaking. It is now known that the western and southern boundaries, at least, are determined by faulting.[2] The Sierra Nevada block of the earth's crust declines westward and passes under the Great Valley, generally (though not everywhere) without faulting and perhaps without change of dip. Around the north end of the valley a peneplain, which seems elsewhere to form the mountain summits, descends to the valley and dips beneath the detrital filling.[3] The downthrow against the Coast Ranges is not in one great fault but in a fault zone wherein are many faults, some parallel, some *en echelon*. The valley is indeed a great complex fault trough.[4]

Some of the faults are of long standing (Fig. 167), movement along them having been renewed at intervals, perhaps for several million years. Relatively late in geologic time, at a time somewhat arbitrarily designated as the beginning of the Quaternary, the mountain belts on both sides received distinct uplifts and probably the valley was much depressed. Much of the unconsolidated filling of the basin has accumulated since that time. As this now extends far below sea-level and as there is no evidence that sea water entered the valley and not even evidence of a widespread lake[5] it must be assumed that the sinking has been gradual and that in the main it was filled with alluvium about as fast as

[1] Redding folio 138, U. S. Geol. Survey, 1906; DILLER, J. S., Guidebook of the Western United States, Shasta Route, U. S. Geol. Survey, *Bull.* 614, p. 69, 1915.

[2] CLARK, BRUCE L., Tectonics of the Valle Grande of California, *Bull.* Amer. Assoc. Petrol. Geol., vol. 13, pp. 199–238, 1929. Studies leading to the newer ideas of structure have been stimulated, first, by studies of earthquakes and, second, by the search for petroleum.

[3] DILLER, J. S., Tertiary Revolution in the Topography of the Pacific Coast, U. S. Geol. Survey, *14th Ann. Rept.*, pt. II, pp. 405, 410, and 421, 1892; Redding folio 138, p. 6, U. S. Geol. Survey, 1906; RANSOME, F. L., *loc. cit.*, p. 376.

[4] CLARK, B., *loc. cit.*, p. 202.

[5] RANSOME, F. L., *loc. cit.*, p. 389.

it sank.[1] Local lakes like those now found in the valley, being retained by alluvial fans, are incidental to alluvial filling; hence some of the sediment is lacustrine.

The topography described above indicates that the valley is still filling, and for aught that is known, still sinking. The evidences of continued aggradation extend from the natural levees in the center to freshly surfaced alluvial fans at the mountain foot.

Ever since the beginning of the pronounced deepening of the valley by the deformation of the old Pliocene surface, the drainage has found its outlet through the sag now marked by the Bay of San Francisco. The now submerged channel probably indicates the course of the master stream for a long time before the last great deformation. It was antecedent to the last uplift of the Coast Ranges and to the faulting which outlines the San Francisco-Santa Clara Valley.[2] The valley though outlined by faulting owes its present form to erosion and submergence. Both the faulting and the erosion necessarily preceded the local sinking which made the bay.

THE CALIFORNIA COAST RANGES

Definition and Boundaries

The name California Coast Range (or Ranges) is applied to the mountains west of the Great Valley of California. These with their included valleys comprise a belt nearly 400 miles long with an average width of at least 50 miles. The section thus designated is bounded on the north by the Klamath Mountains which are distinguished from the California Coast Ranges geologically and to some extent also topographically. The topographic differences are due mainly to the greater strength of the rocks and the longer physiographic history of the Klamath Mountains. As the sections are here distinguished, all rocks older than Jurassic are included in the Klamath section.

---

[1] The 2,000 ft. of unconsolidated sediment mentioned on p. 478 are assumed by Ransome to be of Pleistocene age and to indicate a subsidence of 2,000 ft. since the beginning of the Pleistocene. Even if it were found that the lower part of this material is older than supposed, it would still remain true that the basin was much depressed and its rim elevated at about the beginning of the Quaternary.

[2] San Francisco folio 193, p. 20, U. S. Geol. Survey, 1914.

The California Coast Ranges are distinguished from the Angeles Ranges to the south largely by a difference of trend, the ranges of the northern section trending northwest-southeast, those of the southern section nearly east and west; but near the common boundary some ranges curve or have intermediate trends; hence the southern limit of the California Coast Ranges is not clearly marked. Conventionally the section is made to end with the San Rafael Mountains, the Santa Maria and Santa Ynez Valleys being assigned to the Angeles section.

The eastern boundary of the section is almost everywhere marked by an abrupt rise of the mountains above the nearly flat plain of the Valley of California. A number of faults are known to follow this line approximately. Other faults and echelon folds deviate from this line at low angles and are lost to sight beneath the alluvium of the Great Valley. Detailed study has been mainly south of San Francisco Bay[1] but the mountain front farther north is believed to have the same general character. The whole line is evidently one of sharp deformation, whether by faulting or flexure.[2]

General Description

The Ranges.—This section consists in general of nearly parallel ranges of low mountains with intervening valleys of various widths. Most of the ranges are between 2,000 and 4,000 ft. high. Altitudes above 5,000 ft. are rare. The trend of the belt as a whole is about north 30° west but the individual ranges, especially south of San Francisco, trend more nearly northwest. Thus they end against the coast, and the longitudinal valleys are open to the sea at their northwestern ends. The abrupt termination of the ranges in this singular manner is one of the features that suggests faulting along the shore line.

In the main the ridges are relatively straight and even-topped but less so than the Appalachian ridges. North of San Francisco uniformity of altitude is rather prominent but the several ridges are maturely dissected and no broad summits remain. South of San Francisco there are some broader rolling uplands but interspersed among these are higher crests and the general aspect is less plateau-like than it is farther north. Like the Allegheny

[1] CLARK, BRUCE L., *loc. cit.;* Studies in the Tectonics of the Coast Ranges of California; manuscript unpublished at the time of this writing.

[2] LAWSON, A. C., Calif. Earthquake Comm. *Rept.*, vol. I, p. 12, 1908.

ridges, the California Coast Ranges are generally separated by valleys which are roughly parallel to the strike but the most prominent of these valleys follow faults, as described below.

The Coast.—On the west the mountains of this section rise rather abruptly from the sea. Throughout much of the distance the shore line approximately corresponds with a line of structural deformation, probably involving faulting. A submarine shelf, roughly 25 to 50 miles wide, seems to represent a part of the continental mass though its outer edge is 5,000 ft. below sea-level and therefore much lower than what is commonly called the "Continental Shelf." Beyond that the descent is steep to depths of about 12,000 ft. This relatively abrupt descent likewise represents crustal deformation, not the front of a sedimentary bank.[1]

In so far as the shore line is determined by faulting, the actual line of the fault is now probably covered by the sea because the cliffs must have receded somewhat since the faulting occurred. In any case the last faulting must have been relatively recent, *i.e.*, since the making of the youngest local peneplain.

Throughout a large part of the shore the steep seaward slope is interrupted by old cliffs and narrow wave-cut terraces. These terraces range from sea-level to a maximum altitude of more than 1,500 ft. The maximum height observed is nearly the same from the Klamath Mountains on the north to the islands off the coast of southern California. As these terraces are due to intermittent uplift, the higher ones are necessarily oldest and most eroded. The benches which attract the attention of the casual observer are generally not more than 800 to 1,000 ft. above the sea. Some of these are almost perfectly preserved. The several features of wave-cut terraces are all locally present: old sea cliffs, beach gravels at their bases, deltas, and even borings of marine animals in the rocks.[2] Some of the terraces are a mile to two miles in width. The lowest is essentially a narrow coastal plain, the southerly continuation of that described on page 461, but the

[1] LAWSON, ANDREW C., The Continental Shelf of the Coast of California, Nat. Res. Council, *Bull.* 44, vol. 8, 1924; see also bathymetric chart compiled from data obtained with "sonic depth finder," Hydrographic Office, U. S. Navy. Lawson also describes the Coast of California in the Calif. Earthquake Comm. *Rept.*, vol. I, pp. 13–15, 1908.

[2] LAWSON, A. C., Geology of Carmelo Bay, Univ. Calif. *Bull.*, Dept. Geol. Sci., vol. I, p. 46, 1893.

recent sediments commonly thought of as covering or constituting a coastal plain are in many places almost or quite wanting.

From lat. 38°30′ (50 miles north of the Golden Gate) to Cape Mendocino, wave-cut terraces are almost everywhere found, though any one of them may be interrupted from place to place. Farther north where weak Pliocene rocks border the sea, cliff recession is so rapid that the terraces are in many places cut away. Near San Francisco they are poorly developed; the lowest would in any case have been drowned by the more recent submergence that made San Francisco Bay. Excellent examples are found both north and south of Monterey Bay.[1]

Local Description.—A few of the best known ranges and valleys are as follows: The Diablo Range[2] is the easternmost range south of San Francisco Bay. It is continuous with the Temblor and San Emigdio Ranges to the southeast, the three forming the boundary of the Great Valley of California to its southern extremity where the Tehachapi Range (southern end of Sierra Nevada) curves westward and meets the San Emigdio. For 65 miles at its northern end the Diablo Range is double, its western member being the Mt. Hamilton Range, so named from its most prominent peak. This subrange is topographically continuous with the Berkeley Hills which border San Francisco Bay on the east though the latter have had a different history. West of the Mt. Hamilton Range is the broad, trough-like Santa Clara Valley, submerged at the north beneath the waters of San Francisco Bay. West of this valley and south of the Golden Gate is the Santa Cruz Range which is continuous southeastward with the Gabilan Range.[3] This, in turn, merges with the Diablo Range in latitude about 36°30′. The Santa Cruz Range south of San Francisco borders on the sea but the mountains in line with it farther southeast are separated from the sea by the broad Salinas Valley and the Santa Lucia Range. At its southeastern extremity the Salinas Valley is contiguous with the Carizzo

[1] Santa Cruz folio 163, p. 6, also sheet of illustrations, U. S. Geol. Survey, 1909.

[2] The best general map of central California is sheet J 10 of the International Map of the World; scale 1:1,000,000.

[3] In the Coast Ranges it must not be assumed that topographic continuity indicates unity of physiographic history. Two ranges may form a continuous mass; yet their rocks and their histories may be so different as to require separate treatment. The range names in common use do not always designate physiographic units.

Plain,[1] an elongated desert basin with centripetal drainage, stretching from near lat. 35° to 35°30'.

West of the Salinas Valley and south of the Bay of Monterey is the Santa Lucia Range whose southwestern flank descends steeply to the sea but which, on the opposite side, is more or less subdivided into minor ranges roughly parallel to the main axis and separated by the valleys of longitudinal streams. South of the 35th parallel are the San Rafael Mountains which agree in trend with the California Coast Ranges at the northwest but curve round to a nearly eastward trend parallel with that of the Angeles Ranges.

North of San Francisco Bay are four parallel ranges.[2] Named in order from east to west these ranges are the Yolo, Napa, Sonoma, and Marin. The intervening longitudinal valleys named in the same order are the Berryessa, Napa, and Petaluma, the last named being the southern extension of the Russian River Valley. All of these ranges except the Sonoma and all of the valleys except that of the Russian River lose their continuity within 50 miles of San Francisco Bay. Farther north the ranges are, for the most part, merged into one broad mountain belt without dominant trends and without commanding ridges or great dividing valleys. There are minor exceptions on the east side, and the basin of the Eel River at the northwest embraces several parallel longitudinal valleys.

The most westerly branch of the Eel River, known as the South Fork, is separated from the ocean by the Mendocino Plateau which occupies a belt apparently continuous with the Marin. This is a rugged belt 10 to 20 miles in width, extending from San Francisco to Cape Mendocino. It is for the most part drained by short transverse streams. Most of it is a submaturely dissected upland rising from about 1,600 ft. on the west to 2,100 ft. on the east where it is generally surmounted by somewhat higher residual mountains. The entire belt is called, at least in its northern part, the Mendocino Plateau.[3] The mountains

---

[1] As with the mountains of this section, so also with the valleys, continuity or contiguity does not indicate unity either in character or in history.

[2] OSMONT, VANCE C., A Geological Section of the Coast Ranges North of the Bay of San Francisco, Univ. Calif. *Bull.*, Dept. Geol. Sci., vol. IV, pp. 39–87, 1904.

[3] HOLWAY, R. S., The Russian River, Univ. Calif. *Pub.* in Geogr., no. I, pp. 9–10, 1913.

which rise above this plateau, either as monadnocks on a peneplain or perhaps in part faulted up, constitute a poorly defined ridge, the so-called Mendocino Range, near the eastern margin.

ROCKS AND STRUCTURE

Varying Resistance.—The rocks of the Coast Ranges are in large part resistant sedimentaries. Most widespread are the metamorphosed rocks of the Franciscan and older series with their indurated sandstone, slate, and other resistant rocks.[1] Of almost equal importance are the massive Cretaceous and Tertiary sandstones. These younger rocks are less resistant than the Franciscan yet they take their place as mountain makers though not confined to the mountains. Weaker sediments, of Pliocene age, occupy mainly structural troughs but are not unknown in the ranges. Igneous rocks occupy relatively small areas. The largest of these areas are underlain by granite similar to that of the Sierra Nevada and Klamath Mountains. Unconsolidated Quaternary sediments cover extensive areas in the larger valleys.

All of these rocks except the youngest have been compressed and folded, the older ones several times. They have also been subject to faulting for a long time. The dominant direction of the great faults approaches that of the folds but the absence of close agreement is important. Profound erosion in more than one cycle acting on this folded and faulted mass, has left the several formations outcropping generally in elongate areas or irregular bands. These have none of the regularity of the outcrops in the Appalachian belt. Nor is there here that correspondence between the geologic and topographic maps which is so characteristic of the folded Appalachians. Most of the large valleys are indeed longitudinal but this fact is related chiefly to faulting, some of which has been so pronounced and so recent as to control the drainage and the major topographic features. Inspection of the map shows only one broad area in which there is little or no suggestion of longitudinal drainage and parallel ridges determined by structure. This is in the broad expanse of Franciscan rocks north of Clear Lake (lat. 39°).

---

[1] LAWSON, A. C., Calif. Earthquake Comm. *Rept.*, vol. I, 1908. The age of the Franciscan is variously stated from Triassic to Cretaceous. On the geologic map of California (1916) it is called Jurassic.

But elsewhere, even on this same body of Franciscan rocks, we find the longitudinal valley of the Russian River and some of the parallel tributaries of the Eel River. It is not certain that all longitudinal drainage in this northern part is due to faulting. South of lat. 38°30' faults are abundant and their influence on the relief is much more in evidence than that of differences in hardness of rocks.

Individual Faults.—The best known of the fault lines is the San Andreas Rift made familiar by the San Francisco earthquake in April, 1906, which was due to a slipping along this line. It may be traced for 530 miles southeastward from Point Arenas (lat. 39°). Throughout this distance it is marked by nearly straight valleys, generally at the foot of equally straight mountain fronts. At places these valleys and mountain slopes may be due directly to crustal movement; elsewhere they may result from erosion along a belt much broken up and weakened by multiple faulting. In such cases it may be impossible to determine which side was uplifted or whether all the movement may have been horizontal as it was in the San Francisco earthquake. North of San Francisco this depression makes Tomales Bay and Bolinas Lagoon which partly cut off the Point Reyes peninsula from the mainland. Farther south it traverses the Santa Cruz Mountains and determines the east front of the Gabilan Range and the west front of the Temblor Range. Thence it passes into the next section to the south, following for some distance the boundary between the Angeles Ranges and the Mohave Desert and then the southern side of the San Bernardino Range.

Many similar fault lines are traced for shorter distances.[1] One of these determines the east side of San Francisco Bay and the Santa Clara Valley. There is another at the east front of the Santa Lucia Range where it overlooks Salinas Valley. A great thrust fault determines the westernmost slope of the Klamath Mountains (South Fork Range) for 100 miles. Much of the steep shore is of the same character as the mountain slopes named.

---

[1] LAWSON, A. C., Calif. Earthquake Comm. *Rept.*, pp. 17–19, 1908, also the accompanying Atlas, Map 1; Fault Map of the State of California, Seismol. Soc. Amer., 1922; CLARK, BRUCE L., Tectonics of the Valle Grande of California; Amer. Assoc. Petrol. Geol. *Bull.*, vol. 13, pp. 199–238, 1929. This paper describes many of the fault blocks of the Coast Ranges, giving a brief history of each.

Physiographic History

General Statement.—The physiographic history of the California Coast Ranges can be stated only in general terms. Details differ in different parts. Of many parts the details are unknown. The outstanding fact is that the whole region is divided into fault blocks and that each block must be studied by itself. Each has had its ups and downs, periods when it lay low and received sediments, other periods when it stood high and was eroded, perhaps base-leveled. Some were raised in horizontal position, some tilted or arched.[1] Some blocks were depressed so recently that they are still low and receiving sediments either subaqueous or subaerial. Others whose depression was relatively recent were covered with weak sediments which are again being eroded since uplift. The rising and sinking of the several blocks have not been reduced to system. The movements of each are known only by the records left on that particular block, not by any necessary relation to other members of a system.

Older Cycles.—Of the early epochs of mountain making presumably no direct topographic records are left. The abiding results of those efforts are structural. The Franciscan and older rocks were closely folded and metamorphosed. The strength thus imparted to the rocks and the position thus given to the beds affect the present forms as they must influence all future land forms. Some of the great faults may have begun at the same time. At least they are very old.[2] Movement along them has been intermittent but some of the oldest are still active, determining the outlines of ranges and great valleys of the present day. Of all the faults mapped in this section approximately half are believed to be still active.[3]

Later Cycles.—On the whole, this section has been a rising area but the rise has been irregularly distributed both in time and place. In the meantime there has been great degradation of up-thrown blocks and folds and corresponding filling of troughs, generally fault troughs. Sedimentation in such troughs

---

[1] WILLIS, ROBIN, Physiography of the California Coast Ranges, Geol. Soc. Amer. *Bull.*, vol. 36, pp. 641–678, 1925. In classifying the ranges, Willis has taken into account their structure as well as their physiographic history.

[2] CLARK, BRUCE L., *loc. cit.*, p. 202.

[3] Fault map of the State of California, Seismol. Soc. Amer.. 1922.

in Pliocene time reached a maximum thickness of one mile.[1] At several times up-thrown blocks have been reduced to lowlands (not necessarily peneplains) which merged with extensive deltas in the structural troughs, thus producing an approach to gradation plains by a combination of degradation and aggradation.

Such was the surface over much of the area sometime before the beginning of Quaternary time.[2] It followed severe deformation in the late Miocene or at the close of that period and was in turn followed by similar folding and faulting, largely the latter, at about the close of the Pliocene. In this last great orogenic disturbance the present ranges and great valleys came into being though not without relation to older lineaments, since many of the present features are due to renewal of movement along old faults; nor is it to be understood that there has been no change since that time.

Toward the middle of Pleistocene time a sinking of 1,000 to 2,000 ft. affected the entire Coast Range area. Conditions were similar to those of the Pliocene. The same kind of gradation plain began to develop but its progress was interrupted by reelevation of the land. Its development was mainly on weak rocks, hence south of San Francisco. Meantime important new faulting was in progress, making, among other features, the trough which was later to be submerged, forming the Bay of San Francisco.[3] In the rising that followed the mid-Pleistocene depression the marine terraces were made. Hence it is only in a very general way that the present topographic features can be said to date from the close of the Tertiary or the beginning of Quaternary time.[4]

Remnants of Peneplains.—Many of the California Coast Ranges show undoubted remains of former peneplains. Some of the even crests are thus accounted for. So also are some of the valley floors. Moreover the valley floor may be part of the same

---

[1] LAWSON, A. C., Calif. Earthquake Comm. *Rept.*, vol. I, p. 10, 1908.

[2] LAWSON, A. C., Post-Pliocene Diastrophism on the Coast of Southern California, Univ. Calif. *Bull.*, Dept. Geol. Sci., vol. I, p. 158, 1893.

[3] LAWSON, A. C., San Francisco folio, U. S. Geol. Survey, 1914.

[4] The geologic dating of events here mentioned is the concern of historical geology rather than of physiography or geomorphology. The latter is concerned with sequence only in so far as cause and effect are involved. The reason for giving any dates at all is the assumption that sequences are more easily realized if events are dated than if they are merely arranged in order. The dates may be changed without affecting the explanation.

peneplain which elsewhere forms a mountain crest.[1]   It is therefore impossible to correlate peneplain remnants by their altitudes. It is only in favored cases that they can be correlated at all until the histories of the several structural units (generally fault blocks) have been deciphered independently.

It is not to be assumed that all of the subdued surfaces in this region are to be referred to the two epochs of gradation mentioned above.   Still less can it be assumed that the two peneplains covered the whole area in question.   The second in particular was

FIG. 168.—Capay Valley in northwestern Yolo County, California. The locality is one of steeply dipping Cretaceous rocks peneplaned and perhaps deformed still later by folding and faulting. The range in the background (west) is monoclinal and its crest represents a peneplain. Such crests are common in the Coast Ranges but the peneplains represent several different cycles and throughout most of the area they have been so much faulted that their remnants cannot be correlated by altitude. (*David M. Durst, Univ. Calif. Pub. in Geogr.*)

very restricted.   None the less, the nearly level surfaces which are now most in evidence were produced at the two stages mentioned. When the term cycle is used in connection with these events it is not to be understood that the cycle was complete.

The summit of the Santa Lucia Range south of lat. 36° is described as an even surface at places several miles wide.[2]

[1] WILLIS, R., Physiography of the California Coast Ranges, Geol. Soc. Amer. *Bull.*, vol. 36, p. 672, 1925.

[2] FAIRBANKS, H. W., San Luis folio 101, p. 11, U. S. Geol. Survey, 1904, mentions one place in its middle portion where the rolling surface is 10 miles wide.

Parallel ranges in the San Luis quadrangle are described in similar terms. These uplands are assumed to be remnants of a Pliocene surface, the Santa Lucia peneplain. Other ranges like the Gabilan show at their crests the remains of old past-mature or subdued surfaces, which obviously could not be produced in their present topographic position and quite as obviously are being destroyed.[1]

In the southern part of the section the peneplains of two cycles appear to be in juxtaposition.[2] The younger one is wide-spread in the Salinas Valley from which it has been called locally the Salinas peneplain. Its altitude is some hundreds of feet lower than that of the Santa Lucia peneplain but it rises toward the south where the two levels merge.

The coastal strip of peneplain north of San Francisco, the northern part of which is called the Mendocino Plateau, is no doubt the product of continued erosion for a long time.[3] Its correlation with the peneplains of the Klamath section is not entirely certain but it may be of the same age as that which intervenes between the Klamath Mountains and the northern end of the Sacramento Valley.[4]

The last event throughout most of the section was a moderate sinking whereby the mouths of streams entering the ocean are drowned, generally not more than five or six miles. The sub-merged shelf is locally crossed by deep gorges suggesting drowned erosion valleys[5] but several of them are probably structural.[6] If the gorges are stream-cut the valleys must have been partly cut in an earlier cycle, since the lowest marine terrace now exposed is uneroded.

The Bay of San Francisco was made at this time by greater local sinking. The deepest water in this bay (just inside the strait) is 378 ft. This probably indicates the full amount of

[1] WILLIS, R., *loc. cit.*

[2] FAIRBANKS, H. W., San Luis folio 101, p. 12, U. S. Geol. Survey, 1904.

[3] LAWSON, A. C., Geomorphogeny of the Coast of Northern California, Univ. Calif. *Bull.*, Dept. Geol. Sci., vol. I, p. 242, 1894.

[4] LAWSON, A. C., *loc. cit.*, p. 271, 1894. For a description of the peneplain in this locality see DILLER, J. S., Tertiary Revolution in the Topography of the Pacific Coast, U. S. Geol. Survey, *14th Ann. Rept.*, pt. II, pp. 405–408.

[5] See Bathymetric Chart, Hydrographic Office, U. S. Navy, 1922.

[6] Lawson points out that one of them (Carmelo Bay) is almost in line with a fault, and another (Bay of Monterey) is in the axis of a syncline. See Geology of Carmelo Bay, Univ. Calif. *Bull.*, Dept. Geol. Sci., vol. I, p. 59, 1893.

local subsidence because the bottom is swept by tidal currents and the straits are not filling up.[1] At a single locality 20 miles northeast of San Francisco a raised bench shows that the land has risen six feet since the general submergence which is otherwise the last movement recorded.[2]

Summary of Stream Origins.—The streams of the Coast Ranges are of various types and ages. Some streams north of San Pablo (northern part of San Francisco) Bay follow synclines.[3] This suggests that they may have been consequent on the original folding. They might also have originated as subsequent streams after peneplanation. Stream courses resulting from long adjustment are exemplified by those which flow seaward across the Mendocino Plateau, including the transverse portion of the Russian River and those north of it. These streams merely follow the courses which they acquired on the peneplain. Some of them like the Big River and the transverse portion of the Russian River have beautiful entrenched meanders.

Some streams are plainly subsequent, following the strike of relatively weak beds. Of these, some took their courses in the older erosion cycle and some since the uplift of the last peneplain.[4] The branches of the Eel River east of Cape Mendocino are good examples.

Some of the larger streams have had a complex history. Thus the Santa Clara south of San Francisco Bay and the San Benito in the southeastward extension of the same structural valley flow between up-thrown fault blocks. The Salinas is similarly located. The original streams were doubtless consequent on this structure but the valleys which they carved out (at least that of the Salinas) were partly or wholly filled during submergence. New streams then flowed over these unconsolidated sediments and were thus superposed on the hard rocks of the old valley. In this way the Salinas in the San Luis quadrangle is caused to flow for some distance in a gorge parallel

---

[1] For amount of local depression see LAWSON, A. C., Geomorphogeny of the Coast of Northern California, Univ. Calif. *Bull.*, Dept. Geol. Sci., vol. I, 266–268, 1894; also Santa Cruz folio 163, p. 6, U. S. Geol. Survey, 1909.

[2] LAWSON, A. C., *loc. cit.*, p. 271, 1894.

[3] OSMONT, VANCE C., A Geological Section of the Coast Ranges North of the Bay of San Francisco, Univ. Calif. *Bull.*, Dept. Geol. Sci., vol. IV, pp. 80–82, 1904; also Lawson, cited below.

[4] LAWSON, A. C., *loc. cit.*, pp. 251–252; also Calif. Earthquake Comm. *Rept.*, p. 20.

to the wide-open valley now left by the removal of the soft sediments.[1] The gradual cleaning out of these valleys since the last great submergence (mid-Pleistocene) has left terraces corresponding in altitude to the marine terraces.[2]

The Russian River[3] follows a similar valley east of the Mendocino Range. The original river in the present cycle (since the peneplain was uplifted) flowed seaward along the line of the present lower course down the slope of the peneplain. A northern subsequent tributary had a remarkable headward growth along a belt of gravels and was probably aided in its headward growth by faulting which further extended the line of weakness northward. One after another the seaward-flowing consequent streams were captured. The gravels are now almost completely carried away and the superimposed stream flows through canyons where it crosses spurs which were buried when the course was chosen.

ANGELES SECTION

Distinguishing Features[4]

The lowlands of southern California and the enclosing mountains together constitute a section with a large degree of individuality, but neither logically unified nor clearly delimited. Its most distinguishing feature is the approximate east-west trend of the mountain ranges on its northern margin. The east-

[1] San Luis folio 101, p. 13, U. S. Geol. Survey, 1904.

[2] Lawson, A. C., Calif. Earthquake Comm. *Rept.*, p. 22.

[3] Holway, R. S., The Russian River, Univ. Calif. *Pub.* in Geogr., vol. I, 1913. The reader is referred to this paper for a more exact statement in greater detail.

[4] The following maps will be found most useful in reading about this section:

1. Southern California, a 3-sheet topographic map issued by the U. S. Geol. Survey; scale 4 miles to 1 inch, contour interval 250 ft.

2. Geological map of California; scale 12 miles to 1 inch, State Mining Bureau, 1916.

3. Atlas of the California Earthquake Commission, especially Map 1. Topographic map of California showing fault lines. Published by the Carnegie Institute of Washington, 1908.

4. Irrigation map of California, Pls. I, II, and III of Irrigation Resources of California and Their Utilization, by Frank Adams. Published by U. S. Dept. of Agriculture as Exper. Sta. *Bull.* 254, 1913.

5. Fault map of the state of California, by the Seismological Society of America, 1922.

Fig. 169.—Topography on weak Tertiary beds in the Coalinga oil field, Santa Barbara County, California. The altitude is about 1,000 ft., the climate arid except for brief winter rains, and the rocks weak. Such mature topography of fine texture, though not representative of large areas, is found widely distributed on the younger sedimentaries in the drier parts of the Pacific Border and adjacent provinces. (*U. S. Geol. Survey.*)

west Santa Ynez Range immediately north of the Santa Barbara Channel branches off spur-like from the main belt of Coast Ranges, making an angle of nearly 45 deg. with the ranges to the north, but the trends of the main ranges farther east curve gradually from a southeasterly to an easterly direction (Fig. 132). As here defined, the northern section ends with the San Rafael Range. The southwestern foot of this range is clear, where the mountains rise above Santa Maria and Santa Ynez Valleys. The eastward extent of this section is indefinite. The two physiographic sections are here separated by an arbitrary line drawn from the head of the Santa Ynez River to Antelope Valley, the westernmost point of the Mohave Desert.

South of the ranges with an east-west trend (San Gabriel and San Bernardino) are rather extensive lowlands sometimes called, with doubtful propriety, the Valley of Southern California. The ranges south of these lowlands trend northwest-southeast as do the Coast Ranges farther north. Geologically they are merely faulted portions of the Lower Californian province.

This section may be said to be characterized by mountains due directly to uplift (mainly faulting) rather than to differential erosion; also by lowlands aggraded by alluvium which in large part buries an older topography. The Coast Ranges of central California share these characteristics to some extent but their structure and physiographic history are less obvious. Also a smaller portion of their valleys is being aggraded by alluvium.

Areal Description

Borders of the Santa Barbara Channel.—At Point Conception in lat. 34°30′, the coast of California changes its direction from north-south to east-west. The Santa Ynez Mountain Range follows the coast (in fact determines it) for some 60 miles east from Point Conception. Farther east are other small ranges with similar trends. South of this east-west coast is the Santa Barbara Channel, and in line with it toward the east is the (in part) structural valley of the Santa Clara River. South of this valley are the San Gabriel Range and several small east-west mountain ranges, the most important being the Santa Monica on the coast. In a direct line westward from this range is a line of islands or partly submerged mountains marking the southern border of the Santa Barbara Channel. It thus appears that the dominance of east-west trends in the Angeles section is somewhat greater than it would seem from an inspection of the mainland alone.

The Santa Ynez Range is sharply and maturely dissected but has a fairly even crest 3,000 to 4,000 ft. high declining toward the west end.   At its southern base is a narrow marine terrace followed through its length by the Southern Pacific Railroad. The width of this terrace varies from a few hundred feet to several miles and its altitude from sea-level to several hundred feet (Fig. 170).   It answers to the narrow coastal plain described at

Fig. 170.—Wave-cut terraces in Pleistocene sediments one mile west of Ventura, California, and about one-half mile from the coast.   The plain in the foreground is less than 50 ft. above sea.   The higher terraces are seen in profile. (*Delos and Ralph Arnold, Jour. Geol.*)

various places farther north.   Old strand lines are found locally more than 800 ft. high, but considerably tilted by recent crustal movements.   At the northern base of the range, 6 to 12 miles from the shore and following a pronounced fault line, is the west-flowing Santa Ynez River.   Low mountains and broad plains occupy the area between this and the base of the San Rafael Range.[1]

East of the Santa Ynez Range the most distinct geographic landmark is the Santa Clara Valley, a nearly straight east-west

[1] Good descriptions of the large and small ranges north of the Santa Ynez River are given by Arnold and Anderson in U. S. Geol. Survey, *Bull.* 317, The Santa Maria Oil District.   Arnold, in describing the Summerland district, U. S. Geol. Survey, *Bull.* 321, p. 18, points out that in the mountains of the western part of this section folding has been more prominent than faulting.   The Santa Ynez Range is mainly a great fold overturned toward the south.

valley, in part structural, cutting all the way across from the Mohave Desert to the ocean and followed by the Southern Pacific Railroad. At the west it merges with the Hueneme Plain, an old delta of the Santa Clara River, 15 to 20 miles in extent each way and one of the great agricultural districts of southern California. South of the Santa Clara Valley and separated from it by minor ranges is the San Fernando Valley, an alluvium-filled miniature of the California Trough (25 by 15 miles). South of that basin is the Santa Monica Range whose eastern end separates the San Fernando Valley from the Los Angeles Coastal Plain.

San Gabriel and Similar Ranges.—The most extensive mountain range of southern California is the San Gabriel, an extensive belt of granitic rocks with an east-west length of 60 miles and a maximum width of about 20 miles. It is bounded on the north by Santa Clara Valley and the Mohave Desert, and on the south by the Valley of Southern California and the San Fernando Valley. Cajon Pass at the east separates the San Gabriel from the San Bernardino Range and Fernando Pass at the west end, leading north from the San Fernando Valley to the Santa Clara, separates this range from the Santa Susanna, one of the many small east-west ranges referred to above.

This large area of more than 700 square miles is a maturely or past-maturely dissected highland of granitic rocks. The average crest height is probably above 6,000 ft. Dissection by narrow, deep, and tortuous canyons is complete. Flat uplands and flat-bottomed valleys are alike wanting, and there is no longer an approximate uniformity of altitude among sharp divides.[1] So far as known this description of the topography of the San Gabriel Range applies equally to the other granite mountains[2] northwest of it up to and including the San Emigdio group west of Tejon Pass which is conventionally taken as the limit of the Sierra Nevada.[3]

[1] MENDENHALL, W. C., Two Mountain Ranges of Southern California, Geol. Soc. Amer. *Bull.*, vol. 18, p. 661, 1907.

[2] See geologic map of California, 1916.

[3] On the accompanying map the San Emigdio Mountains are included in the California Coast Ranges. It is possible that when the region has been better studied and when more detailed description is called for, the large granite area west of Tejon Pass may be included with the adjacent granite areas either in the Sierra Nevada province or in the Angeles section of the Pacific Border.

The San Gabriel Range like the adjoining range across the Santa Clara Valley overlooks the Mohave Desert, the southern boundary of which is the great San Andreas fault. The northern face of the mountains is a fault scarp made by uplift on the south, but more recent movement has been in the opposite direction thus raising a line of foothills known as the Portal Ridge. The southern face of the San Gabriel Range is likewise a fault scarp; hence the entire range is an uplifted block.

San Bernardino Range.—Eastward from the San Gabriel Range and separated from it by Cajon Pass, is the San Bernardino Range, a granitic mass uplifted between faults. The fault on the north side is less definitely known but the one on the south side is the continuation of the San Andreas Rift which crosses from the north to the south side of the mountain belt at Cajon Pass.

Approached from either north or south, the San Bernardino Mountains look much like the San Gabriel except that in a commanding view the heights of the ridges are accordant instead of discordant. The borders of the range are deeply dissected by young valleys, less graded than those of the range to the west. Having ascended the precipitous slope, all resemblance to the San Gabriel ceases. The headwaters of the streams are seen to be separated by gently undulating and undissected divides. The common level of these in the western part of the range is at 5,000 to 6,000 ft. Altitudes increase farther east toward San Bernardino Peak (10,666 ft.) and San Gorgonio Peak (11,485 ft.), but the general level is nowhere so high as these peaks. The central part of the range contains extensive areas at the summit level which are broadly rolling and not reached by erosion in the present cycle. There are broad meadows and even some playa lakes. In every way, except for features dependent on climate, the aspect of these areas is that of the Mohave Desert of which the range may recently have been a portion[1] (see below under History).

On the northerly slopes of San Gorgonio Peak, well-formed cirques and moraines indicate former alpine glaciers down to the level of 8,500 ft.[2] The latitude of this peak is a little above 34°.

---

[1] MENDENHALL, W. C., U. S. Geol. Survey, *Wat. Sup. Pap.* 219, p. **17,** 1908.

[2] FAIRBANKS, H. W., and CAREY, E. P., Glaciation in the San Bernardino Range, California, *Science*, vol. XXXI, pp. 32–33, 1910.

So far as known this is the most southerly instance of glaciation in the United States.[1]

San Jacinto and Santa Ana Ranges.—Of the ranges which bound the lowland of southern California on the south, not much is known except their northern ends. The San Jacinto Range which forms the southwestern wall of the Salton Trough is separated from the San Bernardino Range by San Gorgonio Pass, a trough three to four miles wide, partly floored with alluvium.

Fig. 171.—San Jacinto Valley, southern California, looking south from Relief Hot Springs. The locality is at the west foot of the San Jacinto Mountains. Note the inability of the San Jacinto River to cut a permanent channel; also its numerous temporary channels separated by sand bars. The mantle of alluvium laid down by this overloaded stream covers an uneven surface of granite continuous with that of the mountains in the distance. (*U. S. Geol. Survey.*)

This range is continued northwestward in a line of hills or badlands almost to the city of San Bernardino. The San Jacinto Range, which has many crests from 7,000 to 9,000 ft. high, presents steep faces both to the northeast and southwest. Probably it is an uplifted block between faults parallel to the San Andreas Rift. If so, the floor of San Gorgonio Pass, except for its alluvial filling, may well be a portion of the same old surface which now survives in remnants at the top of the two adjacent ranges.

[1] The most southerly surviving glacial ice is mentioned on page 105.

Parallel with the San Jacinto and midway between it and the ocean, is the Santa Ana Range, a spur from the great granitic highland here called the Lower Californian province. It is a fault block tilted seaward, the steep straight scarp on the northeast side being still preserved. Its altitude declines toward the northwest where the uplift runs out into the low complex anticline of the Puente Hills and reaches almost to Los Angeles. The summit level of the Santa Ana Range is a seaward-sloping, little dissected peneplain.[1]

Lowland of Southern California.—The so-called "Valley of Southern California" consists of all the lowlands between the San Gabriel and San Bernardino Mountains on the north, the San Jacinto and Santa Ana on the south, and the Pacific Ocean on the west. The total area is approximately 2,000 square miles but this includes many subdued ridges, knobs, or groups of hills due either to recent uplift, like the Puente Hills already mentioned, or residual on an imperfect peneplain, as are the higher peaks or knobs on the mountain ranges.

These hills subdivide the lowland into more or less distinct valleys or basins. The floors of these basins are generally smooth, made so by the accumulation of wash from the mountains. Such filling is locally of great depth, perhaps several thousand feet. Elsewhere the underlying rock rises above the alluvial surface in isolated hills or groups of hills. At still other places, especially near the southern margin, the underlying rock floor was less depressed or more uplifted, and no alluvium has accumulated. At such places the topography is that of an old erosion surface, generally rolling but with some conspicuous hills or even small mountains.

The largest continuous plain is the so-called "Coastal Plain" on which Los Angeles stands. Its length along the coast from the Santa Monica Mountains on the northwest to the San Joaquin Hills (lat. 33°35′) on the southeast, is 50 miles, and its breadth from the sea back to the Puente Hills is 15 to 20 miles. Its area is approximately 775 square miles. This plain represents mainly the combined deltas of the Los Angeles, San Gabriel, and Santa Ana Rivers. Like the plains more remote from the sea, this one is therefore composed of detritus washed down from the mountains. In this case, however, the alluvium was to some extent

[1] LAWSON, A. C., Calif. Earthquake Comm. *Rept.*, vol. I, p. 24.

worked over and redeposited by waves.[1] The plain at its inner edge is 200 to 300 ft. above the sea and hence slopes 10 to 20 ft. per mile.

North and east of the Puente Hills are two basins at the southern foot of the San Gabriel and San Bernardino Mountains. The western and smaller basin traversed by the San Gabriel River is separated by the San José Hills from the larger eastern basin of the Santa Ana River. Both consist of coalescing alluvial fans sloping south from an altitude of 1,000 to 2,000 ft. at the mountain base to altitudes of 300 to 500 ft. along the southern margin. The alluvial slope near the mountains may be as steep as 500 ft. to the mile but it quickly flattens, and near the southern margin may be 50 ft. to the mile. Even this is three to five times the average slope of the Coastal Plain, whose form is partly the work of waves. In this arid climate and with this porous material, such slopes are insufficient for erosion, and the surface of the plain remains essentially without local relief.

Throughout these valleys or basins, isolated hills or groups of hills rise here and there above the plain of aggradation. Some are of granite, others of sedimentary rocks. These hills are only the higher parts of the old topography which is gradually being inundated by a flood of alluvium. Between hills the buried rock surface lies at unequal depths below the present plain, locally several thousand feet.

Southeast of the Santa Ana River, a valley nearly 25 miles wide between the San Jacinto and Santa Ana Mountains extends to the southeast for at least 40 miles (Fig. 171). Broad irregular belts of alluvium occupy a part of this area, the remainder of which is diversified by hills and low mountains. The name "Perris Plain" taken from the principal town, is properly applied to the main alluvium-covered area. As seen from the mountains on either side, the surface of the entire down-faulted block (graben or moat) is a lowland.

Stream Habits.—The streams of this section are actively degrading their mountain courses and are aggrading their valley reaches with corresponding rapidity. The amount of porous alluvium already laid down is so large that all streams sink in and disappear within a few miles of the mountain base, sometimes

[1] If the term "coastal plain" be so restricted as to exclude plains partly or wholly surfaced by subaerial wash, the term would not be applicable to this area.

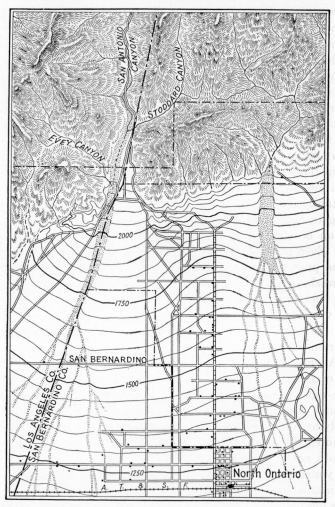

Fig. 172.—A Piedmont alluvial plain or compound alluvial fan in southern California. Contour interval 50 ft. The squares in the northern part indicate miles. Note the number of living streams in the mountain area and the dry, branching sand washes on the plain. It is on such plains as this that the fruits and grapes of southern California are grown. (*U. S. Geol. Survey, Cucamonga sheet.*)

within a few hundred feet.   Beyond the point of their disappearance in dry weather, their courses may be traced as dry "washes" or "sand washes," used only in time of flood when the stream reaches farther out on the alluvial slope.   Such stream courses commonly consist of a network instead of a single channel. The larger streams have more or less continuous washes reaching to the sea but all such streams are "interrupted," *i.e.*, their courses consist of alternating stretches of dry wash and flowing water.   Where the alluvium is deep and porous, the water percolates slowly through it in a down-stream direction but does not appear at the surface except in time of flood.   Where the underlying rock approaches the surface and obstructs percolation, the stream flows at the surface.   The bearing of this on irrigation and on the ground-water supply is evident.   With constantly increasing depth of alluvium the proportion of percolating to flowing water is naturally increased, likewise the proportion of sediment deposited to that carried through to the sea.   Even now the amount of the latter is very small.

The practical value of the percolation of water beneath the dry washes is illustrated by the experience of Los Angeles with its former water supply derived from the San Fernando Valley. The wash of the Tujunga River crosses San Fernando Valley from the San Gabriel Mountain on the north to the Los Angeles River on the south.   From wells sunk in and near these channels Los Angeles derived an abundant water supply until her population exceeded 300,000.   The courts held that the city had the same right to that underflow as it would have had to a surface stream.   Hence the right of private parties to tap the same supply by wells was refused.[1]

Shores and Islands.—The shore line throughout this section, as both north and south of it, gives evidence of recent rising. The young marine terrace on the south side of the Santa Ynez Mountains has already been mentioned.   Remnants of older shore lines are found near Santa Barbara as high as 850 ft.   One of these now declines in altitude eastward at the rate of more than 100 ft. per mile,[2] indicating pronounced crustal warping since the older beaches were made, *i.e.*, in late Pleistocene time.

[1] DILLER, J. S., Guidebook of the Western United States, U. S. Geol. Survey, *Bull.* 614, p. 98, 1915.

[2] ARNOLD, R., Geology and Oil Resources of the Summerland District, California, U. S. Geol. Survey, *Bull.* 321, p. 19, 1907.

That deformation is continuing was shown by the earthquake at Santa Barbara in 1926.

The San Pedro Hills which form the bold headland 20 miles south of Los Angeles are an island similar in every way to the others which lie a few miles off shore, but incidentally connected with the mainland by the abundant deposits of the Los Angeles and San Gabriel Rivers. Its summit is 1,475 ft. above the sea. From sea-level to a height of 1,240 ft. its sides are terraced by old strand lines, perfect below, eroded above.[1]

Off the coast at distances ranging from 25 to 90 miles are six islands of considerable size. Of these it is noteworthy that the two which lie nearest the mainland, Santa Cruz and Santa Catalina, have rugged slopes deeply scored by stream valleys whose lower courses are drowned. The eastern part of Santa Rosa Island is similar, while all the islands lying farther from shore show wave-cut terraces, generally to heights approaching 1,500 ft. It might be inferred from this that the sea bottom has recently sunk along a belt containing the nearer islands while farther out it has been rising, as has the mainland to the east and north. In that case this sinking belt would be analogous to the California and Puget Troughs with which it is almost in line. Reasoning based on the presence or absence of wave-cut terraces alone is not, however, conclusive, since their development and preservation are affected by the nature of the rocks and preexisting slopes. Partly on this account the coast of the mainland, the whole of which is believed to have risen recently, contains stretches of well-marked terraces alternating with others free from such evidence.[2]

All the islands here referred to rise from the structural terrace or "Continental Shelf" described on page 483. This shelf broadens to more than 150 miles where the shore of southern California swings to the east. Its surface is much broken as though by faulting. Among the islands are basins or troughs

---

[1] For details of strand lines on the islands of southern California, see SMITH, W. S. TANGIER, A Topographic Study of the Islands of Southern California, Univ. Calif. *Bull.*, Dept. Geol. Sci., vol. II, no. 7, pp. 179–230, 1900; also LAWSON, A. C., Post-Pliocene Diastrophism of the Coast of Southern California, Univ. Calif. *Bull.*, Dept. Geol. Sci., vol. I, pp. 115–160, 1893.

[2] SMITH, W. S. TANGIER, *loc. cit.*, pp. 208–218, believes that the distribution of hard and soft rocks and the former slopes of these islands are sufficient to account for the remarkable distribution of wave-cut terraces.

reaching depths of more than 6,000 ft. There can be little doubt that the recent structural history of this submerged shelf is similar to that of the adjacent mainland, and that in its larger features the topography is similar. The Channel Islands (south of the Santa Barbara Channel) are probably an anticlinal mountain range. Other islands are upthrown fault blocks, San Clemente being a typical "basin range." The troughs and basins find their analogues in San Fernando Valley of the Angeles section and Death Valley of the Great Basin.[1]

SUMMARY OF PHYSIOGRAPHIC HISTORY

In a general way the physiographic history of this section agrees with that of the section north of it. The mountains are mainly fault blocks, uplifted at different times, now dissecting or dissected, some more, some less, with concurrent alluviation of the valleys. Peneplaning in late Tertiary time may have been prevalent but the lack of synchrony in the physiographic histories of the several ranges makes it difficult to determine how widespread any one peneplain may have been. The outstanding topographic features are mainly structural and due chiefly to faulting, though the faulting did not all occur at the same time. It is a safe inference that the movement which raised the partly dissected San Bernardino and southern ranges came decidedly later than that which raised the maturely dissected San Gabriel Range. It may well be that the summit uplands of the San Bernardino, San Jacinto, and Santa Ana Mountains are all parts of the same peneplain or old rolling surface observed in the floors of the Mohave Desert, San Gorgonio Pass, and the Perris Basin. If so, they might also be correlated with one of the levels shown in the Tehachapi and Sierra Nevada Ranges.[2] It would follow then that the old erosion surface of low altitudes and moderate reliefs which stretched from the Mohave Desert to the sea was, at the time of its making, surmounted by the San Gabriel Range,

[1] LAWSON, A. C., The Continental Shelf of the Coast of California, Nat. Res. Council *Bull.*, vol. 8, no. 44, 1924. This paper discusses the entire area covered by the survey made with the sonic depth finder extending from San Francisco to Mexico, and published as Bathymetric Chart 5194, Hydrographic Office, U. S. Navy, 1922.

[2] HERSHEY, O. H., The Quaternary of Southern California, Univ. Calif. *Bull.*, Dept. Geol. Sci., vol. III, pp. 1–30, 1902; LAWSON, A. C., Geomorphogeny of the Tehachapi Valley System, Univ. Calif. *Bull.*, Dept. Geol. Sci , vol. IV, pp. 431–462, 1904.

as it was by the Sierra Nevada and Tehachapi Ranges, then much lower than they are now.

Without regard to exact correlations it is still true that both up-faulted and down-faulted blocks had former surfaces of relatively small relief, whether or not they were all continuous at one time. The original form of this surface may still be seen in parts of the Perris Valley where it remains uncovered, and in parts of the San Bernardino Mountains where it remains undissected. Where the valleys are deeply filled with alluvium the rock surface is presumably quite as uneven as where it is exposed and not dissected. The burial of rock hills is still progressing.

The main drainage lines of this section are evidently antecedent to the Santa Ana Mountains and presumably established before the last uplift of the San Jacinto and San Bernardino Ranges. The Santa Ana River cuts directly through the Santa Ana Range in a narrow valley nearly 2,000 ft. deep. Certain tributaries plainly owe their courses to fault lines. Such are the east and west forks of the San Gabriel River and those stretches of the San Jacinto which follow the bases of the newly faulted mountains.

RESOURCES

Petroleum is abundant in the Angeles section. It occurs in the relatively young (Miocene to Pliocene) sediments where moderately folded. Suitable structures and large supplies are found from the Puente Hills on the southeast to the Pacific Ocean north of Point Conception.

As agriculture is the greatest industry of southern California, the soil and the water which give it value are necessarily the chief resources. The rainfall is insufficient for farming without irrigation. It is, moreover, confined to the winter months, mainly from November to March or April. The annual rainfall ranges from 20 in. down to 12 in. according to altitude or distance from the higher mountains. All the natural flow of streams was long ago appropriated for irrigation. Irrigation from wells, both flowing and pumped, has long been important. It will be observed that the great thickness of porous alluvium, while causing streams to decrease in size and disappear, is favorable to the conservation of a vast supply of ground water. Fortunately the conditions are such as to favor artesian wells throughout one large area and several small ones. The large one is in the

Coastal Plain southeast of Los Angeles. The sediments in that area occupy a trough or basin in the underlying rock. In general the bedrock surface slopes toward the sea and is many hundreds of feet deep, but near the coast it approaches the surface in a long swell or ridge thus obstructing the seaward movement of the ground water and holding it back in a basin or trough of relatively dense rock.[1] An artesian basin of several hundred square miles is thus produced. There are several similar but much smaller

FIG. 173.—Citrus fruit lands of the Riverside-Highlands irrigation district, southern California. Like most other fruit-growing districts of southern California, this one is on alluvium washed down from the mountains and spread out as alluvial fans or alluvial slopes, partially or wholly submerging the high points of the older rock surface. (*Mendenhall, U. S. Geol. Survey.*)

basins, one of them just east of San Bernardino and another southeast of Pomona.

Outside the area of flowing wells, pumping is necessary. This is now done on a large scale. In 1907 there were in this section 3,000 flowing wells and 1,400 pumping plants. During the pumping season, the combined flow of the flowing wells was about 200 sec.-ft. and the flow from pumps was 300 sec.-ft.[2]

[1] MENDENHALL, W. C., U. S. Geol. Survey, *Wat. Sup. Paps.* 137, 138, 142, and 219.

[2] MENDENHALL, W. C., Ground Waters of the San Joaquin Valley, California, U. S. Geol. Survey, *Wat. Sup. Pap.* 222, p. 27, 1908.

As with practically all other artesian basins where water is valuable, the water is being drawn from these basins more rapidly than it comes in.   The results of this are: (1) the flow from the wells is decreased; (2) the depth of the water table is increased; and (3) the artesian area is shrinking.   In some localities where the water table was formerly 25 ft. deep it is now 50 ft. deep.[1] The surface is thus made drier and the work of pumping increased.

The original area of the Coastal Plain artesian basin was 290 square miles.   This was reduced to 190 square miles in the decade preceding 1904.[2]   Both the shrinkage in area and the fall of the water table were in part due to a decade of deficient rainfall, but the results also indicate excessive use.

The combination of semitropical climate, very rich soil, and artificial watering causes farming in this section to be intensive. Most of the hundred million dollars worth of citrous fruits sold annually from the state of California are produced in this section.[3] Other fruits, grapes, and nuts are also produced on a vast scale. Of field crops, beans and sugar beets are perhaps most important, especially on the low delta plain at the mouth of the Santa Clara River.

LOWER CALIFORNIAN PROVINCE

South of the parallel ranges of block mountains of which the San Jacinto and Santa Ana are best known and extend farthest north, is a broad dissected seaward-sloping granitic upland not unlike that of the Sierra Nevada but of lower altitude, generally not much above 5,000 ft. on its higher (east) side.   On that side it presents a steep face, a series of fault scarps, to the low-lying Salton Trough.

The area here described is arbitrarily limited on the northwest by the Santa Margarita River, since it is convenient to speak of the San Jacinto and Santa Anna Mountains in connection with the other ranges surrounding the lowland of southern California. The Angeles section is in some ways strongly marked but its limits are more or less arbitrary.   Moreover the extensive upland of Lower California must be recognized as a province, but the limit here assigned is a matter of convenience.

[1] U. S. Geol. Survey, *Wat. Sup. Pap.* 138, p. 34.

[2] U. S. Geol. Survey, *Wat. Sup. Pap.* 139, p. 18.

[3] In the census year 1919 the citrous fruits produced in California were valued at $87,000,000.

That part of this long belt which lies in the United States[1] consists largely of rolling uplands surmounted by residual hills and small mountain ranges. The large area is subdivided by deep valleys or polygonal basins into smaller masses sometimes called ranges, at other times mesas. Some of these are remarkably smooth, even cultivated, but they differ in this respect as also in altitude. Some of the uplands are sloping, their several edges being eroded more or less according to the amount or rate of uplift or perhaps according to the time elapsed since the last uplift. The whole region appears to be composed of fault blocks displaced in different ways and at different times, some of them still moving. Meantime erosion has worked with or against diastrophism according as crustal movement was downward or upward. On account of the large number of faults and the recency of some, the details of topography and physiographic history differ for each fault block.

This granitic upland is bordered on the west by a terraced lowland[2] 12 to 18 miles wide and 60 miles long within the limits of the United States. Isolated granitic hills rise above this plain, becoming more numerous toward the east where the plain is gradually lost among spurs and outliers of the upland just described. The plain, whose full height is 800 ft. at the inner edge, is preserved only in remnants, a large part of it being destroyed by transverse streams from the mountains. Alluvial terraces of considerable width extend from the mountains to the shore where they merge with marine terraces, indicating that this part of the coast has shared the recent general uplift of the California Coast. Its gradual or intermittent rise is recorded in its terraces, the lowest and youngest of which may perhaps be correlated with the Los Angeles Coastal Plain. This youngest marine terrace, only slightly above the sea, is several miles wide at the north, but in the southern half it is absent and there are steep sea cliffs.

The entire plain west of the granite upland is a composite delta of many streams. Though still young, it is distinctly older both

[1] SAUER, CARL, Land Forms in the Peninsular Range of California as developed about Warner's Hot Springs and Mesa Grande, Univ. Calif. *Pub.* in Geogr., Vol. 3, pp. 199–290, 1929. This is the most recent and most intensive study of a portion of the area here described.

[2] LAWSON, A. C., Post-Pliocene Diastrophism of the Coast of Southern California. Univ. Calif. *Bull.*. Dept. Geol. Sci., vol. I, pp. 115–160, 1893.

in time and in topographic development than the Los Angeles Coastal Plain.   It embraces a large amount of good arable land, perhaps a third of the entire area, but the water supply is limited. The climate is more arid than further north.   The neighboring mountains are lower and the flow of the streams is correspondingly smaller.   The irrigated acreage in this section in 1913 was less than a tenth of that of the Angeles section.   By the storage of waters in reservoirs the area may be doubled or quadrupled.[1]

San Diego Bay is an exceptionally good example of a lagoon almost shut off from the ocean by a wave-built bar.   The position of this long bar known as Coronado Beach was determined by currents from the south which cut across the open bay from Coronado Heights to Coronado Island.   Behind the islands and bar is a spacious harbor.

[1] ADAMS, FRANK, "Irrigation Resources of California and Their Utilization," U. S. Dept. Agr., Exper. Sta., *Bull.* 254, pp. 38–39.

INDEX

A

Abajo Mountains, 311.

Absaroka Range, 158.

Adams, Frank, Irrigation Resources of California and Their Utilization, 493, 510.

Adams, Geo. I., Geology and Water Resources of the Patrick and Goshen Hole Quadrangles in Eastern Wyoming and Western Nebraska, 19; Physiography of Kansas, 27, 28.

Adams, Geo. I., and others, Gypsum Deposits in the United States, 86.

Agency Plain, 271.

Alden and Stebinger, Pre-Wisconsin Drift in the Region of Glacier National Park, 73.

Alden, Wm. C., Physiographic Development of the Northern Great Plains, 63, 65, 66, 76, 158; Pre-Wisconsin Drift in the Region of Glacier National Park, 73; Yellowstone National Park and Its Environs in the Great Ice Age, 153; Glaciers of Glacier National Park, 207.

Alkali marshes, 386.

Alluvial fans, 340.

American Falls, 241.

American Fork, 175.

Anaconda Range, 214.

Anderson, A. L., Mica Deposits of Latah County, Idaho, 231.

Angeles section, distinguishing features of, 493; local descriptions in, 495, 497, 498, 499, 500; streams of, 501; shore line of,

503; islands off the coast of, 504; physiographic history of, 505; resources of, 506.

Antelope Hills, 136.

Apache Mountains, 382.

Apishapa River, 43.

Aquarius Plateau, 295, 298.

Arapahoe Peak, 101, 103.

Arikaree formation, age of, 17; characteristic topography on, 18; also Fig. 8, p. 17; Fig. 9, p. 20.

Arkansas Hills, 104.

Arkansas River, 22, 25, 27, 33, 35, 104, 110, 128.

Arnold and Anderson, The Santa Maria Oil District, 496.

Arnold, Ralph, Geological Reconnaissance of the Coast of the Olympic Peninsula, Washington, 456; Geology and Oil Resources of the Summerland District, 496, 503.

Arroyos, 371.

Artesian water, classes of, 87.

Atanum-Moxee Valley, 267.

Atwood and Mather, Evidence of Three Distinct Glacial Epochs in the San Juan Mountains, 119; Grand Canyon of the Gunnison River, 125.

Atwood, W. W., Physiographic Studies in the San Juan District, 119; Glaciation of the Uinta and Wasatch Mountains, 175, 178, 181, 182; Physiographic Conditions and Copper Enrichment, 213, 221; A Geographic Study of the Mesa Verde, 309.

Aubrey Cliffs, 382.

Avon Basin, 223.

D